SOLID STATE PHYSICS,

NUCLEAR PHYSICS,

AND

PARTICLE PHYSICS

SOLID STATE PHYSICS, NUCLEAR PHYSICS, AND PARTICLE PHYSICS

NINTH LATIN AMERICAN SCHOOL OF PHYSICS

KENNETH JOHNSON
BERNARD JOUVET
YUVAL NE'EMAN
MICHAEL NAUENBERG
ALEXANDER MAKSYMOWICZ
CHRISTIAN FRONSDAL
ROSCOE WHITE
IVO ŠLAUS AND GUY PAIĆ
SERGIO RODŔIGUEZ
R. F. WOOD
MANUEL CARDONA
H. METCALF, J. BRANDENBERGER, AND J. BAIRD
H. E. STANLEY

W. A. BENJAMIN INC.
New York 1968 Amsterdam

SOLID STATE PHYSICS, NUCLEAR PHYSICS,
AND PARTICLE PHYSICS

Library of Congress Catalog Card Number 68-25424
Manufactured in the United States of America.

*The manuscript was put into production on March 1, 1968;
this volume was published on May 30, 1968.*

W. A. Benjamin, Inc.
New York, New York 10016

Foreword and Acknowledgements

The Ninth Session of the Latin American School of Physics was held in Santiago, Chile, in July 1967, under the auspices of the Faculty of Physics and Mathematics, University of Chile, and the Chilean Atomic Energy Commission.

Throughout the years the Latin American School of Physics has proved itself as an instrument of the utmost importance in the development of physics in this continent.

As it is known, the main purpose of the School is to bring together active Latin American physicists and offer them review courses in advanced fields of research, thus helping them to keep up to-date with current trends of physics. Besides, the School also provides Latin American physicists with the opportunity to discuss their own work with their colleagues attending the School. Through both these ways the School thus effectively combats scientific isolation, one of the most difficult problems physicists working in developing countries must invariably face.

The 1967 Session was devoted to three main subjects :

Particle physics, Low Energy Nuclear Physics and Solid State Physics (the need for covering such a broad spectrum of physics in a School like this is self-evident). Most of the courses given are contained in this book, and it is a great pleasure to express here our gratitude to the respective lecturers for having joined us in our School.

It is also a pleasure to thank the various institutions whose support made this Session of the School possible, namely, the Latin American Centre for Physics (CLAF), the Organization of American States (OEA), the University of California-University of Chile Cooperative Programme, the US Atomic Energy Commission, the French Atomic Energy Commission and the US National Science Foundation.

The total number of participants registered at the School was 115, coming from 10 different countries. In addition to the lectures, a large number of Seminars were given; unfortunately, almost none of them could be included in this book, in order to keep its size reasonable.+

If this Session of the School had any success, this was due (apart from the people and institutions already quoted) to the efforts of a number of people, acting at different levels and at different times. To give a complete list of all of them is clearly an almost impossible task -most probably the list would be both, long and incomplete- but I feel I cannot fail to mention here a few representative names.

\+ There also was an unofficial -and most exciting- Seminar which M. Nauenberg announced as "Some Boundary Problems in the Middle East". The lecturer was Yuval Ne'eman and the date early July (1967).

Dean Enrique d'Etigny and Prof. Gastón Pesse, of the Faculty of Physics and Mathematics, University of Chile, and Prof. Efraín Friedmann, of the Atomic Energy Commission, gave us constant and unfailing support. To my younger colleagues and students, notably Dr. Enrique Tirapegui, who shared with me the full responsability for the School, Mr. Romualdo Tabensky, Dr. Víctor Massida and Mr. Sergio Hojman, to mention only a few of them, I am deeply indebted for their most generous efforts and collaboration. Our Secretary, Miss María Elena Pardo, made life easier and more pleasant for all of us at the School. Finally, the whole book was typed —and at times hand-written— by Miss Irene Davis, who did what I consider a most excellent job. We wish to record here our gratitude to all of them.

Igor Saavedra
Director
IX Latin American School of Physics

Contents

Page

Page

PART II. Nuclear Physics 471

ERRATUM TO THE LECTURES ON

"THE FIELD THEORETICAL APPROACH TO COMPOSITE PARTICLES".

page 114

- Formula (2.40) should read : $T_y(s) \Big|_{\substack{\longrightarrow \\ s\to\infty}} \frac{\varphi^2 \; RX(s)}{s \; Z_3}$

page 141

- The third formula should read

$$\int dk \int da \; e^2 (a) \; \Gamma^2 (p, p-k) \quad \Delta' (p-k) \frac{1}{k - a - i\epsilon}$$

- The fourth formula should read :

$$\delta m_e^{(1)} = - \int da \; e^2 \; (a) \left[\ldots \right]^2 . \left\{ \ldots \right\}$$

- In the last formula, $\approx$ means "asymptotically in a"

page 142

- The signs $=$ should read $\approx$

page 143

- The last formula should read

$$\frac{1}{q^2} \left\{ \ldots \right\}^{-1}$$

page 145

- The formula (3.33) should read

$$e \; \Gamma_V \; (q^2) = e \left\{ 1 - \frac{\ldots}{(\ldots)[\, 1 - \gamma^2 \ldots]} \right\} \times F_V (q^2)$$

page 147

- The formula (3.35) (ii) should read

$$1 - \frac{\gamma^2 \int \ldots}{\gamma^2 \int \ldots} = \ldots$$

page 155

- A_μ is the renormalized axial vector current
- The formula in the middle of the page should read

$$+ f^2 \, p^2 \int (\sigma (a) / (a + p^2 - i \epsilon))da$$

page 186

- The last formula should read

$$\left| \Delta_X^{(\mu)}(s) \right| \xrightarrow[s \to \infty]{} 1/\sqrt{s}$$

page 191

- The expression before formula (5.25) should read

$$D_H = D_O \left(\Delta_H^{(\mu)} \right)^{-1}$$

page 202

- The two integrals should be multiplied by $1/12\pi$

page 203

$$\sigma(s') = \frac{s'}{3\pi} \sqrt{\ldots} \quad (1 + 2\, m^2/s')$$

page 270

- In the second line

$$\xi_\mu \xi_\nu f(\xi^2) = \frac{1}{4} \delta_{\mu\nu} f(\xi^2)$$

Part I

Particle Physics

1

RECENT DEVELOPMENTS IN QUANTUM ELECTRODYNAMICS+

Kenneth Johnson, Massachusetts Institute of Technology, U.S.A.

+ Preliminary notes of these lectures were taken by Drs. Víctor Massida and Bernardo Liberman.

INTRODUCTION

In this series of lectures, I would like to present both a review of old things as well as some recent work in the subject of quantum electrodynamics.

It is not possible in such a short series to present more than a cursory review, so in the first few lectures we will no more than touch upon some formal results which will be needed in the later lectures.

The goal of these lectures will be to discuss some methods which can be used to study the properties of the Green's functions of electrons and photons asymptotically far off the mass shell of the physical particles. We shall try to show that if one believes in the ordinary renormalized perturbation solutions of the Dyson-Schwinger equations for Green's functions, then one may conclude that the so-called bare mass of the electron, m_o, must be zero. We shall try to state clearly all the additional assumptions that are needed along the way in deriving this result. The meaning of this fact we shall find, is that the so-called Lehmann equation for the bare mass, expressed in terms of renormalized spectral functions, would yield $m_o = 0$, and this result would occur as an identity, holding for all values of the physical mass and coupling constant.

We shall also try to show that a similar result holds for the bare charge, namely that it has a fixed value independent of the value of the physical charge as long as it is smaller, and the equation which relates them, $e^2/Z_3(e^2) = e_o^2$ should in fact hold as an identity in e^2 obeyed as long as $0 < e^2 < e_o^2$. We shall obtain an equation for the function f(x) which will determine e_o^2 as the solution of $f(e_o^2) = 0$.

Some of the material to be discussed in these lectures is been given previously in similar series at other places. Y hope that the present version is more or less definitive; many of the questions which were unanswered previously have been cleared up. For more details on special aspects not emphasized here one may refer to notes made of these earlier versions.

Finally, all of the new work which will be described here has been the result of a collaboration with Professor Marshall Baker and in some part also with Dr. R. Willey.

1. MAXWELL EQUATIONS - QUANTIZATION FORMALISM

We begin with Maxwell's equations

$$F_{\mu\nu} = \partial_\mu A_\nu - \partial_\nu A_\mu \qquad (1.1)$$

$$\partial^\mu F_{\mu\nu} = -e_o^2 J_\nu \qquad (1.2)$$

J_μ describes the flux of particles which carry the unit of charge e_o. We shall use a metric such that

$$a^\mu b_\mu = \mathbf{a} \cdot \mathbf{b} + a^o b_o = \mathbf{a} \cdot \mathbf{b} - a_o b_o .$$

Eqs. (1.1) and (1.2) are obtained from the Lagrangian density

$$\mathcal{L} = -\frac{1}{2} F_{\mu\nu} (\partial^\mu A^\nu - \partial^\nu A^\mu) + \frac{1}{4} F_{\mu\nu} F^{\mu\nu} + e_o J_\mu A^\mu \qquad (1.3)$$

It is convenient to replace the field variable A_μ by $(1/e_o) A_\mu$. In order to keep the product $A_\mu F^{\mu\nu}$ unchanged we also replace $F_{\mu\nu}$ by $e_o F_{\mu\nu}$. With this change we get

$$\mathcal{L} = -\frac{1}{2} F_{\mu\nu} (\partial^\mu A^\nu - \partial^\nu A^\mu) + \frac{e_o^2}{4} F_{\mu\nu} F^{\mu\nu} + J_\mu A^\mu \qquad (1.4)$$

The Maxwell equations become

$$e_o^2 F_{\mu\nu} = \partial_\mu A_\nu - \partial_\nu A_\mu \qquad (1.5)$$

$$\partial_\mu F^{\mu\nu} = -J^\nu \qquad (1.5a)$$

If we wish to consider a current which is not conserved, it is easily seen that the present formalism leads to inconsistencies. Indeed, if we take the divergence of Eq. (1.5a), we get $\partial^\mu J_\mu = 0$, so Maxwell's equations are only consistent if charge is locally conserved.

Now, it is convenient, for mathematical reasons, to allow ourselves the freedom of working with non-conserved currents, even though these will have no physical meaning. We shall consider as physical only those processes which locally conserve charge.

To do this it is convenient to work with a formalism which is not completely gauge invariant, by using, instead of (1.4), the following Lagrangian:

$$\mathcal{L} = -\frac{1}{2}F_{\mu\nu}(\partial^{\mu}A^{\nu} - \partial^{\nu}A^{\mu}) + \frac{e_o^2}{4}F_{\mu\nu}F^{\mu\nu} + J_{\mu}A^{\mu}$$

$$- \Im\partial_{\mu}A^{\mu} + \frac{e_o^2}{2}\xi\Im^2 \qquad (1.6)$$

In (1.6), ξ is a free numerical parameter, which would characterize a gauge in the classical theory. The new field equations are

$$e_o^2 F_{\mu\nu} = \partial_{\mu}A_{\nu} - \partial_{\nu}A_{\mu} \qquad (1.7)$$

$$e_o^2\xi\Im = \partial_{\mu}A^{\mu} \qquad (1.7a)$$

$$\partial^{\mu}F_{\mu\nu} = -J_{\nu} - \partial_{\nu}\Im \qquad (1.7b)$$

By taking the divergence of (1.7b) we get now

$$\partial^{\nu}J_{\nu} + \Box^2\Im = 0 \qquad (1.8)$$

which shows explicitly that the current does not need to be conserved.

However, when $\partial^{\nu}J_{\nu} = 0$, $\Im$ is a free field, and for all processes which locally conserve charge, the coupling to $\Im$ will have no effect. Thus physical results will be independent of the choice of the relative strength of the coupling to $\Im$ expressed by the parameter ξ.

2. SOURCES

We wish to consider the case in which the current consists of two terms, $j^{\mu}(x)$ and $J^{\mu}(x)$.

The first term represents the operator current of the electron field which is always conserved: $j^{\mu}(x) = \bar{\psi}(x)\gamma^{\mu}\psi(x)$.

$J^{\mu}(x)$ is an arbitrary external c-number current, which is not necessarily conserved. More generally, we wish to consider the four components J^{μ} as independent, and to use them as variational parameters. With this new form of the current we get the Hamiltonian

$$H_t = H_{J=0}(A_{\mu}, F_{\mu\nu}, j_{\mu}, \psi) - \int d\mathbf{x}\, J_{\mu}(\mathbf{x}, t)A^{\mu}(\mathbf{x}) \tag{2.1}$$

where the explicit time dependence comes from the external current J_{μ}.

Let us work in the Heisenberg representation. The time dependence of an operator B(t) is given by the equation

$$\frac{dB}{dt} = \frac{1}{i}\left[B, H(t)\right] \tag{2.2}$$

The corresponding equation for H(t) will be

$$\frac{dH(t)}{dt} = \frac{1}{i}\left[H(t), H(t)\right] + \frac{\partial H(t)}{\partial t} = \frac{\partial H(t)}{\partial t}$$

$$= - \int d\mathbf{x} \frac{\partial J^{\mu}(\mathbf{x},t)}{\partial t} A_{\mu}(\mathbf{x}, t) \tag{2.3}$$

where
$$H(t) = H_{J=0}\left[A_{\mu}(t), F_{\mu\nu}(t), \text{etc.}\right] - \int d\mathbf{x}\, J_{\mu}(\mathbf{x},t)A^{\mu}(\mathbf{x},t)$$

The field operators $A_{\mu}(\mathbf{x}, t)$ obey the Eq. (2.2).

Let us consider the processes for which the external current J_{μ} vanishes at $t = \pm\infty$. In this case the operators $H(\pm\infty) = H_{J=0}\left[A(\mathbf{x}, \pm\infty), \ldots\right]$ are unitarily related, since (2.2) defines a sequence of unitary transformations.

We shall define an "in" vacuum state by

$$H_{J=0}(-\infty)\,|\,\text{in}, 0 > \, = 0 \tag{2.4}$$

and an "out" vacuum state by

$$H_{J=0}(+\infty)\,|\,\text{out}, 0 > \, = 0 \tag{2.5}$$

We shall find it convenient to construct the amplitude

$$< 0, \text{out}\,|\,0, \text{in} > \tag{2.6}$$

which is a functional of J_μ.

In order to obtain equations which will enable us to do this, we must first derive certain boundary conditions which are obeyed by a matrix element of the form

$$< 0, \text{out}\,|\,B(t)\,|\,0, \text{in} > \tag{2.7}$$

where B(t) is an operator which obeys (2.2). We shall assume that the current $J_\mu(\mathbf{x}, t)$ is turned on only over a finite time interval:

$$J_\mu(\mathbf{x}, t) \neq 0, \qquad t_o < t < t_f \,.$$

For $t < t_o$, $H(t) = H(-\infty) =$ constant, and from Eq. (2.2) we get

$$B(t) = e^{iH(-\infty)t}\, B e^{-iH(-\infty)t} \qquad t < t_o \tag{2.8}$$

where B is a suitable fixed operator. Consequently, if we consider

$$< 0, \text{out}\,|\,B(t)\,|\,0, \text{in} > \, = \sum_c < 0, \text{out}\,|\,c, \text{in} > < c, \text{in}\,|\,e^{iH(-\infty)t}$$

$$B e^{-iH(-\infty)t}\,|\,0, \text{in} > \, =$$

$$= \sum_c \langle 0, \text{out} \mid c, \text{in} \rangle \, e^{iE_c t} \langle c, \text{in} \mid B \mid 0, \text{in} \rangle \tag{2.9}$$

where $|c, \text{in}\rangle$ is a complete set of vectors of the operator $H_{J=0}(-\infty)$, and use is made of Eq. (2.4).

Now, it can be shown that if we define our operators to act in a standard quantum mechanical Hilbert space with a "positive metric", that is, if

$$\langle a \mid b \rangle^{*} = \langle b \mid a \rangle \tag{2.10}$$

for any two states, then $H_{J=0}$ is not a positive definite operator. This is because the additional terms introduced in the Lagrangian which describe the fields, $\exists$ and $J_\mu A_\mu$ carry negative energy. So, it is difficult to define the vacuum as the "lowest" state of energy, since in this case $H_{J=0}$ has no minimum eigenvalue.

In order to avoid mathematical difficulties with an H unbounded from below, we work in a Hilbert space where $H_{J=0}$ has a spectrum bounded from below. This can be done by replacing (2.10) by some other suitable condition (so that we work in an "indefinite metric"). However, since we will never have occasion to make use of the form of the modified version of (2.10), we do not give it explicitly.

When, finally, we deal with physical, local charge conserving processes, and we start with a state in which the unphysical modes are not excited ($H > 0$ in this subspace), we shall make no transitions into such states, and hence, for such processes, (2.10) will hold.

Coming back to Eq. (2.9), since in this way $E_c > 0$ (the vacuum has $E = 0$), this matrix element of B(t) has only negative frequencies in its Fourier resolution for $t < t_o$. This is one boundary condition.

In the same way, we see that the matrix element (2.9) has only positive frequencies in its Fourier resolution for $t > t_f$. This is the second boundary condition.

In addition to this we also need to calculate the matrix element of any time ordered product of operators,

$$< 0, \text{out} \,|\, T\left[B_1(t_1), \ldots B_n(t_n)\right] |\, 0, \text{in} > .$$

as a functional of the external current.

In order to do that, let us write the change in the matrix element caused by the replacement $J_\mu \to J_\mu + \delta J_\mu$. This is given by the "action principle",

$$\delta < 0, \text{out} \,\Big|\, T\left[B_1(t_1), \ldots B_n(t_n)\right] \Big|\, 0, \text{in} > =$$

$$= i\int d^4x\,\delta J_\mu(x) < 0, \text{out} \,|\, T\left[A_\mu(x) B_1(t_1) \ldots B_n(t_n)\right] |\, 0, \text{in} > \tag{2.11}$$

where δJ_μ is an infinitesimal.

We can also express (2.11) in terms of a functional derivative, since no constraint of the type $\partial_\mu \delta J^\mu = 0$ is imposed, so that the variations can be taken as independent:

$$-i\frac{\delta}{\delta J_\mu(x)} < 0, \text{out} \,|\, T\left[B_1(t_1) \ldots B_n(t_n)\right] |\, 0, \text{in} > =$$

$$= < 0, \text{out} \,|\, T\left[A_\mu(\mathbf{x}, t) B_1(t_1) \ldots B_n(t_n)\right] |\, 0, \text{in} > \tag{2.12}$$

3. ELECTROMAGNETIC FIELD GREEN'S FUNCTIONS

Let us apply the action principle to the matrix element $<0, \text{out} | 0, \text{in}>$ in order to obtain its functional dependence of J_μ:

$$\frac{\delta < 0, \text{out} | 0, \text{in} >}{< 0, \text{out} | 0, \text{in} >} = i \int d^4x \frac{<0, \text{out} | A_\mu(x) | 0, \text{in} >}{<0, \text{out} | 0, \text{in} >} \delta J^\mu(x)$$

$$\equiv i \int d^4x < A_\mu(x) > \delta J^\mu(x) \tag{3.1}$$

In Eq. (3.1) and hereafter we use the notation

$$< M > = \frac{< 0, \text{out} | M | 0, \text{in} >}{<0, \text{out} | 0, \text{in} >} \tag{3.2}$$

for any operator M.

When $J_\mu \to 0$, $<M> \to <0|M|0>$ (vacuum expectation value of M).

From the field equations (1.7) we get

$$\Box^2 A_\nu - \partial_\mu \partial_\nu A^\mu + e_o^2 (J_\nu + j_\nu + \partial_\nu \mathcal{E}) = 0 \tag{3.3}$$

In addition we have

$$e_o^2 \xi \mathcal{E} = \partial_\mu A^\mu \tag{1.7a}$$

$$\partial_\nu J^\nu + \Box^2 \mathcal{E} = 0 \tag{1.8}$$

We first find that

$$- \Box^2 < \mathcal{E} > = \partial_\nu J^\nu \tag{3.4}$$

since $\partial_\nu J^\nu$ is a c-number.

In solving this differential equation, we must use the boundary conditions derived above. Thus, we find

$$< \mathfrak{J}(x) > = \int D_F(x-y)\partial_\nu J^\nu(y)d^4y \qquad (3.5)$$

where $D_F(x)$ is the Feynman Green's function, which is the solution of

$$-\Box^2 D_F(x) = \delta^4(x) \qquad (3.6)$$

It has only positive frequencies in its Fourier resolution for $x_o > 0$, and only negative frequencies for $x_o < 0$. Therefore, $< \mathfrak{J}(x) >$ will satisfy the right boundary conditions.

We can easily verify that (3.6) has the solution

$$D_F(x) = \int \frac{d^4q}{(2\pi)^4} \frac{e^{iqx}}{q^2 - i\varepsilon} = \int \frac{d\mathbf{q}}{(2\pi)^3} \frac{i}{2|\mathbf{q}|} e^{i\mathbf{q}\cdot\mathbf{x}} e^{-i|q_o|\cdot|x_o|} \qquad (3.7)$$

where $\varepsilon \rightarrow +0$.

From (3.3) and (1.7a) we get

$$-\Box^2 < A_\nu > = -\partial_\nu e^2 \xi < \mathfrak{J} > + e_o^2 J_\nu + e_o^2 < j_\nu > + e_o^2 \partial_\nu < \mathfrak{J} >$$

$$= e_o^2 J_\nu + e_o^2 \partial_\nu \int D_F(x-y)\partial_\mu J^\mu(y)d^4y(1-\xi) + e_o^2 < j_\nu >$$

By imposing again the same boundary conditions, we find

$$< A_\nu(x) > = e_o^2 \int D_{\mu\nu}(x-y)\left[J^\mu(y) + < j^\mu(y) >\right] d^4y \qquad (3.8)$$

where

$$D_{\mu\nu}(x) = \int \frac{d^4q}{(2\pi)^4} e^{iq\cdot x} D_{\mu\nu}(q) \qquad (3.9)$$

and

$$D_{\mu\nu}(q) = \left[g_{\mu\nu} + (\xi - 1)\frac{q_\mu q_\nu}{q^2 - i\varepsilon}\right]\frac{1}{q^2 - i\varepsilon} \qquad (3.10)$$

We used the fact that $\partial_\mu < j^\mu > = 0$.

Now we come back to (3.1). First of all, we shall obtain an explicit expression of $< 0, \text{out} | 0, \text{in} >$ as a functional of J_μ, in the case when we have only an external current.

Replacing (3.8) into (3.1), we get

$$\frac{\delta < 0, \text{out} \mid 0, \text{in} >}{< 0, \text{out} \mid 0, \text{in} >} = \delta \log < 0, \text{out} \mid 0, \text{in} >$$

$$= i \int d^4 x \delta J^\mu(x) D_{\mu\nu}(x-y) J^\nu(y) d^4 y$$

$$= \delta \left[\frac{i}{2} \int d^4 x d^4 y J^\mu(x) J^\nu(y) D_{\mu\nu}(x-y) \right]$$

where we have used the fact that $D_{\mu\nu}$ is a symmetric tensor. From this we get

$$< 0, \text{out} \mid 0, \text{in} > = e^{\frac{i}{2}\int J^\mu(x) J^\nu(y) D_{\mu\nu}(x-y) d^4 x d^4 y} \tag{3.11}$$

The integration constant must be 1 in order that

$$< 0, \text{out} \mid 0, \text{in} > = < 0 \mid 0 > = 1 \quad \text{for } J_\mu \equiv 0.$$

In the general case, however, $< j_\mu(x) >$ will be a functional of J_μ.

It is convenient to define the photon Green's functional by

$$\bar{D}_{\mu\nu}(x, y) = \frac{\delta < A_\mu(x) >}{\delta J^\nu(y)} = \frac{\delta}{\delta J^\nu(y)} \left[\frac{< 0, \text{out} \mid A_\mu(x) \mid 0, \text{in} >}{< 0, \text{out} \mid 0, \text{in} >} \right]$$

$$= i \frac{< 0, \text{out} \mid T A_\mu(x) A_\nu(y) \mid 0, \text{in} >}{< 0, \text{out} \mid 0, \text{in} >}$$

$$- \frac{i < 0, \text{out} \mid A_\mu(x) \mid 0, \text{in} > < 0, \text{out} \mid A_\nu(y) \mid 0, \text{in} >}{< 0, \text{out} \mid 0, \text{in} >^2}$$

$$= i < T\left[A_\mu(x) A_\nu(y) \right] > - \, i < A_\mu(x) > < A_\nu(y) > \tag{3.12}$$

[In this derivation use is made of (2.12)]. This shows explicitly that $D_{\mu\nu}(x, y)$ is not linear in $A_\mu(x)$. If $J_\mu = 0$, $\bar{D}_{\mu\nu}(x, y)$ reduces to

$i<0|T[A_\mu(x)A_v(y)]|0>$, because of the vanishing of $<0|A_\mu(x)|0>$. It is evident that in this case $\bar{D}_{\mu v}(x,y)$ will be a function of $x - y$ alone, since the only way to distinguish between different points of space-time would be by means of the external current $J_\mu(\mathbf{x},t)$.

On the other hand, by taking the functional derivative of (3.8) we get

$$\bar{D}_{\mu v}(x,y) = e_o^2 D_{\mu v}(x-y) + e_o^2\int D_{\mu\lambda}(x-y')\frac{\delta<j^\lambda(y')>}{\delta J^v(y)}d^4y' \tag{3.13}$$

Since the charges are coupled locally to the field A_μ, $<j_\lambda>$ is most usefully regarded as a functional of $<A>$ rather than J_μ. If we use the chain rule for functional differentiation, we can write

$$\frac{\delta<j^\lambda(y')>}{\delta J^v(y)} = \int\frac{\delta<j^\lambda(y')>}{\delta<A_\alpha(y'')>}\frac{\delta<A_\alpha(y'')>}{\delta<J^v(y)>}d^4y''$$

$$= \int\frac{\delta<j^\lambda(y')>}{\delta<A_\alpha(y'')>}\bar{D}_{\alpha v}(y'',y)d^4y''$$

Replacing into (3.13) we get an integral equation for $\bar{D}_{\mu v}$:

$$\bar{D}_{\mu v}(x,y) = e_o^2 D_{\mu v}(x-y)$$

$$+ e_o^2\int D_{\mu\lambda}(x-y')\frac{\delta<j^\lambda(y')>}{\delta<A_\alpha(y'')>}\bar{D}_{\alpha v}(y'',y)d^4y''d^4y'$$

Let us define the "polarization" or "photon self-energy part" by

$$\pi^{\lambda\alpha}(x,y) = -\frac{\delta<j^\lambda(x)>}{\delta<A_\alpha(y)>} \tag{3.14}$$

The integral equation becomes

$$\bar{D}_{\mu\nu}(x, y) = e_o^2 D_{\mu\nu}(x - y) - e_o^2 \int D_{\mu\lambda}(x - y')\pi^{\lambda\alpha}(y', y'')\bar{D}_{\alpha\nu}(y'', y) d^4y' d^4y'' \tag{3.15}$$

From the conservation of $j_\mu(x)$ it follows that

$$\frac{\partial}{\partial x^\lambda}\pi^{\lambda\alpha}(x, y) = 0 \tag{3.16}$$

From the gauge invariance of $< j_\mu(x) >$, we see that if $A_\mu \rightarrow A_\mu + \partial_\mu \delta\lambda$ [so that $\delta < A_\mu > = \partial_\mu(\delta\lambda)$], we obtain

$$\delta_{(\lambda)} < j^\sigma(x) > = 0 = \int \frac{\delta < j^\sigma(x) >}{\delta < A_\rho(y) >} \frac{\partial}{\partial y^\rho}(\delta\lambda) d^4y$$

$$= - \int \pi^{\sigma\rho}(x, y) \frac{\delta(\delta\lambda)}{\delta y^\rho} d^4y$$

By integrating by parts we get finally

$$\frac{\partial}{\partial y^\alpha}\pi^{\lambda\alpha}(x, y) = 0 \tag{3.17}$$

We may also remark that since $\bar{D}_{\mu\nu}(x, y)$ is symmetric when $\mu \leftrightarrow \nu$ and $x \leftrightarrow y$ (see 3.12), it follows that $\pi^{\mu\nu}(x, y)$ is also symmetric.

Thus, there is an intimate relationship between the local conservation of current expressed by (3.16) and local gauge invariance expressed by (3.17). It can be seen, by using (3.16), that

$$\bar{D}_{\mu\nu}(x, y) = e_o^2 D_{\mu\nu}(x - y) - e_o^2 \int \left[D_F(x - y')\pi_\mu^\alpha(y', y'')\bar{D}_{\alpha\nu}(y'', y) d^4y' d^4y'' \right] \tag{3.18}$$

We shall be particularly interested in the form of the photon Green's functional when $J^{\mu} = 0$, and $|0, in\rangle = |0, out\rangle = 0$. In this case $\langle j^{\mu}\rangle \rightarrow \langle 0| j^{\mu}(x)|0\rangle = 0$, and thus because of (3.8), $\langle A^{\mu}\rangle = 0$.

All of our functions are translation invariant in this limit [as we have already discussed for $\bar{D}_{\mu\nu}(x, y)$].

$$\bar{D}_{\mu\nu}(x, y)\Big|_{J=0} \longrightarrow \bar{D}_{\mu\nu}(x - y) = \int \frac{d^4q}{(2\pi)^4} \bar{D}_{\mu\nu}(q) e^{iq.(x-y)} \tag{3.19}$$

Likewise

$$\Pi_{\mu\nu}(x, y)\Big|_{J=0} \longrightarrow \Pi_{\mu\nu}(x - y) = \int \frac{d^4q}{(2\pi)^4} \Pi_{\mu\nu}(q) e^{iq.(x-y)} \tag{3.20}$$

Because of (3.16) and (3.17), $\Pi_{\mu\nu}(q)$ must have the form

$$\Pi_{\mu\nu}(q) = (g_{\mu\nu} q^2 - q_{\mu} q_{\nu}) \rho(q^2) \tag{3.21}$$

Eq. (3.18) in momentum space becomes

$$\bar{D}_{\mu\nu}(q) = e_o^2 D_{\mu\nu}(q) - e_o^2 D_F(q)(g_{\mu}^{\alpha} q^2 - q_{\mu} q^{\alpha}) \rho(q^2) \bar{D}_{\alpha\nu}(q^2) \tag{3.22}$$

Let us put

$$\bar{D}_{\mu\nu}(q) = \left[g_{\mu\nu} - \frac{q_{\mu} q_{\nu}}{q^2} \right] \bar{D}(q^2) + \frac{q_{\mu} q_{\nu}}{q^2} L$$

where

$$\bar{D}(q^2) = e_o^2 D_F(q) - e_o^2 \rho(q^2) \bar{D}(q^2)$$

or

$$\bar{D}(q^2) = D_F(q) \frac{1}{\frac{1}{e_o^2} + \rho(q^2)}$$

and $L = e_o^2 \xi D_F(q^2)$.

[From Eq. (3.7) we see that $D_F(q^2) = \frac{1}{q^2 - i\varepsilon}$]. Thus,

$$\bar{D}_{\mu\nu}(q) = \left[g_{\mu\nu} - \frac{q_\mu q_\nu}{q^2}\right] \frac{D_F(q^2)}{(1/e_o^2) + \rho(q^2)} + \frac{q_\mu q_\nu}{q^2} e_o^2 \xi D_F(q^2) \tag{3.23}$$

We see that only the term in $\bar{D}_{\mu\nu}$ proportional to $[g_{\mu\nu} - (q_\mu q_\nu / q^2)]$ is affected [through $\rho(q^2)$] by the vacuum polarization of the electrons.

Let us now write down some relations between bare and renormalized charge; for detailed calculations see App. B. As we already saw, when $J_\mu(x) = 0$,

$$\bar{D}_{\mu\nu}(x-y) = i \langle 0 | T[A_\mu(x) A_\nu(y)] | 0 \rangle$$

$$= \int \frac{d^4 q}{(2\pi)^4} e^{iq(x-y)} \bar{D}_{\mu\nu}(q) .$$

The equal time commutation rules impose a constraint on the behavior of $\bar{D}_{\mu\nu}(x-y)$ for $x_o - y_o \rightarrow 0$, or in momentum space, on $\bar{D}_{\mu\nu}(q)$ as $q_o \rightarrow \infty$. Indeed one finds that as $q_o \rightarrow \infty$, it is necessary that

$$\rho(q^2) \rightarrow \rho(-q_o^2) \rightarrow 0. \qquad \text{Therefore, as } q^2 \rightarrow \infty$$

$$\bar{D}_{\mu\nu}(q) \rightarrow \frac{e_o^2}{q^2} \left[g_{\mu\nu} + (\xi - 1) \frac{q_\mu q_\nu}{q^2} \right]$$

which is just the form of the "free" photon Green's function, since the free field and the coupled field share the same commutation rules.

As $q^2 \longrightarrow 0$, on the other hand,

$$\bar{D}_{\mu\nu}(q) \longrightarrow \left[g_{\mu\nu} - \frac{q_\mu q_\nu}{q^2} \right] \frac{1}{q^2} \frac{1}{(1/e_o^2) + \rho(0)}$$

$$+ \frac{q_\mu q_\nu}{q^2} \frac{e_o^2 \mathscr{G}}{q^2}$$

The physical coupling (the first term), which is given at $q^2 = 0$, is governed by the parameter

$$\frac{1}{e_o^2} + \rho(0) \equiv \frac{1}{e^2} \tag{3.24}$$

The constant e is the so-called physical or renormalized charge. We shall show in App. B that it always satisfies $e_o^2 > e^2$.

The renormalization constant Z_3 is defined by

$$Z_3 \equiv \frac{e^2}{e_o^2} = 1 - e^2 \rho(0) \tag{3.25}$$

or

$$\frac{1}{Z_3} = 1 + e_o^2 \rho(0) \tag{3.25a}$$

In terms of e^2, we have

$$\bar{D}_{\mu\nu}(q) = \left[g_{\mu\nu} - \frac{q_\mu q_\nu}{q^2} \right] \frac{1}{q^2} \frac{1}{(1/e^2) + [\rho(q^2) - \rho(0)]}$$

$$+ \frac{q_\mu q_\nu}{q^2} \frac{e^2}{q^2} \frac{\mathscr{G}}{Z_3}$$

where $\rho(q^2) - \rho(0)$ can be calculated in a power series in e^2 with finite coefficients in every order.

4. ELECTRON GREEN'S FUNCTION.
FUNCTIONAL DIFFERENTIAL EQUATIONS

In order to determine $\Pi_{\mu\nu}(x, y)$ in the general case ($J_\mu \neq 0$), we must have a way of calculating $< j_\mu(x) >$ as a functional of $< A_\mu(x) >$. To do this let us look at the equations of motion of the charges.

The relevant part of the Lagrangian is

$$\mathcal{L}' = \bar{\psi}(x)\gamma^\mu \frac{1}{i}\partial_\mu \psi(x) + m_o \bar{\psi}(x)\psi(x) + j_\mu(x)A^\mu(x) \tag{4.1}$$

We use Dirac matrices such

$$\left\{\gamma_\mu, \gamma_\nu\right\} = -2g_{\mu\nu}$$

The resultant equation of motion is the Dirac equation:

$$\left[\gamma_\mu\left(\frac{1}{i}\partial^\mu - A^\mu(x)\right) + m_o\right]\psi(x) = 0 \tag{4.2}$$

m_o is the so-called mechanical mass of the electron.

The field operators obey the equal time canonical commutation rules,

$$\left\{\psi(x), \psi^+(y)\right\}_{x^o = y^o} = \delta^{(3)}(\mathbf{x} - \mathbf{y}) \tag{4.3}$$

Let us define the electron Green's functional

$$S(x, y) \equiv i < T\left[\psi(x)\bar{\psi}(y)\right] > \tag{4.4}$$

From (4.2) and (4.3) we see that $S(x, y)$ satisfies

$$(\gamma_\mu \frac{1}{i}\partial^\mu + m_o)S(x,y) = \delta^4(x - y) + i\gamma_\mu < T\left[A^\mu(x)\psi(x)\bar{\psi}(y)\right] > \tag{4.5}$$

Using the action principle (Eq. 2.12), we have for the last term,

$$< 0, \text{out} \,|\, T\left[A_\mu(x)\psi(x)\bar{\psi}(y)\right] |\, 0, \text{in} > =$$

$$= - i \frac{\delta}{\delta J^{\mu}(x)} < 0, \text{out} \,|\, T\left[\psi(x)\bar{\psi}(y)\right] |\, 0, \text{in} >$$

$$= - \frac{\delta}{\delta J^{\mu}(x)} \left[< 0, \text{out} \,|\, 0, \text{in} > S(x, y) \right]$$

$$= -i < A_{\mu}(x) > < 0, \text{out} \,|\, 0, \text{in} > S(x, y)$$

$$- < 0, \text{out} \,|\, 0, \text{in} > \frac{\delta S(x, y)}{\delta J^{\mu}(x)}$$

Finally,

$$i < T\left[A_{\mu}(x)\psi(x)\bar{\psi}(y)\right] > =$$

$$= -i \frac{\delta S(x, y)}{\delta J^{\mu}(x)} + < A_{\mu}(x) > S(x, y)$$

$$= -i \bar{D}_{\mu v}(x, x') \frac{\delta}{\delta < A_{v}(x') >} S(x, y)$$

$$+ < A_{\mu}(x) > S(x, y) \tag{4.6}$$

Here, and in what follows, we use the convention that repeated primed variables are understood to be integrated over all the four-dimensional space:

$$f(x')\, g(x') \equiv \int d^4x'\, f(x')\, g(x') \tag{4.7}$$

In the derivation of (4.6) we used (3.12). Substitution of (4.6) in (4.5) gives

$$\left[\gamma_{\mu} \left(\frac{1}{i} \partial^{\mu} - < A_{\mu}(x) > \right) + m_o \right] S(x, y) =$$

$$= \delta^4(x - y) - i \gamma_{\mu} \bar{D}^{\mu v}(x,x') \frac{\delta}{\delta < A^{v}(x') >} S(x, y) \tag{4.8}$$

which is the Schwinger functional differential equation for $S(x, y)$.

With S we can calculate $< j_\mu(x) >$ and thus $\Pi_{\mu\nu}$; therefore we have now a closed set of functional differential equations for the basic amplitudes which arise in electrodynamics.

To compute $< j_\mu(x) >$, we may use the formula for the current operator $j_\mu(x)$ in terms of $\bar{\psi}(x)\gamma^\mu\psi(x)$. Here we must be careful, since

$$S(x,y) = i < T\left[\psi(x)\bar{\psi}(y)\right] > ,$$

and as $y \to x$, $S(x,y)$ has the singularity of $\delta^3(x-y)$. Thus we expect that as $y \to x$, $S \sim \frac{1}{(x-y)^3}$.

As a consequence, $j^\mu(x)$ must be expressed as $\bar{\psi}(x)\gamma^\mu\psi(x)$ by taking a suitable limit applied to $\bar{\psi}(y)\gamma^\mu\psi(x)$ as $y \to x$.

We do not wish to dwell on the details here, but only to remark that this limit should be such that $< j_\mu >$ is gauge invariant, that is it should be unaffected if we let $< A_\mu(x) > \to < A_\mu(x) > + \partial_\mu\lambda(x)$. We see from (3.18) that $\bar{D}_{\mu\nu}$ is unaffected by this change in $< A_\mu >$, and therefore from (4.8) we find

$$S(x,y) \longrightarrow e^{i[\lambda(x) - \lambda(y)]}\, S(x,y)$$

This expression shows the importance of a careful definition of $< j_\mu >$, because as $y \to x$ the right-hand side has in general quadratically divergent gauge dependent contributions, like

$$\sim \left.\frac{\lambda(x) - \lambda(y)}{(x-y)^3}\right|_{x \to y} \sim \left.\frac{\partial_\mu\lambda(x)}{(x-y)^2}\right|_{x \to y}$$

We write the function $S(x,y)$ in the following form, which indicates its dependence of the gauge:

$$S(x, y ; < A_\mu > + \partial_\mu \lambda) = e^{i[\lambda(x) - \lambda(y)]} S(x, y; < A_\mu >) \tag{4.9}$$

By differentiating (4.9) with respect to $\lambda(\xi)$, and taking into account that

$$\frac{\delta\lambda(x)}{\delta\lambda(\xi)} = \delta^4(\xi - x), \quad \text{we get}$$

$$i\left[\delta^{(4)}(\xi - x) - \delta^{(4)}(\xi - y)\right] S(x, y)$$

$$= \int \frac{\delta\, S(x, y)}{\delta < A_\mu(\xi') >} \frac{\partial}{\partial \xi'^\mu}\left[\delta^{(4)}(\xi' - \xi)\right] d^4\xi'$$

$$= -\partial^\mu_\xi\left[\frac{\delta\, S(x, y)}{\delta < A^\mu(\xi) >}\right]$$

The quantity

$$\frac{\delta\, S(x, y)}{\delta < A^\mu(\xi) >} \equiv S(x, x')\, \Gamma_\mu(\xi, x', y') S(y', y) \tag{4.10}$$

defines the so-called Dyson vertex function Γ_μ. The identity

$$S(x, x') \frac{1}{i} \partial^\mu_\xi \Gamma_\mu(\xi, x', y') S(y', y)$$

$$= -\left[\delta(\xi - x) - \delta(\xi - y)\right] S(x, y) \tag{4.10'}$$

is the generalized Ward identity.

When $J(x) = 0$, $< A_\mu > = 0$, all functions become translation invariant. Thus, when $< A_\mu > = 0$,

$$\Gamma_\mu(\xi, x', y') = \int \frac{d^4p\, d^4q}{(2\pi)^4 (2\pi)^4} \Gamma_\mu(p + q\, , p)\, e^{i(p + q)x'}\, e^{-ipy'}\, e^{-iq\xi}$$

and

$$S(x,y) = \int \frac{d^4p}{(2\pi)^4} e^{ip(x-y)} S(p) \cdot$$

So (4.10') becomes

$$q^\mu \Gamma_\mu(p+q,\ p) = S^{-1}(p+q) - S^{-1}(p) \tag{4.11}$$

We differentiate it with respect to q_v:

$$\Gamma_v(p+q,\ p) + q^\mu \frac{\partial}{\partial q^v} \Gamma_\mu(p+q,\ p) = \frac{\partial}{\partial p^v}\left[S^{-1}(p+q)\right]$$

If we assume that $\Gamma_\mu(p+q,\ p)$ as a function of q_μ has no singularities at $q \rightarrow 0$, we find by putting $q = 0$,

$$\Gamma_v(p,p) = \frac{\partial}{\partial p^v} S^{-1}(p) \tag{4.12}$$

which is the standard form of the Ward identity.

Since $S(x,y)$ is an amplitude for a process in which charge is not locally conserved, even when $J_\mu = 0$, it will depend upon the parameter ξ. Let us calculate the exact form of this dependence.

We can see in the formula (3.18) for $D_{\mu v}(x,y)$ that we have in the right-hand side an explicit dependence of ξ in the first term, and possibly an implicit dependence in the second one, through $\pi_{\mu v}$.

In order to show that actually both $\pi_{\mu v}$ and $< j_\mu >$ are independent of ξ, let us write (3.18) in the form

$$\bar{D}_{\mu v}(x,y) = \bar{D}^{(T)}_{\mu v}(x,y) + e_o^2 \xi\left[\partial_\mu \partial_v D_F(x-x')\right] D_F(x'-y) \tag{4.13}$$

where

$$\bar{D}^{(T)}_{uv}(x,y) = e_o^2 D^{(T)}_{\mu v}(x-y) - e_o^2 D_F(x-x')\pi_{\mu\sigma}(x',y')\bar{D}^{(T)\sigma}{}_v(y',y) \tag{4.14}$$

and

$$D^{(T)}_{\mu v}(x-y) = \int \frac{d^4q}{(2\pi)^4} e^{iq(x-y)}\left[g_{\mu v} - (q_\mu q_v/q^2)\right](1/q^2) \tag{4.15}$$

If $\partial^\mu \Pi_{\mu\nu} = 0$, it follows from (4.14) and (4.15)

$\partial^\mu \bar{D}^{(T)}_{\mu\nu}(x, y) = 0$. We then have from (4.8)

$$\left[\gamma^\mu\left(\frac{1}{i}\partial_\mu - < A_\mu(x) >\right) + m_o\right] S(x, y) = \delta^4(x - y)$$

$$- i\gamma^\mu \; e_o^2 \xi \partial_\mu \partial_\nu D_F(x - x'') D_F(x'' - x') \frac{\delta S(x, y)}{\delta < A_\nu(x'') >}$$

$$- i\gamma^\mu \bar{D}^{(T)}_{\mu\nu}(x, x') \frac{\delta S(x, y)}{\delta < A_\nu(x') >} \tag{4.16}$$

The solution of (4.16) is given by (see App. C) :

$$S(x, y; < A_\mu >) = e^{ie_o^2 \xi \int \frac{d^4q}{(2\pi)^4} \frac{1}{q^2} \frac{1}{q^2}\left[e^{iq(x - y)} - 1\right]} \cdot S^{(T)}(x - y \tag{4.17}$$

where $S^{(T)}(x,y)$ obeys the functional equation

$$\left[\gamma^\mu\left(\frac{1}{i}\partial_\mu - < A_\mu >\right) + m_o\right] S^{(T)}(x, y) = \delta^4(x - y)$$

$$- i\gamma^\mu \bar{D}^{(T)}_{\mu\nu}(x, x') \frac{\delta S^{(T)}(x, y)}{\delta < A_\nu(x') >} \tag{4.18}$$

We see that as $x \rightarrow y$ the dependence on ξ which appears in (4.17) drops out, and hence the current $< j_\mu >$ can be calculated with $S^{(T)}$ as well as with S. We then have a set of equations for $\Pi_{\mu\nu}$ which contain no ξ dependence.

Thus, $< j_\mu >$ and $\Pi_{\mu\nu}$ are independent of ξ, and the complete dependence of $\bar{D}_{\mu\nu}$ on ξ is given exactly by the second term in (4.13).

This result agrees with our previous remark that in amplitudes for processes which locally conserve charge, the dependence should be trivial or absent.

We remark here that the calculations leading to (4.17) are formal, because the q integration in (4.17) diverges in the ultra-violet region. Since we have made no use of approximate methods of calculation, we see that this means that in general (for arbitrary ξ) S cannot exist.

We also see that the divergence which appears explicitly in (4.17) is multiplicative, and thus a multiplicative renormalization will remove it.

To make the argument less formal let us introduce a cut-off into our functional equations by letting

$$D_{\mu\nu}(q) = \left[g_{\mu\nu} + (\xi - 1)\frac{q_\mu q_\nu}{q^2}\right]\frac{1}{q^2} \longrightarrow$$

$$\longrightarrow \left[g_{\mu\nu} + (\xi - 1)\frac{q_\mu q_\nu}{q^2}\right]\frac{1}{q^2}\left[\frac{\Lambda^2}{q^2 + \Lambda^2}\right] \qquad (4.19)$$

In this case (4.17) becomes

$$S(x, y) = e^{ie_o^2 \xi \int \frac{d^4 q}{(2\pi)^4} \frac{1}{q^2} \frac{1}{q^2}\left[\frac{\Lambda^2}{q^2 + \Lambda^2}\right]\left[e^{iq(x - y)} - 1\right]} S^{(T)}(x,y) \qquad (4.17')$$

In (4.17') the factor $S^{(T)}(x,y)$ is a finite quantity. $S^{(T)}$ also contains Λ. We may now remark that in a certain circunstance, we can choose a finite value for ξ such that as $\Lambda^2 \rightarrow \infty$ (that is, as the cut-off is removed), S approaches a finite limit. To show this we must establish that the dependence of $S^{(T)}$ on Λ^2 is of the same multiplicative type that occurs in the exponential factor, and that it has <u>the same form</u>.

We notice that although the above integral converges near $q = 0$, if we try to separate the part which as $\Lambda^2 \to \infty$ diverges (which comes just from the constant added to $\exp[iq \cdot (x - y)]$), we could introduce a spurious infrared divergence. This is an old problem in electrodynamics. To circumvent this difficulty let us write

$$1 = \frac{m^2}{q^2 + m^2} + \frac{q^2}{q^2 + m^2}$$

where m is a convenient mass parameter, for instance the physical mass of the electron. Then we can write for the exponent

$$ie_o^2 \xi \int \frac{d^4q}{(2\pi)^4} \frac{1}{q^2} \frac{1}{q^2} \frac{\Lambda^2}{q^2 + \Lambda^2} \left[e^{iq \cdot (x - y)} - \frac{m^2}{q^2 + m^2} \right]$$

$$- ie_o^2 \xi \int \frac{d^4q}{(2\pi)^4} \frac{1}{q^2} \frac{\Lambda^2}{q^2 + \Lambda^2} \frac{1}{q^2 + m^2} .$$

The first integral remains finite as $\Lambda^2 \to \infty$, whereas the second becomes

$$e_o^2 \xi \frac{\pi^2}{(2\pi)^4} \log \left[\frac{\Lambda^2}{m^2} \right]$$

Consequently, for $\Lambda^2 \gg m^2$ we find

$$S(x, y) \longrightarrow \left[\frac{\Lambda^2}{m^2} \right]^{e_o^2 \xi \frac{\pi^2}{(2\pi)^4}} .$$

$$\cdot \, e^{ie_o^2 \xi \int \frac{d^4q}{(2\pi)^4} \left[e^{iq(x-y)} - \frac{m^2}{q^2 + m^2} \right] \frac{1}{q^2} \frac{1}{q^2}} \cdot S^{(T)}(x,y)$$

Since we know that in perturbation theory a multiplicative renormalization (defined by a constant Z_2) will make both S and $S^{(T)}$ finite, we find that the relationship between them must be of the form

$$Z_2^{(\xi)} \sim \left[\frac{\Lambda^2}{m^2}\right]^{e_o^2 \xi \frac{\pi^2}{(2\pi)^4}} Z_2^{(0)} \tag{4.18}$$

when $\Lambda^2 >> m^2$.

5. FUNCTIONAL EQUATIONS FOR S(x, y)

To carry our our subsequent analysis, we shall find it convenient to replace the functional differential equations by single, functional equations for S and $\bar{D}_{\mu\nu}$. These at first sight will look complicated. However, the complications will be superficial, in the sense that each term in the equations will have certain features which will be shared by all, and consequently by the solution. They will allow us in a simple way to establish the existence of finite, renormalized solutions, to study the finiteness of the renormalization constant, to investigate symmetry breaking solutions, to study the consequent existence or non-existence of the so-called Goldstone bosons, and finally to consider what happens far off the mass shell.

Let us first define the "electron self-energy part":

$$i\gamma^{\mu}\bar{D}_{\mu\nu}(x, x')\frac{\delta}{\delta < A_\nu(x') >} S(x, y) \equiv \sum(x, x')S(x', y) \tag{5.1}$$

Substituting in (4.18) we have

$$\left[\gamma^{\mu}\left(\frac{1}{i}\partial_{\mu} - \langle A_{\mu}(x)\rangle\right) + m_{o}\right] S(x,y) =$$

$$= \delta^{(4)}(x-y) - \sum(x,x')S(x',y) \qquad (5.2)$$

If we define $\frac{1}{S}(x,y)$ by

$$\frac{1}{S}(x,x') \cdot S(x',y) \equiv \delta^{(4)}(x-y), \qquad (5.3)$$

we get for (5.2) the following formal solution:

$$\frac{1}{S}(x,y) = \left[\gamma^{\mu}\left(\frac{1}{i}\partial_{\mu} - \langle A_{\mu}(x)\rangle\right) + m_{o}\right]\delta^{(4)}(x-y)$$

$$+ \sum(x,y) \qquad (5.4)$$

Combining (5.1) and (5.4) we get

$$\sum(x,y) = i\gamma^{\mu}\bar{D}_{\mu\nu}(x,y)S(x,y)\gamma^{\nu}$$

$$- i\gamma^{\mu}\bar{D}_{\mu\nu}(x,x')S(x,x'')\frac{\delta\sum(x'',y)}{\delta\langle A_{\nu}(x')\rangle} \qquad (5.5)$$

On iteration of this equation we will obtain an infinite series which expresses $\sum(x,y)$ in terms of integrals of powers of S and $\bar{D}_{\mu\nu}$.

At this point it is convenient to introduce the standard graphical notation. Let x y symbolize S(x, y), and ξ η simbolize $\bar{D}_{\mu\nu}(\xi,\eta)$.

The connections at vertices are made with

$\gamma^{\mu}\delta(\xi - x)\delta(x - y)$.

In this way the result of the iteration can be graphically represented by

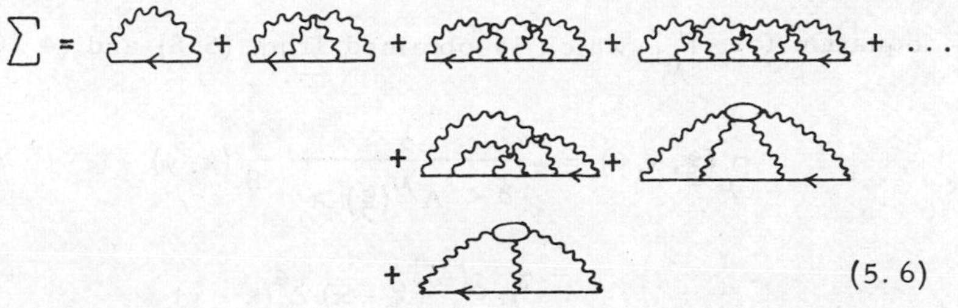

(5.6)

The powers of S increase by two and those of $\bar{D}_{\mu\nu}$ by one from term to term.

We will <u>define</u> by the series (5.6) the <u>functional</u>

$$\sum\left[x,y;\ \bar{D}_{\mu\nu}(\xi,\eta);\ S(u,v)\right] \tag{5.7}$$

for arbitrary S and $\bar{D}$.

In this way for a given $\bar{D}_{\mu\nu}$ we may regard S as the solution of the functional equation

$$\frac{1}{S}(x,y) = \left[\gamma^{\mu}\left(\frac{1}{i}\partial_{\mu} - < A_{\mu} >\right) + m_o\right]\delta^{(4)}(x-y)$$
$$+ \sum\left[x,y;\ \bar{D}(\xi,\eta);\ S(u,v)\right] \tag{5.8}$$

In this functional equation S is the independent variable, while < A > may be considered as a parameter.

Of course, the form of $\bar{D}$ also depends upon S, so really there is another functional equation for $\bar{D}$ in terms of S.

Thus, S and $\bar{D}$ are actually the simultaneous solutions of a pair of coupled equations.

It will simplify matters however, if at first we study the equation for S with $\bar{D}$ assumed as given. We will then study the more general pair of equations later.

Before of doing that, let us write the following integral equation for Γ_μ, which is obtained from (5.8) and (4.10):

$$\Gamma_\mu(\xi, x, y) = - \frac{\delta}{\delta < A^\mu(\xi) >} \frac{1}{S}(x, y)$$

$$= \gamma_\mu \delta^{(4)}(\xi - x)\, \delta^4(x - y)$$

$$- \frac{\delta}{\delta < A^\mu(\xi) >} \sum\left[x, y;\ \bar{D}_{\mu v}(\xi, \eta);\ S(u, v)\right] \qquad (5.9)$$

We shall have to consider Γ_μ only for $J_\mu = 0$ In this case

$$\left. \frac{\delta \bar{D}_{\mu v}(\xi, \eta)}{\delta J_\lambda(\xi)} \right|_{J=0} = - < 0 \left| T\left[A_\mu(\xi) A_v(\eta) A_\lambda(\xi)\right] \right| 0 > = 0$$

because of Furry's Theorem (since A_μ is odd under charge conjugation and $|0>$ is invariant). Consequently when $< A > = 0$

$$\Gamma_\mu(\xi, x, y) = \gamma_\mu \delta^4(\xi - x)\, \delta^{(4)}(x - y)$$

$$- \frac{\delta \sum(x, y;\ \bar{D};\ S)}{\delta S(u', v')} S(u', u'')\, \Gamma_\mu(\xi, u'', v'')\, S(v'', v') \qquad (5.10)$$

where we used (4.10). Defining

$$- \frac{\delta \sum\left[x, y;\ \bar{D}(\xi, \eta);\ S(u, v)\right]}{\delta S(x', y')} \equiv K_{e\bar{e}}(x, y;\ y', x') \, , \qquad (5.11)$$

eq. (5.10) can be written

$$\Gamma_\mu(\xi, x, y) = \gamma_\mu \delta^4(\xi - x)\delta^4(x-y)$$

$$+ K_{e\bar{e}}(x,y; y', x')S(x', x'')\Gamma_\mu(\xi, x'', y'')S(y'', y') \qquad (5.12)$$

Graphically, $K_{e\bar{e}}$ has the form

$K_{e\bar{e}}$ =

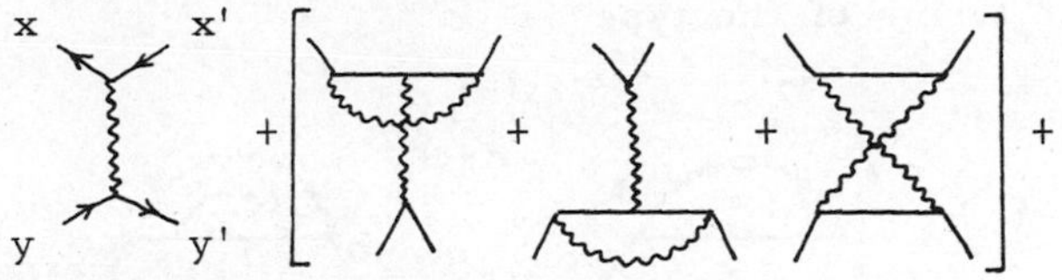

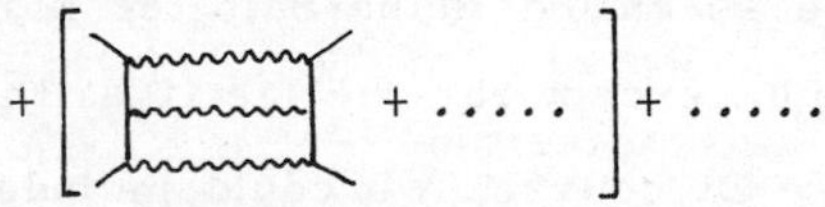

(5.13)

as can be seen by taking the functional derivative with respect to S of (5.6).

Since $\langle A \rangle = 0$, we may write Eq. (5.12) in momentum space and it becomes

$$\Gamma_\mu(p+q, p) = \gamma_\mu + \int K_q(p, k)S(k+q)\,\Gamma_\mu(k+q, k)S(k)d^4k \qquad (5.14)$$

where $K_q(p, k)$ is defined by

$$K(x, y, y', x') = \int \frac{d^4p\, d^4q\, d^4k}{(2\pi)^{12}} K_q(p,k)e^{i(p+q)x}e^{-ipy}e^{i(k+q)x'}e^{-iky'} \qquad (5.15)$$

Notice that we can write K as a function of only three momenta because of the translation invariance of $K(x, y, y', x')$.

Thus, labeled with momenta, the series (5.13) is

$K_{e\bar{e}}$ = 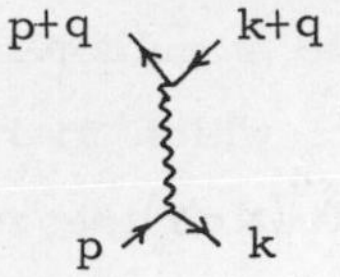

 + ... (5.16)

$K_{e\bar{e}}$ is irreducible with respect to two electron or two photon "cuts" vertically. That is, no term in (5.13) can be broken into two pieces by cutting two electron or two photon lines vertically. (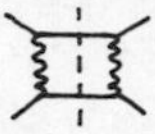 , 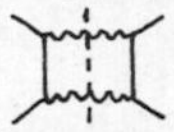); this occurs because in the series (5.6) there are no terms of the type

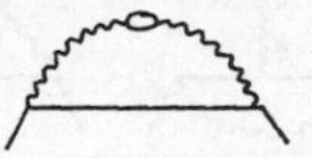 or 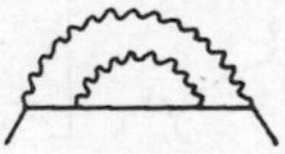

$K_{e\bar{e}}$ would be the so-called Bethe-Salpeter kernel for particle-antiparticle scattering, except for the fact that the "two photon" terms are not present. Of course, we could include them in (5.14) if we wished, since they can give no contribution because of the Furry theorem.

6. GAUGE WITH A FINITE Z_2

It is easy to see that if we graphically represent Γ_μ by 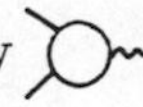, then we may also represent $K_{e\bar{e}}$ in the form

$K_{e\bar{e}}$ =  + 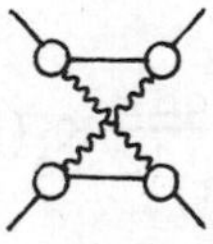 + ... ≡ 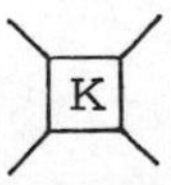

 (6.1)

In these graphs (which are called "skeletons") only vertices of the Γ_μ type appear.

From Eq. (5.14) it can be seen that if we rescale S and Γ in such a way that $S \cdot \Gamma$ = invariant, then KSS is also invariant.

Thus, KSS is invariant with respect to a multiplicative renormalization of S and Γ_μ. It is this feature which makes (5.14) a useful equation to study renormalized perturbation theory. The graphical representation of (5.14) is

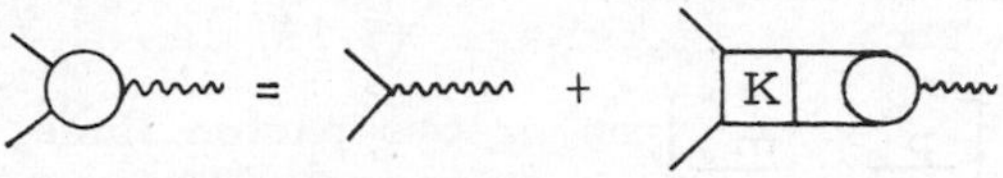

(6.2)

If we try to compute Γ_μ using this equation, without a cut-off, we encounter divergences in perturbation theory. However, we also know that we may make Γ_μ finite by means of a divergent multiplicative renormalization. We now wish to make use of this fact to prove that we may choose a special value of ξ, which makes Γ_μ finite when evaluated using (6.2).

Let us first repeat the argument given by Gell-Mann and Low to show that we can determine the form of the dependence of Γ_μ on the cut-off.

We shall assume that e_o^2 is finite, so that

$$\bar{D}_{\mu\nu}(q) \xrightarrow[q^2 \to \infty]{} e_o^2 D_{\mu\nu}(q)$$

where $\bar{D}_{\mu\nu}$ contains an ultraviolet cut-off, as defined in (4.19).

We shall assume that the part of the contribution to Γ_μ which diverges as $\Lambda \to \infty$, comes from the asymptotic region, so that we may replace $\bar{D}_{\mu\nu}$ by $e_o^2 D_{\mu\nu}$ everywhere in K.

The Gell-Mann and Low argument is the following. Since

$$\Gamma_\mu(p, p) = \frac{\partial}{\partial p^\mu} S^{-1}(p)$$

we can think in terms of S instead of Γ. Then for $p^2 \gg m^2$,

$$S^{-1}(p) \longrightarrow (\gamma \cdot p) B(p^2),$$

where B is a finite, dimensionless function of p^2, Λ^2 and m^2 (m = physical mass of electron):

$$B = B\left[\frac{p^2}{\Lambda^2}, \frac{m^2}{\Lambda^2}\right]$$

It is understood that B depends also of e_o^2. Further we may write

$$B\left[\frac{p^2}{\Lambda^2}, \frac{m^2}{\Lambda^2}\right] = Z_2\left[\frac{m^2}{\Lambda^2}\right] \bar{B}\left[\frac{p^2}{m^2}, \frac{m^2}{\Lambda^2}\right],$$

and we know from renormalized perturbation theory that with a suitable choice for Z_2, $\bar{B}$ is finite in the limit as $\Lambda^2 \rightarrow \infty$.

Further,

$$B\left[\frac{p^2}{\Lambda^2}, \frac{m^2}{\Lambda^2}\right]$$

remains finite when $m \rightarrow 0$ (this fact is less obvious, and we shall give below an argument for it).

If it is so, for p^2, $\Lambda^2 \gg m^2$ we find

$$B\left[\frac{p^2}{\Lambda^2}, 0\right] \sim Z_2\left[\frac{m^2}{\Lambda^2}\right] \bar{B}\left[\frac{p^2}{m^2}, 0\right].$$

If we put $p^2 = \Lambda^2$,

$$B(1, 0) \sim Z_2\left[\frac{m^2}{p^2}\right] \bar{B}\left[\frac{p^2}{m^2}, 0\right]. \quad \text{So}$$

$$B\left[\frac{p^2}{\Lambda^2}, 0\right] \cdot \bar{B}\left[\frac{\Lambda^2}{m^2}, 0\right] = B(1, 0)\bar{B}\left[\frac{p^2}{m^2}, 0\right]$$

Differentiating with respect to p^2 and putting $p^2 = \Lambda^2$, we find

$$\frac{1}{p^2} B'(1,0)\bar{B}\left[\frac{p^2}{m^2}, 0\right] = \frac{1}{m^2} B(1,0)\bar{B}'\left[\frac{p^2}{m^2}, 0\right].$$

The solution of this equation is

$$\bar{B}\left[\frac{p^2}{m^2}, 0\right] = (\text{const.})\left[\frac{p^2}{m^2}\right]^{g(e_o^2)}, \quad \text{where}$$

$g(e_o^2) = \dfrac{B'(1,0)}{B(1,0)}$ is a finite function of e_o^2 So

$$Z_2\left[\frac{m^2}{\Lambda^2}\right] \sim (\text{const.})'\left[\frac{m^2}{\Lambda^2}\right]^{g(e_o^2)} \tag{6. 3}$$

The above argument holds for any value of ξ. Let us apply it for $\xi = 0$; using (4. 18) we get for any ξ

$$Z_2^{\xi}\left[\frac{m^2}{\Lambda^2}\right] \sim Z_2^{o}\left[\frac{m^2}{\Lambda^2}\right]\cdot\left[\frac{m^2}{\Lambda^2}\right]^{\frac{e_o^2 \pi^2}{(2\pi)^4}\xi} =$$

$$= (\text{const.})\left[\frac{m^2}{\Lambda^2}\right]^{\left[g(e_o^2) + \frac{e_o^2 \pi^2}{(2\pi)^4}\xi\right]}$$

We see that if we choose ξ so that

$$g(e_o^2) + \frac{e_o^2 \pi^2}{(2\pi)^4}\xi = 0,$$

then Z_2^{ξ} is finite as $\Lambda^2 \to \infty$, that is in this case no divergent multiplicative renormalization of S or Γ is required.

If we compute g in powers of e_o^2, we find that the series begins with the fourth order term. Therefore, ξ must be of the form $\xi = \xi_1 e_o^2 + \xi_2 e_o^4 + \ldots$ with finite coefficients ξ_i

We may now give the intuitive reason for this result. This intuitive argument is the basis of a proof of (6. 3).

If we look at the integral equation (6.2), the lowest divergent graph is

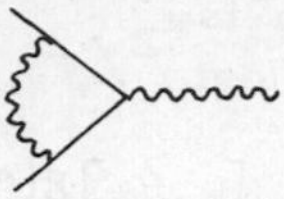 (6.4)

and as is well known this diverges as $\log(\Lambda^2)$ as $\Lambda^2 \rightarrow \infty$. However, the coefficient of the logarithm is a linear function of ξ, and hence it can be made to vanish for some choice of ξ. A simple inspection shows that this occurs for $\xi = 0$. Because of Ward's identity, the coefficient of $\gamma \cdot p$ in the graph 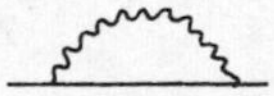 is also finite for this choice of ξ.

In the next order we have the following graphs which are iterations of the kernel  $= K^{(1)}$.

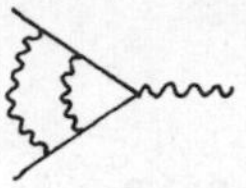 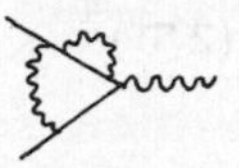, etc.

For the same reason that (6.4) became finite for $\xi = 0$, it can be seen that the graphs above are also finite.

The only possible divergent contributions come from the next terms in K,

$K^{(2)}(p,k) \sim$  + 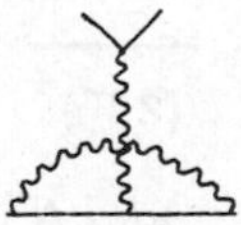 + 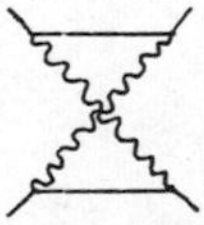

To look at the divergent part of the integration we may put m = 0 in all electron Green's functions. We get

$$\text{div. part} = \int K^{A}_{(2)}(p,q)\,\frac{1}{\gamma \cdot q}\,\gamma_{\mu}\,\frac{1}{\gamma \cdot q}\,d^4q$$

For $m = 0$, $q^2 K_{(2)}$ is of the form $K(p/q)$, and it is clear that if $K(0)$ is finite, this integral will diverge like $\gamma_\mu \cdot \log(\Lambda^2)$. If however, as $p \to 0$, $K(p/q) \to \log(p^2/q^2)$, for example, we could get a divergence of the type $\gamma_\mu (\log \Lambda^2)^2$. We shall show below that $K_{(2)}(0, q)$ is finite, so that only a single $\log(\Lambda^2)$ appears. Therefore, we may cancel this logarithmic term by letting $\xi \to \xi_1 e_o^2$ with a suitable finite choice of ξ_1, since then to this order (e_o^4) the graph (6.4) would also have a single $\log(\Lambda^2)$. We may continue this argument order by order; all that must be shown to prove that the cancellation is possible with a power series $\xi = \xi_1 e_o^2 + \xi_2 e_o^4 + \ldots$ with finite coefficients, is that each contribution to $K(p, q)$ remains finite when $m = 0$ and $p = 0$.

In the example above we have for example

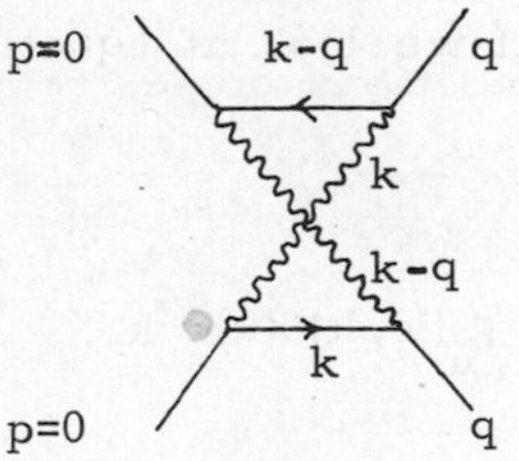

,

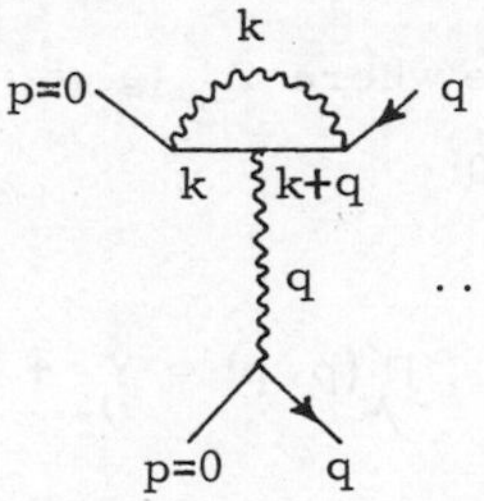

. . . . . .

We see that when $m = 0$ for the first graph the integration over k is convergent both in the ultraviolet and infrared regions, since the denominators vanish at most like k^3 near $k = 0$ or $(k - q)^3$ at $k = q$. The same holds true for the other graphs, where the ultraviolet convergence occurs because of the choice of gauge. Therefore, $K^{(2)}(0, q)$ with $m = 0$ is finite. With the same method we can generalize this proof to an arbitrary order.

From now on it will greatly simplify our considerations to make use of the value of ξ which makes Z_2 finite or, equivalently, makes the unrenormalized S exist.

However, it should be noted that even though S formally exists for this choice of ξ, some care must be exercised since the integrals which yield S or Γ are still singular. Thus, for example, if we put $\xi = 0$ and evaluate the following graph

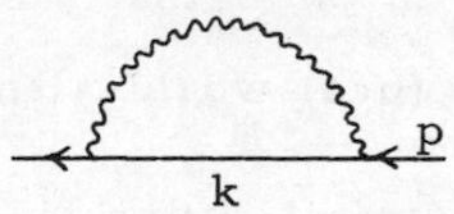

when $S(k) \rightarrow 1/(\gamma \cdot k)$, the integral is only conditionally convergent. Indeed, if we compute the "next largest" contribution given by $-m/k^2$, it diverges (and requires a subtraction from the m_o term in $1/S$). Consequently, the operations imposed to obtain the vertex equation from the self-energy equation still have only a formal significance without the use of a cut-off, even when performed in the gauge where Z_2 is finite. Indeed if we look at equation (5.14) for $q = 0$:

$$\Gamma_\mu(p, p) = \gamma_\mu + \int K(p, k)S(k)\ \Gamma_\mu(k, k)S(k)d^4k$$

and assuming for $p \rightarrow \infty$ that

$$\Gamma_\mu \rightarrow \gamma_\mu, \qquad S \rightarrow \frac{1}{\gamma \cdot k}$$

we get for the asymptotic contributions:

$$\gamma_\mu = \gamma_\mu + \int K^A(p,k) \frac{1}{\gamma \cdot k} \gamma_\mu \frac{1}{\gamma \cdot k} d^4k \qquad (6.5)$$

where

$K^A(p,k) =$ 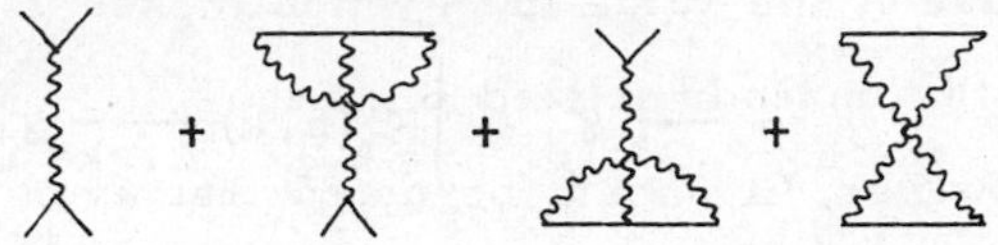 $+ \ldots$

(6. 5')

In K^A we use $S = \frac{1}{\gamma \cdot k}$ for the electron propagator and we work in the gauge defined above.

However, it is easy to show that the second term of (6. 5) does not vanish, but becomes $\gamma_\mu \lambda(e_o^2)$, where $\lambda(e_o^2)$ is a power series in e_o^2 which is finite order by order.

Therefore, (6. 5) is not consistent with $\Gamma_\mu \rightarrow \gamma_\mu$ for $p \rightarrow \infty$. Consequently, what we should in fact say in this gauge is that as $p \rightarrow \infty$, $\Gamma_\mu(p, p) \rightarrow C\gamma_\mu$, where C is a constant.

Then for S we have for $p \rightarrow \infty$

$$S(p) \longrightarrow \frac{1}{C} \frac{1}{\gamma \cdot p}, \quad \text{because of Ward's identity.}$$

Let us define

$$\Gamma'_\mu = \frac{1}{C} \Gamma_\mu(p, p) \qquad (6.6)$$

So $\qquad \Gamma'_u(p, p) \longrightarrow \gamma_\mu$ as $p \longrightarrow \infty$.

Similarly, we define

$$S'(p) = CS(p) \xrightarrow[p \to \infty]{} \frac{1}{\gamma \cdot p}.$$

We see that

$$KSS \longrightarrow K'S'S'$$

by replacing Γ by Γ' and S by S'. Therefore,

$$\Gamma'_\mu(p,p) = \frac{1}{C}\gamma_\mu + \int K'(p,k)S'(k)\,\Gamma'_\mu(k,k)S'(k)d^4k \qquad (6.7)$$

which asymptotically becomes

$$\gamma_\mu = \frac{1}{C}\gamma_\mu + \int K'_A(p,k)\frac{1}{\gamma\cdot k}\gamma_\mu\frac{1}{\gamma\cdot k}d^4k \qquad (6.7')$$

where

$K'_A(p,k) =$ 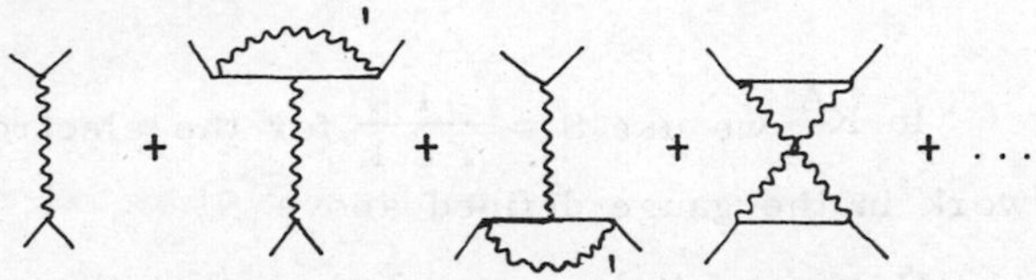

with $S' = \frac{1}{\gamma\cdot k}$ in all electron lines, and where each vertex correction in K'_A has a finite subtraction made from it so that $\Gamma_\mu^{(n)}(p+k,p) = 0$ when $n = 0$; we indicate this with a prime.

The integral in (6.7') then has the form

$$\lambda'(e_o^2)\gamma_\mu, \text{ with } \lambda'(e_o^2) \text{ a finite power series.}$$

Our result is then consistent if we take $\frac{1}{C} + \lambda'(e_o^2) = 1$.

With this simple remark our equations are consistent with the limiting behavior

$$\Gamma'_\mu(p,p) \longrightarrow \gamma_\mu \quad \text{and} \quad S'(p) \longrightarrow \frac{1}{\gamma\cdot p}.$$

far off the mass shell in this gauge.

The final result is then to put a finite constant $\neq 1$ in the inhomogeneous term of the integral equation for Γ_μ.

Hereafter we shall assume that this is done in the kernel and we will no longer indicate with a prime the corrected vertex and S functions.

7. THE ELECTRON BARE MASS

The equation for the electron Green's function when $\langle A \rangle = 0$ can be written (see Eq. 5.8)

$$\frac{1}{S(p)} = \gamma \cdot p + m_o + \sum\left[p;\ \bar{D}(q);\ S(k)\right] \qquad (7.1)$$

We wish to study this equation in the asymptotic region. As in the case of Γ, we replace $\bar{D}(q)$ by its asymptotic form,

$$\bar{D}_{\mu v}(q) \longrightarrow e_o^2 D_{\mu v}(q).$$

Further, if we work in the gauge defined in the previous section no cut-off in $\bar{D}_{\mu v}$ will be needed to make $S(k)$ exist without renormalization. However, in perturbation theory only the combination $m_o + \sum(p)$ will be finite; that is, if we let $m_o = m - \delta m$ (m = physical mass of the electron and δm = electromagnetic mass) only $-\delta m + \sum(p)$ is finite in perturbation theory in the limit $\Lambda^2 \rightarrow \infty$. We shall find it convenient instead of working with m, to use the parameter

$$m'_o = m_o + \sum(0)$$

where m'_o is a finite quantity (its relation to m is finite in perturbation theory). Therefore, (7.1) becomes asymptotically

$$\frac{1}{S(p)} = \gamma \cdot p + m'_o + \Big[\sum[p;\ e_o^2 D(q);\ S(k)]$$

$$- \sum[0;\ e_o^2 D(q);\ S(k)]\Big] \qquad (7.2)$$

In our further discussion it will be useful to study this equation regarding it as exact. This amounts to studying the usual theory omitting all diagrams with insertions into single photon lines.

This theory and the exact one will share the same asymptotic electron Green's function provided e_o^2 is finite.

Let us now scale Eq. (7.2):

$$\frac{1}{\lambda S(\lambda p)} = \gamma \cdot p + \frac{m_o'}{\lambda} + \frac{1}{\lambda}\left[\Sigma(\lambda p;\ e_o^2 D;\ S) - \Sigma(0;\ e_o^2 D;\ S)\right]$$

If we make use of (5.6), we find

$$\frac{1}{\lambda S(\lambda p)} = \gamma \cdot p + \frac{m_o'}{\lambda} + \left[\Sigma\left(p;\ e_o^2 D;\ \lambda S(\lambda k)\right) - \Sigma\left(0;\ e_o^2 D;\ \lambda S(\lambda k)\right)\right] \qquad (7.3)$$

which expresses the fact that m_o' is the only parameter which sets the scale in (7.2).

Let us define

$$m(p) \equiv -\frac{\partial}{\partial\lambda}\left[\frac{1}{\lambda S(\lambda p)}\right]_{\lambda=1} \qquad (7.4)$$

If we differentiate (7.3), we get

$$m(p) = m_o' + \int\left[K(p,k) - K(0,k)\right] S(k)m(k)S(k)d^4k \qquad (7.5)$$

where

$$K(p,k) = -\frac{\delta\Sigma(p)}{\delta S(k)} = K_{q=0}(p,k)$$

is the Bethe-Salpeter kernel previously defined.

We may use (7.4) to compute m(p) as a power series in e_o^2 which is finite order by order. We must of course supplement (7.5) with an equation which allows us to construct S from m.

Since

$$\frac{1}{S(p)} = \gamma \cdot p\, B(p^2) + A(p^2), \quad \text{using (7.4), we get}$$

$$m(p) = \gamma \cdot p \left[-2p^2 B'(p^2)\right] + A(p^2) - 2p^2 A'(p^2) \equiv$$

$$\equiv \gamma \cdot p\, \beta(p^2) + \alpha(p^2).$$

Therefore:

$$B(p^2) = 1 + \frac{1}{2} \int_{p^2}^{\infty} \frac{dx}{x} \beta(x)$$

This integral converges since we know that in our gauge, S is consistent with the asymptotic behavior

$$\frac{1}{S} \longrightarrow \gamma \cdot p \quad \text{for } p^2 \longrightarrow \infty. \text{ We also find}$$

$$A(p^2) = \frac{1}{2} \int_{1}^{\infty} \frac{dx}{x^{3/2}} \alpha(p^2 x) + (\text{const.}) \sqrt{p^2}\,.$$

Since A should have no square root singularity at $p^2 = 0$, the constant must be zero. Therefore:

$$A(p^2) = \frac{1}{2} \int_{1}^{\infty} \frac{dx}{x^{3/2}} \alpha(p^2 x).$$

In zeroth order, $m(p) = m_o'$, so

$$\beta = 0, \quad B = 1 \quad \text{and} \quad \alpha = m_o', \quad A = m_o'. \quad \text{Thus}$$

$$\frac{1}{S} = \gamma \cdot p + m_o'$$

Consequently to zeroth order $m_o' = m$, where m is the physical mass. If we substitute

$$S = \frac{1}{\gamma \cdot p + m_o'}$$

into K we can calculate m(p) to the next order. If we continue in this fashion we will construct a finite iterative solution to the equation for m(p), in terms of e_o^2 and m_o'.

Let us consider the case in which the complete solution to the equation for m(p) is such that we get an S which makes $\sum(p)$ exist without a cut-off [i.e., the exact solution to (7.1) is such that m_o exists and is finite]; then it is interesting to notice that we could scale (7.1) itself without a cut-off. In this case we would find

$$m(p) = m_o + \int K(p,k)\, S(k)\, m(k)\, S(k)\, d^4k \qquad (7.5')$$

From this it follows immediately

$$m(0) = m_o + \int K(0,k)\, S(k)\, m(k)\, S(k)\, d^4k \qquad (7.5'')$$

or

$$m(p) = m(0) + \int \left[K(p,k) - K(0,k)\right] S(k)\, m(k)\, S(k)\, d^4k \qquad (7.5''')$$

Comparing with (7.5) we get $m(0) = m_o'$, that is, when m_o is finite, we can compute it using (7.5') or (7.5'') with m(0) replaced by m_o'. Eq. (7.5'') in this case would give the supposed finite relationship between m_o and m_o'.

Let us now study (7.5) in the asymptotic region $p^2 \gg m_o'^2 \sim m^2$. Then

$$m(p) = \gamma \cdot p\beta(p^2) + \alpha(p^2) \longrightarrow \alpha(p^2), \text{ since in general}$$

$$\beta \sim 0\left[\frac{m^2}{p^2}\right] \quad \text{for} \quad p^2 \gg m^2 \quad \text{in our gauge.}$$

Thus, if both p^2 and p'^2 are large,

$$\alpha(p^2) \simeq m'_o + \int \left[K(p,k) - K(0,k)\right] S(k)\, m(k)\, S(k)\, d^4k$$

$$\alpha(p'^2) \simeq m'_o + \int \left[K(p',k) - K(0,k)\right] S(k) m(k)\, S(k)\, d^4k$$

and therefore

$$\alpha(p^2) \simeq \alpha(p'^2) + \int \left[K(p,k) - K(p',k)\right] S(k)\alpha(k)\, S(k)\, d^4k \ ,$$

where we also replace m by α in the integrand since we are interested in the asymptotic contribution to the integral.

If we put m = 0 in the kernel, the equation approaches to the finite limit

$$\alpha(p^2) \simeq \alpha(p'^2) + \int \left[K_A(p,k) - K_A(p',k)\right] \frac{1}{\gamma \cdot k}\alpha(k)\frac{1}{\gamma \cdot k}\, d^4k \qquad (7.6)$$

where K_A is the asymptotic kernel defined in (6.5'). (7.6) is a linear integral equation, and we see that

$$\alpha(p^2) = \alpha(p'^2)\, f\left[\frac{p^2}{p'^2},\ e_o^2\right]$$

where

$$f\left[\frac{p^2}{p'^2},\ e_o^2\right] = 1 - \int \left[K_A(p,k) - K_A(p',k)\right] \frac{1}{k^2} f\left[\frac{k^2}{p'^2},\ e_o^2\right] d^4k.$$

If we differentiate (7.6) with respect to p^2 and put $p'^2 = p^2$, we get

$$\frac{\alpha'(p^2)}{\alpha(p^2)} = p^2 f(e_o^2), \qquad \text{where}$$

$$f(e_o^2) = \frac{\partial}{\partial x} f(x, e_o^2)\Big|_{x=1}$$

Therefore,

$$\alpha(p^2) \sim \left[\frac{p^2}{m^2}\right]^{f(e_o^2)} \cdot \text{(constant)}$$

is the asymptotic form of $\alpha(p^2)$ valid when $p^2 \gg m^2$.

$f(e_o^2)$ can be calculated as a finite power series in e_o^2 using (7.6). Let us illustrate the lowest order calculation. In lowest order,

$K_A =$ 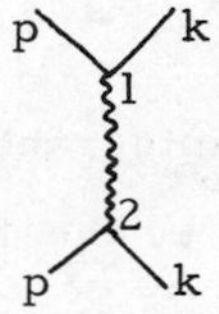

$$= -\frac{ie_o^2}{(2\pi)^4}\gamma^{\mu}_{(1)} D_{\mu\nu}(p-k)\gamma^{\nu}_{(2)}$$

with $\xi = 0$. So,

$$f\left[\frac{p^2}{p'^2}, e_o^2\right] = 1 + ie_o^2 \int \frac{d^4k}{(2\pi)^4}\left[\gamma^{\mu} D_{\mu\nu}(p-k)\gamma^{\nu}\right.$$

$$\left. - \gamma^{\mu} D_{\mu\nu}(p'-k)\gamma^{\nu}\right]\frac{1}{k^2} f\left[\frac{k^2}{p'^2}, e_o^2\right] d^4k =$$

$$= 1 - 3ie_o^2 \int \frac{d^4k}{(2\pi)^4}\left[\frac{1}{(p-k)^2} - \frac{1}{(p'-k)}\right] \cdot$$

$$\cdot \frac{1}{k^2} f\left[\frac{k^2}{p'^2}, e_o^2\right] d^4k$$

Going to an euclidean metric, we have (for example, if $p > p'$)

$$f\left[\frac{p^2}{p'^2}, e_o^2\right] = 1 - \frac{3e_o^2\pi^2}{(2\pi)^4}\int_{p'^2}^{p^2}\frac{dk^2}{k^2} f\left[\frac{k^2}{p'^2}, e_o^2\right] =$$

$$= 1 - \frac{3e_o^2 \pi^2}{(2\pi)^4} \int_1^{p^2/p'^2} \frac{dx}{x} f(x).$$

Therefore

$$f(e_o^2) = - \frac{3e_o^2 \pi^2}{(2\pi)^4} = - \frac{3\alpha_o}{4\pi},$$

and in the lowest order,

$$\alpha(p^2) \longrightarrow \left[\frac{m^2}{p^2}\right]^{\frac{3\alpha_o}{4\pi}} \cdot \text{(const.)}.$$

In the next order we have to include the graphs

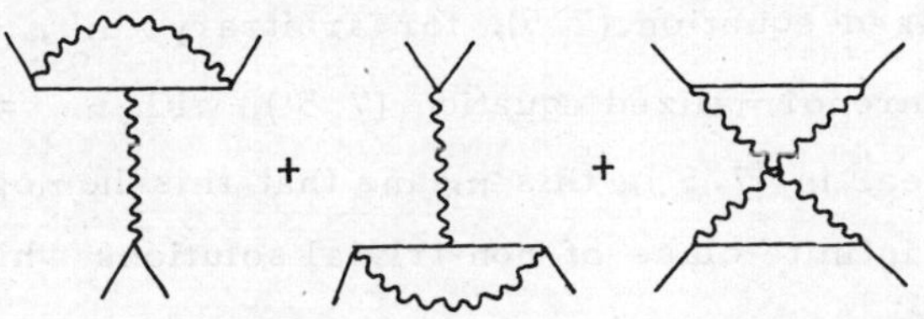

plus the gauge modification of  .

We see that

$$f(e_o^2) = - \frac{3e_o^2}{16\pi^2} + \cdots ,$$

so that if e_o^2 is small enough, f is negative, and

$$\alpha(p^2) \longrightarrow \left[\frac{m^2}{p^2}\right]^{-f} \longrightarrow 0.$$

If we suppose that for the actual e_o^2 f remains negative, then

$$m(p) \longrightarrow \alpha(p^2) \longrightarrow 0 \quad \text{as} \quad p^2 \longrightarrow \infty .$$

As a consequence, the unsubtracted integral

$$\int K(p,k)\, S(k)\, m(k)\, S(k)\, d^4k$$

exists and yields a function which vanishes for $p^2 \longrightarrow \infty$. Using (7.5') we find, since $m(p) \longrightarrow 0$, that

$$m_o \equiv 0 ,$$

that is, the bare mass of the electron vanishes. To obtain this result we have summed up the ordinary renormalized perturbation solution of the equations, which are expressed in terms of an arbitrary finite physical mass.

Since the bare mass vanishes, we find that taking the solution of the renormalized equation (7.5), for arbitrary m_o', we get the solution to the unrenormalized equation (7.5'), with $m_o = 0$. Since m_o' does not appear in (7.5'), this means that this homogeneous equation has an infinite class of non-trivial solutions which are related to each other by the scaling law $m_o' \longrightarrow \lambda m_o'$ for arbitrary λ. We see also that since m(p) obeys (7.5') with $m_o = 0$, Eq. (7.5") is just a trivial identity in m_o'.

8.-SYMMETRY BREAKING

From the discussion at the end of the last section we have seen that since $m_o = 0$ the renormalized theory gives an infinite number of finite solutions for m(p) (one for each value of m_o'), which are not scale invariant.

However, the unrenormalized equation (7.5') is invariant under a scale transformation. Therefore, the renormalized perturbation theory breaks the symmetry of the unrenormalized equation.

Let us prove now that if we have a spontaneously broken theory with a conserved current, then there must be particles of zero mass. This is the Goldstone theorem.

Let us represent m(p) by

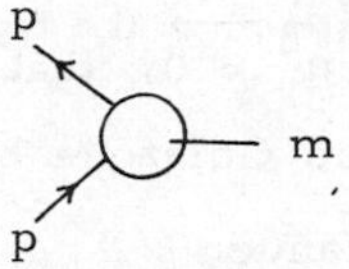

(8.1)

and the homogeneous Eq. (7.5') with $m_o = 0$ by

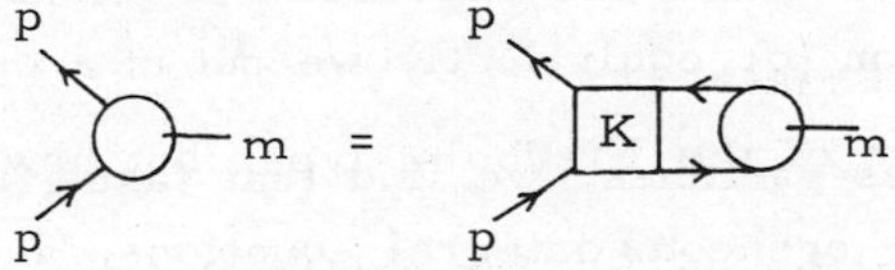

(8.2)

Now suppose we were to consider putting into our Lagrangian, a coupling to an external scalar field, that is, a term $\bar{\psi}(x)\psi(x)K(x) = S(x)K(x)$ where K(x) is a given c-number function.

Then we would define a corresponding scalar vertex function $\Gamma(\xi, x, y)$ which when $k \longrightarrow 0$, would obey the equation

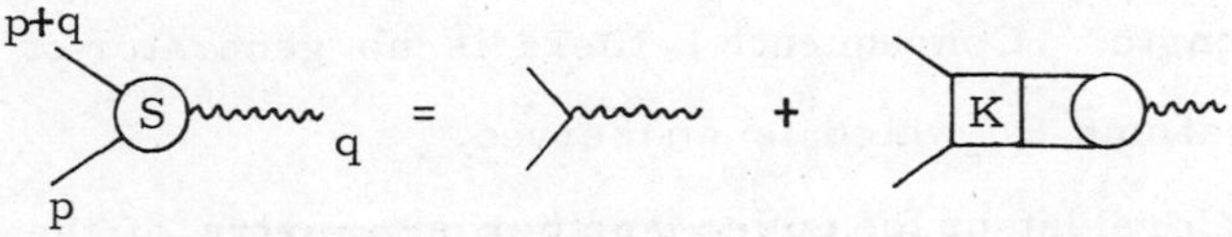

(8.2')

where 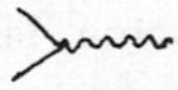 stands for the Dirac matrix 1. We see that when $q^\mu = 0$, this equation is identical to (8.2), except for the absence of the inhomogeneous term in (8.2).

Now, if these integral equations were of the Fredholm type (which they are not), then we could write for the Fredholm determinant of (8.2'),

$$\det(1 - KSS) = f(q^2),$$

where because of Lorentz invariance, f would depend only on q^2. Since we see that (8.2) has a solution with $q^\mu = 0$, this would mean that $f(0) = 0$, and hence we would find that the homogeneous equation of (8.2') would have a solution with only the requirement that $q^2 = 0$, not $q^\mu = 0$. This would then imply the existence of a pole in $\Gamma(q+p, p)$ at $q^2 = 0$, that is, a zero mass scalar particle. This would be the Golstone boson associated with the breaking of scale invariance.

However, the above argument, while suggestive, is not a proof because (8.2) and (8.2') are not Fredholm kernels. Further, if we make a subtraction (or equivalently we put in a cut-off), the subtracted equations are of the Fredholm type, but now both (8.2) and (8.2') become inhomogeneous integral equations, and we can no longer use the argument given in the above paragraph.

We should therefore like to try to construct an alternative argument which makes use of a conservation law and the associated Ward identity. Even when $m_o = 0$ and the equations of the theory are scale invariant, the Hamiltonian is not scale invariant, but only scale "covariant" since it carries the dimension of an inverse length. Consequently, there is no generator of scale transformations S which is conserved.

Therefore let us consider another symmetry of the Lagrangian which does have associated with it a formal conservation law, namely γ_5 invariance.

The unrenormalized equation for the electron propagator with $m_o = 0$ is (see Eq. 7.1)

$$\frac{1}{S(p)} = \gamma \cdot p + \sum \left[p;\ \bar{D}(q);\ S(k)\right] \tag{8.3}$$

From this we can write

$$e^{i\alpha\gamma_5}\frac{1}{S(p)}e^{i\alpha\gamma_5} = \gamma\cdot p + e^{i\alpha\gamma_5}\sum e^{i\alpha\gamma_5} =$$

$$= \gamma\cdot p + \sum\left[p;\ \bar{D}(q);\ e^{-i\alpha\gamma_5}S(k)\,e^{-i\alpha\gamma_5}\right] \qquad (8.4)$$

since

$$e^{i\alpha\gamma_5}\gamma_\mu e^{i\alpha\gamma_5} = \gamma_\mu .$$

Differentiating (8. 4) with respect to α and putting $\alpha = 0$, we get

$$\left\{i\gamma_5, \frac{1}{S(p)}\right\} = -\int\frac{\delta\sum(p)}{\delta S(k)}\left\{i\gamma_5, S(k)\right\}d^4k.$$

Let us put

$$J_5(p) \equiv \left\{\gamma_5, \frac{1}{S(p)}\right\}.$$ Then we have

$$J_5(p) = \int K(p,k)\,S(k)\,J_5(k)\,S(k)\,d^4k \qquad (8.5)$$

which is of the same form of (7. 5').

Thus, if we choose a solution to the renormalized equations which give a non-vanishing mass, then

$$\left\{\gamma_5, \frac{1}{S(p)}\right\} \neq 0,$$

and therefore we also broke the γ_5 invariance of the unrenormalized equations.

However, as in the case of scale invariance considered above, we cannot prove the existence of Goldstone bosons from these equations. Therefore we turn to an alternative method using a "conservation law method".

We study first the equation for S in the coordinate space, with a bare mass term (5. 3):

$$\frac{1}{S}(x, y) = \left\{\gamma^{\mu} \frac{1}{i} \partial_{\mu} + m_o\right\} \delta^4(x - y) + \sum\left[x, y;\ \bar{D};\ S(u, v)\right]$$

Let us make a local γ_5 transformation (which destroys translation invariance):

$$e^{i\alpha(x)\gamma_5} \frac{1}{S} e^{i\alpha(y)\gamma_5} = \left\{\gamma^{\mu} \partial_{\mu} \alpha(x) \gamma_5 \right.$$

$$\left. + m_o e^{2i\alpha(x)\gamma_5}\right\} \delta^4(x - y)$$

$$+ \sum\left[x, y;\ \bar{D};\ e^{-i\alpha(u)\gamma_5} S(u, v)\, e^{-i\alpha(v)\gamma_5}\right].$$

Now we functionally differentiate with respect to $\alpha(\xi)$, and then we put $\alpha = 0$, so that translation invariance is restored. Going to momentum space we find

$$\frac{1}{S(p + q)} \gamma_5 + \gamma_5 \frac{1}{S(p)} = (\gamma \cdot q)\gamma_5 + 2m_o \gamma_5$$

$$+ \int K_q(p, k)\, S(k + q) \left[\frac{1}{S(k + q)} \gamma_5\right.$$

$$\left. + \gamma_5 \frac{1}{S(k)}\right] S(k)\, d^4k \tag{8.6}$$

We see that this equation reduces to (8.5) if we take $q = 0$ and $m_o = 0$.

Let us define now the axial vector current

$$A_{\mu}(\xi) = \psi(\xi) \gamma_{\mu} \gamma_5 \psi(\xi) \tag{8.7}$$

and the corresponding vertex operator Γ_5^{μ} by

$$i < 0 | T\left[A^{\mu}(\xi)\psi(x)\bar{\psi}(y)\right] | 0 > \equiv$$

$$\equiv S(x, x')\,\Gamma_5^{\mu}(x', y'; \xi)\,S(y', y) \qquad (8.8)$$

We find that Γ_5^{μ} obeys

$$\Gamma_5^{\mu}(p+q,\ p) = \gamma^{\mu}\gamma_5 + \int K_q(p,k)\,S(k+q)\,\Gamma_5^{\mu}(k+q,\ k)S(k)d^4k \qquad (8.9)$$

Equivalently, if we write this equation as the definition of Γ_5^{μ}, we can take (8.8) to define the operator A^{μ} at least for a limited class of matrix elements.

If we multiply (8.9) by q_{μ} and subtract from it (8.6), we get

$$J_5(p+q,\ p) = 2m_o\gamma_5 + \int K_q(p, k)S(k+q)J_5(k+q, k)S(k)d^4k \qquad (8.10)$$

where

$$J_5(p+q,\ p) \equiv q_{\mu}\Gamma_5^{\mu}(p+q,\ p) - \frac{1}{S(p+q)}\gamma_5 - \gamma_5\frac{1}{S(p)}$$

J_5 is related to A_{μ} by

$$S(x, x')\,J_5(\xi,\ x', y')\,S(y', y) = i < 0 | T\left[\partial_{\mu}A^{\mu}(\xi)\psi(x)\bar{\psi}(y)\right] | 0 >$$

Thus, if $\partial_{\mu}A^{\mu} = 0$, then $J_5 = 0$, and if $J_5 \neq 0$, then $\partial_{\mu}A^{\mu} \neq 0$.

We see that formally the mechanical mass breaks the conservation of the current, at least to lowest order. In higher orders J_5 itself acts to break the conservation law.

If we assume that the only solution of (8.10) for $m_o = 0$ is given by $J_5 = 0$, then we recover a Ward identity

$$q^{\mu}\Gamma^{5}_{\mu}(p+q,p) = S^{-1}(p+q)\gamma_5 + \gamma_5 S^{-1}(p)$$

If we further assume that $S^{-1}(p)\gamma_5 + \gamma_5 S^{-1}(p) \neq 0$, which is the case in our problem, then we find that as $q \rightarrow 0$,

$$q^{\mu}\Gamma^{5}_{\mu}(p+q,p) \not\rightarrow 0$$

Therefore, we must have singular terms in Γ^{5}_{μ} at $q = 0$. These correspond to zero mass intermediate states, i.e., Goldstone bosons. If, however, there are non-trivial solutions to (8.10) for $m_o = 0$, then it is not necessary that $\partial_{\mu} A^{\mu} = 0$, even when $m_o = 0$. This, in fact, is the case in renormalized perturbation theory.

Thus, suppose we study the equation for Γ^{5}_{μ}, using our perturbation solutions; we find that it is regular at $q = 0$. Consequently, using such a solution order by order we get

$$S^{-1}(p)\gamma_5 + \gamma_5 S^{-1}(p) = J_5(p,p)\ , \quad \text{and we see that}$$

$$2A(p)\gamma_5 = J_5(p,p), \quad \text{since } S^{-1} = \gamma\cdot pB + A.$$

The unrenormalized equation for A would be

$$\gamma_5 A(p) = m_o\gamma_5 + \int K(p,k)\, S(k)\, A(k)\, \gamma_5\, S(k)\, d^4k$$

If we make a subtraction at $p = 0$ we get

$$A(p)\gamma_5 = A(0)\gamma_5 + \int\left[K(p,k) - K(0,k)\right] S(k)\, A(k)\,\gamma_5\, S(k)\, d^4k$$

It can be shown that A(p) obeys this equation if

$$m(p) = m(0) + \int\left[K(p,k) - K(0,k)\right] S(k)\, m(k)\, S(k)\, d^4k.$$

Consequently, our ordinary renormalized perturbation theory yields symmetry breaking solutions of the unrenormalized equations which also break the conservation law $\partial_\mu A^\mu(\xi) = 0$.

Therefore, Goldstone theorem does not apply.

9. VACUUM POLARIZATION

Up to now we have considered only the question of the electron Green's function, with the assumption that the photon Green's function $\bar{D}_{\mu\nu}(q)$ approaches asymptotically $e_o^2 D_{\mu\nu}(q)$ with finite e_o^2.

Let us examine now the validity of this procedure. We shall use a method which is an extension of the one originally employed by Gell-Mann and Low some years ago and which has become known as the "renormalization group" (in my opinion an unfortunate name). However, before beginning the discussion of this method, I would like to summarize the conclusions about vacuum polarization which are obtained in a more or less straight-forward way and are described in detail in Baker, Johnson, Willey, to be published, Phys. Rev..

Let us define a photon "self-energy part" functional $\pi^{\alpha\beta}(q;\bar{D})$ by the following graphs:

$\pi^{\alpha\beta}(q;\bar{D}) =$

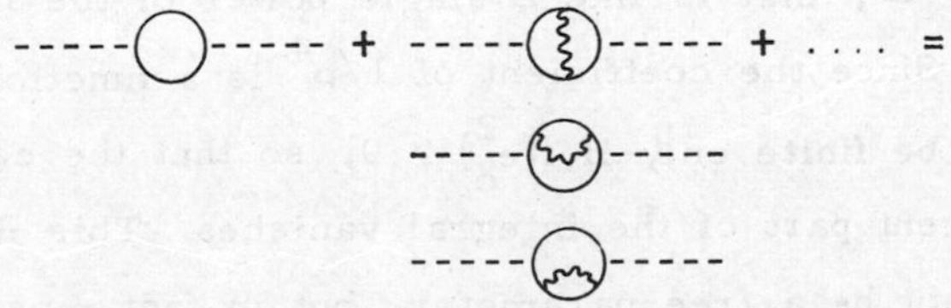

$$= (g^{\alpha\beta} q^2 - q^\alpha q^\beta)\rho(q^2;\bar{D}) \qquad (9.1)$$

The graphs are irreducible with respect to insertions into single photon lines (so that ~~~~ stands for $\bar{D}$).

Then the photon Green's function may be regarded as the solution of the following functional equation

$$\left[\frac{1}{\bar{D}(q)}\right]_{\alpha\beta} = (q^2 g^{\alpha\beta} - q^\alpha q^\beta)\left[\frac{1}{e_o^2} + \rho(q^2; \bar{D})\right] + q^\alpha q^\beta \frac{1}{e_o^2 \xi} \tag{9.2}$$

Now, if the solution of this equation is such that $\rho \to 0$ as $q^2 \to \infty$, then $\bar{D}_{\alpha\beta}(q) \to e_o^2 D_{\alpha\beta}(q)$.

Further, in order to evaluate $\rho(q^2)$ for $q^2 \gg m^2$, we must take into account the fact that the most slowly vanishing contributions to it will come from the region of integration in the functional where $\bar{D}_{\mu\nu}$ has the asymptote:

$$\bar{D}_{\mu\nu}(q) \longrightarrow e_o^2 D_{\mu\nu}(q) - e_o^4 \left[g_{\mu\nu} - \frac{q_\mu q_\nu}{q^2}\right] \frac{1}{q^2} \rho(q^2) \tag{9.3}$$

When the second term is inserted into the photon lines in (9.1) we get a contribution which is smaller than the one which comes from $e_o^2 \bar{D}_{\mu\nu}$, provided that $\rho \to 0$ as $q^2 \to \infty$. Consequently, it is interesting to consider $\Pi_{\alpha\beta}$ when we insert just $e_o^2 D_{\mu\nu}$ into the photon lines.

It can then be shown that every term in the above series in e_o^2 is given by an integral which diverges like $\int d^4p \frac{1}{p^4}$ as $p \to \infty$, that is like a single power of the logarithm of a cut-off.

Since the coefficient of $1/p^4$ is a function $f(e_o^2)$, the theory can be finite only if $f(e_o^2) = 0$, so that the coefficient of the divergent part of the integral vanishes. This means that e_o^2 cannot be a free parameter, but in fact must be the solution of an eigenvalue equation. If e_o^2 is such that $f(e_o^2) = 0$, then the leading contribution to $\rho(q^2)$ comes from the second term in (9.3), that is from ρ itself.

Thus, we get the following equation:

$$\rho(q^2) \simeq \int \frac{\delta\rho(q^2;\bar{D})}{\delta\bar{D}_{\alpha\beta}(k)}\bigg|_{\bar{D}=e_o^2 D} \left[-e_o^4\right]\left[g_{\alpha\beta} - \frac{k_\alpha k_\beta}{k^2}\right]\frac{\rho(k^2)}{k^2}\, d^4k \tag{9.4}$$

This is a homogeneous, linear integral equation for ρ valid when $q^2 >> m^2$.

The solution of (9.4) has the form

$$\rho(q^2) \simeq C\left[\frac{m^2}{q^2}\right]^{g(e_o^2)}, \quad \text{provided} \quad g > 0.$$

$g(e_o^2)$ is a finite power series in e_o^2. When e_o^2 is small it can be shown that

$$g(e_o^2) \simeq -e_o^4 f'(e_o^2),$$

where $f(e_o^2)$ is the same function as before

Since $f(e_o^2)$ is positive for very small values of e_o^2, if it has a zero it must have the form

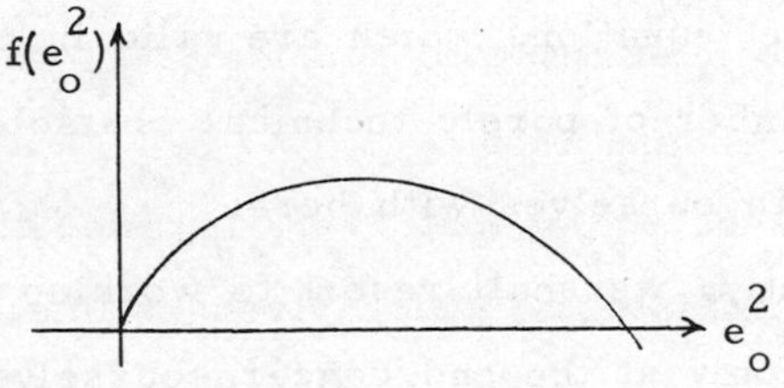

Therefore, if it vanishes it will do so with negative slope, leading to a positive g. Then we have a consistent solution of (9.4).

Since the constant C is arbitrary, we would then find that the asymptotic form of ρ is not completely specified by the uniquely given e_o^2.

The constant C and thus ρ can therefore depend only on e^2, the so-called "physical" or renormalized coupling constant.

Thus, we reach the conclusion that although e_o^2 must be a uniquely specified quantity, the renormalized coupling constant e^2 is still a free parameter.

Now we shall turn to an alternative method of studying the asymptotic form of ρ, first used by Gell-Mann and Low and which leads to the same conclusions.

In analogy with the definition (5.6) for Σ let us define $\pi(q; \bar{D}; S)$ as a functional of the exact photon and electron Green's functions, by the following series

 (9.5)

We omit diagrams of the form , since we are using the exact electron Green's function S in the electron lines in (9.5)

To handle the coupled electron and photon problem in such a way that we get equations which are valid in perturbation theory presents a number of purely technical obstacles that we do not wish to concern ourselves with here.

Consequently, we shall resort to working with diagram equations and only at the end concern ourselves with the subtractions and forth, which are required to make the equations correct.

Let us represent

$$m(p) = -\frac{\partial}{\partial\lambda}\left[\frac{1}{\lambda S(\lambda k)}\right]_{\lambda=1} \quad \text{by}$$ 

and the analogous quantity for photons, namely,

$$\mu(q^2)(g^{\mu\nu}q^2 - q^\mu q^\nu) = -\frac{1}{2}\frac{\partial}{\partial\lambda}\left[\frac{1}{\lambda^2}\pi^{\mu\nu}(\lambda q)\right]_{\lambda=1}$$

$$= -\frac{1}{2}\frac{\partial}{\partial\lambda}\left[(g^{\mu\nu}q^2 - q^\mu q^\nu)\rho(\lambda^2 q^2)\right]_{\lambda=1}$$ by

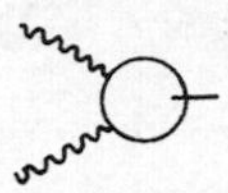

We see that:

$$\mu(q^2) = -q^2\rho'(q^2).$$

If we scale the equation for the electron Green's function including now the effects of scaling the photon terms we get the diagramatic equation (with $m_o = 0$):

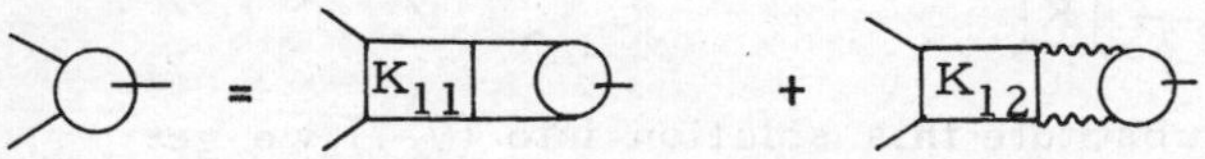

(9.6)

where 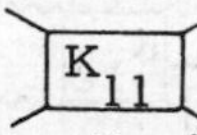

is a Bethe-Salpeter type kernel for electron-positron scattering which is also irreducible with respect to vertically cutting two photon lines; 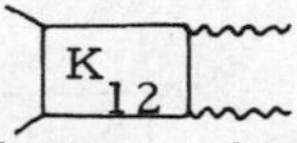

is a similar kernel for annihilation into two photons which is irreducible with respect to both two photon and two electron cuts.

In a similar way, if we scale (9.5) and differentiate it we get

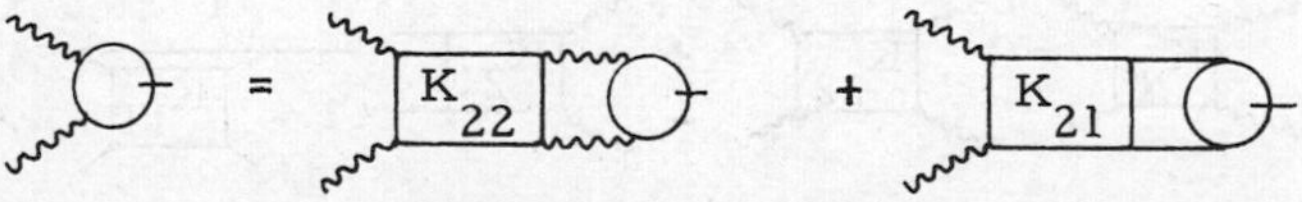

(9.7)

where both K_{22} and K_{21} are irreducible with respect to two photon and two electron cuts.

The equation which we previously considered (see Eq. 8.2) was

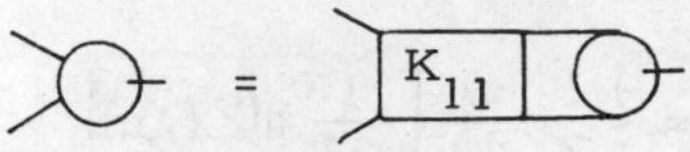

$$\bowtie\!-\ =\ \boxed{K_{11}}\!-\!\!\circ\!-\qquad\qquad (9.8')$$

where we had $e_o^2 D_{\mu\nu}(q)$ instead of $\bar{D}_{\mu\nu}(q)$ for the photon lines.

Let us denote the solution of (9.8') for a given physical mass for the particle by $\bowtie\!(H)\!-$, i.e.,

$$\bowtie\!(K)\!-\ =\ \boxed{K_{11}}\!(H)\!-\qquad\qquad (9.8)$$

Then the complete solution of (9.6) can be written as

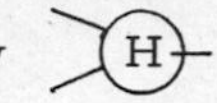

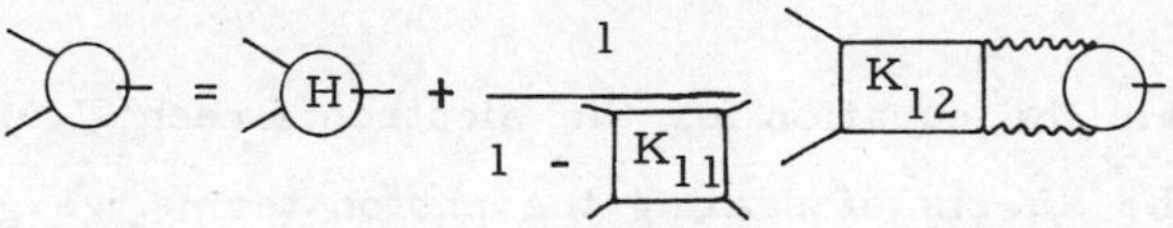

$$\bowtie\!-\ =\ \bowtie\!(H)\!-\ +\ \frac{1}{1\ -\ \boxed{K_{11}}}\ \boxed{K_{12}}\!\!\!\sim\!\!\!\circ\!-\qquad (9.9)$$

where

$$\frac{1}{1\ -\ \boxed{K}}\quad\text{stands for}\quad 1\ +\ \boxed{K}\ +\ \boxed{K}\,\boxed{K}\ +\ \ldots$$

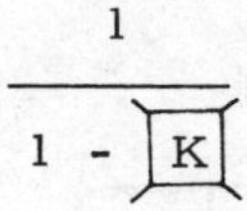

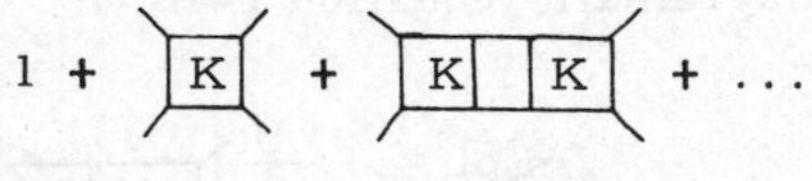

If we substitute this solution into (9.7) we get

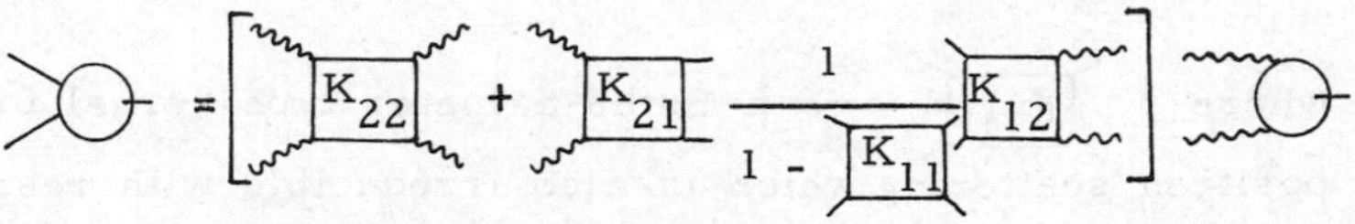

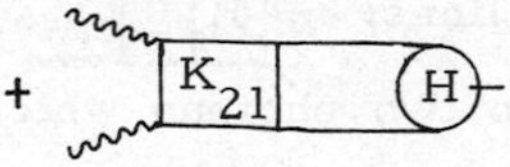

$$\bowtie\!-\ =\ \left[\ \boxed{K_{22}}\ +\ \boxed{K_{21}}\ \frac{1}{1\ -\ \boxed{K_{11}}}\ \boxed{K_{12}}\ \right]\!\!\sim\!\!\circ\!-$$

$$+\ \boxed{K_{21}}\!(H)\!-\qquad\qquad (9.10)$$

The first term involves the kernel

$$\boxed{K_\gamma}\ =\ \boxed{K_{22}}\ +\ \boxed{K_{21}}\ \frac{1}{1\ -\ \boxed{K_{11}}}\ \boxed{K_{12}}$$

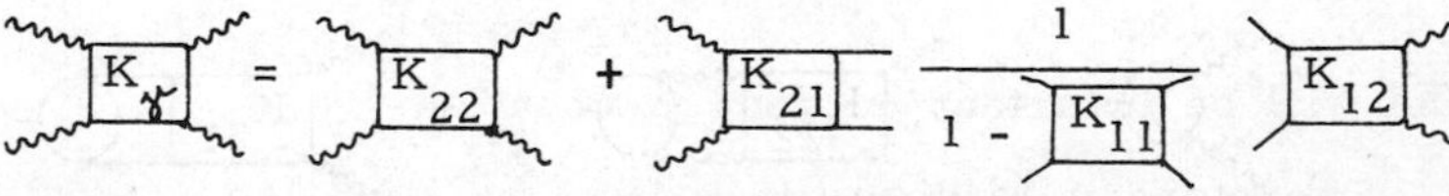

which contains all graphs which cannot be reduced by cutting two photon lines. Thus, K_γ is the ordinary kernel for the scattering of light by light. In terms of K_γ we have

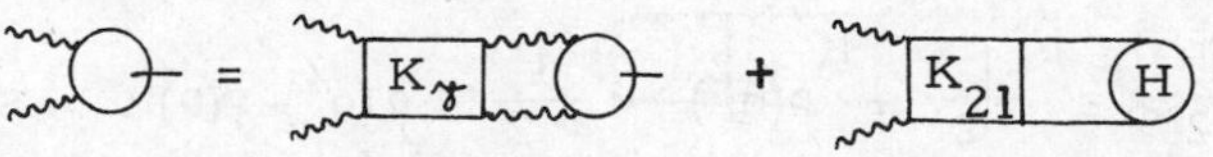

(9.11)

If we study the kernel K_γ, we find that it may be expressed in terms of skeletons by

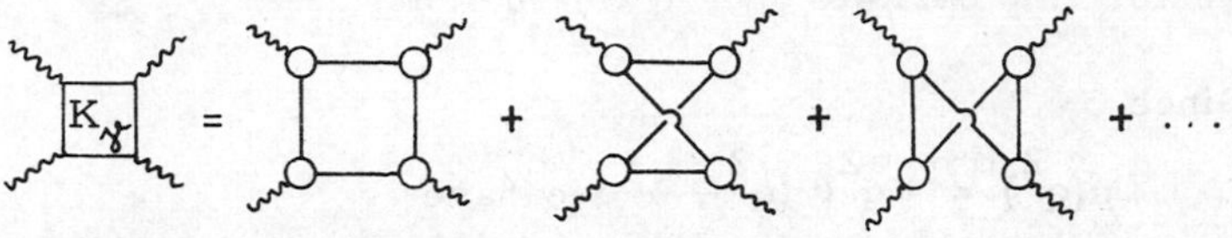

It is clear that this is invariant with respect to the multiplicative renormalizations

$$S \longrightarrow Z_2 \overline{S} \quad ; \qquad \Gamma_\mu \longrightarrow \frac{1}{Z_2} \overline{\Gamma}_\mu$$

In a similar way, since

$$m(p) = - \frac{\partial}{\partial \lambda} \left[\frac{1}{\lambda S(\lambda p)} \right]_{\lambda = 1} \longrightarrow \frac{1}{Z_2} \overline{m}(p)$$

with

$$\overline{m}(p) = - \frac{\partial}{\partial \lambda} \left[\frac{1}{\lambda \overline{S}(\lambda p)} \right]_{\lambda = 1} ,$$

we see that the second term of (9.11) expressed in terms of skeletons, namely

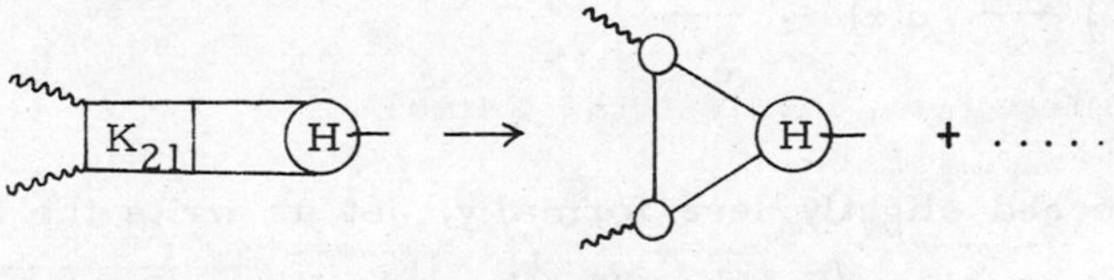

also will be invariant on renormalization.

Therefore it is possible to find by iteration a solution of (9.11) which is finite order by order in perturbation theory.

We of course must have a recipe for constructing $\overline{D}$ in terms of $\mu(q^2)$. Let us define

$$\frac{1}{d(q^2)} \equiv \frac{1}{e_o^2} + \rho(q^2) = \frac{1}{e^2} + \rho(q^2) - \rho(0) . \quad \text{So,}$$

$$\bar{D}_{\mu v}(q) = \left[g_{\mu v} - \frac{q_\mu q_v}{q^2} \right] \frac{1}{q^2} d(q^2) + (\text{gauge terms})$$

Since

$$\mu(q^2) = - q^2 \rho'(q^2), \quad \text{we have}$$

$$\frac{1}{d(q^2)} = \frac{1}{e^2} - \int_0^{q^2} \frac{dx}{x} \mu(x).$$

Since if $\rho \longrightarrow 0$, $d(\infty) = e_o^2$, we see that

$$\frac{1}{e_o^2} = \frac{1}{e^2} - \int_0^{\infty} \frac{dx}{x} \mu(x).$$

The convergence of the integral requires that $\mu(q^2) \longrightarrow 0$ as $q^2 \longrightarrow \infty$. Since $\mu > 0$, this is also the requirement that no "ghost" zero in $1/d(q^2)$ appears. In fact, the requirement that no ghosts are present, enforces the stronger requirement:

$$\int_0^{\infty} \frac{dx}{x} \mu(x) \leqslant \frac{1}{e^2} .$$

To proceed slightly less formally, let us write the form of the integral equation (9.11). The kernel $K_{\gamma;\alpha\beta}(k, q)_{\mu v}$

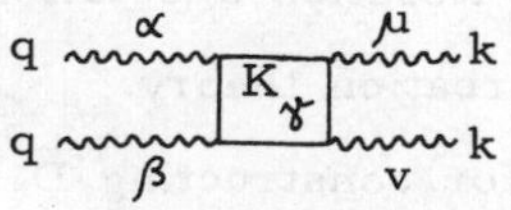

is gauge invariant and satisfies

$$k^{\alpha} K_{\gamma} = 0 \qquad q^{\mu} K_{\gamma} = 0$$

After integrating over the angles of q, we have the following form for the first term:

$$(g^{\alpha\beta} k^2 - k^{\alpha} k^{\beta}) \int d^4q\, K(k,q)\, d^2(q) \mu(q) =$$ 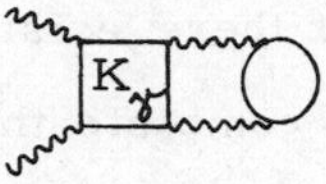

In a similar way the second term of (9.11) is also gauge invariant and let us write for it

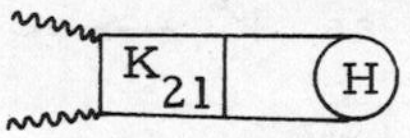
$$= (g^{\alpha\beta} k^2 - k^{\alpha} k^{\beta})\, i(k)$$

So, Eq. (9.11) can be written as

$$\mu(k^2) = \int d^4q\, K(k,q)\, d^2(q) \mu(q) + i(k) \tag{9.11'}$$

Since $\mu(k^2) = -k^2 \rho'(k^2)$, if $\rho(k^2)$ is regular at $k^2 = 0$ (and it should be so in perturbation theory), it follows that

$$\mu(0) = 0, \quad \text{i.e.,}$$

$$\int d^4q\, K(0,q)\, d^2(q) \mu(q) + i(0) = 0 \tag{9.12}$$

In fact, if we try to use renormalized perturbation theory, (9.12) does not hold order by order. The reason is that (9.11) cannot be derived from the equation (9.1) in a way that is valid using the perturbation version of (9.1), since that diverges.

If we put a cut-off into (9.1) (so that we can use perturbation theory), then we could not scale (9.1) without also scaling the cut-off. However, if we subtract (9.12) from (9.11'), we find

$$\mu(k^2) = \int d^4q\left[K(k,q) - K(0,q)\right] d^2(q)\mu(q) + i(k^2) - i(0) \qquad (9.13)$$

Equation (9.13) is a consistent one which yields renormalized perturbation theory.

If there exists an exact solution to (9.13) consistent with a finite complete theory without a ghost, then as $k \longrightarrow \infty$, $\mu \longrightarrow 0$, the separate integral in (9.13) converge and the first one will asymptotically vanish.

We shall see that $i(k^2)$ is finite order by order in renormalized perturbation theory and vanishes as $k^2 \longrightarrow \infty$. Consequently, if $\mu \longrightarrow 0$ as $k^2 \longrightarrow \infty$, we get:

$$0 = -\int d^4q\, K(0,q)\, d^2(q)\mu(q) - i(0) \,,$$

which is equation (9.12).

To illustrate the use of (9.13) to construct renormalized perturbation theory, let us give an example in lowest order.

In this case only the second term in (9.13) is present, and we have 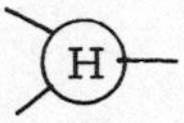 = m, where m is the physical mass of the electron.

Further we get i(0) from the kernel

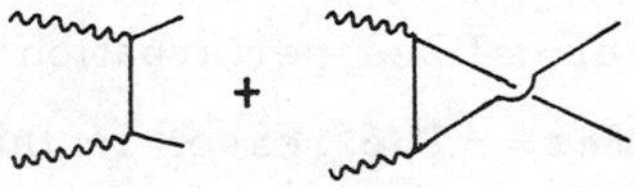

with $S = \dfrac{1}{\gamma \cdot p + m}$. Thus we have just the graphs:

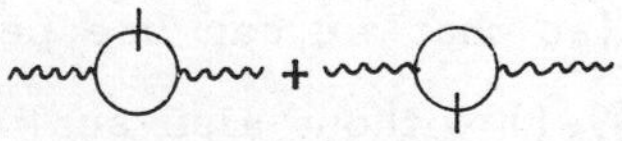

where  stands for SmS.

Although the integral in the above graphs at first sight has a linear (or, if the integrand is symmetric, a logarithmic) divergence, by calculation it can be seen that it is in fact finite.

One must exercise the usual care to obtain a gauge invariant result; in our case there is only a finite constant in the above graphs which violates conservation, and it can be removed with a gauge invariant definition of the current.

We get then for $i(k^2)$ the finite expression

$$i(k^2) = -\frac{1}{2\pi^2}\int_0^1 dx \frac{m^2 x(1-x)}{k^2 x(1-x) + m^2}$$

which as $k^2 \longrightarrow \infty$ is of the order m^2/k^2.

Since $i(k^2) = i(k^2/m^2)$ is finite and formally proportional to m, it vanishes as $m \longrightarrow 0$, or equivalently, as $k^2 \longrightarrow \infty$, order by order in renormalized perturbation theory.

Consequently, the second term in (9.13), as $k^2 \longrightarrow \infty$ tends to the constant $-i(0)$ $(+1/12\pi^2$ for $e^2 = 0)$, and thus gives a contribution to μ such that

$$\frac{1}{d(q^2)} \longrightarrow \frac{1}{e^2} - \int_0^{q^2} \frac{dx}{x}\left[-i(0)\right] \longrightarrow \frac{1}{e^2} + i(0)\log(q^2).$$

We see that the first term in (9.13) is of fourth order in e. If $\mu \longrightarrow -i(0)$, inserting it into the integrals we find that

$$\int K(k,q)\, e^4\left[-i(0)\right] d^4q$$

diverges logarithmically; the difference which appears in (9.13), however, converges and asymptotically $(q^2 \longrightarrow \infty)$ it becomes

$\log(q^2)$. If as $q^2 \to \infty$ $\mu(q^2) \to \log q^2$, then as $k^2 \to \infty$

$$\frac{1}{d(k^2)} \longrightarrow -\int_0^{q^2} \frac{dx}{x} \log x \longrightarrow -(\log q^2)^2 .$$

This is the way that higher powers of $\log q^2$ appear in perturbation theory. The $\log^2$ term corresponds to the graphs

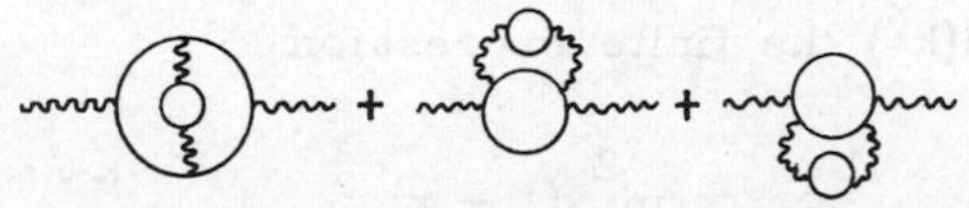

We now turn to a discussion of how to study in general such terms in $d(q^2)$.

10. THE IMPLICATIONS OF RENORMALIZED PERTURBATION THEORY CONCERNING THE FINITENESS OF THE UNRENORMALIZED FIELD THEORY

If we wish to study Eq. (9.13), to determine what we can learn about $\mu(k^2)$ when $k^2 \gg m^2$, we proceed in a similar way as in earlier sections.

Thus, let k^2 and k'^2 be such that k^2, $k'^2 \gg m^2$. Then

$$\mu(k'^2) = \int d^4q \left[K(k', q) - K(0, q)\right] d^2(q)\mu(q) + i(k'^2) - i(0) \tag{9.13'}$$

Subtracting this equation from (9.13) we get

$$\mu(k^2) = \mu(k'^2) + \int d^4q \left[K(k, q) - K(k', q)\right] d^2(q)\mu(q) + i(k^2) - i(k'^2) \tag{10.1}$$

Further

$$\frac{1}{d(k^2)} = \frac{1}{e^2} - \int_0^{k^2} \frac{dx}{x}\,\mu(x) = \frac{1}{d(k'^2)} - \int_{k'^2}^{k^2} \frac{dx}{x}\,\mu(x) \qquad (10.2)$$

Let us use the two last equations to fix $\mu(k^2)$ in terms of the two quantities $\mu(k'^2)$ and $d(k'^2)$, when k^2, $k'^2 >> m^2$. Since in this case $i(k^2)$, $i(k'^2) \rightarrow 0$, we get

$$\mu(k^2) = \mu(k'^2) + \int d^4q\left[K(k,q) - K(k',q)\right] d^2(q)\mu(q).$$

Now we define

$$\mu(k^2) \equiv \mu(k'^2)\, F\left[\frac{k^2}{k'^2};\ d(k'^2),\ \mu(k'^2)\, d(k'^2)\right] \qquad (10.3)$$

where

$$F\left[\frac{k^2}{k'^2}, x, y\right] = 1 + \int d^4q\left[K(k,q) - K(k',q)\right] d^2(q) F\left[\frac{q^2}{k'^2}; x, y\right] \qquad (10.4)$$

Eq. (10.2) becomes

$$\frac{1}{d(k^2)} = \frac{1}{x}\left[1 - y\int_{k'^2}^{k^2} \frac{dz}{z}\, F(z/k'^2)\right] \qquad (10.2')$$

If we put m = 0 everywhere in kernel K in (10.4), then the equation for F approaches a finite limit.

Differentiating (10.3) with respect to k^2 and putting $k'^2 = k^2$, we get

$$\frac{\partial}{\partial \log k^2}\left[\mu(k^2)\right] = \mu(k^2)\, d^2(k^2)\Psi\left[d(k^2),\ \mu(k^2)\, d(k^2)\right] \qquad (10.5)$$

where $\quad x^2\Psi(x,y) \equiv \frac{\partial}{\partial z} F(z; x, y)\Big|_{z=1} \qquad (10.6)$

defines Ψ as a power series in x and y which is gotten from (10.4) by iteration.

To solve (10.5) let us define another function ψ by the equation

$$\mu(k^2) = \psi\left[d(k^2)\right] = -\frac{\partial}{\partial \log k^2}\left[\frac{1}{d(k^2)}\right] =$$

$$= \frac{1}{d^2(k^2)}\left[\frac{\partial}{\partial \log k^2} d(k^2)\right] \qquad (10.7)$$

Then we get

$$\frac{\partial}{\partial \log k^2}\psi\left[d(k^2)\right] = \psi\left[d(k^2)\right]d^2(k^2)\Psi\left[d(k^2), \psi\left(d(k^2)\right)d(k^2)\right]$$

or

$$\psi'\left[d(k^2)\right]d^2(k^2)\psi\left[d(k^2)\right] = \psi\left[d(k^2)\right]d^2(k^2)\Psi\left[d(k^2), \psi\left(d(k^2)\right)d(k^2)\right]$$

or more simply

$$\psi'(x) = \Psi\left[x, \; x\psi(x)\right] \qquad (10.8)$$

Integrating equation (10.7) we get

$$\int_{d(k'^2)}^{d(k^2)} \frac{dx}{x^2\psi(x)} = \log\left[\frac{k^2}{k'^2}\right] \qquad (10.9)$$

Equation (10.9) is an implicit relation between $d(k^2)$ and $d(k'^2)$ when $k^2, k'^2 \gg m^2$.

This equation was first obtained by Gell-Mann and Low.

In our case ψ can be computed using (10.8) and $\Psi(x,y)$ from (10.6) and (10.4). Notice that none of these equations contains any reference to the coupling constant e^2.

Now, as $k^2 \to \infty$, $d(k^2) \to e_o^2$ if e_o^2 is finite. However, the right-hand side of (10.9) diverges as $k^2 \to \infty$. The only way for the integral on the left to diverge as $d(k^2) \to e_o^2$ is $\psi(e_o^2) = 0$, that is, it is necessary that e_o^2 obeys an eigenvalue equation.

In this case, when $k^2 >> m^2$, we can write

$$\int_{d(k'^2)}^{d(k^2)} \frac{dx}{e_o^4 (x - e_o^2)\psi'(e_o^2)} \sim \log\left[\frac{k^2}{k'^2}\right]$$

so that

$$\log \frac{d(k^2) - e_o^2}{d(k'^2) - e_o^2} \sim \log\left[\frac{k^2}{k'^2}\right]^{e_o^4 \psi'(e_o^2)}$$

Therefore,

$$d(k^2) \sim e_o^2 - \left[e_o^2 - d(k'^2)\right]\left[\frac{k^2}{k'^2}\right]^{e_o^4 \psi'(e_o^2)} \qquad (10.10)$$

Since ψ must approach zero from positive values, we have

$$\psi'(e_o^2) < 0 .$$

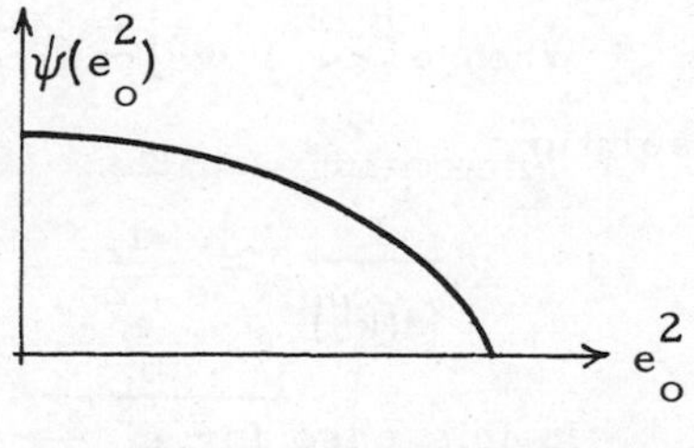

Moreover, from (10.8),

$$\psi'(e_o^2) = \Psi(e_o^2, 0).$$

Putting y = 0 in (10.2') we see that $d(k^2) = x$, so we neglect all graphs in K with insertions in photon lines. The integral becomes linear.

It is not difficult to show that $\Psi(e_o^2, 0) \simeq f'(e_o^2)$, where $f(e_o^2)$ is the function defined earlier which gave the eigenvalue equation. Thus, the exponent in Eq. (10.10) is consistent with that obtained in Section 9 when we considered the series

.....

The Gell - Mann - Low eigenvalue equation is however

$$\psi(e_o^2) = 0.$$

Let us investigate if it is equivalent to the equation $f(e_o^2) = 0$.

In (10.8) $\Psi(x, y)$ is defined independently of the charge e^2. In principle, there could be a dependence of e^2 in the constant of integration:

$$\psi(x) = \psi(0) + \int_0^x dx \Psi[z, z\psi(z)]$$

In order to get information about $\psi(0)$ let us consider (10.7), which holds for $k^2 \gg m^2$.

When $e^2 \ll 1$ we can compute $d(k^2)$ using the lowest order solution:

$$\frac{1}{d(k^2)} \simeq \frac{1}{e^2} - \frac{1}{12\pi^2} \log\left[\frac{k^2}{m^2}\right] + 0(e^2).$$

In this case for $e^2 \to 0$, $d(k^2) \to 0$, so that

$$\psi(0) = (12\pi^2)^{-1}$$

Thus the constant $\psi(0)$ is also independent of e^2. Consequently,

$$\psi(x) = \frac{1}{12\pi^2} + \int_0^x dz\, \Psi[z, z\psi(z)]$$

and therefore the eigenvalue equation (10.8) is independent of the physical charge e^2. The form of $d(k^2)$ in the asymptotic region is determined in terms of $\psi'(e_o^2)$, which can be computed from $\Psi(e_o^2, 0)$ (that is, without insertions into photon lines). However, the Gell-Mann and Low eigenvalue equation

$$\psi(e_o^2) = 0 = \frac{1}{12\pi^2} + \int_0^{e_o^2} dz\, \Psi[z, z\psi(z)] \tag{10.11}$$

seems to involve the full function Ψ.

We have not yet shown that the solution to (10.11) is the same as the solution to the equation $f(e_o^2) = 0$.

Since both methods give the same answer for d asymptotically, it is plausible that this point can be straightened out.

In any event, the final conclusion is that although in the renormalized theory the parameters m and e^2 are free, if we use this theory to compute m_o and e_o^2 we find that $m_o = 0$ and e_o^2 is the solution of an eigenvalue equation.

Thus, the parameters m_o and e_o^2 in the Hamiltonian are not free; rather, the renormalized theory parametrized by e^2 and m comes from a single operator H. Thus, there are a class of solutions to the Green function equation which come from H. These different solutions correspond to different vacuum states, labeled by m and e: $|0; m; e\rangle$. Because the vacuum fills all of space, any excitation of the vacuum $|0; m; e\rangle$ will be orthogonal to any excitation of $|0; m'; e'\rangle$.

Hence this multiplicity of solutions has no physical consequences, within electrodynamics as a closed theory. We must remember however, that the world of electrons and photons also must join with the rest of physics. Presumably, it is the rest of the world which provides the boundary conditions to determine the values of m and e^2.

APPENDIX A

Eq. (2.11) is a special case of the action principle of Schwinger. Since it assumes a slightly unconventional use of the time dependent formalism on states, which may not be familiar to all, let us derive it.

Suppose $H_t = H_{ot} + H_{1t}$, where both H_o and H_1 may have an explicit time dependence.

We may define time dependent states by

$$i\frac{\partial}{\partial t} {}_H\!\langle a, t | = {}_H\!\langle a, t | H(t) \qquad \text{(A. 1)}$$

or

$$i\frac{\partial}{\partial t} {}_{H_o}\!\langle a, t | = {}_{H_o}\!\langle a, t | H_o(t)$$

where

$$\frac{dH_H(t)}{dt} = \frac{1}{i}\left[H_H(t), H_H(t)\right] + \frac{\partial H}{\partial t} = \frac{\partial H}{\partial t}$$

This is the reverse of the usual convention

$$i\frac{\partial}{\partial t} | a_t \rangle = H(t) | a_t \rangle$$

and

$$-i\frac{\partial}{\partial t} \langle a_t | = \langle a_t | H(t).$$

The subscript notation ${}_H\!\langle a, t|$ is intended to indicate the Hamiltonian which specifies the time dependence. We note that, with this definition of time dependent states,

$${}_H\!\langle a, t | B_H(t) | c, t \rangle_H = \text{time independent and therefore H independent} \qquad \text{(A. 2)}$$

where the time dependence of B is given by

$$\frac{d B_H(t)}{dt} = \frac{1}{i}\left[B_H(t), H(t)\right] .$$

Let us define now a unitary operator U(t, t') by the identity

$$_H\langle a,t \mid b,t' \rangle_H \equiv {}_{H_o}\langle a,t \mid U(t,t') \mid b,t' \rangle_{H_o} \tag{A. 3}$$

Using (A. 1) and (A. 3) we have

$$_H\langle a,t \mid H(t) \mid b,t' \rangle_H = {}_{H_o}\langle a,t \mid H_o(t)\, U(t,t') +$$

$$+ i\frac{\partial U}{\partial t}(t, t') \mid b, t' \rangle_{H_o}$$

But:

$$_H\langle a,t \mid H(t) \mid b,t' \rangle_H = \sum_c {}_H\langle a,t \mid H(t) \mid c,t \rangle_H \, {}_H\langle c,t \mid b,t' \rangle_H$$

$$= \sum_c {}_{H_o}\langle a,t \mid H_{H_o}(t) \mid c,t \rangle_{H_o} \, {}_{H_o}\langle c,t \mid U(t,t') \mid b,t' \rangle_H$$

where we used (A. 2) and (A. 3).

Therefore,

$$i\frac{\partial}{\partial t} U(t, t') = \left[H_{H_o}(t) - H_o(t)\right] U(t, t') =$$

$$= H_{1, H_o}(t)\, U(t, t') \tag{A. 4}$$

So:

$$U(t, t') = T\left[e^{-i\int_{t'}^{t} d\tau H_{1, H_o}(\tau)}\right] \tag{A. 5}$$

Therefore, from (A. 3) we get

$$ {}_{H}\langle a,t\,|\,b,t'\rangle_{H} = {}_{H_o}\langle a,t\,|\,T\left[e^{-i\int_{t'}^{t} d\tau H_{1,H_o}(\tau)}\right]|b,t'\rangle_{H_o} \tag{A. 6} $$

which is the standard result.

If we vary $H_{1,H_o}(\tau)$ in an infinitesimal neighbourhood $\Delta\tau'$ about $\tau = \tau'$ which is between the interval t, t' we will have for (A. 6)

$$ {}_{H}\langle a,t\,|\,b,t'\rangle_{H} = {}_{H_o}\langle a,t\,|\,T\left[e^{\int_{\tau'+\Delta\tau'}^{t} d\tau H_{1,H_o}(\tau)}\right] \cdot $$

$$ \cdot\left[1 - i\Delta\tau'\,\delta H_{1,H_o}(\tau')\right] T\left[e^{-\int_{t'}^{\tau'-\Delta\tau'} d\tau H_{1,H_o}(\tau)}\right]|b,t'\rangle_{H_o} $$

therefore:

$$ \delta_{H}\langle a,t\,|\,b,t'\rangle_{H} = {}_{H_o}\langle a,t\,|\,T\left[e^{-i\int_{\tau'}^{t} d\tau H_{1,H_o}(\tau)}\right] $$

$$ \left[(-i\,\Delta\tau'\,\delta H_{1,H_o}(\tau')\right] T\left[e^{-\int_{t'}^{\tau'} d\tau H_{1,H_o}(\tau)}\right]|b,t'\rangle_{H_o} $$

If we insert complete sets of states and use (A. 2) and (A. 3) we get

$$ \delta_{H}\langle a,t\,|\,b,t'\rangle_{H} = {}_{H}\langle a,t\,|\,(-i)\,\Delta\tau'\,\delta H_{1,H}(\tau')\,|b,t'\rangle_{H} $$

Therefore in general, if the variation occurs throughout the region between t and t',

$$\delta < a, t | b, t' > = -i \int_{t'}^{t} d\tau' < a, b | \delta H_1(\tau') | b, t' > \qquad (A.7)$$

where all time dependence is governed by the Hamiltonian H.

The relation (A.7) is the "action principle".

APPENDIX B

We are going to show that $\lim_{q^2 \to \infty} \rho(q^2) = 0$. We know that for $J_\mu = 0$,

$$\bar{D}_{\mu\nu}(x,y) = i < 0 | T\left[A_\mu(x) A_\nu(y)\right] | 0 >$$

$$= \int \frac{d^4 q}{(2\pi)^4} e^{iq(x-y)} \bar{D}^{\mu\nu}(q) \qquad (B.1)$$

$\bar{D}_{\mu\nu}(q)$ is given by (3.23). For $x_o > y_o$, taking the limit $y_o \to x_o$, we get

$$i < 0 | A_\mu(x) A_\nu(y) | 0 > = \int \frac{d\mathbf{q}}{(2\pi)^3} e^{i\mathbf{q}\cdot(\mathbf{x}-\mathbf{y})} \int \frac{dq_o}{2\pi} \bar{D}_{\mu\nu}(q) \qquad (B.2)$$

where the path of integration is closed at $\mathrm{Im}(q_o) < 0$, in order that $e^{iq_o(x_o - y_o)}$ does not diverge.

Analogously, for $y_o > x_o$, $y_o \to x_o$,

$$i < 0 | A_\nu(y) A_\mu(x) | 0 > = \int \frac{d\mathbf{q}}{(2\pi)^3} e^{i\mathbf{q}\cdot(\mathbf{x}-\mathbf{y})} \int \frac{dq_o}{2\pi} \bar{D}_{\mu\nu}(q) \qquad (B.3)$$

Subtracting (B.3) from (B.2) we get

$$i < 0 | \left[A_{\mu}(x), A_{v}(y) \right]_{x_o = y_o} | 0 > = \int \frac{d\mathbf{q}}{(2\pi)^3} e^{i\mathbf{q}.(\mathbf{x}-\mathbf{y})} \oint \frac{dq_o}{2\pi} \bar{D}_{\mu v}(q)$$

In order that the right hand side vanishes, as required by the canonical commutation rules, we see that $\lim_{q_o \to \infty} \bar{D}_{\mu v}(q) \sim \frac{1}{q_o^2}$ (or higher negative powers); then, from (3.23), we conclude that

$$\frac{1}{\frac{1}{e_o^2} + \rho(q^2)} \not\to q_0 \quad \text{when } q_o \to \infty .$$

By applying the same procedure to $\frac{\partial}{\partial x_o} \bar{D}_{\mu v}(x, y)$, we obtain

$$i < 0 | \left[\dot{A}_{\mu}(x), A_{v}(y) \right]_{x_o = y_o} | 0 > = \int \frac{d\mathbf{q}}{(2\pi)^3} e^{i\mathbf{q}.(\mathbf{x}-\mathbf{y})} \oint \frac{dq_o}{2\pi} \bar{D}_{\mu v}(q)(-iq_o)$$

From the commutation relations

$$\left[\dot{A}_i(x), A_j(y) \right]_{x_o = y_o} = ie_o^2 \, \delta_{ij} \, \delta(\mathbf{x} - \mathbf{y})$$

$$\left[\dot{A}_o(x), A_o(y) \right]_{x_o = y_o} = ie_o^2 \xi \, \delta(\mathbf{x} - \mathbf{y})$$

and from (3.23) we conclude that

$$\lim_{q_o \to \infty} \rho(q^2) = 0 \qquad \text{(B. 4)}$$

Another property of $\rho(q^2)$ can be deduced from (B. 1). In fact, we can see by introduction of a complete set of intermediate states, that $\bar{D}_{\mu v}(q^2)$ has a cut in the q^2 plane along the negative real axis (corresponding to time-like q vectors).

From (3.23), we see that only $\rho(q^2)$ can account for this cut. This fact allows us to use the following representation:

$$\rho(q^2) = \int_0^\infty dk^2 \frac{\sigma(k^2)}{k^2 + q^2} \tag{B.5}$$

We have added no polynomial to the right-hand side because of (B.4).

Looking at (3.23) for $q^2 \rightarrow 0$, and assuming that no poles are present, we can define the physical charge by

$$\frac{1}{\frac{1}{e_o^2} + \rho(0)} \equiv e^2 \tag{B.6'}$$

because in that limit $\bar{D}_{\mu\nu}$ must tend to the propagator of physical photons. Eq. (B.6') can be written as

$$\frac{1}{e^2} = \frac{1}{e_o^2} + \rho(0) \tag{B.6}$$

From the fact that the function σ in (B.5) is always positive we conclude that $e^2 < e_o^2$.

Let us write (B.6) in the form

$$\frac{1}{e_o^2} + \rho(q^2) = \frac{1}{e^2} + \rho(q^2) - \rho(0) = \frac{1}{e^2} - q^2 \int_0^\infty dk^2 \frac{\sigma(k^2)}{k^2(k^2+q^2)} \tag{B.7}$$

If $q^2 \rightarrow +\infty$, we see from (B.7) that $(1/e_o^2) + \rho(q^2)$ can be negative, so that it must vanish at some intermediate point.

This corresponds to a singularity of $\bar{D}_{\mu\nu}$ for a space-like value of q. Such a singularity is physically not acceptable, and it is called a "ghost". Even if $\bar{D}_{\mu\nu}$ is renormalizable there can be a singularity, for a sufficiently high value of q^2. If the ghost occurs at infinity, from (B. 4) and (B. 7) we see that $e_o^2 = \infty$. We also see in this case that

$$\int_0^\infty dk^2 \frac{\sigma(k^2)}{k^2} \text{ must converge.}$$

The result of this discussion can be visualized in the plot of the figure.

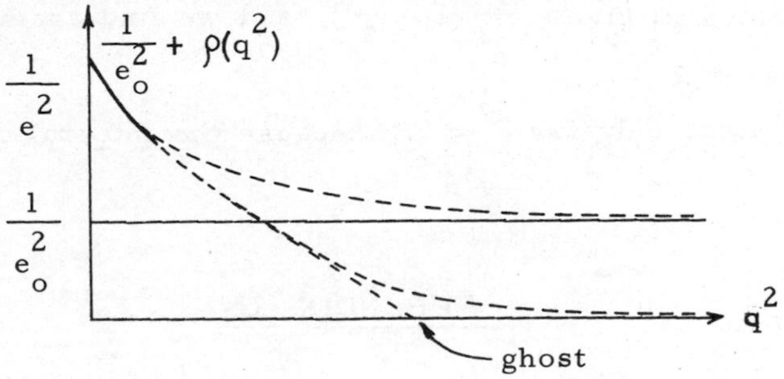

As we have seen, for $q^2 \rightarrow \infty$ we have

$$\frac{1}{e^2} - \int_0^\infty dk^2 \frac{\sigma(k^2)}{k^2} = \frac{1}{e_o^2} \tag{B. 8}$$

which relates e_o and e.

When the ghost is at infinity, (B 8) is an identity with respect to e^2, in the sense that $e_o^2 = \infty$ for any value of it.

If the left-hand side of (B. 8) is finite, we still have an identity with respect to e^2.

Let us give two examples of that.

Take $\sigma(k^2) = \frac{1}{(12\pi^2)}\left[\frac{m^2}{k^2}\right]^{e^2/12\pi^2} \Theta(k^2 - m^2)$

In this case the integral in (B.8) is equal to $1/e^2$, so that $1/e_o^2$ is identically equal to zero.

As a second example we take

$$\sigma(k^2) = \frac{1}{(12\pi^2)}\left[\frac{m^2}{k^2}\right]^{\frac{e^2}{12\pi^2(1 - \frac{e^2}{7})}} \Theta(k^2 - m^2)$$

The integral gives $\frac{1}{e^2}(1 - \frac{e^2}{7})$, and we find again an identity for e_o^2: $e_o^2 = 7$.

This holds only for $e^2 < 7$, because the integral diverges for $e^2 > 7$.

APPENDIX C

We have the equation

$$\left[\gamma^\mu\left(\frac{1}{i}\partial_\mu - \langle A_\mu(x)\rangle\right) + m_o\right] S(x, y) = \delta^{(4)}(x - y)$$

$$- ie_o^2 \xi \gamma^\mu \partial_\mu \partial_\nu D_F(x - x'') D_F(x'' - x') \frac{\delta S(x, y)}{\delta \langle A_\nu(x')\rangle}$$

$$- i\gamma^\mu \bar{D}^{(T)}_{\mu\nu}(x, x') \frac{\delta S(x, y)}{\delta \langle A_\nu(x')\rangle} \qquad \text{(C. 1)}$$

Let $M(x - x') \equiv e_o^2 \xi D_F(x - x'') D_F(x'' - x') =$

$$= e_o^2 \xi \int \frac{d^4q}{(2\pi)^4} e^{iq(x - x')}\left[\frac{1}{q^2}\right]^2 \qquad \text{(C. 2)}$$

Since M is infrared divergent let $q^2 \rightarrow q^2 + \lambda^2$ for a moment (there is no such divergence in $\partial_\mu \partial_\nu M$). Then (C. 1) becomes

$$\left[\gamma^{\mu}\left(\frac{1}{i}\partial_{\mu} - \langle A_{\mu}(x)\rangle\right) + m_{o}\right] S(x,y)$$

$$= \delta^{(4)}(x-y) - i\gamma^{\mu}\partial_{\mu}\partial_{v} M(x-x') \frac{\delta\, S(x,y)}{\delta \langle A_{v}(x')\rangle}$$

$$- i\gamma^{\mu} \bar{D}_{\mu v}^{(T)}(x,x') \frac{\delta\, S(x,y)}{\delta \langle A_{v}(x')\rangle} \qquad (C.3)$$

Now we multiply both sides of (C. 3) by the operator

$$\exp\left[-\left(\partial_{\lambda} M(x-x')\right) \frac{\delta}{\delta \langle A_{\lambda}(x')\rangle}\right]$$

acting on any functional of $\langle A \rangle$:

$$\left\{\exp\left[-\left(\partial_{\lambda} M(x-x')\right) \frac{\delta}{\delta \langle A_{\lambda}(x')\rangle}\right]\right\} F\left\{A_{\lambda}(\xi)\right\}$$

$$= F\left\{A_{\lambda}(\xi) - \partial_{\lambda} M(x-\xi)\right\}$$

Further

$$\partial_{\lambda} M(x-\xi)\Big|_{\xi \to x} = 0 \,,$$

since M is an even function. Finally,

$$\left\{\exp\left[-\left(\partial_{\lambda} M(x-x')\right) \frac{\delta}{\delta \langle A_{\lambda}(x')\rangle}\right]\right\} \frac{1}{i}\partial_{\mu}$$

$$= \frac{1}{i}\partial_{\mu} e^{-\left[\partial_{\lambda} M(x-x')\right] \frac{\delta}{\delta \langle A_{v}(x')\rangle}}$$

$$- i\partial_{\mu}\left[\partial_{\lambda} M(x-x')\right] \frac{\delta}{\delta \langle A_{\lambda}(x')\rangle}$$

Consequently we find

$$\left[\gamma^{\mu}\left(\frac{1}{i}\partial_{\mu} - \langle A_{\mu}(x)\rangle\right) + m_{o}\right] S\left[x, y; \langle A_{\mu}(\xi)\rangle - \partial_{\mu} M(x-\xi)\right]$$

$$= \delta^{(4)}(x-y) - i\gamma^{\mu}\bar{D}^{(T)}_{\mu\nu}(x, x')\frac{\delta}{\delta\langle A_{\nu}(x')\rangle} S$$

$$\cdot \left[x, y; \langle A_{\mu}(\xi)\rangle - \partial_{\mu} M(x-\xi)\right]$$

We have also made use of the fact that the functional $\bar{D}$ should be gauge invariant, and therefore unchanged when

$$\langle A_{\mu}(\xi)\rangle \longrightarrow \langle A_{\mu}(\xi)\rangle - \partial_{\mu} M(x-\xi) =$$

$$= \langle A_{\mu}(\xi)\rangle + \frac{\partial}{\partial \xi^{\mu}} M(x-\xi)$$

We define

$$S^{(T)}\left[x, y; \langle A_{\mu}(\xi)\rangle\right] \equiv S\left[x, y; \langle A_{\mu}(\xi)\rangle + \frac{\partial}{\partial \xi^{\mu}} M(x-\xi)\right]$$

If we use (4.9) we find

$$S\left[x, y; \langle A_{\mu}(\xi)\rangle + \frac{\partial}{\partial \xi^{\mu}} M(x-\xi)\right] =$$

$$= e^{i\left[M(0) - M(x-y)\right]} S\left[x, y; \langle A_{\mu}(\xi)\rangle\right]$$

and thus we have established (4.16).

In the above formula we can let $\lambda \rightarrow 0$, since $M(x-y) - M(0)$ approaches an infrared finite limit.

REFERENCES

J. Schwinger, Phys. Rev. 91, 713 (1953).

J. Schwinger, Proc. Natl. Acad. Sci. US, 37, 452 (1951).

F. J. Dyson, Phys. Rev. 75, 486, 1736 (1949).

J. C. Ward, Phys. Rev. 78, 1824 (1950).

Y. Takahashi, Nuovo Cimento 6, 370 (1957).

K. Johnson, B. Zumino, Phys. Rev. Letters 3, 351 (1959).

B. Zumino, Jour. Math. Phys. 1, 1 (1960).

M. Gell-Mann, F. E. Low, Phys. Rev. 1300 (1954).

K. Johnson, M. Baker, R. Willey, Phys. Rev. 136, B1111 (1964).

R. Haag, Th. Maris, Phys. Rev. 132, 2325 (1963).

Y. Nambu, G. Jona-Lasinio, Phys. Rev. 124, 246 (1961).

J. Goldstone, A. Salam, S. Weinberg, Phys. Rev. 127, 965 (1962).

M. Baker, K. Johnson, B. Lee, Phys. Rev. 133, B209 (1964).

Th. A. J. Maris, G. Jacob, Phys. Rev. Letters 17, 1300 (1966).

M. Gell-Mann, F. E. Low, op. cit.

R. Jost, J. M. Luttinger, Helv. Phys. Acta 23, 201 (1950).

L. D. Landau, A. A. Abrikosov, I. M. Halatnikov, Dokl. Acad. Nayk. SSSR 95, 497, 773, 1177 (1954).

K. Johnson, R. Willey, M. Baker, Phys. Rev. (in press).

The method of differentiation of the self-energy part was first suggested by Ward. Ambiguities in the original proposal were pointed out by Yang and Mills. These objections do not apply to the method of differentiation used here.

J. C. Ward, Proc. Phys. Soc. (London) A 64, 54 (1951).

C. N. Yang, R. Mills, Prog. Theo. Phys. Suppl. 37 38, 507 (1966).

See also

J. D. Bjorken, S. Drell, "Relativistic Quantum Fields", Mc Graw Hill Inc. N. Y. (1965) for an alternative method.

Earlier notes on the same subject as these lectures:

Lectures on Particles and Field Theory, Englewood Cliffs N. J. Prentice Hall (1965).

Acta Physica Austriaca, Suppl. 2 (1965).

2

THE FIELD THEORETICAL APPROACH TO COMPOSITE PARTICLES[+]

Bernard Jouvet, Collège de France, Paris

+ Translated into (bad) English from the original French by Dr. Enrique Tirapegui.

1. THE CONCEPT OF COMPOSITE PARTICLE

The problem of defining intrinsically and in an observable way a composite system has received historically a great number of solutions.

I) The first notion of a composite system comes from the Greeks, it is that of divisibility: a system is composite if it may be divided, it is elementary if it may not be divided "α-τομος". The atoms were then elementary systems, and this was so until it was possible to break them.

The molecular hypothesis and afterwards the discovery of the molecules and atoms brought as a consequence the distinction of two types of divisibility: the elements in which a composite body could be separated were:

- of the same nature, i.e. with the same physical or chemical properties (excluding the mass) of the original body;
- of a different nature.

For instance a lump of sugar may be divided into several pieces of sugar of the same type, and this is possible as far as the limit of the sugar molecules (it is then composed of elements identical to itself) is reached. The sugar molecule may then be divided in elements of a different nature. We shall call this two notions homo-divisibility [I(1)] and allo-divisibility [I(2)] respectively.

II) At the same time an evident <u>mass rule</u> appears as a characteristic of composite systems: The mass of the composite system is approximately equal to the sum of the masses of the constituents (it was the case of the mass of the molecules, the mass of the atoms, afterwards this was experimentally verified as a good approximation still for the nucleus).

III) With the Bohr model of the hydrogen atom and the Schrödinger equation two new notions of composite systems appear. We shall call them weak solubility(°) and total solubility.

IIIa. <u>Weak Solubility</u>. If the forces between some given particles are attractive, bound states may appear. The existence of these states is in this way deduced from the given particles and their properties of interaction (for instance the first models of the deuteron). The properties of the given particles (constituents) imply for the bound state, if it exists, a certain number of properties such as integer or half integer spin, proper quantum number for charge, baryonic number, strangeness, isospin, etc.

IIIb. <u>Total solubility</u>. In the case for which the forces between the constituents have a sufficiently simple structure such that we are able to calculate with unlimited precision all the parameters characterizing the dynamical properties of bound states (mass, radius, etc) as an explicit function of the properties of the constituents, then one has an objective test of compositeness if

---

(°) "deductibilité faible et deductibilité total" in the French manuscript.

these parameters are in agreement with experiment.

Nowadays the objective criterion of divisibility and validity of the mass rule, and the subjective criterion of weak solubility are the only ones that allow us to think that nuclei are composite systems. But over this statement nobody doubts.

IV. With the Quantum Theory of Fields the Concept of Elementary Particle appears. It was first used for indivisible particles (i.e. non composite in the sense of criterion I) like the electron, the proton and the photon -this last particle could be absorbed or created but not "divided"- in a more strict sense before the discovery of the positive electron.

According to this concept one postulates a field associated to each type of particle its dynamics is completely characterized by spin, mass parameters and couplings with all the other fields. But the result is that the elementary particles defined in this way are in general divisible (in contradiction with criterion I), and their properties of divisibility form a class which is greater than those we have already defined.

Indeed the allo-divisibility I(2) which traduces the properties of reactions such as

$$\gamma \rightarrow e^{+} + e^{-}$$

$$\pi \rightarrow N + \overline{N}$$

is necessarily associated with a new type of divisibility which we may call hetero-divisibility I(3) which traduces the notion that the products of the division of an elementary particle may contain the particle itself with other particles of different form, for instance

$$e \rightarrow \gamma + e$$

$$N \rightarrow \pi + N$$

The homo-divisibility I(1) exists also for instance in the reaction

$$\pi^o \rightarrow 3\pi^o$$

We should also notice that even if some physical parameters of the elementary particle must be postulated (mass, spin, couplings, isospin, charge, baryon number, strangeness) there are other parameters which are deduced (radius, magnetic moment, etc.). We may also see that the existence of very general conservation rules is enough to deduce for elementary particles all the properties of weak solubility (IIIa) of composite models. For instance, if we accept the isospin invariance and the Lorentz invariance as fundamental postulates of field theory, then the elementary π-meson has necessarily integer spin and integer isospin if it interacts with the nucleons.

The quantum theory of fields introduces, as we have just seen, a concept of "elementary particle" which is not the complement of the previous concept of a composite system. The problem is then to choose properties or concepts suitable to define and distinguish composite particles from this new point of view. We may try to define composite particles by the property of "not being elementary" and also to conserve the compatibility of the previous criterion with this one. This implies for our last criterion the following properties:

The total solubility (IIIb), which implies, after the definition of elementary particles (IV), the possibility of proving the existence of the composite particle and that of calculating its mass (m) and the coupling constants G_i with other fields.

We remark that it is certainly impossible to conserve the mass criterion in the form (II) (though this is not forbidden by the definition of elementary particles (IV)) and that it seems difficult to generalize it in an acceptable way if we take into account the results that are available for the known particles. Furthermore the distinction of the particles that may be considered as "constituents" of another system is not at all evident in the high energy domain because the notions of solubility, even weak, divisibility and mass rule, which were in coincidence for low energies (and made possible in that case the identification of constituents) do not have now unambiguous relations among themselves. For instance, manifestations of natural divisibility such as the decay modes of pions and the mass rule would lead us to think that the π-meson is formed of $\mu + \nu_\mu$, while the notion of "solubility" implies on the contrary that the π-meson is formed of $N - \bar{N}$ in spite of the fact that the divisibility of the π in baryons-antibaryons is energetically more difficult to realize. We may then say from a theoretical point of view that leptons and baryons must be both constituents of the pions if these particles are composite, but it is also clear that a hierarchy of constituents must be considered according to which the most important constituents from the point of view of the solubility are those for which the divisibility is weaker and the mass rule (II) is violated in the worse way. An extreme example of this anomaly is given by the quark models, based only on the solubility criterion, the divisibility being not yet proved. Another example is the case of the photon: if it is possible to satisfy the mass criterion and the weak solubility in a neutrino theory of photons, it is also evident that the main property of photons, that of interacting with charged particles, cannot be deduced if one does not take into account the existence of the charged particles, which completely break the mass criterion. In this sense the Fermi-Yang model is historically the first to have emphatically rejected the mass criterion, using instead that of solubility.

We must then conclude that in the high energy domain the only criterion for the composite nature of a particle is that of "total solubility", which we have previously explained in the case of field theory. But that criterion alone is not satisfactory, firstly because the notion of constituent is badly defined, and also because of the existence of the simple counter-example of the Lee model ($V \rightarrow N + \theta$), in which a second complex pole appears in the propagator. We may suppose that the first pole is that of an elementary particle of given mass m_v and given coupling constant G, whereas the complex pole corresponds to an unstable particle V^* completely deduced from the given data ("total solubility") its mass m_v^* and coupling constant G^* being explicit functions of the parameters of the constituents V, N, and θ. But in the same model it is also possible to consider as given the parameters m_v^* and G^* defining particle V^*, and this determines completely the propagator and therefore the particle V. Then in this case there is nothing to tell us how to decide which of the two particles V or V^* is elementary, apart from the subjective and arbitrary roles of "postulated" and "deduced" particle which we may assign to them.

Clearly, however, one "feels" that there exists an essential difference between the solubility of the V^* particle and that of the states of the hydrogen atom or of the deuteron, for instance. The problem is then to see what is that difference. We must then find a precise definition of a composite particle which should express not only the solubility (which is in most cases, due to the difficulties of the calculations, a more or less subjective criterion) but which should also be capable of giving results connected to observable phenomena, that is, with objective facts.

2. THE DEFINITION OF THE COMPOSITE CHARACTER

2.1. Our purpose being to give an intrinsic definition of composite particles, we shall study now a soluble model with a bound state, which we may consider as a typical example of a particle described as composite. Afterwards we shall study the particular properties which such particle may have, in comparison to those that it would have if it were elementary.

Let us consider the non-relativistic Hamiltonian[1]:

$$H_X = \int d^3k \left[\frac{1}{2u}\mathbf{k}^2 + \mu\right]\theta^+(\mathbf{k})\theta(\mathbf{k}) + m\int d^3p N^+(\mathbf{p})N(\mathbf{p})$$

$$-\frac{\lambda}{(2\pi)^3}\int d^3k_1 d^3k_2 d^3k_3\, \delta^{(3)}(\mathbf{k}_1 + \mathbf{k}_2 - \mathbf{k}_3 - \mathbf{k}_4)$$

$$f_o(k_1^2)f_o(k_3^2)\theta^+(\mathbf{k}_1)N^+(\mathbf{k}_2)\theta(\mathbf{k}_3)N(\mathbf{k}_4) \qquad (2.1)$$

where we have postulated the existence of the field $\theta(\mathbf{k})$ of elementary bosons of mass μ, coupled locally to the static fermions field N of mass m. The function $f_o(k^2)$ is a form factor normalized at some given value of k^2.

The basic interaction is analogous to the four field interaction first introduced by Fermi. Moreover, it has the property of being separable: to recall these properties (separable coupling of four fields) we shall designate by X this type of coupling.

The matrix $T_{X(N,\theta)}(s)$ is represented by the series of graphs (Fig. 1)

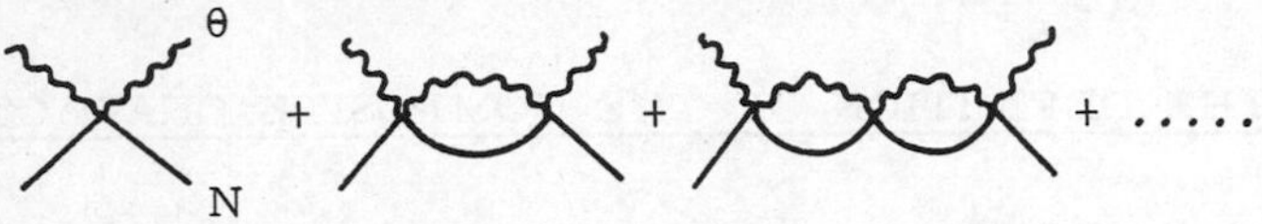

Fig. 1

and expressed as a function of the parameters characterizing N and θ has the form

$$T_{X(N,\theta)}(s) = \frac{\lambda_o \varphi_o^2(s)}{1 - \lambda_o B(s)} \qquad (2.2)$$

$$s = m + \mu + \frac{k^2}{2\mu} = \text{total energy of } (N+\theta) \text{ particles}$$

We may suppose without lost of generality that the function $f_o(k^2)$ is normalized at some point s_o:

$$f_o(k^2) = \varphi_o(s) \quad , \quad \varphi_o(s_o) = 1$$

One has

$$B(s) = \bar{B}(s) + i B_1(s)$$

$$B(s) = \frac{i}{(2\pi)^4} \int \frac{d^4k' f_o^2(k'^2)}{(s - k'_o - m + i\varepsilon)(k'_o - \frac{k'^2}{2\mu} - \mu + i\varepsilon)}$$

which can be written as

$$B(s) = \frac{\mu^{3/2}}{\sqrt{2}\,\pi^2} \int_{m+\mu}^{\infty} \frac{\varphi_o^2(s')\sqrt{s'-(m+\mu)}}{s'-s-i\varepsilon}\, ds'$$

We shall put

$$\sigma(s) = \frac{\mu^{3/2}}{\sqrt{2}\,\pi^2}\sqrt{s-(m+\mu)}$$

The integral for B(s) will be convergent if

$$\varphi_o^2(s)\Big|_{s\to\infty} < s^{-1/2}$$

The function $\overline{B}(s)$ is real and increases with s for $s < m+\mu$.
If

$$B(m+\mu) > \frac{1}{\lambda_o} > 0 \quad \text{condition I} \qquad (2.3)$$

we have a bound state corresponding to a particle which we shall call V_c whose mass M_c is defined by the pole $s = M_c$ of T(s) for $s < M+\mu$ (see Fig. 2).

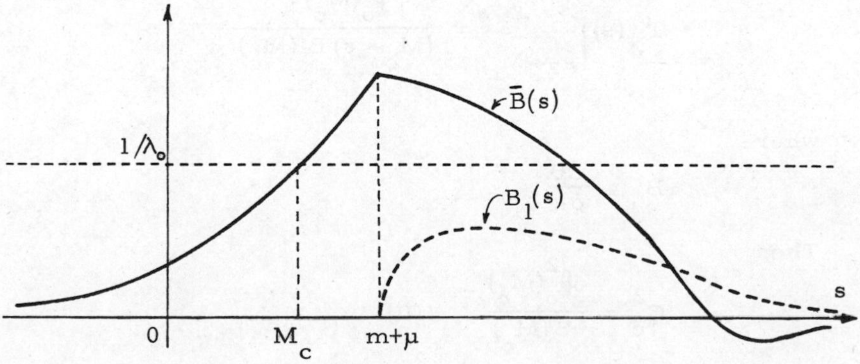

Fig. 2

We see then that (I) is the condition for the existence of a bound state.

The mass M_c is such that

$$B(M_c) = \frac{1}{\lambda_o} \quad \text{(II)} \tag{2.4}$$

We call (II) the <u>mass relation</u>.

We may write (2.2) in the form

$$T_X(s) = \frac{\varphi_o^2(s)}{\frac{1}{\lambda_o} - B(s)} = \frac{\varphi_o^2(s)}{B(M_c) - B(s)} \tag{2.5}$$

In the same way as for the case in which we deal with elementary particles, the renormalized coupling constants may be defined by the residues at the poles of the S matrix $\left[\text{which in the neighborhood of this poles has the form } -G^2/[p - M + i\varepsilon]\right]$.

The coupling constant G_c of the V_c particle with its constituents is then given by the residue at the pole $s = M_c$ of $T_X(s)$. In the neighborhood of $s = M_c$ we have

$$T_X(s)\Big|_{s \to M_c} = \frac{\varphi_o^2(M_c)}{(M_c - s)\, B'(M_c)} \tag{2.6}$$

where

$$B' \equiv \frac{\partial B}{\partial s}$$

Then

$$G_c^2 = \frac{\varphi_o^2(M_c)}{B'(M_c)} \quad \text{(III)} \tag{2.7}$$

which we call the <u>coupling relation</u>.

The matrix $T_X(s)$ may then be written

$$T_X(s) = \frac{\varphi_o^2(s)}{(M_c - s)B'(M_c)\left[1 - \frac{M_c - s}{B'(M_c)}\int \frac{\varphi_o^2(s')\sigma(s')\,ds'}{(s'-M_c)^2(s'-s-i\varepsilon)}\right]} \tag{2.8}$$

We shall now write $T_X(s)$ in a way displaying its explicit dependence on the constants characterizing the bound state V_c: (M_c, G_c^2) and on the form factor of the vertex $V_c \longrightarrow N+\theta$ (which must be normalized for $s = M_c$).

Let us define

$$\varphi_N(s) \equiv \frac{\varphi_o(s)}{\varphi_o(M_c)} \equiv Z_1(M_c)\,\varphi_o(s) \tag{2.9}$$

and

$$B_N(s) \equiv \frac{B(s)}{\varphi_o^2(M_c)} \tag{2.10}$$

Then

$$T_{X(V_c, N, \theta)} = +G_c^2 \frac{\varphi_N^2(s)}{(M_c - s)\left[1 - G_c^2(M_c - s)\int \frac{\sigma(s')\varphi_N^2(s')ds'}{(s'-M_c)^2(s'-s-i\varepsilon)}\right]} \tag{2.11}$$

where

$$G_c^2 = \frac{1}{B_N'(M_c)} \tag{2.12}$$

is just our coupling relation (III).

The two relations II(2.4) and III(2.7) [or (2.12)] determine the mass and the coupling constant of the bound state V_c as functions of the parameters of the particles N and θ and of their properties [masses (m , μ) and their coupling [coupling constant λ_o and form factor $\wp_o(s)$]]. These two relations express then the fact that the composite particle V_c is completely deduced (total solubility) from the parameters of the particles N and θ only.

But now we face the fundamental problem mentioned in the preceding section: suppose we know all the properties of the particles N and θ and we find in nature a particle we call V_E, which has the same types of interaction as the particle V_c, i.e. it has the same quantum numbers as a system (N+ θ) and it may effectively be divided in the two particles N and θ; then how can we assert that such a particle is composed of the particles N and θ and that it corresponds to the particle V_c? From all we have said so far the only method would consist in an explicit calculation of M_c and G_c^2 and in the verification that these values are exactly the experimental ones, M_E and G_E^2. But here we face the difficulty that only rarely is possible to explicitly calculate those values with an arbitrary precision, and one may then ask whether there are other properties characterizing the composite particle V_c which could be used as a more practical criterion.

Taking into account the fact that the knowledge of the field equation of an interacting field allows the deduction of <u>all</u> the properties of the particle represented by that field, the only way to obtain all the properties of the composite particle V_c appears to be the knowledge of the evolution equation of the field of that composite particle, which we may think should be different from the equation for an elementary particle V_E.

We may try in general to determine such a field equation using the following method: consider as given the most general field equation for a particle of type V_E (whose free field equation may have a priori a non linear structure and the couplings with the fields N and θ may have a complicated form) and try to identify the S matrix for such a system with the matrix S_x of the system in which the V_c composite particle appears. If such identification is possible we have thereby determined a field equation which traduces all the observable properties of the composite particle and in that sense we may then say that we have determined the field equation of a composite particle, V_c.

b) In the case of the preceding model the solution of the problem is simple. We assume, a priori, an elementary and static particle V_E, whose free field equation is of the usual linear form, and whose coupling traduces in the most simple way the desired divisibility property ($V \rightarrow N+\theta$), namely, the Hamiltonian is of the type of T. D. Lee's:

$$H_Y \equiv \int d^3k\, M_E^o\, V_E^{o+}(\mathbf{k})\, V_E^o(\mathbf{k}) + \int d^3p\, m\, N^+(\mathbf{p})\, N(\mathbf{p})$$
$$+ \int d^3k \left[\frac{k^2}{2\mu} + \mu\right] \theta^+(\mathbf{k})\, \theta(\mathbf{k}) + \frac{G_E^o}{\sqrt{2\pi}} \int d^3k_1 d^3k_2$$
$$d^3k_3\, \delta(\mathbf{k}_3 - \mathbf{k}_1 - \mathbf{k}_2) \Big[V_E^o(\mathbf{k}_3)\, \theta^+(\mathbf{k}_1)\, N^+(\mathbf{k}_2)\, f_o(\mathbf{k}_1^2)$$
$$+ \text{h.c.} \Big] \qquad (2.13)$$

Here V_E^o is the bare field associated to the particle V_E, M_E^o its bare mass and G_E^o its bare coupling constant. The coupling introduced in this way is the local product of the three fields (V, N and θ) (analogous to the case of the Lorentz and the Yukawa couplings), and we use the index Y to characterize this kind of coupling.

The scattering amplitude (Nθ) is represented by the series of graphs of Fig. 3.

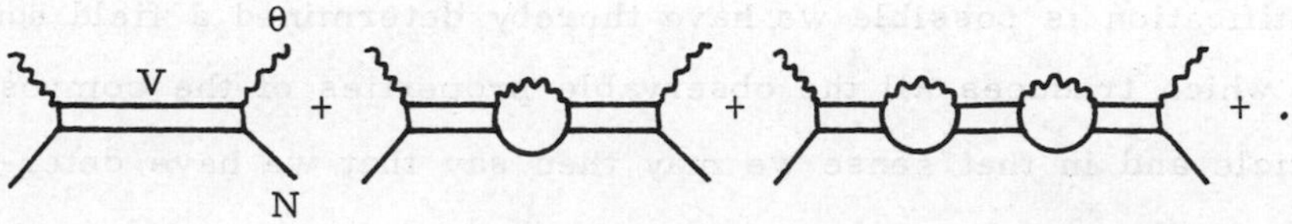

Fig. 3

Its value is

$$T_Y(s) = \frac{-G_o^2 \varphi_o^2(s)}{-s + M_o - G_o^2 B(s)} \tag{2.14}$$

where B(s) is the same function we found in the preceding X model.

The physical mass M_E and the observed coupling constant G_E are here given a priori, and they must be the poles of $T_Y(s)$. These latter properties are realized by determining, as functions of G_E^2 and M_E, the renormalization constants $\delta\nu$, Z_3, Z_1 defined through the relations

$$M_E^o = M_E + \frac{\delta\nu}{Z_3} \tag{2.15}$$

$$G_E^o = \frac{G_E}{\sqrt{Z_3}} Z_1 \quad , \quad (V_E^o = \sqrt{Z_3}\, V_E),$$

which, together with Eq. (2.14) give

$$T_Y(s) = \frac{G_E^2 \varphi_N^2(s)}{Z_3(M_E - s) + \delta\nu - G_E^2 B(s)}$$

$$= \frac{G_E^2 \varphi_N^2(s)}{M_E - s - G_E^2 B_R(s)} \qquad (2.16)$$

where

$$\varphi_N(s) = \frac{\varphi_o(s)}{\varphi_o(M_E)} = Z_1(M_E)\varphi_o(s) \quad , \quad \varphi_N(M_E = 1 \qquad (2.17)$$

$$B_R(s) = \left[Z_1(M_E)\right]^2 \left[B(s) - B(M_E) - (s - M_E)B'(M_E)\right]$$

Then

$$B_R(M_E) = B'_R(M_E) = 0$$

Writing

$$Z_1^2 B(s) = B_N(s)$$

we have

$$Z_3(G_E^2, M_E) = 1 - G_E^2 B'_N(M_E) \qquad (2.18)$$

$$\delta\nu(G_E^2, M_E) = G_E^2 B_N(M_E) \qquad (2.18')$$

and we may write $T_{Y(V_E, N, \theta)}(s)$ in an identical form to that of $T_{X(V_c, N, \theta)}(s)$, M_E and G_E replacing in (2.16) the constants M_c and G_c.

The identification of the matrix element of the elementary particle theory T_Y with the matrix element T_X of the composite particle theory is then easy to perform, and it is obtained when the constants M_E and G_E in T_Y tend to M_c and G_c.

The first condition is then expressed by

$$B_N(M_E \rightarrow M_c) \equiv B(M_c)Z_1^2(M_c) = \frac{\delta\nu}{G_c^2} = \frac{Z_1^2(M_c)}{\lambda_o} \qquad (2.19)$$

Then

$$\frac{G_c^2 Z_1^2(M_c)}{\delta\nu(G_c^2, M_c)} = \lambda_o \quad : \quad \underline{\text{mass equation}}\ (\text{IV}) \qquad (2.20)$$

The second condition expresses the fact that G_c^2 is determined by the equation

$$Z_3(G_c^2, M_c) = 0 \quad : \quad \underline{\text{coupling equation}}\ (\text{V}) \qquad (2.21)$$

Therefore, the Y theory of an elementary particle V_E, in the limit $Z_3 = 0$ and when $\delta\nu$ is given by the condition (2.2) is identical, in the sense previously defined, to the X theory of the composite particle V_c. We remark here that the concept of elementary particle in field theory is characterized by the fact that spins, masses and coupling constants are given a priori; we also see that in the preceding example, for which there is no problem of spin, we obtain exactly two equations, (2.20) and (2.21), to determine the two parameters of the composite particle. The existence of these two equations (even if we are not able to give them an explicit form to deduce two relations) characterizes then the "total solubility" of the composite particle. In the case of real theories (of pseudoscalar mesons, vector mesons, etc.) the coupling constants are frequently dimensionless, in contrast to the constant λ_o of the Fermi type which has the dimension M^{-2}. Furthermore in the case in which the fermions have a bare mass equal to zero, only this constant λ_o permits the introduction of a mass dimension and hence the production by Eq. (IV)(2.20) of the masses of the mesons and in consequence that of the fermions[5]. Equation V(2.21) characterizes therefore the equation for the coupling constant, and we may identify Eq. IV(2.20) as the equation for the mass of the composite particle. It should be noted that the dimensionless coupling constant G^2 is related, by the dimensionless relation V(2.21) to the ratios of the masses of fermions and bosons, and depends implicitly on λ_o only through the composite boson mass value.

c) Before a more detailed discussion, we shall give two other useful proofs of the equivalence of the matrices S_X and S_Y. The proof we have just given is characterized by the use of a limiting procedure only over the observable quantities (G_E and M_E) of the Yukawa theory. We shall now study the effect of that limit on the bare constants of the Yukawa theory[6]: using (2.15) we have ($\delta\nu$ being finite and different from zero):

$$M_o = M + \frac{\delta\nu}{Z_3}\bigg|_{Z_3 \to 0} \to \infty \tag{2.22}$$

and

$$G_o = G\frac{Z_1}{\sqrt{Z_3}}\bigg|_{Z_3 \to 0} \to \infty$$

But (using Eq. 2.20)

$$\left.\frac{G_o^2}{M_o}\right|_{Z_3\to 0} = \frac{G_c^2 Z_1^2}{\delta\nu} = \lambda_o \qquad (2.23)$$

Dividing numerator and denominator of T_y by $M_o - s$ before taking the limit $M_o \to \infty$ we obtain

$$\left. T_y(s)\right|_{Z_3\to 0} \equiv \left. \frac{\frac{G_o^2}{M_o - s}\varphi_o^2(s)}{1 - \frac{G_o^2}{M_o - s}B(s)} \right|_{Z_3\to 0} =$$

$$= \frac{\lambda_o \varphi_o^2(s)}{1 - \lambda_o B(s)} \equiv T_x(s) \qquad (2.24)$$

In fact this identity is equivalent to replace in the graphs of Fig. 3 the elements of graphs which contain the bare field propagator $1/(M_o - s)$ and the bare coupling constant G_o^2, e.g.,

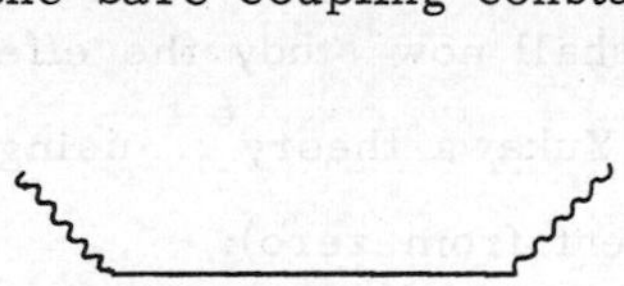

by

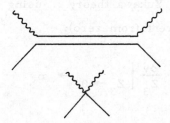

which amounts to replace $G_o^2/(M_o - s)$ by λ_o in the computations.

We see that the series of graphs 3 goes into the series of graphs 1 (Fig. 1).

We remark here that the condition $Z_3 = 0$ is sufficient to ensure that the Yukawa theory reduces to a Fermi-type theory where λ_o is arbitrary (positive if the particle is stable).

It may also be useful to consider the renormalized quantities of the Fermi theory; indeed the fact that we find in nature interactions of the Fermi type for which it is not known whether they involve bound or composite unstable states that may have unknown masses, or if they result from fundamental Lagrangian Fermi couplings, makes it necessary to consider the possibility that the Fermi interaction we observe might result from "masked" Yukawa theories.

Let us suppose for instance that in our Yukawa theory the physical mass M_E is greater than the energy domain which has been explored up to now. It is then clear that it would not be convenient to discuss that theory in terms of the completely unknown parameters M_E and G_E.

Let us suppose then that we have fixed by a direct measurement the value of T(s) for a certain energy $s = s_1$ and define the observable contact interaction constant to be

$$T_y(s_1) = \lambda_{obs} \tag{2.25}$$

If this theory is of the Yukawa type we have

$$\lambda_{obs} = \frac{G_E^2 \varphi_N^2(s_1)}{M_E - s_1 - G_E^2 B_R(s_1)} \tag{2.26}$$

and we deduce easily the expression of $T_y(s)$ in function of λ_{obs}:

$$T_y(s) = \frac{\lambda_{obs} \dfrac{\varphi_o^2(s)}{\varphi_o^2(s_1)}}{1 - \dfrac{\lambda_{obs}}{\left[\varphi_o^2(s_1)\right]^2}\left[B(s) - B(s_1) - Z_3(s - s_1)\right]} \tag{2.27}$$

Putting

$$\varphi_{RX}(s) = \frac{\varphi_o(s)}{\varphi_o(s_1)} = \varphi_o(s)\, Z_{1X},\quad \varphi_{RX}(s_1) = 1 \tag{2.28}$$

$$B_{RX}(s) = \frac{1}{\left[\varphi_o(s_1)\right]^2}\left[B(s) - B(s_1)\right] = (Z_{1X})^2\left[B(s) - B(s_1)\right]$$

$$B_{RX}(s_1) = 0$$

we obtain

$$T_y(s) = \frac{\lambda_{obs}\, \varphi_{RX}^2(s)}{1 - \lambda_{obs}\, B_{RX}(s) + \lambda_{obs}\, Z_3(s - s_1)} \tag{2.29}$$

In this last form the two parameters M_E and G_E of the Yukawa theory have been replaced by the observable constant λ_{obs} and the unknown constant Z_3 which might be detected at low energy providing the functions $\varphi_o(s)$ and $B(s)$ are known. We see then that in the limit $Z_3 = 0$

$$T_y(s) \rightarrow T_x(s) = \frac{\lambda_{obs}\, \varphi^2_{RX}(s)}{1 - \lambda_{obs}\, B_{RX}(s)} = \frac{\lambda_o\, \varphi_o^2(s)}{1 - \lambda_o B_o(s)} \tag{2.30}$$

$$\lambda_o = \frac{\dfrac{\lambda_{obs}}{\varphi_o^2(s_1)}}{1 + \lambda_{obs} \dfrac{B(s_1)}{\varphi_o^2(s_1)}} = \frac{\lambda_{obs}\, Z^2_{1X}}{1 + \lambda_{obs}\, Z^2_{1X}\, B(s_1)} \tag{2.31}$$

It may be verified that in this limit the definition of λ_{obs} by equation (2.26) is equivalent to the mass equation (2.20).

2.2. The properties of "solubility" and of "allo-compositeness" we have just found and characterized by the property $Z_3 = 0$ for the composite particle are also exhibited from various points of view:

a. Hilbert space: It is possible to show, at least in a soluble model where the state vectors can explicitly be constructed, that the state vector of the composite particle is contained in the Hilbert space spanned by the state vectors of its constituents, which expresses clearly the allo-composite character. The calculations for the model defined by H_y for $Z_3 \neq 0$ give:[1,2,3]

$$| V_E(\mathbf{p}) > = Z_3 V_E^+(\mathbf{p}) \,|\, 0 > + \frac{G_E}{4\pi^{3/2}} \int \Big[d^3q d^3k \delta(\mathbf{p} - \mathbf{q} - \mathbf{k}) \frac{f(\mathbf{k})}{(\frac{k^2}{2\mu} + \mu + m - M_E)} \times N^+(\mathbf{q})\theta^+(k) \,|\, 0 > \Big] \tag{2.32}$$

$$| N_{\mathbf{q}_1} \theta_{\mathbf{k}_1} >^{\pm} = N^{+}_{\mathbf{q}_1} \theta^{+}_{\mathbf{k}_1} | 0 > - \frac{G_E}{4\pi^{3/2}} \times$$

$$\frac{f(\mathbf{k})}{\left[\frac{k^2}{2\mu} + \mu + m - M_E\right]\left[\bar{B}_R(s) \pm iB_1(s)\right]} \times$$

$$\times \Big\{ Z_3 \int d^3 p \delta(\mathbf{p} - \mathbf{q}_1 - \mathbf{k}_1) V^{+}_E(\mathbf{p}) | 0 >$$

$$+ \frac{G_E}{4\pi^{3/2}} \int\Big[d^3 q d^3 k \delta(\mathbf{q} + \mathbf{k} - \mathbf{q}_1 - \mathbf{k}_1) \frac{f(k)}{\left[\frac{k^2}{2\mu} - \frac{k_1^2}{2\mu} \bar{+} i\varepsilon\right]} \times$$

$$N^{+}(\mathbf{q}) \theta^{+}(\mathbf{k}) | 0 > \Big] \Big\}$$

and the limit $Z_3 = 0$ gives then*

$$\lim_{Z_3 \to 0} | V_E(\mathbf{p}) > \equiv | V_c(\mathbf{p}) > = \int \ldots\ldots\ldots\ldots N^{+} \theta^{+} | 0 > \tag{2.33}$$

b. <u>Field equations.</u> The Lagrangian L_y from which H_y is obtained has in the limit $Z_3 \to 0$ a very singular form because $V^{\circ}_E = \sqrt{Z_3}\; V_E \to 0$ while M°_E and G°_E tend to infinity.

But the limits $V^{\circ}_E M^{\circ}_E \to V_E \delta\nu$ and $G^{\circ}_E V^{\circ}_E = G_E V_E$ are finite.

---

* It is clear that the physical states $|N\theta>^{+}$ and $|V_c>$ are orthogonal (for a discussion of this model from the point of view of "physical operators" see Ref. 7).

Only the dynamical term

$$V_E^{\circ +}\left(i\frac{\partial}{\partial t} - M_E\right)V_E^{\circ} = ZV_E^{+}\left(i\frac{\partial}{\partial t} - M_E\right)V_E$$

disappears completely from L_y.

The equation of motion for the field V_E

$$Z_3\left(i\frac{\partial}{\partial t} - M_E\right)V_E - \delta\nu V_E = G_E Z_1 N\mathcal{A} \tag{2.34}$$

where $\mathcal{A}$ = Fourier transform of $f\theta$,

reduces for $Z_3 \to 0$ to the constraint relation[1]

$$V_E\Big|_{Z_3 \to 0} \equiv V_c = \frac{G_c Z_1}{\delta\nu} N\mathcal{A} \tag{2.35}$$

This relation clearly traduces the allo-composite character of the field V_c which is expressed solely in terms of the operators of other fields. The possibility of representing a composite particle by a "quasi-local field" has been shown in general by Haag, and it may be verified that the field (2.35) satisfies, as all the quasi-local fields, the asymptotic condition.[9] But the field V_c defined by the constraint $Z_3 = 0$ is the only one to satisfy, like the field of an elementary particle, the norm condition[9]

$$< 0 \mid V_c(x) \mid V_{\mathbf{p}} > = \frac{1}{(2\pi)^{3/2}} e^{i(\mathbf{p}\cdot\mathbf{x} - M_c t)} \tag{2.36}$$

The constraint condition also permits the elimination of the field V_c from the Lagrangian L_y, to obtain the Lagrangian[1]:

$$(L_y)_{Z_3 = 0} = L^{\bullet}_N + L^{\bullet}_{\theta} + \frac{1}{2} \frac{G_c^2 Z_1^2}{\delta\nu} (N\mathcal{A})(N^+ \mathcal{A}^+) \qquad (2.37)$$

which (taking into account the value of λ_o) is nothing but the Lagrangian L_x in which the non linear contact coupling between the fields N and θ appears.

The absence of the field V_c from the Lagrangian traduces its character of "solubility"*.

We note however that the property for a field of being eliminated from the Lagrangian is not sufficient to guarantee the composite character of that field. For instance:

a. The component A_4 of the electromagnetic potential of the photon, considered as elementary, may also be eliminated of the Lagrangian of electrodynamics replacing it by a non linear but also non local interaction

$$\int J_o(x) \frac{1}{|\mathbf{x} - \mathbf{x}'|} \delta(t - t') J_o(x') d^4x'$$

b. In a Yukawa theory of elementary particles it is also possible to eliminate from the Lagrangian the meson field, replacing its effect by an "action at a distance" term

$$\frac{G_o^2}{2} \int J(x) \Delta_F(x - x') J(x') d^4x'$$

The complex character of $\Delta_F = \bar{\Delta} + i\Delta_1$ reflects the fact that

---

* "deductibilité" in the French manuscript.

the matrix $(S_y)_{[0\ \text{meson}]}$ defined in the space of the operators forming the currents is not unitary, and only in the limit $Z_3 = 0$, which implies $G_o^2 \Delta_F(x) \rightarrow \lambda_o \delta^{(4)}(x)$, the matrix $(S_y)_{[0\ \text{meson}]}$ becomes unitary and the interaction local.

c. We shall see in Chapter 3 the distinction, from the point of view of the Lagrangian, between the case mentioned in the introduction (Lee model with particles V_c and V_c^*) and the composite case.

2.3. We have seen the different forms in which the general properties of "solubility" and "allo-compositeness" of a soluble model of composite particle show themselves, all those properties being in fact a consequence of the only condition $Z_3 = 0$.

But up to now we have dealt only with theoretical properties, and then our next step must be to look for an objective criterion different from the always weak possibility of using total solubility to distinguish a composite particle.

There are some indications suggesting a positive answer to this question: in the case of elementary bosons the canonical commutation rules imply

$$\left[\varphi(x), \dot{\varphi}(x')\right]_{t=t'} \approx \frac{1}{Z_3} \delta^{(3)}(\mathbf{x} - \mathbf{x}')$$

In the model we are considering we have

$$\left\{V_E, V_E^+\right\} \approx \frac{1}{Z_3} \tag{2.38}$$

Relations of this type imply that if the renormalized propagators have the Källen-Lehmann causal form

$$\Delta'(s) = \int \frac{\rho(s')}{s - s' + i\varepsilon} ds'$$

we have

$$\int \rho(s') ds' = \frac{1}{Z_3}$$

and then

$$s \Delta'(s') \Big|_{s \to \infty} \longrightarrow \frac{1}{Z_3} \tag{2.39}$$

We may therefore expect that the propagators of composite particles (defined as the limit when $Z_3 \to 0$ of the propagators of elementary particles) should be more singular at infinity than those of the elementary ones. <u>This asymptotic property which is in principle observable</u>, might then be used as a basis to make an objective distinction between a composite particle and an elementary one.

We also note that the fact that the field of a composite particle can be expressed in terms of the other fields, for instance C = AB... implies that C does not necessarily commute with the operators of its constituents (for instance A), and this must also imply characteristic asymptotic properties for certain scattering amplitudes.

A difference of that kind appears clearly in (2.29):

$$B_{RX}(s) \Big|_{s \to \infty} \longrightarrow \text{constant} \tag{2.40}$$

$$T_y(s) \Big|_{s \to \infty} \longrightarrow \frac{\varphi^2_{RX}(s)}{Z_3} \qquad \text{if } Z_3 \neq 0,$$

or tends to $\lambda_o \varphi_o^2(s)$ if $Z_3 = 0$.

The preceding study suggests that the condition $Z_3 = 0$ may be a good intrinsic definition of a composite particle:

1. This condition implies a group of properties, in agreement between themselves, expressing the notion of compositeness we have discussed in the previous chapter.

2. This condition takes the form of a mathematical relation, well defined and general, and it is then possible in principle to analize its consequences in a complete way.

3. This condition implies observable consequences which may provide then objective criterions for compositeness*.

The generalization of the example we have studied to more realistic cases faces various problems (whose discussion in detail will be given in the next chapters):

A. The first type of question is the following: Once we have accepted the $Z_3 = 0$ definition for compositeness, is it possible, in order to recognize whether a particle is elementary or composite, to determine with precision which are effectively the observable and characteristic physical properties of composite particles resulting from $Z_3 = 0$ in comparison with those of elementary particles for which $Z_3 \neq 0$? Is it possible to measure directly the constants Z_3 ? Is it possible to effectively calculate the constant Z_3 and then deduce from this at least half of the information required by total solubility (the mass is still to be determined) ?

B. A second type of questions must be studied also: The example we have studied was based on a contact (four fields coupling) interaction, and once the coupling constant was given the mass

* For completeness we quote the original work in which the $Z_3 = 0$ condition for compositeness was first proposed: B. Jouvet, Nuovo Cimento 5, 1 (1957) (note of the translator).

equation followed. But it is well known that there are also bound states produced by non local forces (for instance the Hydrogen atom).

It may be shown that such systems which we may call H-types of composite particles are also characterized by the property $Z_3 = 0$ and also that they have different properties with respect to elementary particles. Obviously the mass equation of H particles is different from that of X particles, and we also have observable differences between the two types of composite systems.

C. Finally, how general is the constraint $Z_3 = 0$ as a definition of composite particles:

i. In theories in which there are many particles.

ii. In the general covariant theory of fields.

iii. In the case where the composite particle is not built with particles different from itself (allo-compositeness) but it is composed of itself and other particles or of itself alone (auto-compositeness) ?

REFERENCES

The models we have studied here and there principal properties have been first considered in

1. J. C. Houard, B. Jouvet, Nuovo Cimento 18, 466 (1960).
2. Y. Ataka, Prog. Theor. Phys. 25, 369 (1961).
3. M. T. Vaughn, R. Aaron, R. D. Amado, Phys. Rev. 124, 1258 (1961).

Recent references and also the simplifications we have used here with respect to the models in Refs. 1, 2 and 3 are given in Ref. 4.

4. J. M. Levy-Leblond, Comm. Math. Phys. 4, 157 (1967).

5. W. Heisenberg, Zeits. J. Naturforschrift 9a, 292 (1954).

6. B. Jouvet, Nuovo Cimento 3, 1133 (1956).

7. M. Sirugue-Collin, Thèse, Marseille.

8. B. Jouvet, Nuovo Cimento 5, 1 (1957).

9. J. C. Houard, Cahiers de Physique 189-190, (1966) p. 161.

3. OBSERVABLE PROPERTIES OF THE COMPOSITE CHARACTER

In this chapter we shall limit ourselves to a class of models defined by interactions which contain at least one local or separable interaction. With a convenient choice of the coupling constant of that interaction it is always possible to fix the value of the mass of the composite particle at any value, and then the only properties of the composite character which should be studied are those resulting from the fact that the coupling constant satisfies the equation $Z_3 = 0$.

We shall distinguish two situations:

- The elastic case (where the inelasticity is zero)
- The case of processes where the inelasticity may be treated in the lowest order of perturbation theory.

3.1. The elastic case. A great variety of models have been proposed and may be used to study this case; all of them suppose the reaction $E \rightarrow A + B$ and the only condition to be fulfilled is the convergence of the integral for Z_3.

We give here some examples of those models:

a. local coupling

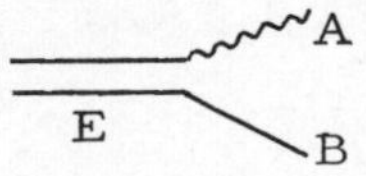

scalar covariant model (AB scalar field)

F. Zachariasen, Phys. Rev. 121, 1851 (1961)

M. L. Whippman, L. S. Gerstein, Phys. Rev. 134, 1123, (1964).

Lee model invariant under the Galilei group (non relativistic)

Ref. 4 of chapter 2.

S. Machida, Prog. Theor. Phys. 14, 407, (1965).

M. Sirugue-Colin, These, Marseille (1967).

b. coupling with a form factor

Lee model, T. D. Lee, Phys. Rev. 95, 1329 (1954).

c. coupling with vertex effects (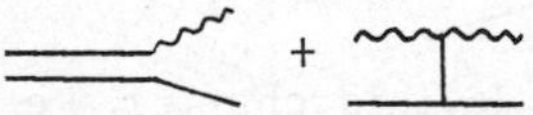),

A. Jacquemin, B. Jouvet, Nuovo Cimento 37, 20, (1965).

a. Differences in the asymptotic behavior of the matrix elements of the S matrix for composite particles and elementary particles. Levinson's Theorem and phase shifts[1]. Let us come back to the models studied in chapter 2. Taking T(s) in the form (2.16),

$$T_y(s) = \frac{G^2 \varphi_N^2(s)}{Z(M-s) - G^2\left[\bar{B}(s) - \bar{B}(M) + i\pi B_1(s)\right]} \qquad (3.1)$$

we may write the matrix $S_y = 1 + 2i\pi q T_y(s)$ as

$$S_y(s) = \frac{Z(M-s) - G^2\left[\bar{B}(s) - \bar{B}(M) - i\pi B_1(s)\right]}{Z(M-s) - G^2\left[\bar{B}(s) - \bar{B}(M) + i\pi B_1(s)\right]} = \frac{D^*(s)}{D(s)}$$

$$= e^{2i\delta(s)} \qquad (3.2)$$

with

$$B_1(s) = q\varphi_N^2(s)$$

$$S_y(s) = -1 \quad \text{when} \quad \mathrm{Re}\, D(s) = 0$$

$\bar{B}(s)$ has the form $\sim -1/s$ when $s \to \infty$, as it is shown in the figure below.

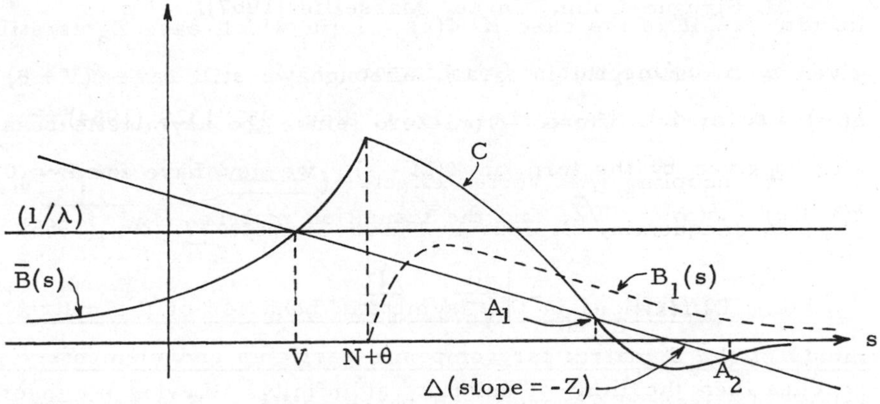

The zeros of Re D(s) are given by the intersection of the line Δ of slope $(-Z)$ with the curve C. The phase shift is chosen to be zero for $s = N + \theta$ and reaches the value $-\pi/2$ at A_1 and A_2, decreasing at A_1 and increasing at A_2, going finally to zero for $s = \infty$. It is known that if we have a pole on the second Riemann sheet near the real axis, the phase shift reaches $\pi/2$ by increasing values in the neighborhood of the pole. Indeed, a detailed study of the model permits the determination of this pole. When $Z \to 0$ and M is held constant the intersection point A_2 tends to infinity.

$S_x(s) = \lim_{Z \to 0} S_y(s)$ is real at infinity because $\bar{B}(s)$ and $B_1(s)$ tend to zero for $s \to \infty$, and therefore $\delta_\infty(Z=0) = \pi$.

These results are in accordance with Levinson's theorem, whose content may be expressed as follows

$$\delta(V+\theta) - \delta(\infty) = 0 \quad \text{for} \quad Z \neq 0 \quad \text{elementary particle}$$

$$\delta(V+\theta) - \delta(\infty) = \pi \quad \text{for} \quad Z = 0 \quad \text{bound state (composite particle)}$$

Nevertheless if $B_1(s)$ is different from zero when s tends to infinity, as it is the case if $\varphi(s) = 1$ (in which case Z_3 is still given by a convergent integral), although we still have $\delta(V+\theta) - \delta(\infty) = 0$ for Z_3 different from zero (since the asymptotic behavior is given by the term in $Z(M - s)$), we now have for $Z = 0$, $\delta(V+\theta) - \delta(\infty) = \pi/2$, and the transition matrix

$$|T(s)|_{Z\to 0} = \left|\frac{i}{\sqrt{s}}\right| = \frac{1}{\sqrt{s}}$$

reaches then the limit of unitarity at infinity. Levinson's theorem must be generalized in that case.[2]

<u>The propagators.</u>[3] In chapter 2 we have determined the propagator of the V particle in the elementary case, and have shown that in the limit Z tends to zero it becomes more singular at infinity; in fact we have in the present model

$$S'(s)\Big|_{s\to\infty} \longrightarrow \frac{1}{Zs} \quad \text{if} \quad Z \neq 0$$

and

$$\left[S_1'(s) = \lim_{Z\to 0} S'(s)\right]_{s\to\infty} \longrightarrow \frac{1}{\delta\nu} \tag{3.3}$$

$\varphi^2(s)G^2S'(s)$ is given in perturbation theory in terms of the bare constants by the limit (Fig. 1 in Ch. 2) of the graphs of Fig. 3 (Ch. 2), the constant $G^2/\delta\nu = \lambda$ coming from the limit as $Z \to 0$ of the first graph of Fig. 3 of Ch. 2.

Clearly the propagator $S'_1(s) = \lim_{Z\to 0} S'(s)$ cannot satisfy the usual Lehmann representation, and the divergence in the limit $Z \to 0$ of the integral that represents $1/Z$ makes it appear that a subtraction would be necessary; nevertheless, that is not what happens here.

Let us consider the propagator in the elementary case:

$$S'(s) = \int \frac{\rho(s')ds'}{s - s' + i\varepsilon} = F < 0 \mid T(V_E , V'^*_E) \mid 0 > \qquad (3.4)$$

where F is the Fourier transform; $\rho(s)$ is given by

$$\rho(s) = \delta(s - M_E) + G^2 \varphi_N^2(s) \mid S'(s) \mid^2 \sigma(s) \qquad (3.5)$$

(where $\sigma(s)$ is the phase space factor) and can be deduced from

$$F \sum_\alpha < 0 \mid V_E \mid \alpha > < \alpha \mid V'^*_E \mid 0 > \qquad (3.6)$$

where the states $\mid\alpha >$ are the physical states $\mid V_E >$ and $\mid N\theta >$.

If Z goes to zero

$$\rho_1(s) \equiv \lim_{Z\to 0} \rho(s) = \delta(s - M_c) + G_c^2 \varphi_N^2(s) \mid S'_1(s) \mid^2 \sqrt{s - (m+\mu)}$$

$$= \delta(s - M_c) - \frac{1}{2\pi i} \left[S'_1(s + i\varepsilon) - S'_1(s - i\varepsilon) \right] \qquad (3.7)$$

where $$S'_1(s) = \frac{\lambda_o/G_c^2}{1 - \lambda_o B(s)} = \lim_{Z\to 0} S'(s)$$

It is remarkable that $\rho_1(s)$ can be deduced exactly from the calculation of $F < 0 \mid V_c , V_c'^{*} \mid 0 >$ with $V_c = \lim_{Z \to 0} V_E = NA$; the second term of $\rho_1(s)$ clearly comes from

$$|< 0 | NA | N\theta >|^2 = | \quad + \quad + \quad + \ldots |^2$$

$$= |S_1'|^2 \; \mathrm{Im}\, B$$

while the term $\delta(s - M_c)$ is suitably normalized according to formula (2.36) and we therefore have:

$$\lim_{Z \to 0} < 0 | V_E , V_E'^{*} | 0 > = < 0 | V_c , V_c'^{*} | 0 > , \quad t \neq t' \tag{3.8}$$

and similarly for

$$< 0 \mid [V_E , V_E'^{*}] | 0 > \quad \text{and} \quad < 0 | \{V_E , V_E'^{*}\} | 0 > .$$

Clearly, provided $\varphi_N^2(s) \to 0$ sufficiently rapidly, the integral

$$J_1(s) \equiv \int \frac{\rho_1(s')\, ds'}{s - s' + i\varepsilon} \tag{3.9}$$

converges and

$$J_1(s) \Big|_{s \to \infty} \longrightarrow 0$$

Calculated by the residue theorem with the aid of (3.7) and integrating over the contour

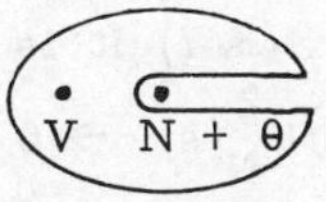

we obtain

$$J_1(s) = \frac{\lambda_o/G^2 Z_1^2}{1 - \lambda_o B(s)} - \frac{\lambda_o}{G^2 Z_1^2} \qquad (3.10)$$

the constant term coming from the contribution of the integral over the large circle at infinity, which is different from zero since $S_1'(s) \rightarrow 1/\delta\nu$, and making sure that $J_1(s) \underset{s \to \infty}{\longrightarrow} 0$, we have

$$\lim_{Z \to 0} S'(s) = \lim_{Z \to 0} F < 0 \mid T(V_E, V_E'^{*}) \mid 0 >$$

$$\equiv S_1'(s) = \frac{\lambda}{G^2 Z_1^2} + \int \frac{\rho_1(s')\,ds'}{s - s' + i\varepsilon} \qquad (3.11)$$

and hence

$$< 0 \mid T(V_c, V_c'^{*}) \mid 0 > \neq \lim_{Z \to 0} < 0 \mid T(V_E, V_E'^{*}) \mid 0 > \qquad (3.12)$$

Let us also consider the expression $\int \rho(s)ds$.

If $Z \neq 0$ we have $\frac{1}{Z} = \int \rho(s)ds$ which defines Z taking into account the canonical relations and in agrement with the relation[4] $Z = 1 - G_E^2 B'(M_E)$.

But when $G \rightarrow G_c$ so that $G_c^2 B'(M_c) = 1 \Rightarrow Z = 0$, the canonical relations are no longer valid, and the question arises whether the relation $\int (\rho(s))_{Z \to 0}\, ds = (1/Z)_{Z \to 0} = \infty$ still holds.

In view of the form of $\rho_1(s)$ in Eq. (3.7) it is clear that $\int \rho_1(s)ds$ does not necessarily diverge if $\varphi_N^2(s) \rightarrow 0$ sufficiently rapidly.

An explicit calculation shows in fact that we have

$$\left.\begin{aligned} \int \rho_1(s)ds &= \frac{G_c^2}{(2\pi\delta\nu)^2}\left\{\int dk \frac{k^2\varphi_N^2}{\omega_k}\right. \\ &\equiv 4\pi^2 < 0 \mid A(t)A^*(t) \mid 0 > \end{aligned}\right\}, \qquad (3.13)$$

[A(x) is defined here by

$$A(x) = \int d^3x' f(\mathbf{x} - \mathbf{x}') A(\mathbf{x}', t)$$

where $f(\mathbf{x})$ is the form factor in configuration space], an expression that can also be obtained from

$$< 0 \mid \{V_c , V_c'^*\} \mid 0 >_{t=t'} = \delta(\mathbf{x} - \mathbf{x}') \int \rho_1(s)ds \qquad (3.14)$$

<u>Dispersion relations.</u> Let us now consider the calculation of the amplitude $N\theta \rightarrow N\theta$ by the method of dispersion relations. We have

$$S_{fi} = < N_{\mathbf{q}'} \, \theta_{\mathbf{k}'} \text{ out} \mid N_{\mathbf{q}} \, \theta_{\mathbf{k}} \text{ in} >$$

which by the standard methods of contraction can be written[3]

$$S_{fi} = \delta_{fi} - \frac{G^2}{(2\pi)^6} \iint \Big\{ dx\, dx' \; e^{-ix(q+k)} \; e^{ix'(q'+k')} \; .$$

$$\cdot \left[\theta_{\mathbf{k}'} \mid T(j_N(x') j_N^+(x)) \mid \theta_{\mathbf{k}} \right>$$

$$+ i\delta(t - t') < \theta_{\mathbf{k}'} \mid \{N(x'), j_N^+(x)\} \mid \theta_{\mathbf{k}} > \Big] \qquad (3.15)$$

Considering that $j_N(x) \equiv (i\partial_t - m_N) N(x) \equiv -GA^+(x)V(x)$ and that the physical states of θ are identical to the bare states, the first term in the square bracket becomes

$$< 0 \mid T(V(x'), V^+(x)) \mid 0 > f(\omega_{\mathbf{k}}) f(\omega_{\mathbf{k}'})$$

In the case in which V is elementary, $j_N^+(x) = -GA(x)V_E^*(x)$, and the last term of the square bracket in (2.15) vanishes, since N anticommutes with V_E^+.

In the case in which V is composite we have, on the contrary, $V_c^+ = -\frac{G}{\delta\nu} N^+ A^+$ and the last term of the square bracket in (2.15) is not null, as it contains the expression $\{N, N'^+\} AA'^+$ which involves the non-zero anti-commutator $\{N, N'^+\}$. This terms gives rise in S_{fi} to a contact term proportional to $-(i/\pi^2)(G^2/\delta\nu) f f' \delta^4(f-i)$, and the transition matrix M defined by

$$S_{fi} = \delta_{fi} - \frac{1}{2\pi i} f f' \delta^{(4)}(f - i) M$$

now satisfies the dispersion relation

$$\mathrm{Re}\, M(s) = K - \frac{G^2}{4\pi} \frac{1}{s - M_c} + \frac{1}{\pi} P \int ds' \frac{\mathrm{Im}\, M(s')}{s' - s} \qquad (3.16)$$

which contains the constant $K = -G^2/4\pi\delta\nu$ whose presence is characteristic of the fact that Z is zero. Clearly the existence of the constant can only be determined insofar as the integral needs no subtraction, i.e. it converges.

Discussion. Having brought out, for the case of elastic interactions, the differences in behavior of certain elements of the S-matrix, depending on whether the intermediate particle exchanged by scattering is elementary or composite, we may ask to what extent these differences can actually be observed, in order that we may distinguish by experiment between elementary and composite particles. We shall see that owing to the fact that these differences only arise from the effects of very high energies, it seems to be impossible to decide whether Z is exactly zero or not, and the best we can hope for is to determine an upper limit for the constant Z, which can then be called the degree of "elementariness" of a particle.

This situation is similar to the situation that arises in actual measurements of the masses of supposedly massless particles (photon or neutrino); whereas mathematically the theories of the photon and of the neutrino present essential differences (invariance groups, particular singularity of the commutation relations) according to whether the masses are exactly zero or not, in practice the limits m_γ and $m_\nu \rightarrow 0$ can be taken without any remarkable physical consequences, and the experiment can at most provide limits for these parameters.

We have seen, for example, that Levinson's theorem provides a test which would enable us in principle to determine whether a particle is elementary or composite, but in actual fact the test assumes that we can observe the phase shift at infinity, which is clearly impossible and the problem is rather to determine the energy at which the phase shift begins to show an anomaly characteristic of the compositeness of the intermediate particle. Keeping Z finite but small it is easy to see that T(s) presents a complex pole in the neighborhood of A_2, giving rise to a resonance[5] characterized by its mass M' and its width Γ; if Z is sufficiently small and M' sufficiently big so that $\bar{B}(M') << \bar{B}(M_E)$ we have

$$M' - i\frac{\Gamma}{2} = M_E + \frac{G_E^2}{Z}(\bar{B}(M_E) - i\pi B_1(M')) \quad (3.17)$$

The mass M' is then practically equal to the bare mass $M^\circ_{V_E}$ of the V_E particle, and tends to infinity with 1/Z, whereas the width Γ, which increases when Z diminishes, effectively depends on the value of $B_1(M')$, which tends to zero. As a consequence, the appearance of such a resonance at a finite distance could be an argument in favour of the "elementariness" of the V particle, whereas the absence of observed resonances implies only that M' is greater than the limit E_{max} of the energies attained experimentally; it does not, therefore, allow us to assert that the particle is composite, but only that it is less and less elementary as E_{max} grows greater and greater. Moreover, as we have seen from Levinson's theorem, that resonance does not exist unless $\bar{B}(s)\big|_{s\to\infty} \longrightarrow 0$, which is equivalent to $\delta\nu$ being convergent.

The dispersion relation (without subtraction) given above, or its generalization to concrete cases, could also in principle serve as a basis to estimate the compositeness of certain particles. Nevertheless, it is also necessary in this case, in order to determine the characteristic constant K, to estimate with precision the dispersion integral. The computation of this integral is now clearly limited by the fact that we can only measure Im M(s) up to some finite energy E_{max}. Let us suppose then that with this data, limited in energy, experiment shows on the one hand the lack of a resonance in the domain $E < E_{max}$ and shows on the other hand the need to introduce a constant $K_{exp} \neq 0$ to assure the consistency of the dispersion relation.

It is easy to see that if the particle V is elementary the unobserved resonance of mass $M' > E_{max}$ contributes to the integral through the term

$$\int_{E_{max}}^{\infty} \frac{\mathrm{Im}\, M(s')}{s' - s}\, ds' \approx \frac{G^2}{4\pi M'Z}$$

This term, necessarily omitted in the experimental fit, may well be the explanation of the need to introduce the constant K_{exp}.

Nevertheless, an explicit determination of a constant K_{exp} obtained from an experiment, together with a failure to observe a resonance for $E < E_{max}$ implies the inequality

$$Z < \frac{G^2}{4\pi K_{exp} E_{max}} \tag{3.18}$$

which provides an upper bound to the degree of elementariness of the particle V.

b. Measurability of the parameter Z of "elementariness". Another possible way to determine whether a particle is composite would be to measure directly the degree of elementariness Z of the particle. In principle we could, in effect, calculate Z with the aid of one of its spectral expressions

$$Z = 1 - G^2 \int \frac{|\Gamma|^2 \sigma(a)\, da}{(a - M)^2}$$

or (3.19)

$$\frac{1}{Z} = \int \rho(a) da$$

In the first one G^2_{exp} and $|\Gamma|^2 \sigma(a)_{exp}$ could in principle be deduced from experiments up to an energy E_{max}, which would thus determine an upper limit for Z.[6]

The use of the second relation, in which appear the matrix elements $|\langle 0 | \varphi | \xi \rangle|^2$, which are easily measured, is nevertheless more delicate because although the divergence of $\int \rho(a) da$ guarantees that Z is null, its convergence does not exclude this possibility. In fact if Z is small and different from zero we can easily see that the divergence of the limit: $\lim_{Z \to 0} (\int \rho da)$ arises precisely from the contribution of the resonance in the vicinity of the bare mass M', so that as long as the resonance occurs at an energy higher than the observed energy, this expression can only provide a very poor estimate of Z. This trouble does not arise in the first case, but the problem now is to deduce from the scattering amplitude the expression $|\Gamma|^2 \sigma(a)$.

Nevertheless, the first method has been used successfully by Weinberg[7], and Ezawa et al[8] in the case of deuteron, which offers a series of advantages which make the calculation possible up to a good approximation.

1. The n and p are bound mainly in an S wave (triplet spin state*), the phase space function $\sigma(a) \sim \sqrt{1 - (4m^2/a)} \sim \sqrt{P/E}$ is as

---

* The value of the quadrupole moment of the deuteron shows the smallness of the relative probability of finding the deuteron in the $\ell = 2$ state.

convergent as possible, and the spectral relation for Z converges without a form factor at the vertex.

2. The binding energy is very small and the range of the n-p forces is relatively short, so that the variation of the slowly varying vertex function, between, on the one hand, the position of the pole of the deuteron, and, on the other, the domain in which this function contributes substantially to the integral defining Z (the vicinity of positive s), is too weak and can therefore be neglected (the situation is not the same in the case of the hydrogen atom because of the infinite range of the potential).

Furthermore the relatively short range of the n-p forces, due to the exchange of pions, allows us to assume that the influence of the exchange terms in the scattering amplitude is very small in any case at the beginning of the physical domain, i.e. near the pole of the deuteron.

Neglecting therefore the form factor and the exchange term, we have

$$T(s) = \frac{g^2}{(s+B)\left[1 + (s+B)g^2\,\eta\int\frac{s'\,ds'}{(s'+B)^2(s'-s-i\varepsilon)}\right]}$$

where $\quad s = k^2/2m$

B = Binding energy

$$\eta = \frac{4\pi}{(2m^3)^{1/2}}$$

$$k\cot\delta = -(1/a_t) + (r_e/2)k^2$$

a_t = triplet scattering length , r_e = effective range

a_t and r_e can be expressed as functions of B and of g^2; using

$$Z_D = 1 - g^2 \eta \int \frac{\sqrt{s'}\, ds'}{(s' + B)^2} \longrightarrow g^2 \approx 2\sqrt{B}(1 - Z)/r_e \eta$$

we then have, in terms of B and Z_D,

$$a_t = \frac{2(1 - Z_D)}{2 - Z_D} \frac{1}{\sqrt{2mB}} < \frac{1}{\sqrt{2mB}} = 4.31 \text{ F}$$

$$r_e = - \frac{1}{\sqrt{2mB}} \frac{Z_D}{1 - Z_D} \leq 0 \quad .$$

Experimentally, $a_t = 5.41$ F and $r = 1.75$ F, and the difference between $(r_e)_{Z_D = 0}$ and $(a_t)_{Z_D = 0}$ and the values obtained experimentally is of the order of 1 Fermi $\approx 1/m_\pi$, and can therefore be attributed to the contribution of the exchange term. It is clear on the other hand that Z cannot differ noticeably from 0. Aaron et al[9] have also determined the constant of "elementariness" Z_D of the deuteron experimentally by making a detailed study of the neutron-deuteron elastic scattering, and of the bound state of that system, the triton. They found the best fit with the experimental data by taking Z = 0.0496; the fact that Z_D is slightly different from zero shows according to them, the proportion of the time that the physical deuteron is not in the bare state, but rather in the state with angular momentum $\ell = 2$ which thay had not taken into account. It is reassuring that such good results could be obtained from the study of a particle which one could by no means imagine to be elementary.

3.2. Effect of weak inelasticity on composite particles. Although the study of elastic processes has enabled us to account exactly for the relative properties of composite particles as compared with elementary particles, the concrete cases in which these properties can be brought out unambiguously are extremely rare. We shall now study the case in which the field that constitutes the composite particle interacts with other fields.

1. The problem of external fields. It has long been thought that we can explain the various physical phenomena by means of supposedly known laws and a set of a certain number of fundamental and immutable constants which are, for example, the relative masses of the electron-proton, electron-pion, the charge of the electron, etc., and some most extraordinary ideas have been put forward to explain these numbers. The foundations of the quantum theory of fields and renormalization, and later the axiomatic and dispersion relations approach to the S matrix, rest on the basic idea that elementary particles are defined once and for all by the list of their masses and observed couplings, the bare coupling constants and bare masses being introduced into the canonical theories with great reluctance, and only as a provisional trick which allows one to get rid of the embarrassing infinities arising in perturbation theory, or even being completely eliminated in other formulations.

The intrinsic interest of the properties we have brought out in chapter 2 for the case in which the bare constants have a well-defined mathematical meaning cannot fail to lead us to pose the question of the possibility of extending these properties to all known particles, in spite of certain difficulties arising in the present formulation of the quantum theory of fields. We are therefore led to take seriously the theory of bare fields, admitting the concept of the physical existence of the bare quantities. One of the first consequences to be drawn from this is that the universal catalogue of the elementary particles from which the physical world is built contains not the observed constants, but the bare constants, whose values we do not know.

On the other hand, by defining composite particles as those with Z = 0 the fundamental bare constants become universally infinite, while the observable coupling constants are now solutions of equations which we can define but which we cannot give explicitly and which should be solved in the future.

Having now taken the constants down from the pedestal on which we once believed them immutably placed, since we can now understand at least qualitatively the mechanism through which they exist (even if we cannot yet understand why they take on such and such values), the question arises naturally as to whether is possible to modify the conditions of their existence, for example, by means of external fields, in such a way as to change their values, which would clearly open the way for as yet unimaginable applications.

In the framework of the present study of the notion of compositeness, the question is whether the external fields applied to a system containing particles modifies in a different way the constants characteristic of elementary and composite particles. To fix ideas, let us consider the case of a photon in a uniform Newtonian field; for an elementary photon this fact can be taken into account by including in the usual electrodynamic Lagrangian, in which e_o is a universal constant given a priori, the coupling $KV\bar{\psi}\psi$ whose effect can be regarded as a modification of the bare mass of the electron

$m_o \rightarrow m_o + KV$, which changes the vacuum polarization function B and consequently also Z_3. The universality of

$$\alpha_o = \frac{\alpha}{Z_3(\alpha)} = \frac{\alpha_v}{Z_3(\alpha_v)}$$

with

$$Z_3(\alpha_v) = 1 - \alpha_v B'_v(0)$$

implies the relation

$$\frac{\alpha_v - \alpha}{\alpha_v} = -\alpha(B'_v - B') \tag{3.20}$$

On the contrary, in the composite case the condition for a pole gives for all V:

$$Z_3(\alpha) = Z_3(\alpha_v) = 0 \longrightarrow \alpha B' = \alpha_v B'_v = 1$$

and it is easy to verify that relation (3.20) is also satisfied in this case. Consequently, even though the variation due to the external field of the "fundamental constants" of particles is a direct consequence of the concept of a bare field for elementary particles, this variation does not allow us to distinguish between elementary and composite particles. The difference between these particles can now arise only when an external field is sufficiently intense and acts so as to decrease B'_v, the coupling constant α_v increases and tends to α_o which is finite for elementary particles and without limit for composite particles. Conversely we can also see that if α_v decreases, this has the consequence that the physical mass in this case tends towards the bare mass.

It seems difficult to find a way of bringing out these phenomena, given the weakness of the macroscopic fields at our disposal, but it may be that they play an important part in the superdense states of matter (for instance, in neutron stars the few charged particles (p, e) not yet collapsed in $n + \nu$ might interact with an anomalous electric charge, forming atom-like objects emitting red shifted photons[10]).

2. Electromagnetic interactions.

a. It is evident that in virtue of the conservation of current the charge of a composite particle is equal to the sum of the charges of its components. From the point of view of the S-matrix, the electromagnetic interaction to the first order in e of a charged virtual elementary boson is given by the sum of the two graphs

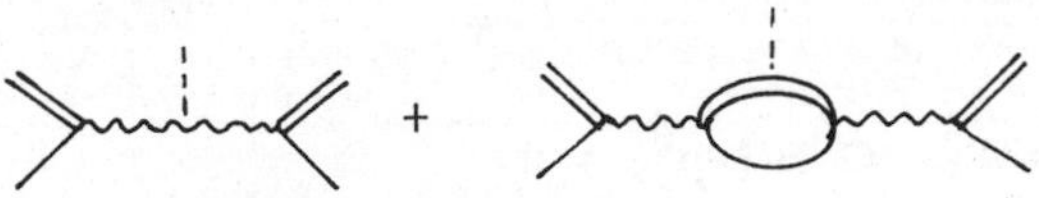

$$\approx \frac{G^2 e A_\mu}{(p^2+\mu^2)\left[(p-k)^2+\mu^2\right]}\left[Z_3(2p-k)_\mu + G^2\Gamma_\mu(p, p-k)\right]$$

(Here, the lines ═══ and ∿∿∿ represent charged particles).
In the limit $k = 0$, we have

$$\Gamma_\mu(p, p-k)\Big|_{k\to 0} = \partial_\mu B(p^2) = 2p_\mu B'(p^2)$$

and the charge of the real particle ($p^2 = -\mu^2$) is $e(Z_3 + G^2 B'(-\mu^2)) = e$, since $Z_3 = 1 - G^2 B'(-\mu^2)$. The coefficient eZ_3 of the first graph comes from the coupling in the Lagrangian $iZ_1 eA_\mu J_\mu$, Z_1 being identical to Z_3 according to Ward's identity.

For a composite particle, the process considered becomes

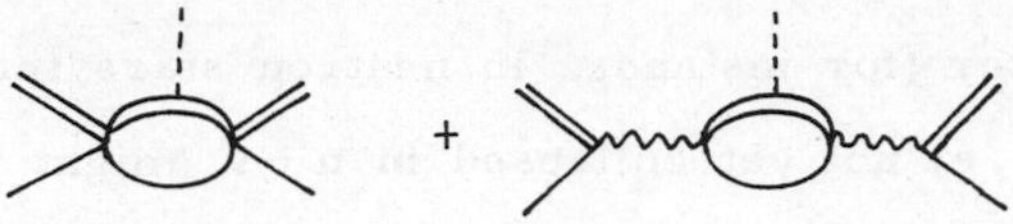

$$\sim eG_c^2 A_\mu(k)\Delta_c'(p^2)\Delta_c'\left[(p-k)^2\right]\Gamma_\mu(p, p-k)$$

and at the poles ($p^2 = -\mu_c^2$ and $(p-k)^2 = -\mu_c^2$) of the propagators Δ_c' of the composite particles, and for $k \to 0$, we have

$$G_c^2 \Gamma_\mu(p,p)\Big|_{p^2 = -\mu_c^2} = 2p_\mu G_c^2 B'(-\mu_c^2) = 2p_\mu \, ,$$

provided that

$$Z_3(G_c^2) = 1 - G_c^2 B'(-\mu_c^2) = 0.$$

As a consequence, the condition

$$G_c^2 \Gamma_\mu(p,p)\Big|_{p^2 + \mu_c^2 = 0} = 2p_\mu \qquad (3.21)$$

is equivalent to the condition that the particle is composite[11].

To the second order in e for an elementary boson, in addition to the iterations of the foregoing graphs, i.e. graphs such as

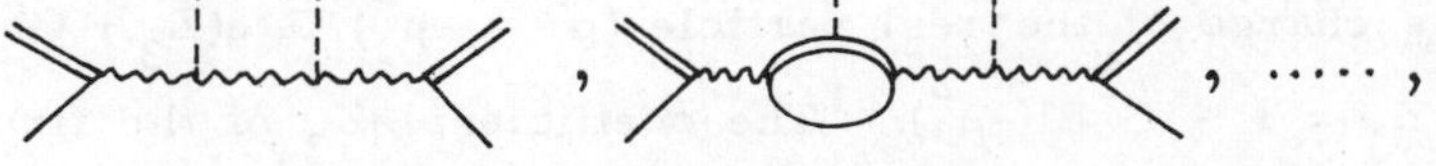

there are graphs such as

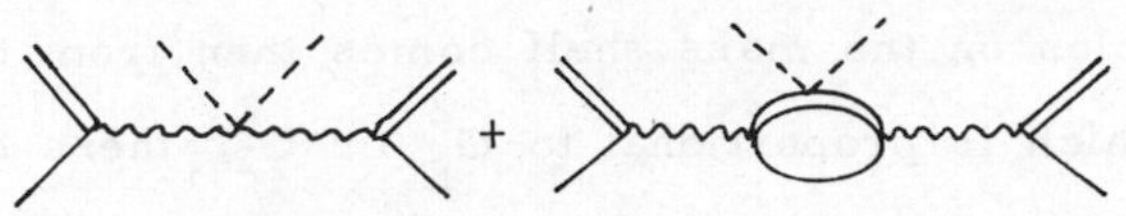

$$\approx \frac{G^2 e^2 A_\mu(k) A_\nu(k-\ell)}{(p^2+\mu^2)\left[(p-\ell)^2+\mu^2\right]} \left\{ 2Z_3 \delta_{\mu\nu} + G^2 \Gamma_{\mu\nu}(p, p-\ell, k, \ell) \right\}$$

where the first term comes from the coupling of the interaction Lagrangian $e^2 Z_3 \varphi^* \varphi A_\mu A^\mu$, the coefficient of Z_3 being a direct consequence of the gauge invariance which implies the substitution $\partial \rightarrow \partial + ieA$ in the dynamic term of the Lagrangian $Z_3 \partial\varphi^x \partial\varphi$.

For a composite field φ, the corresponding interactions are

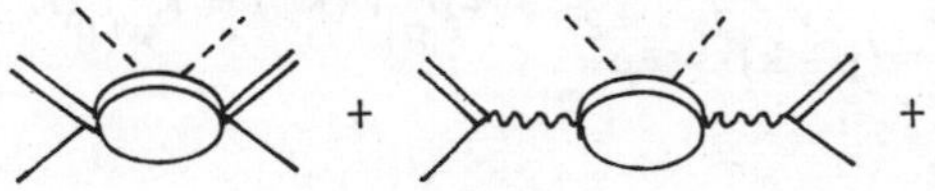 + [iterations of the preceding graphs

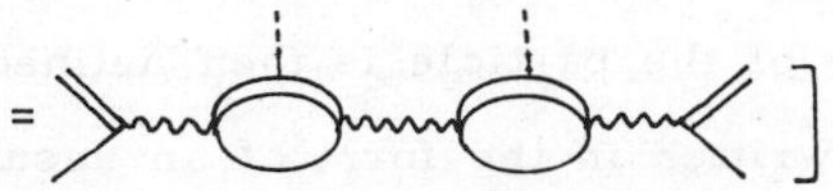

On the mass shell ($p^2 = (p-\ell)^2 = -\mu_c^2$) and for k and ℓ tending to zero, the interactions in $A_\mu A^\mu \varphi_c \varphi_c^*$ of composite and elementary particles are proportional to e^2. Indeed

$$\Gamma_{\mu\nu}(p, p) = \partial_\mu \partial_\nu B(p^2) = 2\delta_{\mu\nu} B'(p^2) + 4p_\mu p_\nu B''(p^2)$$

and

$$1 = Z_3 + G^2 B'(-\mu^2) \quad \text{for any value of } Z_3.$$

The only (unimportant) difference between elementary and

composite particles on the mass shell comes then from the term in $p_\mu p_\nu A^\mu A^\nu$, which is proportional to G_E^2 or G_c^2, these two constants being different.

Let us note that from the Lagrangian point of view the elimination of the charged composite field does not pose any difficulty, since the terms in A_μ proportional to Z_3 disappear from the constraint relations.

Nevertheless, differences between elementary and composite particles can appear for large values of the momenta of certain matrix elements; indeed, for particles on the mass shell and a photon off-shell, we can write

$$\Gamma_\mu(p, p-k)\Big|_{p^2=(p-k)^2=-\mu^2} = 2p_\mu \Gamma(k^2) + k_\mu \Gamma_{\parallel}(k^2)$$

the second term not being observable in scattering. The observable form factor of the particle is then defined by $F(k^2) = Z_3 + \Gamma(k^2)$. If $\Gamma(k^2)$ can be written in the form of an unsubtracted dispersion relation

$$\Gamma(k^2) = \int \frac{\gamma(s)ds}{k^2 - s + i\varepsilon} = -\int \frac{\gamma(s)ds}{s} + k^2 \int \frac{\gamma(s)ds}{(k^2-s)s}$$

we have (since

$$Z_3 + \Gamma(0) = 1, \qquad F(k^2) = 1 + k^2 \int \frac{\gamma(s)ds}{s(k^2-s)} \quad),$$

$$F(\infty) = 1 + \int \frac{\gamma(s)}{s} ds = Z_3 \qquad (3.22)$$

As a consequence the electromagnetic form factor of a composite particle should vanish at infinity.

b. One might be tempted to think that as a result of the above property, the electromagnetic self-energy of a composite particle is more convergent than that of an elementary particle, the graph

being made convergent by the vertex form factor that tends to zero

however, the advantage of having vertices that tend to zero is necessarily upset by the fact that the intermediate propagator of a composite particle is more singular, which considerably weakens the above mentioned advantage. This situation is easily illustrated by the following zero dimensional model[12] (one time dimension only) in which Ward's relation is obvious.

$$L = L_1 + L_2$$

$$L_1 = V^* \left[Z(i\partial_t - m_v) - \delta m_v \right] V + N^*(i\partial_t - m_N)N$$

$$+ \theta^*(i\partial_t - m_\theta)\theta + G(V^*\theta N + \text{h.c.})$$

$$L_2 = + \sum_a \left[[\gamma_a^*(i\partial_t - a)\gamma_a] + e_a(ZV^*V + \theta^*\theta)(\gamma_a + \gamma_a^*) \right]$$

L_1 is the zero dimensional Lee model, and setting in the matrix elements in energy space,

$$E = p_o \equiv p, \quad m_v = V, \quad m_v^o = V^o, \ldots \Sigma = m_N + m_\theta, \ldots,$$

we have

$$\Delta'_v(p) = \frac{1}{p - v} + \frac{\frac{1}{Z} - 1}{p - \frac{\Sigma}{Z} + V(\frac{1}{Z} - 1)}$$

$$= \frac{1}{(p - V)\left[1 - \frac{G^2(p - V)}{(p - \Sigma)(V - \Sigma)^2}\right]}$$

$$V^o = V + \frac{1 - Z}{Z}(\Sigma - V) ,$$

the second pole V' of Δ'_V ,

$$V' = V + \frac{\Sigma - V}{Z} , \quad \left(V^o - V' = -Z(\Sigma - V)\right),$$

$$Z = 1 - \frac{G^2}{(V - \Sigma)^2} ,$$

for $Z = 0$ $\quad G_c^2 = (V - \Sigma)^2$ and $(\Delta'_V)_{Z \to 0} = \frac{1}{p - V} + \frac{1}{V - \Sigma}$

L_2 is the "electromagnetic interaction" of the charged fields V and θ, with the "photon fields" $(\gamma_a + \gamma^*_a)$ whose masses are "a" and whose coupling constants are e_a.

The vertex $V^*_p V_{p-k}(\gamma_a + \gamma^*_a)_k$ off-shell is

$$\Gamma(p, p-k) = \left[Z + \frac{G^2}{(p - k - \Sigma)(p - \Sigma)}\right],$$

and on the mass shell we have

$$\Gamma(V, V-k) = \left[Z + \frac{G^2}{(V - \Sigma)(V - \Sigma - k)}\right] ,$$

with the normalization

$$\Gamma(V, V) = 1,$$

and the asymptotic behavior

$$\Gamma(V, V-k)\Big|_{k\to\infty} \longrightarrow Z$$

The "electromagnetic" self-energy is then

$$\int da\, e^2(a)\, \Gamma^2(p, p-k) G^2 \Delta'_v(p-k) \frac{1}{k - a - i\varepsilon}$$

For p = V we obtain

$$\delta m_e^{(1)} = -\int da\, e^2(a) \left[Z + \frac{G^2}{(V-\Sigma)(V-\Sigma-a)^2} \right] \cdot$$

$$\cdot \left\{ \frac{1}{a} - \frac{\frac{1}{Z} - 1}{\frac{V-\Sigma}{Z} - a} \right\},$$

plus a term

$$= \delta m_e^{(2)} = \int da \frac{e^2(a) G^2}{(V - \Sigma - a)(V - \Sigma)^2}$$

If V is elementary, then $Z \approx 1$ and

$$\delta m_e^{(1)} \approx -\int da\, e_a^2\, Z^2 \frac{1}{Za} = -Z \int \frac{e_a^2}{a}\, da \quad ;$$

if V is composite, then Z = 0 and

$$\delta m_e^{(1)} = -\int e_a^2 \frac{G_c^4\, da}{(V-\Sigma)^2 a^2} \frac{1}{\Sigma - V} = -(\Sigma - V)\int \frac{e_a^2\, da}{a^2} ,$$

and the convergence is improved, although less than what we would obtain if we approximated the composite propagator by its only pole, in which case the result would be

$$\delta m_e^{(1)} = -\int da\, e^2 \frac{G_c^4}{(V-\Sigma)^2} \frac{1}{a^3}$$

Moreover, we have

$$\delta m_e^{(1)} + \delta m_e^{(2)} = -\left[Z + \frac{G^2}{(V-\Sigma)^2}\right]\int \frac{e^2}{a}\, da + \text{(more convergent terms)} ,$$

and we see that, bearing in mind the fact that $\delta m^{(2)}$ increases as $Z \to 0$, the most divergent term is independent of Z.

3. <u>The case when Z is directly measurable at low energy.</u> Let us now mention a class of phenomena in which the constants Z appear in a directly observable way at low energy, a fact that makes them accesible to direct measurement.

Such are the matrix elements for a particle, assumed to be elementary, in interaction with a current J that dresses it, which suffers a transition to a state (particle or current) that we may legitimately suppose to be coupled locally to the current by a known coupling constant which is sufficiently small to be treated in the lowest order of perturbation theory. We will consider as examples the transitions

$$\gamma \overset{(e)}{\Longrightarrow} (e\,\bar{e}) \xrightarrow{g_F} \bar{\nu}_e \nu_e \quad :$$

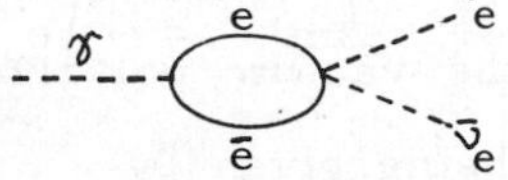

$$\rho^{o} \overset{\gamma_\rho}{\Longrightarrow} (h\,\bar{h}) \xrightarrow{e} \gamma \quad :$$

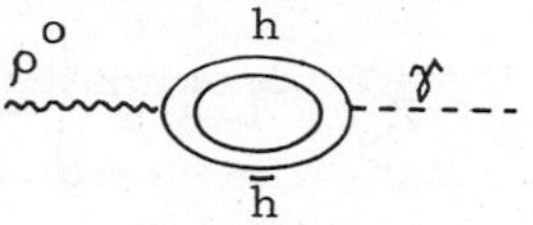

where h stands for hadrons, and

$$\pi^{+} \overset{G_\pi}{\Longrightarrow} (h\,\bar{h}) \xrightarrow{g_F} \bar{\mu}\,\nu_\mu \quad :$$

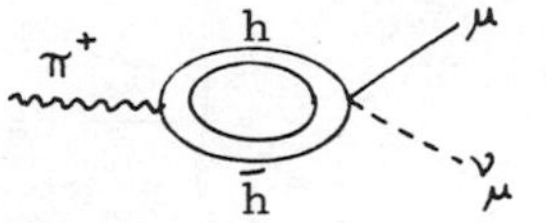

where g_F is the local weak coupling constant.

a. As a simple illustration of the first of these cases, let us suppose that electrons are the only existing charged particles, and that there exists a weak local Fermi coupling of vector type between electron and neutrino (resulting for instance from the universal coupling

$$(\bar{e}\,\gamma'_\mu \nu)(\bar{\nu}\,\gamma'_\mu e) \quad , \quad \gamma'_\mu = \gamma_\mu(1 + \gamma_5) \;).$$

The S-matrix element for the transition $\gamma \leftrightarrow \nu\bar{\nu}$, $A_\mu T^{\mu\sigma}_{[\gamma-\nu]}(\bar{\nu}\,\gamma'_\sigma\,\nu)$, brings in the gauge invariant tensor

$$T^{\mu\nu} = -eg_F(q^2\delta_{\mu\nu} - q_\mu q_\nu)\int \frac{\sigma_e(a)}{a(a+q^2)}\,da$$

On the other hand, the propagator of the photon is given by the expression

$$\frac{1}{q^2}\left\{1 - e^2q^2\int \frac{\sigma_e(a)da}{a^2(a+q^2-i\varepsilon)}\right\}$$

which makes use of the same spectral function $\sigma_e(a)$ which determines the vacuum polarization loop, the constant $Z_3 \equiv Z_3^{\gamma}$ of the photon being given by

$$Z_3^{\gamma} = 1 - e^2 \int \frac{\sigma_e(a)\, da}{a^2}$$

For small q^2, one has for the term proportional to $\delta_{\mu\nu}$ in $T_{\mu\nu}$

$$-q^2 e\, g_F \int \frac{\sigma_e}{a^2} da = - \frac{g_F}{e} q^2 (1 - Z_3^{\gamma})$$

and therefore the observable part of the electron-neutrino vector interaction, given by the sum of the graphs

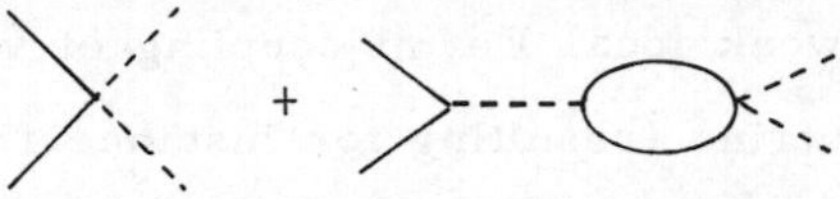

is[13]

$$g_{e\nu} = g_F + \frac{e}{q^2} T_{[\gamma-\nu]} = g_F Z_3^{\gamma} \qquad (3.29)$$

b. The same kind of argument holds as well for the $\rho^0 \rightarrow \gamma$ transition if the fields ρ^0 and γ are coupled with coupling constants γ_ρ and e, respectively, to the <u>same</u> isovector current.[14] The gauge invariant matrix element for the transition $\rho^0 - \gamma$ is therefore

$$T^{\mu\nu}_{[\rho-\gamma]} = -e\gamma_\rho \int \frac{\sigma_1(a)\, da}{a(a + q^2)} (q^2 \delta_{\mu\nu} - q_\mu q_\nu) \qquad (3.30)$$

Furthermore, we have

$$Z_3^{\rho} = 1 - \gamma_\rho^2 \int \frac{\sigma_1(a)\, da}{(a - \rho^2)^2} \tag{3.31}$$

The explicit computation of $T^{\mu\nu}_{[\rho-\gamma]}$ leads to logarithmic divergences in perturbation theory, whereas for a calculation through intermediate states the result is strongly dependent on form factors which are not well-known; this is not surprising because $T^{\mu\nu}_{[\rho-\gamma]}$ brings in the analogue of a renormalization constant. Instead of calculating this expression (necessarily incorrectly) one can use the relation (3.31) and obtain for the coefficient $T_{[\rho-\gamma]}$ of $q^2\delta_{\mu\nu}$ in $T^{\mu\nu}_{[\rho-\gamma]}$

$$-\frac{T_{[\rho-\gamma]}}{e\gamma_\rho} - \frac{1 - Z_3^{\rho}}{\gamma_\rho^2} = \int \sigma_1(a) \left(\frac{1}{a(a + q^2)} - \frac{1}{(a - \rho^2)^2} \right) da \tag{3.32}$$

an expression which, like the Uehling term in electromagnetism, brings in a more convergent dispersion relation which can then be approximately calculated, without much error, because only the small mass terms in $\sigma_1(a)$ play a significant role.

The isovector vertex of the nucleon, sum of the two graphs

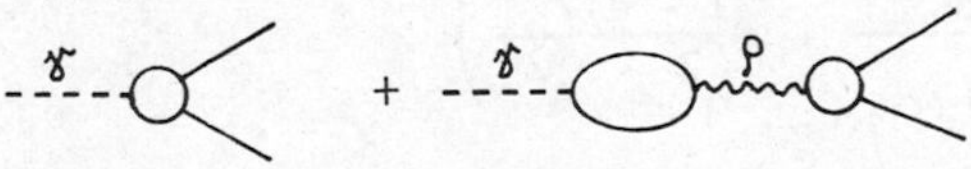

has then the form

$$e\Gamma_\nu(q^2) = e \left\{ 1 - \frac{q^2 \gamma_\rho^2 \displaystyle\int \frac{\sigma_1(a)\, da}{a(a^2 + q^2 - i\varepsilon)}}{(q^2 + \rho^2)\left[1 + \gamma_\rho^2 (q^2 + \rho^2) \displaystyle\int \frac{\sigma_1(a)\, da}{(a - \rho^2)^2 (a + q^2 - i\varepsilon)} \right]} \right\} \cdot F_\nu(q^2) \tag{3.33}$$

where $F_\nu(q^2)$ is a form factor taking into account all the intermediat states not contained in the dressed propagator of the ρ meson and the vertex corrections for the nucleon such as

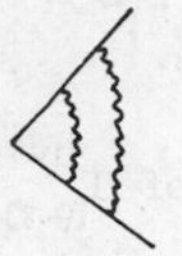

The curly bracket in Eq. (3.33) can be written as

$$1 - \frac{q^2}{q^2+\rho^2}\left[\frac{1 - Z_3^\rho + \gamma_\rho^2\left(\int\frac{\sigma_1\,da}{a(a+q^2)} - \int\frac{\sigma_1\,da}{(a-\rho^2)^2}\right)}{1 - \gamma_\rho^2(q^2+\rho^2)\int\frac{\sigma_1\,da}{(a-\rho^2)^2(a+q^2)}}\right]$$

$$= 1 + \frac{q^2}{q^2+\rho^2}\left[Z_3^\rho - 1 + \varepsilon(q^2)\right] , \qquad (3.34)$$

where $\epsilon(q^2)$ can be approximately calculated without great error to be $\lesssim 1/10$ for $q^2 < M^2$.

Assuming the one-parameter form $\Lambda^2/(\Lambda^2 + q^2)$ for $F_\nu(q^2)$, then the function $\Gamma_\nu(q^2)$ has the general form

$$\left(\frac{c\rho^2}{q^2+\rho^2} + \frac{(1-c)\Lambda^2}{q^2+\Lambda^2}\right)$$

and a "best fit" allows one to determine c and Λ^2, and therefore the coefficient $\left[1 - (Z_3^\rho + \bar{\epsilon})\right]$, $\bar{\epsilon}$ being an average of $\epsilon(q^2)$ over the range of energy in which the fit is made. The fit of Hand et al[15] gives

$$1 - (Z_3^{\rho} + \bar{\epsilon}) = 1.032$$

or

$$1 - (Z_3^{\rho} + \bar{\epsilon}) = 0.94 \quad ,$$

the form factor F_M being in the latter case

$$\frac{\Lambda^2}{q^2 + \Lambda^2} \, \frac{4M^2}{q^2 + 4M^2}$$

These results are compatible with $Z_3^{\rho} \approx 0$.

Let us remark that if one a priori assumes that $Z_3^{\rho} \approx 0$ and neglects the vacuum polarization corrections, one obtains

$$e\Gamma(q^2) = e \frac{\rho^2}{q^2 + \rho^2} F(q^2) \quad ,$$

a form very often used and deduced by Gell-Mann[16] from the property of the composite ρ of having an infinite bare mass.

Although this expression is certainly a good approximation for q^2 not too large, one can see that the expression given by Eq. (3.34) when q^2 goes to infinity behaves like

$$\text{i.} \quad 1 - \frac{\gamma^2 \int \frac{\sigma_1 \, da}{a}}{Z_3^{\rho} q^2} \longrightarrow 1 \quad \text{if} \quad Z_3^{\rho} \neq 0 \qquad (3.35)$$

$$\text{ii.} \quad \frac{1 - \gamma^2 \int \frac{\sigma_1 \, da}{a}}{\gamma^2 \int \frac{\sigma_1 \, da}{(a - \rho^2)}} = \frac{\rho^2 \gamma^2 \int \frac{\sigma_1 \, da}{a(a - \rho^2)}}{\gamma^2 \int \frac{\sigma_1 \, da}{(a - \rho^2)}} \approx \frac{\rho^2}{\delta \nu_{\rho}^2}$$

$$\text{if} \quad Z_3^{\rho} = 0 \quad ,$$

where the latter expression can vanish if $\delta\nu_\rho^2$ diverges.

The experimental knowledge of the constant γ_ρ^2 and the fact that the hypothesis that the ρ meson is composite is compatible with the experimental evidence, allows one to estimate the hadron contribution to the renormalization constant of the photon, which can be written as

$$Z_3^\gamma = 1 - e^2(B_{lept.} + B_1 + B_o) \quad ,$$

B_1 and B_o being the hadron isospin 1 and 0 states contributions. It follows immediately from $Z_3^\rho = 0$ that $e^2 B_1 \approx e^2/\gamma_\rho^2$.

The isoscalar form factors are too badly known at the moment and the generalization of the previous argument to the case T = 0 is complicated by the $\omega - \varphi$ mixing problem.

However, if φ^o is also composite, one has $e^2 B_o \approx e^2/\gamma_\varphi^2$ and $\gamma_\varphi^2 \approx 3\,\gamma_\rho^2$ according to SU(3). Therefore,

$$e^2 B_{hadrons} \approx e^2 \frac{1}{\gamma_\rho^2}(1 + \frac{1}{3}) \approx \frac{2\alpha}{3} \quad ,$$

with $$\frac{\gamma_\rho^2}{4\pi} \approx 2 \qquad (3.36)$$

Therefore, if the photon is a composite particle then the role of the hadrons is negligible in the explanation of the fine structure constant, solution of the equation $Z_3^\gamma(\alpha) = 0$.

It is however worth remarking that one has accepted here that the photon interacts only with the isocurrents T = 0, 1; however, if it turned out that the photon can generate transitions $\Delta T > 1$ and if the coupling constants of the (hypothetical) vector mesons with $T > 1$ with hadrons were very small, the previous conclusions would have to be revised.

Photons and neutrinos.

c. Given Eq. (3.32) of paragraph (b) one can generalize[13] the results of paragraph (a) to the realistic case of the photon interacting with all charged particles (hadrons of isospin 0 and 1 and leptons: electrons, muons, etc.). If, just like in (a) one accepts the existence of a local Fermi coupling V-A for leptons, yielding the vector couplings

$$g_F\left[(\bar{e}\, e)(\bar{\nu}_e\, \nu_e) + (\bar{\mu}\, \mu)(\bar{\nu}_\mu\, \nu_\mu)\right]$$

the vector interaction of a neutrino $\nu_e (\nu_\mu)$ with a proton or a muon (electron) is $g_F e^2 \bar{B}_e (\bar{B}_\mu)$, whereas with an electron (muon) is $g_F[1 - e^2 \bar{B}_\mu]$ $(g_F[1 - e^2 \bar{B}_\mu])$, $\bar{B}_e$ and $\bar{B}_\mu$ being here the graphs

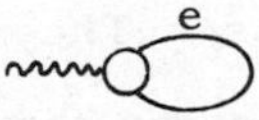

and
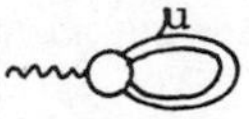

, respectively,

in which the vertex may bring in the currents of other particles

(e.g. 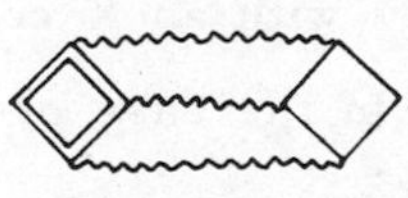). One also has

$$Z_3^{\gamma} = \left[1 - e^2(\bar{B}_e + \bar{B}_\mu) + 0\left(\frac{2\alpha}{3}\right)\right]$$

if there exist no leptons other than e and μ.

Now, it turns out from the experimental limits for ν_μ elastic scattering cross sections that $e^2\bar{B}_\mu \lesssim 1/4$. There arise then several possibilities:

i. The muons and electrons give the same contribution to Z_3; if we further assume that there are no other leptons then we must have $Z_3 \geqslant 1/2$;

ii. $Z_3 = 0$, and it should exist (as yet unknown) leptons other than electrons and muons; or

iii. The contributions to Z_3 from the leptons <u>decrease fast when their masses increase</u> (e.g. $\bar{B}_\mu < (1/3)\bar{B}_e$). Such a law cannot be explained in perturbation theory because $B(\mu) - B(e) \sim \log(m_\mu/m_e)$ which indicates a very slow variation with m. The effect of the distance from the beginning of the singularity of the spectral function is very small on slowly convergent integrals (or in weakly divergent integrals as in perturbation theory). A universal cut-off or a particular importance of the lower mass states of the photon propagator in the computation of the functions B_e and B_μ may explain that phenomena. This is the reason why the information of experimental work on neutrinos could be very important for our understanding of high energy electrodynamics. The measurement of the elastic interactions of ν_e are important for that purpose.

d. <u>Electromagnetic interaction of the W meson.</u> We explained in chapter 2 that it is possible for a theory with an X coupling (Ferm coupling) to be a masked Yukawa theory. In the case of the V-A interaction, if this is so, then the intermediate meson is a charged vector meson, $W^{\pm}$, say. In the hypothesis of a Fermi coupling (J)(J), where $J = J_{\text{hadrons}} + J_{\text{leptons}}$, only one meson is necessary to obtain the equivalence theorem (see chapter 4) and in that case we have (very roughly)

$$g_F \approx \frac{G_W^2}{M_W^2}$$

The electromagnetic interaction of the composite meson with a photon is represented in perturbation theory by the graph

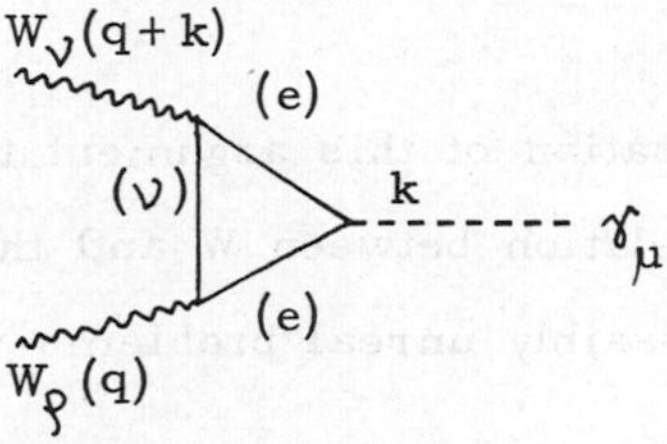

This graph yields[17]

$$T^{[w-\gamma]}_{\mu\rho\nu}(k,q) = e\,G_W^2\,(t^D_{\mu\rho\nu} + t^C_{\mu\rho\nu})$$

where the divergent part $t^D_{\mu\rho\nu}$ has the form

$$t^D_{\mu\rho\nu} = A_1\Big\{\Big[\delta_{\nu\rho}(q+k)_\mu + \delta_{\nu\rho}q_\mu\Big] - \Big[\delta_{\mu\rho}(k+q)_\nu + \delta_{\mu\nu}q_\rho\Big]$$

$$+ 2(\delta_{\mu\rho}k_\nu - \delta_{\mu\nu}k_\rho)\Big\} \equiv A_1 \tau_{\mu\rho\nu}$$

Furthermore, if $k \to 0$ the condition that the charge of W be e is expressed as (using $Z_3^W(G_W^2) = 0$ for the composite meson)

$$e = e\Big[G_W^2(A_1 + \delta A_1)\Big]$$

where δA_1 is finite. Therefore,

$$T^{[w-\gamma]}_{\mu\rho\nu} = e(1 - G_W^2\,\delta A_1)\,\tau_{\mu\rho\nu} + eG_W^2\,t^C_{\mu\rho\nu}$$

and hence, subject to finite corrections, which will be small if G_W is sufficiently small, $T^{[W-\gamma]}_{\mu\rho\nu} \approx e\tau_{\mu\rho\nu}$; in this expression the term $2(\delta_{\mu\rho} k_\nu - \delta_{\mu\nu} k_\rho)$ in the right hand side indicates that the W meson will have a normal magnetic moment equal to two Bohr magnetons. It is interesting to note that, precisely for this value, the radiative corrections of the production of W take on a particularly remarkable shape.[18]

The generalization of this argument to the more general case and the possible relation between W and the photon, raise very complicated and possibly unreal problems which we will not touch upon here.

e. The transition $\pi^+ \rightarrow \mu^+ \nu_\mu$ corresponds to the same type of process. It is well known that the Goldberger-Treiman relation may be obtained by various methods which in different aspects seem related to the composite nature of the pion. Nevertheless a coherent proof for $Z_\pi = 0$ has not yet been given.

Let us consider the pseudoscalar coupling of the pion with the nucleons. The loop in the transition $\pi^+ \rightarrow \mu^+ \nu$ calculated in perturbation theory with the only intermediate state of nucleons has the imaginary part

$$B^1_\mu(p) \approx 2g_F G_{\pi^+} \int \mathrm{Tr}\left[\gamma_\mu \gamma_5 S^1(k) \gamma_5 S^1(p-k)\right] d^4k = k_\mu B^1(p^2)$$

Taking into account the formula

$$S^1(k)(p \cdot \gamma)\gamma_5 S^1(p-k) = 2MS^1(k)\gamma_5 S^1(p-k)$$

we obtain

$$p_\mu B^1_\mu = p^2 B^1(p^2) = 2g_F G_{\pi^+} 2M \int \mathrm{Tr}\left[\gamma_5 S^1(k) \gamma_5 S^1(p-k)\right] d^4k$$

where

$$2\int \mathrm{Tr}\left[\gamma_5 S^1_{(k)} \gamma_5 S^1_{(p-k)}\right] d^4k$$

is also the imaginary part $\sigma_B(p^2)$ of the vacuum polarization of the pion.

We have, in the lowest order in $G^2_{\pi^+}$,

$$Z_3^\pi = 1 - G^2_\pi \int \frac{\sigma_B(a)\, da}{(a - \mu_\pi^2)^2} \tag{3.37}$$

and for the $\pi^+ \to \mu^+\nu$ element of the transition matrix with the π on the mass shell

$$\bar{B}_\mu = g_F 2M p_\mu \int \frac{\sigma_B(a) da}{a(a - \mu_\pi^2)} = p_\mu F_{(\pi\mu\nu)} \tag{3.38}$$

The integrals in Z_3 and B have the same divergence and the difference of both is finite and small $\left[0(\mu^2/M^2)\right]$. Replacing the integral in Eq. (3.38) by its expression in terms of Z_3^π and $G^2_{\pi^+}$ we obtain

$$\bar{B}_\mu = g_F 2MG_{\pi^+} k_\mu \left(\frac{1 - Z_3^\pi}{G^2_{\pi^+}} \right) \tag{3.39}$$

which finally gives the Goldberger-Treiman relation[19] if $Z_3^\pi = 0$. However, to make this heuristic argument consistent it would be necessary a) to justify the approximation of the intermediate state nucleon-antinucleon, b) to prove (in order to avoid the divergence of Z_3^π so as to be able to compare exactly relations (3.37) and (3.38)) that the axial vertex has the form $\gamma_\mu \gamma_5 \Gamma_\pi(k^2)$, where $\Gamma_\pi(k^2)$ is the pseudoscalar form factor of the nucleon, and that it does not contain a term proportional to $k_\mu \gamma_5 F(k^2)$ (or that this term is small as compared with the first one).

The proof given by Ida[20], which is equivalent to justify point b), gives (in the approximation of intermediate states being reduced to $\bar{N}N$) the relations

$$F_{(\pi u \nu)} = F^{(G.T.)}_{(\pi \mu \nu)} \left[\frac{\int_{S_o}^{\infty} \frac{s - \mu^2}{s} \sigma_N(s)\, ds}{1 + \int_{S_o}^{\infty} \sigma_N(s)\, ds} \right]$$

and

$$\frac{1}{Z_3^\pi} = 1 + \int_{S_o}^{\infty} \sigma_N(s)\, ds$$

from which we obtain

$$F_{(\pi\mu\nu)} \longrightarrow F^{(G.T.)}_{(\pi \mu \nu)}$$

if

$$\int \sigma_N(s)\, ds \longrightarrow \infty \quad (\text{i.e. } \frac{1}{Z_3^\pi} \longrightarrow \infty)$$

Nevertheless, the case $Z_3^\pi = 0$ exactly encounters some difficulties which are not as yet understood, and it would be interesting to know their exact source (constraints over the strong interactions parameters or consequences of the fact that one may have

$$\int \left[\lim_{Z_3 \to 0} \sigma_N(s) \right] ds < \infty \quad ;$$

this last point has been discussed in connection with the vertex function).[21]

In the pseudo-vector theory (if it is renormalizable in some sense) the condition $Z^{(\pi)} = 0$ gives for the pion field

$$\varphi_\pi = \frac{f Z_1}{\delta\nu^2 Z_2} (\partial_\mu A_\mu)$$

where A_μ is the unrenormalized axial vector current, and it is known that the Goldberger-Treiman relation follows if it is possible to show that $\delta\nu^2 \approx \mu_\pi^2$. The vacuum polarization operator of the pion has the subtracted and convergent form

$$-f^2 p^2 \int \frac{\sigma(a)\, da}{a(a + p^2 - i\varepsilon)} \quad ;$$

we also have

$$\delta\nu^2 = -f^2 \mu^2 \int \frac{\sigma(a)\, da}{a - \mu^2}$$

and

$$Z^\pi = 1 - f^2 \left[\int \frac{\sigma(a)\, da}{a - \mu^2} + \mu^2 \int \frac{\sigma(a)\, da}{(a - \mu^2)^2} \right] = 0 \quad ,$$

then

$$\delta\nu^2 = -\mu^2 \left[1 + \mu^2 \int \frac{\sigma(a)\, da}{(a - \mu^2)^2} \right] .$$

REFERENCES

1. Ref. 3 of chapter 2.
2. K. Sekine, Cahiers de Phys. 186, 41, (1966) and references included there.
3. J. C. Houard, Nuovo Cimento 35, 194, (1965) and Thèse (Ref. 8 of chapter 2).
4. H. Lehmann, Nuovo Cimento 11, 342, (1954).
5. K. W. Ford, Nuovo Cimento 24, 467, (1962).
6. A practical method has not been given yet; see however R. M. Rockmore, Phys. Rev. 151, 1228, (1966).
7. S. Weinberg, Phys. Rev. 137B, 672, (1965).
8. H. Ezawa, T. Muta, H. Umezawa, Prog. Theor. Phys. 29, 877, (1963).
9. R. Aaron, R. D. Amado, Y. Y. Yam, Phys. Rev. 140B, 1291, (1965).
10. B. Jouvet, Nuovo Cimento 46B, 122, (1966).
11. This condition for compositeness has been studied by:
    L. S. Liu, Phys. Rev. 125, 761, (1962).
    N. M. Rockmore, Phys. Rev. 132, 878, (1963).
    R. G. Cawley, Phys. Rev. 153, 1712, (1967).
12. B. Jouvet and E. Tirapegui, "Zero-dimensional Physics, Stairs, Continued Fractions and Convergence Problems", to be published in Nuovo Cimento.
13. B. Jouvet, Nuovo Cimento 38, 951 (1965) and references contained therein.
14. B. Jouvet, Phys. Lett. 6, 307, (1963).

15. C. N. Hand, D. G. Miller, R. Wilson, Rev. Mod. Phys. 35, 335 (1963).

16. M. Gell-Mann and F. Zachariasen, Phys. Rev. 124, 953 (1961).

17. E. Tirapegui, Comptes Rendus Ac. Sc. 263, 721 (1966).

18. L. V. Lyagin, I. S. Tsukarman JETP 15, 1123 (1962).
E. S. Ginsberg, R. H. Pratt, Phys. Rev. 130, 2105 (1963).
V. V. Solov'ev, I. S. Tsukarman, JETP 15, 868 (1962).

19. M. L. Goldberger, S. B. Treiman, Phys. Rev. 110, 1178 (1958) and 111, 354 (1958).

20. M. Ida, Phys. Rev. 132, 401 (1963).
Cf. for complements, G. Barton, Dispersion Techniques in Field Theory, Benjamin (1965).

21. E. Tirapegui, Nuovo Cimento 47, 400 (1967).

4. GENERALIZATION OF THE COMPOSITENESS EQUATIONS TO THE CASE OF MANY PARTICLES WITH THE SAME QUANTUM NUMBERS

In the last chapter we examined the ρ-γ system (which may be generalized to the ω, φ, γ, or even to the γ-positronium system), and also the system γ-$(e\,\bar{e})$-$(\nu\,\bar{\nu})$, where the photon could be composed of electrons and positrons, and interacts with neutrinos by means of the couplings

$$g_{ee} J^{\mu}_{e} J^{\mu}_{e} + g_{F} J^{\mu}_{e} J^{\mu}_{\nu} .$$

These examples lead us in a natural way to treat on the one hand the general case where a composite and an elementary particle, having interactions of the same type, appear as different poles in the same scattering amplitudes, and, on the other, to study how can the equivalence theorem be generalized to the cases in which there exist contact interactions between many currents.

The last problem is, like the first one (although a priori they look very different), a particular case of the general problem of two particles with the same quantum numbers, interacting with two (generally different) currents. Indeed, it is easily seen that the scattering amplitude $T_{a \to b}$ obtained from a Fermi interaction $gJ_a J_b$ and evaluated in the chain approximation

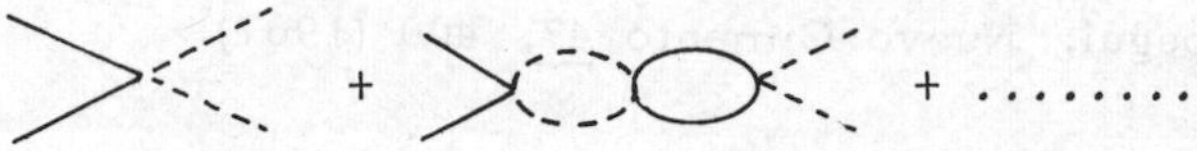

is given by expressions of the type

$$T_{a-b} \sim \frac{g}{1 - g^2 B_a(s) B_b(s)} \quad \text{or} \quad T_{b-b} \sim \frac{g^2 B_2}{1 - g^2 B_a(s) B_b(s)}$$

which may contain two poles[1], since we have, for sufficiently high values of the cut-offs,

$$B_i(s) \approx B_i(0) + sB_i'(0) \quad , \quad \text{for} \quad |s| < M_a, M_b \; .$$

The first problem has been investigated by several authors[2] who have often reached opposite conclusions.

We shall examine here models in which two particles, characterized by the observable fields φ_ℓ, $\ell = 1, 2$, have given finite masses μ_ℓ and interact through Yukawa couplings of given strength G_u^ℓ ($u = 1, 2$) with two currents of different kind J_u.

In addition we assume the existence of three different vacuum polarization bubbles $K_{uv}(s)$ ($u, v = 1, 2$; $K_{12} = K_{21}$), whose forms are given a priori, and the absence of internal radiative corrections (which avoids the complicate vertex renormalization)[3].

The generalization of the Lee model proposed by Vaughn[2] with the coupling

$$\sum_{i,u}\left[\psi_v^i(p)G_i^u\left(\psi_N^*(p-k)f_u(k)\theta^*(k)\right)\right]$$

(where the form factors $f_u(k)$, $u = 1, 2$, are different), is the simplest of the exactly solvable models of this type we know, J_u and φ_i being, respectively, $\psi_N^* f_u \theta^*$ and ψ_v^i.

4.1. Elementary case. Definition of the renormalization constants.

The observable quantities μ_ℓ^2 and G_u^ℓ ($\ell, u = 1, 2$) can be defined by two poles of the scattering amplitudes and four conditions on the residues:

$$\text{Res}\, T_y^{uv}(s = \mu_\ell^2) = \left\{(s - \mu_\ell^2)\left[G_j^u \Delta'_{jk}(s) G_k^v\right]\right\}_{s=\mu^2} = G_u^\ell G_v^\ell \tag{4.1}$$

To make sure that the S matrix deduced from the Lagrangian $\mathcal{L}(\varphi_\ell, \psi_u, G, \mu^2)$ satisfies such conditions, it is necessary to correct the displacements of residues and poles caused by the "dressing" effect of the vacuum polarization functions $K_{uv}(s)$, which appear in the scattering amplitude in the form of the bubbles

$$B_{\ell m}(s) = \sum_{u,v} G^{\ell}_{u} K_{uv}(s) G^{m}_{v}$$

The two subtractions to each of the three functions $B_{\ell m}(s)$ can be performed in a canonically consistent way by adding to the Lagrangian suitable counterterms involving the products $\varphi_\ell \varphi_m$ and $\varphi_\ell \Box \varphi_m$ or $\partial_\mu \varphi_\ell \partial_\mu \varphi_m$ $(\ell, m = 1, 2)$.

The appropriate Lagrangian can then be written in terms of observable quantities in the general form[3]

$$\mathcal{L} = \mathcal{L}_o(\psi_u, \psi_v) - \frac{1}{2} \sum_{\ell, m} \partial_\mu \varphi_\ell Z^{\ell m} \partial_\mu \varphi_m$$

$$- \frac{1}{2} \sum_{\ell, m} \varphi_\ell (Z_{\ell m} \mu_\ell^2 \delta_{\ell m} + \delta\nu^2_{\ell m}) \varphi_m + \varphi_\ell G^\ell_u J_u ,$$

or

$$\mathcal{L} = \mathcal{L}(\psi) - \frac{1}{2} \partial_\mu \tilde{\varphi} Z \partial_\mu \varphi - \frac{1}{2} \tilde{\varphi}(\nu + \delta\nu)\varphi + \tilde{\varphi} G J \qquad (4.2)$$

In writing this, we have defined the symmetric renormalization matrices $Z = Z_{\ell m}$ of the fields and the mass matrix

$$\nu + \delta\nu = Z_{\ell m} \mu_\ell^2 \delta_{\ell m} + \delta\nu^2_{\ell m} \quad ;$$

they are the formal generalization of the renormalization constants Z_3 and $Z_3 \mu^2 + \delta\nu^2$ which appear in the Matthews-Salam method for the case of one field φ.

The propagators are

$$F < 0 | T(\varphi_i \varphi_j') | 0 > = \Delta'_{ij}(s) = \left[-Zs + \nu + \delta\nu - \tilde{G}KG \right]^{-1} \tag{4.3}$$

It can be verified that the conditions for the poles and the residues which are expressed by

$$\det\left[\left(\Delta'(s) \right)^{-1} \right] = 0 \quad \text{and} \quad \tilde{G}R(\ell)G = \tilde{G}G \ , \tag{4.4}$$

where

$$R(\ell) = \left[(s - \mu_\ell^2) \Delta'(s) \right]_{s \to \mu_\ell^2}$$

uniquely determine, provided that det $G \neq 0$, the six constants Z and $\delta\nu$ as functions of G, μ^2, and the expressions of the K_{uv} functions.

The poles of the propagators $F < 0 | T(\varphi_j \varphi_k') | 0 >$ are

$$\delta_{j\ell} \delta_{k\ell} \frac{1}{s - \mu_\ell^2} + \delta_{jm} \delta_{km} \frac{1}{s - \mu_m^2}$$

The matrices

$$R(\ell) = E_\ell \quad \left(E_1 = \begin{bmatrix} 1 & 0 \\ 0 & 0 \end{bmatrix} , \ E_2 = \begin{bmatrix} 0 & 0 \\ 0 & 1 \end{bmatrix} \right) \tag{4.5}$$

are the only solutions of Eq. (4.4), and as a consequence the propagator $F < 0 | T(\varphi_\ell \varphi'_m) | 0 >$, $\ell \neq m$, has no poles for $s = \mu_\ell^2, \mu_m^2$. From this it follows

$$< 0 | \varphi_\ell | m > = \delta_{\ell m} \tag{4.6}$$

The Lagrangian can be diagonalized in the following unique way:

$$\mathcal{L} = \mathcal{L}_o(\psi) - \frac{1}{2}\sum_\ell \partial_\mu \varphi_\ell^{(0)} \partial_\mu \varphi_\ell^{(0)}$$

$$- \frac{1}{2}\sum_\ell \mu_\ell^{(0)^2} \varphi_\ell^{(0)} \varphi_\ell^{(0)} + \varphi_\ell^{(0)} G_u^{(0)\ell} J_u \tag{4.7}$$

by finding a matrix $A = \| A_{\ell m} \|$ (playing a role analogous to $\sqrt{Z_3}$ in the case of one particle), such that the bare fields are

$$\varphi_\ell^{(0)} = \sum_m A_{\ell m} \varphi_m$$

and that

$$\tilde{A}A = Z \quad , \quad \varphi^{(0)} = A\varphi \ ,$$
$$\tilde{A}^{-1}(\nu + \delta\nu)A^{-1} = \mu^{(0)^2} \quad , \tag{4.8}$$

the matrix $\mu^{(0)^2}$ being diagonal. The elements of the matrix $\mu^{(0)^2}$ are the bare masses $\mu_\ell^{(0)^2}$ and $\mu_m^{(0)^2}$ and one has

$$\mu_1^{(0)^2} \mu_2^{(0)^2} = \frac{\det(\nu + \delta\nu)}{\det Z} \tag{4.9}$$

The bare coupling constants are defined by

$$G^{(0)} = \tilde{A}^{-1} G \tag{4.10}$$

The A matrix is real and uniquely defined if det Z > 0 and we have

$$< 0 \mid \varphi_\ell^{(0)} \mid m > = A_{\ell m} \tag{4.11}$$

The canonical relations following from the Lagrangian are

$$\left[\varphi_\ell , \dot{\varphi}'_m\right]_{t=t'} = i\delta(\mathbf{x} - \mathbf{x}')(Z^{-1})_{\ell m} \qquad (4.12)$$

They are related to the asymptotic form of the propagators

$$\Delta'_{\ell m}(s) \longrightarrow \frac{1}{s}(Z^{-1})_{\ell m} \qquad (4.13)$$

Quite different definitions and notations are used in the literature for the renormalization constants Z: for instance, Alexanian et al[2] define the constants $\bar{Z}_{ij}$ which are related to our A_{ij} by $\bar{Z}_{ij} = (A_{ij})^2$. They also define

$$\tilde{Z}_3^{(i)} = (s\Delta'_{ii})_{s\to\infty} = (Z^{-1})_{ii} \;,$$ which leads for instance to

$$\tilde{Z}_3^{(1)} = (Z^{-1})_{11} = \frac{Z_{22}}{\det Z} = \sum_i \frac{A_{i2}A_{i2}}{(\det A)^2} = \frac{\bar{Z}_{12} + \bar{Z}_{22}}{\det \bar{Z}}$$

On the other hand, Choudhury and Srivastava[2] define Z'_{ij} such that

$$\left[\varphi_i , \dot{\varphi}'_k\right] = i\frac{1}{Z'_{ik}}\delta(\mathbf{x} - \mathbf{x}')$$

Such differences in the notation are only relevant when one wishes to give a correct definition for the compositeness condition generalizing that which is given for one particle. This is the problem we are now going to investigate.

4.2. <u>Case of total compositeness.</u> Let us start with the case in which there are contact interactions between two currents,

$$\mathcal{L}_{\text{int.}} = \sum_{u,v} g_{uv} J_u J_v = J g J \tag{4.14}$$

and no elementary particle is present.

The Fermi amplitude satisfies the matrix equation

$$F(s) = g + gK(s)F(s) \longrightarrow F(s) = g\left[1 - gK(s)\right]^{-1} \tag{4.15}$$

If det $g \neq 0$, then

$$F(s) = \left[(g)^{-1} - K(s)\right]$$

The poles $s = \mu_\ell^2, \mu_m^2$, are solutions of

$$D(s) \equiv \det\left(1 - gK(s)\right) = 0$$

If there exist several poles, it is necessary, in order to be able to associate them with particles coupled to the currents by the constants G_u^ℓ, that the residues

$$R_{uv}(\ell) = -(s - \mu_\ell^2)F_{uv}(s)\Big|_{s=\mu_\ell^2}$$

can be put in the form

$$R_{uv}(\ell) = G_u^\ell G_v^\ell$$

for any ℓ, u, v. Then we must have for any ℓ such that $D(\mu_\ell^2) = 0$,

$$\det R(\ell) = 0 \ , \qquad (4.16)$$

an equation which can easily be proved.[1,5]

Let us admit the existence of two poles in the amplitudes $T_x \equiv F$; then we can establish the conditions that must be satisfied in order that a field theory postulating two elementary mesons with a Yukawa coupling with the currents J_u, becomes identical to the preceding theory.

The method using the bare mass and coupling constants will be sufficient to deduce these relations; more details can be found in Ref. 5. We must have

$$\sum_\ell \frac{G_u^{(0)\ell} G_v^{(0)\ell}}{s - \mu_\ell^{(0)2}} = -g_{uv} \qquad (4.17)$$

which implies

$$G_u^{(0)\ell} = \infty \ , \quad \mu_\ell^{(0)2} = \infty \ , \quad \frac{G_u^{(0)\ell} G_v^{(0)\ell}}{\mu_\ell^{(0)2}} = g_{uv}$$

which is ensured by the conditions

$$Z = 0 \qquad \text{(3 conditions)}$$

and $\qquad (4.18)$

$$g = \tilde{G} \delta \nu^{-1} G \qquad \text{(3 conditions)}$$

Conditions (4.18) are the generalization of those given in chapter 2. If we give explicitly these conditions in terms of the renormalized quantities we can verify that they are equivalent to the equations

(4.16) determining μ_ℓ^2 and G_u^ℓ.

Contrary to the single meson case, the <u>triple</u> constraint Z = 0 does not determine now the four coupling constants; they are now deduced from

$$\frac{G_u^\ell}{G_v^\ell} = \frac{\left[K(\ell) - \frac{1}{g}\right]_{vu}}{\left[K(\ell) - \frac{1}{g}\right]_{uu}} \left[\equiv \frac{\left[K(\ell) - \frac{1}{g}\right]_{vv}}{\left[K(\ell) - \frac{1}{g}\right]_{vu}} \quad \text{if} \quad \det D(\ell) = 0 \right] \tag{4.19}$$

and

$$\sum_{u,v} G_u^\ell G_v^\ell K'_{uv}(\ell) = -1$$

4.3. <u>Degenerate cases.</u> Between the totally elementary case of paragraph 4.1 and the totally composite case of paragraph 4.2, characterized by <u>six</u> relations, there is a great variety of intermediate cases. For instance,

- not all the three compositeness constraints Z = 0 are satisfied; or
- some of the G, g matrices are singular (e.g., when the interaction between currents takes the form

$$g(J_1 + J_2)^2 \longrightarrow \det g = 0 ,$$

it is sufficient to postulate a single meson in the Yukawa theory in order to prove the equivalence theorem — $J_1 + J_2$ playing the role of a single current).

a. There is an interesting class of cases, which have been studied by several authors[2], namely the one in which there exist <u>two mesons</u> and <u>a single current</u>; the matrix

$$G = \begin{bmatrix} G_1 & G_2 \\ 0 & 0 \end{bmatrix}$$

is clearly singular: det $G = 0$. The renormalization condition for the residue will be

$$\tilde{G} R(\ell) G = \tilde{G} G = G_\ell^2$$

The matrices

$$R(\ell) = E_1 , E_2$$

are manifestly a solution, as also is

$$R(\ell) = B E_\ell \tilde{B}$$

provided that B satisfies $\tilde{B} G = G$.

Thus B depends of two parameters and can be expressed in general by[6]

$$B^{-1} = \begin{bmatrix} u & (G_2/G_1)(1 - v) \\ (G_1/G_2)(1 - u) & v \end{bmatrix}$$

This double indetermination clearly reflects itself in the expressions of the six constants Z and $\delta\nu$, since there are only four equations (two for the masses and two for the coupling constants) to determine them.

One can ask what condition must be imposed in order that <u>one of the two fields associated with the two particles becomes composite</u>: a natural condition, which generalizes the property

$$\langle 0 | \varphi_c^{(0)} | c \rangle \sim \sqrt{Z}\Big|_{Z=0} = 0$$

can be that

$$\langle 0 | \varphi_2^{(0)} | 1 \rangle = \langle 0 | \varphi_2^{(0)} | 2 \rangle = 0 \,, \qquad (4.20)$$

implying

$$A_{21} = A_{22} = 0 \quad ,$$

while $\langle 0 | \varphi_1^{(0)} | 1 \rangle$ and $\langle 0 | \varphi_1^{(0)} | 2 \rangle$ are not equal to zero; these relations ensure the compositeness of the field $\varphi_2^{(0)}$.

From this it follows that

$$\det Z = (\det A)^2 = 0 \qquad (4.21)$$

which implies (from 4.9) that $\mu_1^{(0)2}\, \mu_2^{(0)2} = \infty$ and then, for instance, $\mu_2^{(0)2} = \infty$.

Conversely, it can be shown that if the Houard-Le Guillou condition[2] $\det Z = 0$ is fulfilled, then $\mu_2^{(0)2}$ for instance is infinite and the A matrix can be written as

$$A = \frac{1}{\sqrt{Z_{11}}} \begin{bmatrix} Z_{11} & Z_{12} \\ 0 & 0 \end{bmatrix} \qquad (4.22)$$

Writing

$$\lambda_o = - \frac{G_2^{(0)2}}{\mu_2^{(0)2}} \quad ,$$

(λ_o is assumed finite, i.e. $G_2^{(0)2} \longrightarrow \infty$) T(s) takes the form

$$T(s) = \frac{\lambda_o + \dfrac{G_1^{(0)2}}{s - \mu_1^{(0)2}}}{1 - \left[\lambda_o + \dfrac{G_1^{(0)2}}{s - \mu_1^{(0)2}}\right] K(s)} \qquad (4.23)$$

Clearly, such a theory arises from the bare fundamental interactions characterized by the two graphs

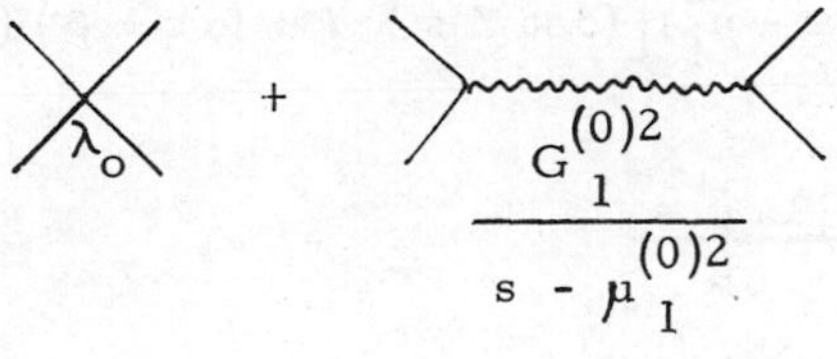

The first one, which corresponds to the exchange term of the bare meson propagator of $\varphi_2^{(0)}$, is "contracted" in a contact interaction. From the Lagrangian point of view, expressed in terms of the observed fields, the condition det Z = 0 implies that the two conjugate momenta $\pi_i = Z_{ij}\dot{\varphi}_j$ for $i = \ell, m$ are proportional; therefore one of them can be made to vanish by means of a linear transformation of the fields φ_i, and the corresponding field can be eliminated by the constraint relation coming from the Lagrange equation associated to it.

As for the single particle case, the canonical relations which involve

$$\left[\frac{1}{Z}\right]_{ij} = \frac{\mathrm{Min}\, Z_{ij}}{\det Z}$$

are more singular (if the unhappy "definition" of the renormalization constants

$$\frac{1}{Z'_{ij}} = \left[\frac{1}{Z}\right]_{ij}$$

is used, all of these are null).

It follows from this that the scattering amplitude becomes more singular at infinity when det Z = 0. For instance, in the model where K(s) is a bubble of scalar mesons, T(s) takes the form

$$T(s) = \frac{\alpha s + \beta}{(s - \mu_1^2)\left[(\det Z)s + \gamma + (\alpha s + \beta)I(s)\right]}$$

with

$$I(s) \sim \frac{\text{Log } s}{s}$$

and the asymptotic behavior of this expression crucially depends on the vanishing of det Z.

It must be understood that this model serves only to the purposes of illustration and that the fact of having dressed vertex functions does not modify the conclusions.

Contrary to the single particle case, the present one has the two following characteristics:

1. The only remaining bare field behaves symmetrically with respect to the two physical particles and it is impossible to say which one of them is composite;

2. The renormalization constants A are defined up to the arbitrariness of the B(u, v) matrix; this can be related to the existence of a renormalization group which can be interpreted as coming from the possibility of considering the contact interaction

as the contraction of an elementary propagator

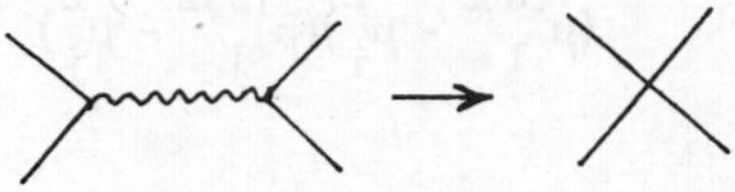

or as a term of potential interaction producing vertex effects

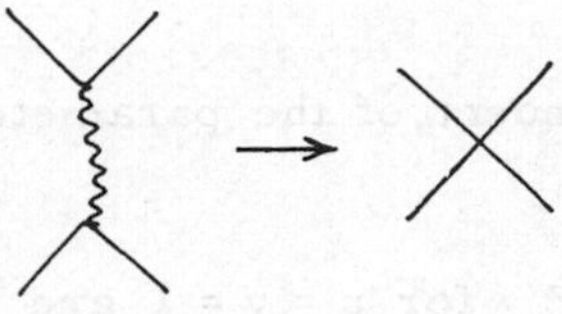

However, a "natural" definition of the renormalization constant associated with each particle can be given by the asymptotic (and in principle observable) limit of the electromagnetic form factors. By repeating the argument of chapter 3, that the graphs

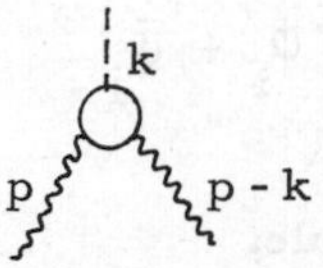

tend to zero if $k^2 \rightarrow \infty$ (p^2 and $(p-k)^2$ being on the mass shells μ_1^2 and μ_2^2), the asymptotic electromagnetic form factors

$$\Gamma(k^2, \mu_i^2, \mu_j^2)$$

come only from the graphs in which the photon is attached to the bare propagator of $\varphi_1^{(0)}$

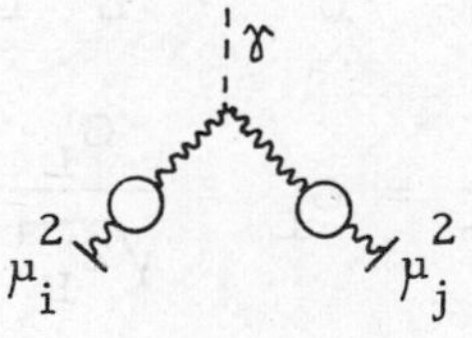

Then we have

$$T(k^2, \mu_i^2, \mu_j^2) \longrightarrow \frac{G_1^{(0)2} K(\mu_i^2) K(\mu_j^2) G_i G_j}{(\mu_1^{(0)2} - \mu_i^2)(\mu_1^{(0)2} - \mu_j^2)}$$

$$= \frac{G_i G_j}{G_1^{(0)2}} \left[1 - \lambda_o K(\mu_i^2)\right]\left[(1 - \lambda_o K(\mu_j^2)\right]$$

This expression is independent of the parameters u and v, and it is equal to $Z_{ij}(u = v = 1)$.

Thus the constants Z_{ij} for $u = v = 1$ are the degrees of elementarity, in principle observable, of the couple of physical particles φ_i and φ_j. For scalar or pseudoscalar particles, for instance, the three constants $|Z_{ij}|$ can in principle be measured separately in the reactions

$$e^+ + e^- \longrightarrow \varphi_i + \bar{\varphi}_j$$

where the φ_i can be unstable.

b. An interesting limiting case of the preceding class occurs when the usual amplitude Nθ of the Lee model, where the V field is elementary, has two poles V_1 and V_2, the second one being complex. One can then build the theory either by giving (like Lee) the field V associated to the pole V_1, whence one deduces the bare field $V_L^o = \sqrt{Z_L}\, V_L$, or by giving a field V'_L associated to the pole V_2, whence one deduces $V'^o_L = \sqrt{Z'_L}\, V'_L$; it is clear that

$$G_L^o \equiv \frac{G_L}{\sqrt{Z_L}} = G'^o_L \equiv \frac{G'_L}{\sqrt{Z'_L}} \quad , \quad \text{and} \quad M_L^o = M'^o_L \quad ,$$

the matrix elements in terms of the bare quantities being the same.

From these relations it follows formally that the two particles V_1 and V_2 become simultaneously composite when $Z_L \rightarrow 0$; however such a result is illusory because as we saw in chapter 2, the pole V_2 goes to infinity if $Z \rightarrow 0$.

Alternatively, we can postulate (as above, 4.3 b) the existence of the two fields V_1 and V_2 associated with the two poles and look for the conditions which make it possible for this system to be identified with the Lee model[8]. It can be seen that the renormalization constants depend on a new arbitrary parameter coming from the fact that the masses M_1 and M_2 satisfy the relation

$$M_L^o - M_1 - G_L^{o2} K(M_1) = M_L^o - M_2 - G_L^{o2} K(M_2) \ ,$$

which says that they are the two poles of the same Lee propagator.

The identification of the scattering amplitude Nθ which postulates two elementary particles with the Lee model amplitude in which two poles come from a single elementary particle, can be obtained in terms of the unrenormalized constants of the Lagrangian with two fields by requiring

$$\frac{G_1^{(0)2}}{s - M_1^{o2}} + \frac{G_2^{(0)2}}{s - M_2^{o2}} = \frac{G_L^{o2}}{s - M_L^{o2}}$$

From this it follows that either

a. $M_2^o \neq M_1^o$ and for instance $M_1^o = M_L^o$, in which case only one bare field V_1^o is coupled ($G_2^{(0)} = 0$). A detailed calculation shows that V_1^o is given by the linear combination

$$V_1^{(0)} = \frac{\sqrt{Z_1}}{G_1}\left[G_1 V_1 + G_2 V_2\right] ,$$

the other one being then an arbitrary combination of the fields V_1 and V_2; or

b. $M_1^o = M_2^o = M_L^o$ and $G_1^{o2} + G_2^{o2} = G_L^{o2}$, which amounts to replace the field V_L^o by a degenerate isospinor

$$\begin{bmatrix} V_1^o \\ V_2^o \end{bmatrix}$$

It is then possible by means of a rotation to decouple one of its components, the only bare field being determined as before in terms of V_1 and V_2.

Therefore, from the Lagrangian point of view the difference between the composite particles defined by the constraint $Z = 0$ and the particle V_2 which is deduced from the Lee model, consists in the following: in the first case, the composite field variable can be expressed in terms of the remaining operators and then be eliminated from the Lagrangian, which takes on a new form; in the second case, on the contrary, the deduced field variable becomes a redundant variable which can be simply suppressed.

The arbitrariness of the subjective situations of "postulated" or "deduced" for the particles V_1 and V_2 is here mathematically expressed by the fact that the renormalization constants depend, in the case of the Lee model, of one additional parameter with respect to the case where the V_1 and V_2 particles are independently postulated and do not have any particular relation between them.

REFERENCES

1. B. Jouvet, Nuovo Cimento, Suppl. 2, 941 (1955).
2. S. Rai Choudhury and K. Srivastava, Nuovo Cimento 39, 650 (1965); Nuovo Cimento 43A, 239 (1966).
   H. Yabuki, Progr. Theor. Phys. 35 , 889 (1966).
   J. C. Houard and J. C. Le Guillou, Nuovo Cimento 44, 484 (1966).
   K. Kang, Phys. Rev. 152, 1234 (1966).
   M. T. Vaughn, Nuovo Cimento 47A, 252 (1967).
   M. Alexanian and R. L. Zimmerman, Nuovo Cimento 48A, 386 and 709 (1967).
3. J. P. Adam and B. Jouvet, Nuovo Cimento, 29, 53 (1963). (The delicate question of vertex renormalization is also studied in this article).
4. See Ref. 3 and M. T. Vaughn, Ref. 2.
5. B. Jouvet and J. P. Adam, Nuovo Cimento 29, 275 (1963).
6. This group (which has been studied by J. C. Houard and J. C. Le Guillou, Ref. 2) is a particular and simple case of the group $G(Z_1^2, Z_3)$, a restriction of the general renormalization group (see M. Astaud and B. Jouvet, Comptes Rendus Acad. Sc. 264, 1433 (1967) (Paris), and to be published in Nuovo Cimento).
7. B. Diu, Nuovo Cimento 28, 83 (1963).
8. T. Leray, Thèse 3ème Cycle, Paris (1960), unpublished.

5. THE MASS EQUATIONS AND THE DIFFERENT TYPES OF COMPOSITE PARTICLES

In the preceding chapters we have discussed only the characteristic properties connected with the vanishing of the field renormalization constants. To achieve this we studied in chapter 2 an ad-hoc model in which it is always possible to fix the mass of the composite particle at the desired value, this value being determined by the a priori arbitrary constant λ_o and the arbitrary form factor $f(k^2)$. We have seen in that case how the mass equation was a relation between the self-energy and the constant λ_o. More precisely, using formula (2.31), we have concluded that the relation fixing the mass was equivalent to the knowledge of the amplitude $T_x(s)$ at some value $s = s_1$ $\left[T_x(s = s_1) = \lambda_{obs}\right]$; it is then clear that the determination of the mass of a composite particle cannot be made if we do not know the form factors and the coupling constant λ_o which appears in the exact physical case. Moreover, in the case of real particles, for instance in the relativistic interactions of pseudoscalar and vector mesons, the problem of the form factors appears already when trying to obtain an expression, even approximate, of the function $Z_3(G^2)$, which must be finite and capable of vanishing for a critical value of G^2. (The model of a scalar field with scalar coupling $\chi \rightarrow \varphi + \varphi^+$, not realized in the physical world, is the only type of relativistic coupling for which the constant Z_3 is finite in perturbation theory, i.e. without form factor, but $\delta\nu^2$ is nevertheless logarithmically divergent in that case).

In the covariant field theory models and in the elastic approximation we may introduce in various ways cut off effects which make convergent the expressions for the renormalization constants:

a) We may suppose that some propagators of the constituent particles are more convergent than usual, but this implies violations of unitarity and is against the tendency of nature because the propagators of composite particles are more divergent than the bare propagators;

b) We may take into account (in the elastic approximation) vertex effects (dressed vertex functions) which may have the property of making convergent the integrals appearing in the definition of the constants $Z_{2,3}$ and $\delta\nu$;

c) We may also consider the two constituent particles in a non local interaction produced by a given potential (when one of the particles is static) or resulting from the exchange of particles between the constituent particles.

We shall study successively some properties of the last two types of models, which will be designed by X and H, the letters representing the properties of contact or non local interactions between the constituent particles. Our study of the properties of these models will be made in the frame of Schrödinger's equation, because with this equation it is possible to construct vast classes of models suitable to illustrate and to study accurately the properties of the interactions of type X and H.

In this framework the interactions are always elastic and the generalization to the case of relativistic elastic interactions is trivial because the only change consists in replacing the non relativistic phase space function $k/m = \sqrt{(s/m^2)}$ by $\sqrt{1 - (4m^2/s)}$ (where $s = E - \mathbf{p}^2$) for the $\ell = 0$ waves which are the only ones we shall consider here.

Let us consider the Lagrangian[1]

$$\mathcal{L}(V, \lambda_o) = i\psi^*\partial_t\psi - \frac{\partial_i\psi^*\partial_i\psi}{2m} - \psi^* V(r)\psi - \lambda_o\psi^*\delta^{(3)}(x)\psi \tag{5.1}$$

which contains a potential V(r) producing a non local interaction H between the particle ψ and a fixed source and also a contact interaction X defined by the given bare constant λ_o. The fundamental graphs are thus

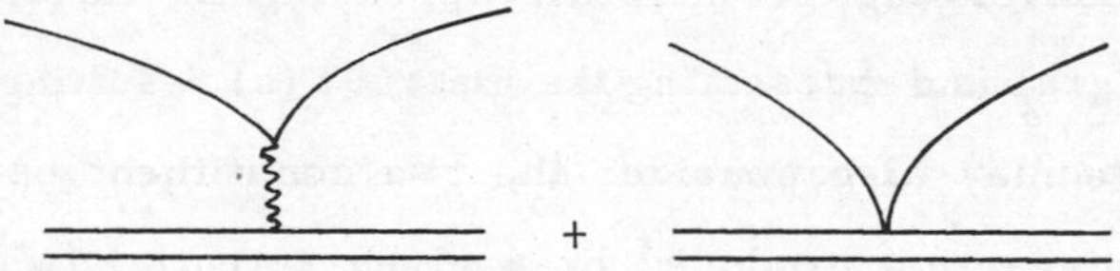

We may also think of the preceding equation as representing the equation of motion of a system of two particles of the same mass $\frac{1}{2}m$ referred to the center of mass system, and having an instantaneous non local interaction $V(\mathbf{x} - \mathbf{x}')$ and an instantaneous contact interaction $\lambda_o\delta(\mathbf{x} - \mathbf{x}')$. Graphically,

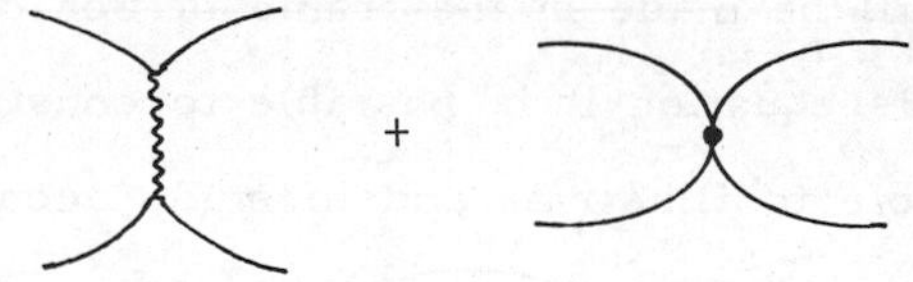

By changing the potential V(r), which can be regular or singular and such that by itself (i.e. when λ_o is null) may or not generate bound states, we are able to study with all the accuracy we need a great variety of cases. It is important to note that the contact coupling in L produces exactly the same mathematical difficulties one finds in relativistic field theories, but the existence here of an equation of motion permits a rigorous mathematical analysis of the renormalization process[2] (principally from the point of view of functional space) as well as the study of the relations between the renormalization constants and the asymptotic behavior of physical amplitudes. Finally, the study of the analytic properties of those problems is considerably simpler than in the relativistic case (restricted to be elastic, which limits the total energy of the system) and has been the object of many rigorous works which we may use.

The graphs representing the matrix $t_x(s)$ resulting from $L(V, \lambda_o)$ can be expanded in powers of λ_o. We have then

$t_x(s) = \sum_n$ 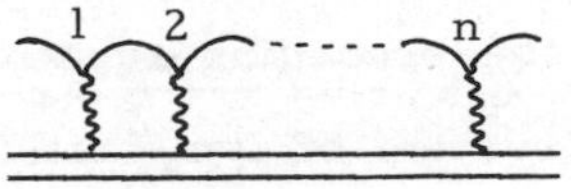

$+ \sum_{n,n'}$ 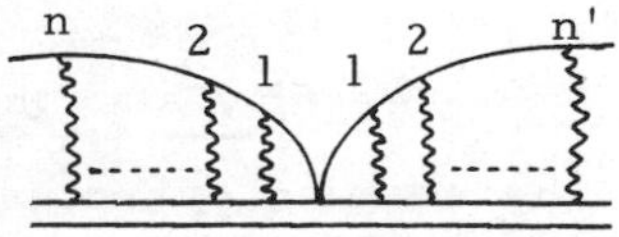

$+ \sum_{n,n',n''}$ 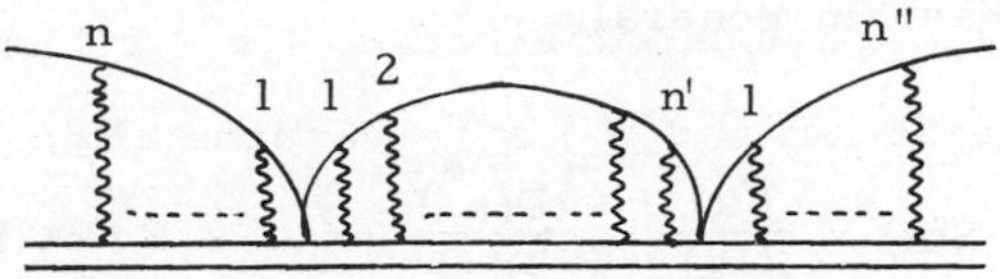

$+ \sum$ 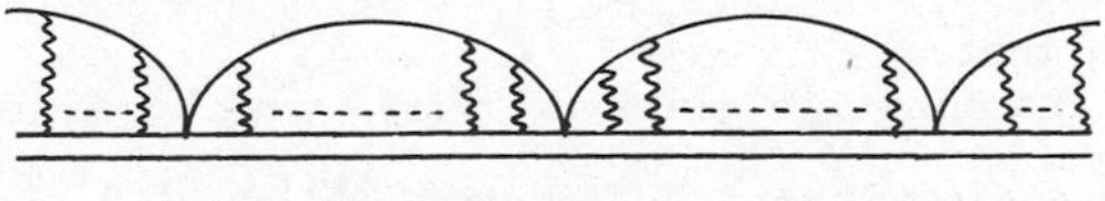 $+ \ldots\ldots$

$$= t_H(s) + \lambda_o\left[\Gamma_o(s)\right]^2 + \lambda_o^2\left[\Gamma_o(s)\right]^2 B_o(s) + \ldots\ldots$$

$$= t_H(s) + \frac{\lambda_o\left[\Gamma_o(s)\right]^2}{1 - \lambda_o B_o(s)} \qquad (5.2)$$

In this decomposition we find the amplitude $t_H(s)$ produced by all non local exchanges, a vertex function $\Gamma_o(s)$ and the vacuum polarization bubble $B_o(s)$.

These functions can be explicitly computed if one knows how to solve exactly the equation in which λ_o is null. The difficulties related to the contact interaction are treated recalling the expression

$$\delta(\mathbf{x}) = \lim_{r_o \to 0} \frac{1}{4\pi r_o^2} \delta(r - r_o)$$

The component of the wave function corresponding to an s-wave, $\psi(x)\big|_{\ell=0} \equiv \frac{\chi(r)}{r}$ satisfies then the equation

$$\left[\frac{d^2}{dr^2} + k^2 - V(r)\right] \chi(k, r) = \frac{\lambda_o}{4\pi r_o^2} \delta(r - r_o) \chi(k, r) \qquad (5.3)$$

One has, in general,

$$S(k) = \frac{f(k)}{f(-k)} = \frac{D(s^*)}{D(s)} = 1 + 2ikt(k) \qquad (5.4)$$

where $f(k) = \lim_{r \to 0} f(k, r)$, $f(\pm k, r)$ being the Jost solutions of Eq. (5.3) such that

$$f(\pm k, r)\Big|_{r \to \infty} \longrightarrow e^{\pm ikr}$$

For $\lambda_o = 0$, let us put $f(\pm k, r) = y_{\binom{1}{2}}(k, r)$, and let us define the unitary matrix

$$S_H(k) = S(k, \lambda_o \equiv 0) = \frac{D_H(s^*)}{D_H(s)} = e^{2i\delta_H(s)} \qquad (5.5)$$

for $s = k^2 > 0$.

For $\lambda_o \neq 0$ we may always write, S_x and S_H being unitary,

$$S_x(k;\, V,\, \lambda_o) = S_H(k;\, V,\, 0)\, S_\lambda(k;\, V,\, \lambda) \tag{5.6}$$

$$D_x = D_H D_\lambda$$

and then deduce

$$t_x = t_H + S_H t_\lambda\ , \tag{5.6'}$$

a decomposition analogous to (5.2).

We shall now consider several situations:

1. <u>The potentials V(r) are regular and do not produce poles in $t_H(s)$</u>. This regular potentials are defined by

$$\int_o^{c<\infty} r\,|V(r)|\,dr < \infty$$

and

$$\int_{c'>0}^{\infty} |V(r)|\,dr < \infty$$

It is then possible to show that[1]

$$S_x = \frac{y_1 - \dfrac{\lambda_o}{4\pi}\dfrac{1}{r_o}y_1 - \dfrac{\lambda_o}{4\pi}y_1'}{y_2 - \dfrac{\lambda_o}{4\pi}\dfrac{1}{r_o}y_2 - \dfrac{\lambda_o}{4\pi}y_2'} \equiv \frac{D_x(s^*)}{D_x(s)}\ , \tag{5.7}$$

with

$$y'_{\frac{1}{2}}(k) \equiv \left[\frac{\partial}{\partial r} y_{\frac{1}{2}}(k, r)\right]_{r \to 0} \quad ; \quad y_{\frac{1}{2}} = y_{\frac{1}{2}}(k) = \left[y_{\frac{1}{2}}(k, r)\right]_{r \to 0}$$

Putting

$$D_x(s) = D_H(s) D_\lambda^{(0)}(s) = y_2\left[1 - \frac{\lambda_o}{4\pi r_o} - \frac{\lambda_o}{4\pi}\frac{y'_2}{y_2}\right] \tag{5.8}$$

we have

$$S_H S_\lambda = \frac{y_1}{y_2}\left\{1 + \frac{2ik\lambda_o}{4\pi y_1 y_2\left(1 - \frac{\lambda_o}{4\pi r_o} - \frac{\lambda_o}{4\pi}\frac{y'_2}{y_2}\right)}\right\} \tag{5.8'}$$

if y_2 has no zeros, and

$$t_x = t_H + \frac{\frac{\lambda_o}{4\pi}}{(y_2)^2\left[1 - \frac{\lambda_o}{4\pi}\left(\frac{1}{r_o} + \frac{y'_2}{y_2}\right)\right]} \tag{5.9}$$

where

$$t_H(k) \equiv \frac{\frac{y_1(k) - y_2(k)}{2ik}}{y_2(k)} \equiv \frac{N_H(s)}{D_H(s)} \tag{5.10}$$

In the physical domain $y_1(s) = y_2^*(s)$, $\operatorname{Im} D_H(s) = \sqrt{s}\, N_H(s)$, and $y_2(s)\big|_{s \to \infty} = 1$, then

$$D_H(s) = 1 - \frac{1}{\pi}\int_0^\infty \frac{\sqrt{s'}\, N_H(s')\, ds'}{s' - s - i\varepsilon} \tag{5.11}$$

It is also possible to show that

$$N_H(s) = \frac{1}{\pi}\int_{-\infty}^0 \frac{D_H(s')\operatorname{Im} t_H(s')\, ds'}{s' - s - i\varepsilon} \tag{5.12}$$

Comparison of the formal expression of field theory, Eq. (5.2), and solution (5.9) shows then that[3]

$$\Gamma_o(s) = \frac{1}{D_H(s)} = e^{1/\pi \int \frac{\delta_H(s')\, ds'}{s' - s - i\varepsilon}} = \text{Omnès integral} , \tag{5.13}$$

and

$$B_o(s) = \frac{1}{4\pi}\left[\frac{1}{r_o} + \frac{y_2'}{y_2}\right]_{r_o \to 0}$$

Taking into account the expression of the Wronskian (independent of r),

$$y_1 y_2' - y_2 y_1' = 2ik$$

and that

$$\Gamma_o(s)\Big|_{s\to\infty} \longrightarrow 1 + 0(s^{-1/2})$$

one has

$$\operatorname{Im} B_o(s) = \frac{1}{4\pi}\frac{y_2' y_1}{y_2 y_2^*} = \frac{1}{4\pi}\frac{k}{y_2 y_2^*} = \frac{\sqrt{s}}{4\pi}\left|\Gamma_o(s)\right|^2$$

and

$$4\pi B_o(s) = \left(\frac{1}{r_o} + i\sqrt{s}\right)\Big|_{r_o\to 0} + \frac{1}{r}\int_0^\infty \frac{\sqrt{s'}\left[\left|\Gamma_o(s')\right|^2 - 1\right] ds'}{s' - s - i\varepsilon}$$

$$4\pi B_o(s) = \lim_{r_o\to 0} \frac{1}{\pi}\int_0^{1/r_o} \frac{\sqrt{s'}\;\left|\Gamma_o(s')\right|^2 ds'}{s' - s - i\varepsilon} \tag{5.14}$$

It is then clear that the contact interaction does not have any effect on t_x because $B_o(s)\big|_{r_o \to \infty} = \infty$. But the situation changes if one makes a renormalization of the constant λ_o. This renormalization may be done as in chapter 2 by defining

$$\lambda_{obs.} = t_\lambda(s = s_1)$$

and the renormalized vertex

$$\Gamma_R(s) = Z_1(s_1)\,\Gamma_o(s) \equiv \frac{\Gamma_o(s)}{\Gamma_o(s_1)}$$

$Z_1(s_1)$ is finite, and

$$\lambda_{obs.} = \frac{\lambda_o \left|\Gamma_o(s_1)\right|^2}{1 - \lambda_o B_o(s_1)} \tag{5.15}$$

then

$$t_\lambda(s) = \frac{\lambda_{obs.} \left|\Gamma_R(s)\right|^2}{1 - \lambda_{obs.} B_{RX}(s)}$$

and

$$B_{RX}(s) = \frac{s - s_1}{4\pi^2} \int_0^\infty \frac{\left|\Gamma_R(s')\right|^2 \sqrt{s'}\, ds'}{(s' - s_1)(s' - s - i\varepsilon)}$$

We have then

$$\lambda_o = \lambda_{obs.} Z_1^2 Z_x \tag{5.16}$$

with

$$Z_x = \left(1 + \lambda_{obs.} B_o(s_1)\right)^{-1} = 0 \tag{5.16'}$$

This renormalization traduces itself in the decomposition (5.8) $D_x = D_H D_\lambda^{(0)}$ by the definition of a new

$$D_{x\,ren.} = D_H \frac{D_\lambda^{(0)}(s)}{D_\lambda^{(0)}(s = s_1)}$$

which we shall denote by $D_x = D_H D_\lambda$, with

$$D_\lambda = 1 - \lambda_{obs.} B_{RX}(s)$$

By a suitable choice of the constant λ_o the amplitude t_λ <u>may have a pole $s = \mu^2$</u> such that

$$B_{RX}(\mu^2) = \frac{1}{\lambda_{obs.}} ,$$

and it may be shown the equivalence of the theory $L_x(V, \lambda_o)$ with a Yukawa theory by postulating a static field $\phi(t)$ of mass μ coupled with ψ through a coupling $g\phi(t)\psi(x,t)\delta(x)$; the equivalence holds when the renormalization constant Z_ϕ of the field ϕ vanishes for a critical value g_μ of g, such that

$$g_\mu^2 \int \frac{\sqrt{s'}\,|\Gamma_x^{(\mu)}(s')|^2 \, ds'}{(s' - \mu^2)^2} = 1 , \qquad (5.17)$$

and

$$\Gamma_x^{(\mu)}(s) = Z_1(\mu)\Gamma_o(s) = \frac{\Gamma_o(s)}{\Gamma_o(\mu^2)}$$

The unitary amplitude t_x can then be written, in terms of the unitary amplitude t_H which has no poles, as

$$t_x = t_H - g_\mu^2 \frac{\left[\Gamma_x^{(\mu)}(s)\right]^2}{(s-\mu^2)\left[1+g_\mu^2(s-\mu^2)\int \frac{|\Gamma_x^{(\mu)}(s')|^2\sqrt{s'}\,ds'}{(s'-s-i\varepsilon)(s'-\mu^2)^2}\right]}$$

$$= t_H - g_\mu^2\left[\Gamma_x^{(\mu)}(s)\right]^2 \Delta_x^{(\mu)}(s) \qquad (5.18)$$

As one has

$$t_H(s)\Big|_{s\to\infty} \longrightarrow 0(s^{-1}) \quad ,$$

one then has

$$t_x(s) \underset{s\to\infty}{\longrightarrow} \frac{i}{\sqrt{s}}$$

(this last behavior is an effect of adding the contact term).

We remark here that if we normalize in a different way the function $D_\lambda(s)$ which is (up to a constant) $\left[\Delta_x^\mu(s)\right]^{-1}$ it is possible to make the decomposition

$$D_x = D_H \cdot \left[\Delta_x^\mu(s)\right]^{-1} \qquad (5.19)$$

While for the regular non relativistic case in which the phase space function is proportional to $\sqrt{s}$ we have

$$|\Delta_x^{(\mu)}(s)| \underset{s\to\infty}{\longrightarrow} 1 \quad , \quad \Gamma_x^{(\mu)}(s) \longrightarrow \text{constant} \quad ,$$

in the relativistic case where the phase space function is

$$\rho(s) = \sqrt{1 - \frac{4m^2}{s}} \quad ,$$

we have ($\Gamma_x(s)$ still behaving as a constant for $s \to \infty$)

$$\Delta_x^{(\mu)}(s)\Big|_{s\to\infty} \longrightarrow \frac{1}{\text{Log } s}$$

In the relativistic case a decomposition of the form (5.18) has been obtained by Lee et al[4]. These authors also give the expression of the vertex $\Gamma_x^{(\mu)}$ as a function, not of $D_H(s)$ but of $D_x = (s - \mu^2)\mathcal{D}_x(s)$, where

$$\mathcal{D}_x(s)\Big|_{s\to\infty} \sim \frac{(\text{Log } s)^n}{s} \quad , \qquad n > \frac{1}{2} \ :$$

$$\left[\Gamma_x^{(\mu)}(s)\right]^{-1} = \mathcal{D}_x(s)\left[1 + \frac{s - \mu^2}{\pi} g_\mu^2 \int \frac{ds'\, \rho(s')}{(s - s')(s' - \mu^2)^2} \left|\frac{1}{\mathcal{D}_x(s')}\right|^2\right] \tag{5.20}$$

Such a form is also valid in the case of non relativistic X particles because $\mathcal{D}_x(s) \sim 1/\sqrt{s}$, $\rho \sim \sqrt{s}$, and the integral appearing in $\Gamma_x^{(\mu)}$ converges.

2. <u>V(r) is a singular potential not producing poles in t_H</u>.

In the case of more singular potentials (for instance

$$V(r)\Big|_{r\to 0} \sim \frac{\nu^2 - (1/4)}{r^2} \quad , \qquad \nu^2 > 0 \ )$$

a form analogous to the preceding one may also be established; but now $\delta_H(s)\big|_{s\to\infty} \neq 0$ and the bare vertex function and the loop are divergent.

The vertex function normalized at an arbitrary point μ^2,

$$\Gamma_x^{(\mu)}(s) = \frac{\Gamma_o(s)}{\Gamma_o(u)} = \exp\left\{\frac{1}{\pi}(s-\mu^2)\int \frac{\delta_H(s')\,ds'}{(s'-\mu^2)(s'-s-i\varepsilon)}\right\} \tag{5.21}$$

tends to zero at infinity, while

$$Z_1 \equiv \frac{1}{\Gamma_o(\mu^2)} \equiv 0$$

for all μ^2. After vertex renormalization the integral representing the loop is finite if $\delta_H(\infty) > \pi/4$ (which happens for more singular potentials than those considered here). Nevertheless $\lambda_o = \lambda_{obs.} Z_1^2 Z_x$ is always null because either $\Gamma_x^{(\mu)} \to$ constant which implies

$$Z_1 \text{ finite} \neq 0 \Longrightarrow Z_x = 0 \quad ;$$

or because

$$Z_x \neq 0 \Longrightarrow \Gamma_x^{(\mu)} \longrightarrow 0 \Longrightarrow Z_1 \equiv 0 \ .$$

We see then that from the point of view of field theory Eq. (5.1) contains the constant $\lambda_o = 0$ in the limit $r_o \to 0$.

3. <u>Properties of composite particles of type H</u> (regular potential case). For the first known particles (Hydrogen atom) the bound state results of a given and regular attractive potential V(r). The mass of the bound state μ_H^2 is given[5] by the pole con-

dition of the $t_H(s)$ amplitude

$$D_H(\mu_H^2) = 0 \tag{5.22}$$

whereas the coupling constant is defined by the residue condition

$$g_\mu^2 = - \frac{N_H(\mu_H^2)}{D'_H(\mu_H^2)} \tag{5.23}$$

It is clear from expressions (5.10) and (5.11) that the amplitude $t_H(s)$ has a similar form[6] to that of the amplitude $t_\lambda(s)$, in Eq. (5.15), N(s) taking the place of the vertex function $|\Gamma(s)|^2$. Nevertheless a first difference arises from the fact that N(s) is not necessarily positive definite for positive s and has a right hand cut, which does not appear in $\Gamma(s)$. Another difference comes from the fact that whereas in the case X one must fix the constant λ_o, which has to be renormalized in the case in which the vertex has a true dynamical origin, so that one must fix in practice one observable parameter (the mass of the bound state or the constant $\lambda_{obs.}$), in the case H on the contrary the amplitude is completely determined if one knows the regular potential V(r).

The question therefore is to know under which conditions the residue equation (5.23) is equivalent to the equation $Z(g_c^2) = 0$, and also what is the meaning of the pole condition (5.22), which clearly must be different from the mass equation of X particles, since it does not contain the λ constant. From what we have seen in the first part of this chapter the bare vertex function $\Gamma_o(s)$, given by $\Gamma_o(s) = 1/D_H(s)$, would also be that of an arbitrary particle φ

(elementary or composite) provided this particle be coupled locally by $g_E \varphi \psi(x)\delta(x)$. Now, if such a particle had the mass μ_E, then, defining its renormalized vertex by

$$\Gamma_{\text{ren.}(\mu_E)}(s) \equiv \frac{\Gamma_o(s)}{\Gamma_o(\mu_E^2)} = Z_1(\mu_E)\,\Gamma_o(s)$$

we would have for $s \approx \mu_E^2 \approx \mu_c^2$

$$\Gamma_{\text{ren.}(\mu_E)}(s) \approx \frac{\mu_E^2 - \mu_H^2}{s - \mu_H^2}$$

and

$$Z_1(\mu_E) \approx \text{const.}\,(\mu_E^2 - \mu_H^2)$$

The mass equation is therefore equivalent to require that[7]

$$Z_1(\mu_E)\Big|_{\mu_E \to \mu_H} = 0 \quad .$$

Nevertheless

$$\Gamma_{\text{ren.}(\mu_E)}(s)\Big|_{\mu_E \to \mu_H} = 0 \quad \text{for all} \quad s \neq \mu_H^2 \quad ,$$

and for this reason it is not possible to define the compositeness condition of the field of particles of type H in the same way as we have done for the X particles: indeed the condition $Z_1 = 0$ (and eventually $Z_3 = 0$) in the equations or in the Lagrangian does not leave any constraint traducing the composite and deduced nature of an eventual field of the particle of type H; the composite field becomes simply uncoupled when the constraints are imposed in the Lagrangian. For this reason we think that the problem of establishing a correct formulation of the field theory of composite particles of type H is still open[8].

Nevertheless, in spite of the absence of a correct Lagrangian formulation, Ida[9] has been able to define propagators and vertex functions of composite particles of type H, by generalizing to the t_H amplitudes the decomposition method given by Lee et al[4]; he obtains, associated to the decomposition $D_H = D_o \Delta_H^{-1}$, the formula

$$t_H = t_o - g_\mu^2 \left[\Gamma_H^{(\mu)}\right]^2 \Delta_H^{(\mu)} \qquad (5.25)$$

similar to Eq. (5.18), in which the last term has no left hand cut. But in this case we have an important difference with the case discussed by Lee et al: the integral which appears in expression (5.20) for the vertex (where $\mathcal{D}_x(s)$ is replaced by $\mathcal{D}_H(s)$ which is such that $\mathcal{D}_H(s) \underset{s \to \infty}{\sim} 1/s$) is divergent. One must then make a subtraction which implies that in $\Gamma_H^{(\mu)}(s)$, normalized at $s = \mu^2$, an arbitrary parameter appears. One also finds that the propagator $\Delta_H^{(\mu)}$, with residue 1 at $s = \mu^2$, necessarily admits a zero and the vertex a pole at a point m^2 with arbitrary position, but such that $m^2 > \mu^2$ ($t_H^{(\mu)}(s)$ does not have such a pole introduced by the decomposition; this pole appears in $t_o(s)$ and cancels with the one of the second term).

We may then write

$$t_H^{(\mu)}(s) = t_o^{(m)}(s) - g_\mu^2 \left[\Gamma_H^{(\mu)}(s)\right]^2 \Delta_H^{(\mu)}(s) \qquad (5.26)$$

More generally, for any regular or singular potential, if $t_H(s)$ has a pole μ_H it is not possible to construct a unitary amplitude $t_o(s)$ having the same left hand cut as $t_H(s)$ and without poles. It is possible to verify that from the decomposition (5.26) one has the conditions

$$Z_3^H(g_\mu^2) = 0 \quad \text{and} \quad \delta\nu_H^2(\mu^2) = 0$$

The possibility that $\delta\nu^2$ be null comes from the fact that the spectral contribution of the state of mass m^2 has a sign opposite to that of the positive integral over the continuous spectrum. Moreover

$$\Gamma_H^{(\mu)}(s)\Big|_{s\to\infty} \longrightarrow 0 \qquad \text{i.e.} \qquad Z_1 \equiv 0$$

4. Particles of type X in the case of a regular potential V(r) producing a pole in t_H. The argument of section (1) may be generalized here. If S_H has a pole at μ^2 (zero of $y_2(k)$) it is clear that S_x defined by (5.7) does not have that pole, but it may anyway have a displaced pole. The displacement is finite only to the lowest order in λ, as it is the case, for instance, for the effect of the Uelhing term in the s states of the Hydrogen atom treated with the Schrödinger equation. But, more generally, to all order in λ the presence of the bound state in S_H does not change the difficulties of divergence of $B_o(s)$ and a renormalization must again be carried out either by fixing $\lambda_{obs.}$ or by giving the position of the pole $s = m^2$ of S_x. The vertex $\Gamma^o(s) = 1/y_2(s)$ presents now a pole at μ^2, while the propagator of the composite X particle,

$$\Delta'^{(0)}_x = \frac{\lambda_o}{1 - \lambda_o B_o(s)} ,$$

has a zero at μ^2; then the term $\Delta'^{(0)}_x \Gamma^o(s)^2$ has a simple pole which cancels with that of t_H; one still has the decompositions

$$D_x = D_H \Delta_m^{-1} \tag{5.28}$$

and

$$t_x^m = t_H^\mu - g_m^2 \left[\Gamma_x^{(m)}(s)\right]^2 \Delta_x^{(m)}(s) ,$$

with

$$\Gamma_x^{(m)}(s) = \frac{D_H(-m^2)}{D_H(s)}$$

Then

$$\left[\Delta_x^{(m)}(s)\right]^{-1} = g_m^2 (s - m^2) \left[\frac{1}{\pi} \int_0^\infty \frac{\sqrt{s'} |\Gamma_x^{(m)}(s')|^2 ds'}{(s' - m^2)(s' - s - i\varepsilon)} - \frac{m^2 - \mu^2}{g_\mu^2} \frac{\mathcal{D}_H^2(-m^2)}{s - \mu^2} \right]$$

with

$$D_H = (s - \mu^2) \mathcal{D}_H(s)$$

and

$$g_\mu^2 = - \frac{N_H(\mu^2)}{D'_H(\mu^2)}$$

The constant g_m^2 is a solution of the equation

$$Z_3(g_m^2) = 1 - g_m^2 \left[\frac{1}{\pi} \int \frac{\sqrt{s'}\, |\Gamma_x^{(m)}(s')|^2}{(s' - m^2)^2} ds' \right.$$

$$\left. + \frac{\mathcal{D}_H^2(m^2)}{g_\mu^2} \right] = 0 \qquad (5.29)$$

The supplementary terms in Δ_x^{-1} and Z_3 (in comparison with the case of section 1) arise from the spectral contribution of the pole of the vertex at μ^2.

5. Comparison X/H.

a. The decomposition (5.26) of the amplitude t_H when it has a pole and the expression (5.28) of the amplitude t_x in the same case present an evident similarity. Indeed these two amplitudes have the same left hand cut and contain contributions from a pole m whose position is arbitrary in $t_o^{(m)}$ or fixed a priori in $t_x^{(m)}$. In fact one may verify that the expression $t_o^{(m)}$ deduced from Eq. (5.26),

$$t_o^{(m)} = t_H^{(\mu)} + g_\mu^2 \left[\Gamma_H^{(\mu)}\right]^2 \Delta_H^{(\mu)}(s) \quad ,$$

in which the arbitrary pole ($s = m^2$) coming from $\left[\Gamma_H^{(\mu)}\right]^2 \Delta_H^{(\mu)}(s)$ appears explicitly, is identical to the X amplitude $t_x^{(m)}$ of Eq. (5.28).

We may then give the following interpretation for the process leading to the decomposition of $t_H(s)$. Instead of directly considering V(r), which gives $t_H = N_H/D_H$, we may write

$$V(r) = \left[V(r) + \lambda_1 \delta(\mathbf{x}) - \lambda_2 \delta(\mathbf{x})\right]_{\lambda_1 = \lambda_2}$$

The singular potential $W_{\lambda_1} \equiv V(r) + \lambda_1 \delta(\mathbf{x})$ gives rise to an amplitude $t_x^{(m_1)}(s, W_{\lambda_1})$ of the form (5.28), which does not contain any pole at μ^2, but whose pole at m_1^2 must be fixed a priori; then one has

$$D_{x(\lambda_1)} = D_H \Delta_{x(\lambda_1)}^{(m_1)\, -1}$$

The term $\lambda_2 \delta(\mathbf{x})$ added now to the potential W_{λ_1} adds to $t_x(s, W_1)$ an amplitude t_{λ_2} which has a vertex pole and a zero of $\Delta_{x(\lambda_2)}^{(m_2)}$ in m_1^2; but we may choose the pole at $m_2^2 = \mu^2$, which is equivalent to impose $\lambda_1 = \lambda_2$. We then have

$$D_{x(\lambda_2)} = D_{x(\lambda_1)} \left[\Delta_{x(\lambda_2)}^{(m_2 = \mu)} \right]^{-1} = D_H = D_o \left[\Delta_H^{(\mu)} \right]^{-1}$$

It is indeed possible to verify that one has

$$\left[\Delta_{x(\lambda)}^{(\mu)} \right]^{-1} \cdot \left[\Delta_{x(\lambda)}^{(m_1)} \right]^{-1} = 1 \Rightarrow \left[\Delta_H^{(\mu)} \right]^{-1} = \Delta_x^{(m_1)}$$

In this way the decomposition of t_H has a very artificial character, but it may be eventually useful when the domain of the physical values of s is small, if one chooses the position of m^2 (or the value of $\lambda_{obs.}$) in such a way that $t_o^{(m)}(s)$ remains small as compared to the term $\Gamma^2 \Delta'$, which is easier to deal with. This method is presented in a more general form by Vaughn et al[10] who make the decomposition

$$V(p-p') = \left[V(p-p') - \lambda W_p W_{p'}\right] + \lambda W_p W_{p'}$$

in which W_p is such that t_o is small.

b. The question should be asked how can one know whether the observed particles are of type X or H. Apart from the obvious difference in the "sum rules" (5.17) and (5.23) which determine g^2 [11], the following distinctions may be established for the case V(r) regular:

i. Difference in the asymptotic behavior ($\delta_H(\infty) \rightarrow -\pi$, $\delta_x(\infty) \rightarrow -\pi/2$, for the bound state).

ii. Difference in the dispersion relations and Regge poles (in the model we consider here the H particles of mass μ_H belong to a Regge trajectory). In the case X studied through the limiting process $r_o \rightarrow 0$, one shows that the trajectory goes into the Re $\ell = 0$ axis. This is due to the fact that both the denominator and numerator functions, $D_o(-k, r_o)$ and $N_o(-k, r_o)$, respectively, become then identically zero and the scattering matrix has a pole at the point m_x located to the left of the initial trajectory. If one wants to generalize these results to the relativistic case, one may admit the Mandelstam representation, i.e. a dispersion relation in t with a finite number of subtractions, and then conjecture that the H particle is still located on a Regge trajectory, i.e. that the amplitude t_H is the analytic continuation in ℓ at the point $\ell = 0$ of the amplitude t. Since

$$A_x(s,t) = A_H(s,t) - g^2 \Gamma^2(s)\Delta(s) \quad ,$$

we have
$$\lim_{t\rightarrow\infty} A_x(s,t) = t^{\alpha_H}(s) + \text{constant}$$

Moreover, if one admits that, as in the non relativistic case, the slope of the trajectory is positive at Re $\ell = 0$, then in the neighborhood of $s = 0$, $\alpha_H(s)$ is negative.

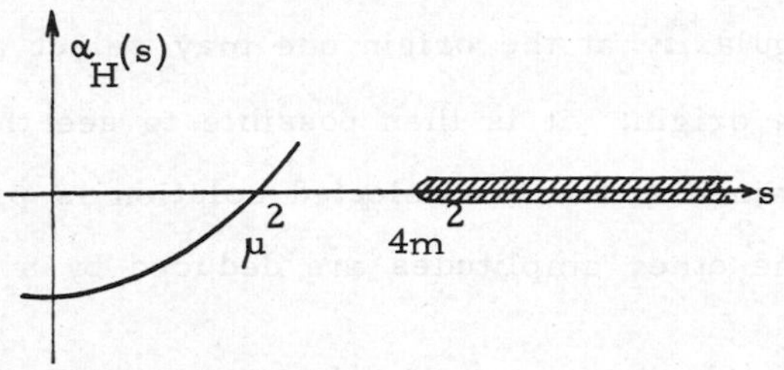

Then, if the exchanged particle is of type X, the scattering amplitude in the crossed channel goes asymptotically to a constant while if the exchanged particle is of the H type it decreases as $t^{\alpha_H(s)}$. Several authors have studied under which conditions an elementary particle is located on a Regge trajectory [13].

<u>The case of weakly singular potentials.</u>* It is remarkable that in this case the two types of solution X and H satisfy the same N/D equations [14] which then have an infinity of solutions depending on one parameter. From the point of view of the Schrödinger equation this degeneracy comes from the fact that the partial wave equation admits of infinite regular solutions at the origin

$$y_\alpha = y_+ + \alpha y_- \quad \text{where} \quad y_\pm\Big|_{r\to 0} \sim r^{\pm\nu + 1/2}$$

and this gives a class of Jost functions all having the same analytic

---

* Example: $r^2 V(r)\Big|_{r\to 0} = \nu^2 - 1/4, \quad 0 < \nu < 1/2.$

properties [15]; amongst all the N/D solutions a particular amplitude has an asymptotic behavior characterized by the minimal value of $\delta(\infty)$.

By a regularization procedure of the potential which eliminates the singularity at the origin one may select a unique solution regular at the origin; it is then possible to see that this unique amplitude obtained from this selected solution is precisely the H amplitude; the other amplitudes are deduced by a relation such as

$$t_\lambda = t_H - \frac{\lambda \Gamma^2}{1 - \lambda B} ,$$

where λ can be interpreted as a contact interaction.

The H solution is analytic in the coupling constant of the potential V(r) and can be obtained in perturbation theory by the N/D method [16]; nevertheless the asymptotic behavior in each order of perturbation theory is in general very different from the asymptotic behavior of the global solution, unlike the regular case.

REFERENCES

1. A. Jacquemin and B. Jouvet, Nuovo Cimento 37, 20 (1965).
2. K. Sekine, Acta Physica Austriaca Suppl. III 440 (1966).
3. For a definition of the vertex in potential theory see also, L. Bertochi, M. Macmillan, F. Predazzi and M. Tonin, Nuovo Cimento 31, 1352 (1964) and Nuovo Cimento 32, 746 (1964).
   R. Rockmore, Ann. of Phys. 32, 114 (1965).

G. Furlan and G. Mahouk, Nuovo Cimento 36, 215 (1965).

4. B. W. Lee, K. T. Mahanthappa, I. S. Gerstein and M. L. Whippman, Ann. of Phys. 28, 466 (1964).

5. G. F. Chew and S. Mandelstam, Phys. Rev. 119, 467 (1960).

6. R. Acharya, Nuovo Cimento 24, 870 (1962).

7. A. Salam, Nuovo Cimento 25, 224 (1962).

8. M. A. Braun, JETP 18, 547 (1963); 19, 460 (1964).

9. M. Ida, Prog. Th. Phys. 34, 82 (1965).
T. Akiba, S. Aito and F. Takayi, Nuovo Cimento 39, 316 (1965).
A. Jacquemin, Nuovo Cimento 44, 390 (1966).
M. L. Whippman and I. S. Gerstein, Phys. Rev. 134, 1123 (1964).
I. S. Gerstein and N. G. Deshpande, Phys. Rev. 140, 1643 (1965).
N. G. Deshpande, Nuovo Cimento 44, 147 (1966).
T. Saito, Phys. Rev. 145, 1309 (1966).

10. M. T. Vaughn, R. Aaron and R. D. Amado, Phys. Rev. 124, 1258 (1961).

11. M. M. Uehara, Prog. Th. Phys. 32, 306 (1964).
G. Clément, A. Jacquemin and B. Jouvet, Nuovo Cimento 26, 287 (1965).

12. A. Jacquemin, Comptes Rendus Ac. Sciences 260, 4311 (1965).

13. P. Kaus and F. Zachariasen, Phys. Rev. 138, 1304 (1965), M. Ida, Prog. Th. Phys. 34, 990 (1965), T. Saito, Ref. 9.

14. G. Clément and A. Jacquemin, Nuovo Cimento 47, A589 (1967); Nuovo Cimento 45, 852 (1966).

15. K. Meetz, Nuovo Cimento 34, 690 (1964).

16. D. Atkinson and A. P. Contogouris, Nuovo Cimento 39, 1082 (1965). (It is possible to show that for weak values of the coupling constant G^2 of the potential the discontinuity in the left hand cut is proportional to G^2, and one may verify that the H amplitude is the solution analytic in G^2).

6. ALLO-COMPOSITE RELATIVISTIC PARTICLES.

We have studied until now cases that were based on the following essential assumptions:

I. We neglected the effects of inelasticity; to take these into account it would be necessary:

a. To introduce the various two particles channels; this can be easily done by using the formalism developed in chapter 4.

b. To dress the constituent particles.

c. To replace the non relativistic potentials as well as the Schrödinger type equations and their N/D generalization, by using the Bethe-Salpeter equations which have the effect of introducing n particles states.

II. We have also neglected the crossing symmetry, the binding force being given a priori.

Some examples of the validity of these approximations are known (Hydrogen atom and the deuteron), but there is no reason to think that this should still hold in the problem of constructing the particles usually called elementary.

The problems having their origin in the complications due to the inelasticity and the requirement of crossing symmetry are extremely vast and therefore we shall deal here only with some particular points.

A. Many attempts have been made in order to try and calculate the coupling constants and masses of composite particles in the elastic approximation considering the crossing symmetry. This last fact, in the case of H particles fixes the exchange potential and should lead in principle to the determination of G and μ: it is the allo-composite "bootstrap"[1].

Almost always the following approximations are made:

1. The binding force is represented by the left hand cut which results from the exchange of a single pole, corresponding to the lowest mass state of the propagator (philosophy of the nearest singularity).

2. The system thus determined is solved by the iterative method (which corresponds to particles of type H).

If some successes have been obtained in the N^*_{33} calculations, it was possible to expect them a priori because the static model works well with a cutoff mass of the order predicted by the π-nucleon interaction. The results for the ρ calculation are bad and for pions simply do not exist.

From the Quantum Field Theory point of view and taking the mass of the ρ as given, it is clear that in order that

$$\gamma_{\rho\pi\pi}^2/4\pi \approx 2$$

be the solution of $Z_3^\rho(\gamma_\rho^2) = 0$, we must have

$$\int_{4\mu^2}^{\infty} \frac{|\Gamma_{\rho\pi\pi}(s')|^2}{(s'-\rho^2)^2} s'\left(1-\frac{4\mu^2}{s'}\right)^{3/2} ds' \approx 1/2$$

in the elastic approximation. $\Gamma_{\rho\pi\pi}$ is here the form factor (normalized at $s = \rho^2$) which arises from the nonlocality in the case H or from the vertex factor in case X. The integral is logarithmically divergent if $\Gamma = 1$, so Γ must have the effect of a cutoff function (whose explicit form is of little importance), thus introducing a cutoff-mass Λ^2 such that

$$\int_{4\mu^2}^{\Lambda^2} \frac{ds'\,s'}{(s'-\rho^2)^2} \approx 1/2 \quad , \quad \text{which implies} \quad \Lambda \approx 7 \cdot 10^6 \text{ MeV.}$$

This value is very different from the range $\Lambda \approx M_\rho \approx 10^3$ MeV of π-π interactions. It is then impossible to explain the ρ with an exchange mechanism of ρ between pions when approximating this effect by a pole located at the beginning of the left cut which leads to regular potential type N/D solutions.

This value of Λ also suggests that the hypothesis of the dominance of the nearest singularities (on the left and right cuts — elastic approximation) in the calculation of fundamental constants is not so good. In spite of this it is evident that for quantities which can be written as spectral integrals subtracted many times, this philosophy must be true because the form of an analytic function in a small domain is more and more modified when a singularity gets nearer, but the height and slope of the curves can depend on the conditions far away. Physically this property is the basis of renormalization and electrodynamics is a good example of this phenomenon. Indeed, although it is not possible to calculate α by

$$\frac{1}{\alpha} = \int \frac{\sigma(s')ds'}{s'^2}, \quad \sigma(s') = \frac{s'}{3\pi}\sqrt{1-(4m^2/s')}\;(1-2m^2/s')$$

or even

$$\frac{1}{\alpha} = \int \frac{\sigma(s')\,|\Gamma(s')|^2 ds'}{s'^2}$$

where Γ is the vertex function of the electron which results from the nearest left singularities, it is nevertheless possible to calculate Uehling's constant with $\int(\sigma/s'^3)ds'$, the other corrections being small and in consequence can be neglected in a first approximation.

In the case of the ρ, the potential due to the exchange of a ρ can be a singular potential, and this fact modifies the importance of the nearest singularity. If that potential is approximated by the singular potential which results from the exchange of only one ρ taken as elementary the exact N/D solution can be obtained [2] and leads to an acceptable value of γ^2; nevertheless an infinity of ghosts appear then in the amplitudes, $\gamma^2_{\rho\pi\pi}$ being greater than the critical value $\gamma_c^2 = \frac{2}{\pi}$ which is a limit point in the sense that beyond it violations of unitarity appear and then the introduction of a cutoff is necessary. We do not yet know if the failures in the explicit calculation of the ρ are a consequence of 1) the approximation of exchanging only one ρ between the pions to define the left cut; 2) not taking into account the various effects of inelasticity (an asymptotically null vertex (Z_1=0) implies in a theory with conserved current a stronger singularity for the pion asymptotic propagators ($Z_2 = 0$) and this implies an important inelasticity); 3) the fact that it is not consistent to suppose for the t channel the exchange of an elementary ρ coupled to the pions without form factors, because this leads to an asymptotic behavior in t very different to the one which is deduced for the s channel, producing then a violation of crossing symmetry in the asymptotic regions. The only consistent attempts from that point of view are the calculations by bootstrap of Regge trajectories[3].

B. Relativistic generalizations of the equivalence theorem $X = Y(Z_3 = 0)$. We have shown the equivalence of a theory $Y(Z_3 = 0)$ with an X theory in the model with a cutoff of chapter 2. This was done in the case when the composite particle appeared as a virtual particle in the intermediate states and with finite but arbitrary energy and momentum.

We have seen that the various ways to approach the problem, namely,

– in terms of the observable parameters of Y,

$$S_Y(G) \longrightarrow S_X(g_o) \quad \text{when} \quad G \longrightarrow G(Z_3 = 0) \equiv C_c \, ,$$

with $g_o = G_c^2 Z_1^2/\delta\nu$,

– in terms of the bare parameters of Y,

$$S_Y(G_o, \mu_o^2) \longrightarrow S_X(g_o)$$

when $\quad G_o^2 \longrightarrow \infty \, , \quad \mu_o^2 \longrightarrow \infty \quad$ and $\quad G_o^2/\mu_o^2 = g_o$,

– in terms of the parameters of X:

$$S_Y(g_F, Z)\big|_{Z\to 0} \longrightarrow S_X(g_F) \longrightarrow S_X(g_o) \, ,$$

all give the same results.

The same proofs can also be given in the cases (mentioned in the references of chapter 3) in which the spectral integral for Z converges, in perturbation theory or globally if the vertex function tends to zero fast enough.

However in a relativistic theory[5] two essential difficulties appear which must be examined:

1. We cannot exclude the composite particle from virtual processes where a summation is done over all energy and momentum values of the propagator of the composite particle;

2. Except the case of a scalar field with scalar coupling to other S or PS fields,[6] the function $Z_3(G^2)$ is, in perturbation theory, a series of infinite terms. For these reasons it is not at all evident that the equivalence shown for the preceding models still holds here.

On the contrary, an evident argument against the equivalence theorem can be given and it is that the Yukawa theory is renormalizable and the Fermi theory is not, and as a consequence a proof of the theorem is at first sight paradoxical and certainly a delicate question. We shall describe here the different points of view and discuss the various "proofs" of the Equivalence Theorem. To fix ideas we shall consider the case of a Yukawa pseudoscalar coupling $G_o \varphi_o J_5^o$ and of a Fermi ps-ps coupling $(g_o/2)J_5^o J_5^o$ (the factor 1/2 comes from the fact that the fermions scattering matrix elements include to the lowest order in g_o a factor $(2g_o/2)$. We shall study successively the two difficult points 1 and 2.

1. Renormalizability of the X theory.

a. Regularization point of view.

a.1. Effective regularization. If we are not afraid of playing with "ghosts" we can give a proof which is mainly an "illustration" of the equivalence theorem, which states that

$$S_Y(G_o, \mu_o, \Lambda) \xrightarrow[\begin{Bmatrix} G_o^2 \to \infty \\ \mu_o^2 \to \infty \end{Bmatrix}]{} S_X(g_o, \Lambda)$$

at any order of perturbation theory (in G_o^2 or on g_o). This can be done by modifying the fermions propagators [7] :

$$S(p) = (i\gamma \cdot p + m_o)^{-1} \longrightarrow S(p, \Lambda) = S(p)F(p^2/\Lambda^2)$$

where $F(p^2/\Lambda^2)$ is a cutoff function such that $F(\infty) = 0$ and such that the bubble function $B_o(p^2, m_o^2, \Lambda^2)$ is convergent and goes asymptotically as $(1/p^2)$ in the lowest order of perturbation theory. Such a propagator implies the existence of states with negative norm. With this modification the theory can be renormalized at any order in G_o^2, and the limit $G_o^2 \to \infty$, $\mu_o^2 \to \infty$, can be performed without introducing new divergences other than eventually that which results from contracting the graph 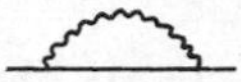 , but which can be absorbed in the fermion mass renormalization.

Furthermore in this case it is possible to calculate the solution of $Z_3(G^2, \Lambda^2) = 0$ in perturbation theory, G^2 being finite and a function of Λ^2 at any order of that theory. The two physical parameters G^2 and μ^2 are then deduced, but in fact they are deduced as a function of two unknown parameters g_o and Λ^2 taken as given, and in this way such a theory implies for the composite particle only the properties of weak solubility ("déductibilité faible", see chapter 1). In spite of the difficulties associated with ghosts this theory would have nevertheless some interest if Nature was sufficiently kind so as to produce one fundamental, universal, and large (large enough) cutoff such that the theory is reasonable within a reasonable energy range. But the fact is that to explain the values of $\alpha = 1/137$, $\gamma^2_{\rho\pi\pi}$ and G^2_π, one must use completely different cutoffs, namely, $\Lambda_\alpha \sim 10^{68}$ MeV, $\Lambda_\rho \sim 10^7$ MeV and $\Lambda_\pi \sim 10^3$ MeV, respectively.

Moreover, in the case of gauge invariant current-current interactions, the presence of a cutoff in the fermion propagators violates this invariance, which can only be restored by adding new couplings which again introduce divergences into $B_o(p)$ (for instance the fact that photons interact with bosons whose propagators are more convergent than the fermion propagators does not change the nature of the divergence of $B_o(p^2)$ in perturbation theory). Nevertheless, if both theories X and Y exist for any finite value of Λ^2, an interesting question (though not soluble in this version of the theory) is that of knowing if the limit $\Lambda^2 \rightarrow \infty$, performed after taking the limit $Z = 0$, still gives an acceptable theory, i.e. a) a theory where all the observable matrix elements are finite and without ghosts and b) such that $Z(G_c^2) = 0$ has a solution

$$G_c^2 = G_c^2(\Lambda^2 \rightarrow \infty) \neq 0$$

a.2. Formal regularization. With respect to the infinities we have encountered in perturbation theory, the following point of view has sometimes been defended, and it can be used in the problem in which we are now interested. It consists in saying that those infinities are the result of products of mathematical entities which are not well defined (products of distributions) and that by means of a more sophisticated mathematical analysis the infinite constants of perturbation theory could be replaced by arbitrary constants[8], such a formal regularization being then equivalent to the substitution

$$\infty \rightarrow C_{(i)}, \quad \text{with} \quad C_{(i)} = \text{finite arbitrary constants.}$$

In this way $B_o(p)$, which in perturbation theory diverges quadratically, could be written as

$$B_o^{reg}(p) = C_o^{(1)} + C_o^{(2)} p^2 + R_{reg}(p^2),$$

where $R_{reg}(p^2)$ can be chosen in such a way that

$$R_{reg}(0) \quad \text{and} \quad R'_{reg}(0) = 0,$$

and has the asymptotic form

$$R_{reg}(p^2) \longrightarrow \sim p^2 \log p^2$$

With this method the counterterms in the Lagrangian, namely $\delta\nu^2$ and Z_3, are arbitrary at any order of perturbation theory and are no longer related to the asymptotic behavior of the propagators. Using these ideas the X theory can be treated at any order, provided that one performs from the beginning partial summations of graphs[9]. Indeed, let us define the propagator of the first approximation

$$\Delta^{(1)}_{x(reg)} = \frac{g_o}{1 - g_o B_o^{reg}(p^2)} \left(\xrightarrow[p^2 \to \infty]{} \sim \frac{1}{p^2 \operatorname{Log} p^2} \right)$$

≡  + ...

This propagator, which can have a pole μ_1^2 and a residue G_1^2 fixed by giving g_o, $C_o^{(1)}$ and $C_o^{(2)}$, and therefore g_F and $C_o^{(2)}$, can be considered as the propagator of a dressed meson to the lowest order in G_1^2. When this propagator is introduced in the calculation of the different corrections (self-energy, vertex), one can complete its dressing by calculating $\Delta^{(2)}_{x(reg)}$, ... $\Delta^{(n)}_{x(reg)}$, including the corrections

$\delta B_o^{reg} \sim$ 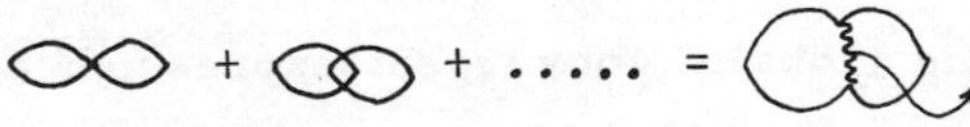 $\Delta^{(1)}_{x(reg)}$

in $\Delta^{(1)}_{x(reg)}$. Such expressions do not diverge here more than in the Yukawa theory, and this implies that the matrix $S_X^{(reg)}$ is renormalizable and finite (i.e., all the arbitrary regularization constants are eliminated from the physical matrix elements). Only μ^2 and G^2 are expressed in terms of the constant g_o and of two series of arbitrary constants $C_i^{(1)}$ and $C_i^{(2)}$, and can therefore be given a priori. The above method allows one to show in a simple manner the essential reason for the non-renormalizability of the Fermi theory in perturbation theory (it is renormalizable if it is treated in a different way). The series expansion of

$$\Delta^{(1)}_{x(reg)} = g_o + g_o^2 B_o^{reg}(p^2) + \ldots..$$

converges only for

$$\left| g_o B^{reg}(p^2) \right| < 1 \ , \quad \text{i.e.} \quad p^2 < \mu_1^2 \ ,$$

the series being divergent for $p^2 > \mu_1^2$: this is the classical divergence of the Born series at a bound state. Whereas in a process where p^2 remains fixed it is easy to sum up the series or to formulate the theory in such a way that the complete propagator is constructed from the beginning, on the contrary, when such a series appears in a process in which one has to integrate over p (e.g. in the scattering graphs

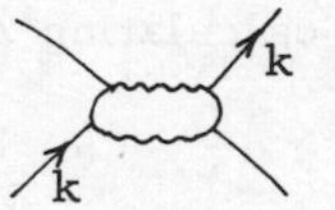

)

the following globally convergent expression appears

$$\int d^4 p \, S(k+p) S(k+p) \Delta^{(1)}_{x(reg)}(p^2) \Delta^{(1)}_{x(reg)}(p^2)$$

which in a perturbation expansion in g_o gives the series of integrals

$$\sum_N \int d^4 p \frac{1}{(p+k)^2 + m^2} \eta_N g_o^N B^{N+2}_{o(reg)}(p^2)$$

$$\sim \sum_N \int \frac{d^4 p}{p^2} \eta_N \left[p^2 \operatorname{Log} p^2 \right]^{N+2} g_o^N \ ,$$

(η_N being a constant) whose divergences (rather, their degrees of divergence) are related to the power of g_o. The regularization of these expressions and their successive renormalization requires then an increasing number of counterterms of different types; then $S_x^{reg}(g_o)$ depends on an infinite number of arbitrary parameters, and then the theory is not renormalizable in perturbation theory in g_o (since by definition the method limits the expansion to an arbitrary finite order g_o^N). However the method of formal regularization, which has some heuristic advantages, is not really correct and is physically poor, if not wrong. Indeed, the propagator $\Delta^{(1)}_{x(reg)}$ is more convergent than a free propagator, and this certainly implies the presence of ghosts with negative norm. The more serious thing is the fact that ghosts can appear for imaginary masses $\mu^2 < 0$, which leads to difficulties with causality and therefore with covariance. On the other hand, from a physical point of view the parameters of the composite particle are certainly arbitrary and only the weak solubility ("déductilité faible") is preserved. Finally, even more serious is the fact that the connection between the existence of the solution of Z = 0 (which here is arbitrary) and the asymptotic behavior of the propagator is completely lost, the latter not having any particular asymptotic property.

b. The global point of view. The two preceding methods allowed us to point out clearly two of the essential difficulties of the proof of the equivalence theorem in the relativistic case. They are:

1. The question of the existence of the solution of the equation $Z_3(G^2) = 0$, and

2. The appearance of divergences related to the perturbation expansion of the Fermi theory.

The last trouble is certainly best delimited and easier to

remove. One way of avoiding it is to start with the Yukawa theory and to suppose first that it exists as long as $Z_3 \neq 0$, and then to study in detail what kind of accidents can appear when one takes in that theory the limit $Z \rightarrow 0$. It is clear that we must also suppose that the Yukawa theory is such that the renormalization constant $Z_3(G^2)$ is a well-defined expression of G^2 and that it has at least one root G_c^2 such that $Z_3(G^2)\Big|_{G^2 \rightarrow G_c^2} \longrightarrow 0$.

This is certainly not the case for perturbation theory in G^2, but nothing prevents us from thinking either that the perturbation series for $Z_3(G^2)$ sums up to an acceptable expression, or that we can find a suitable method of calculation (for instance, by an expansion in intermediate states, where the vertex can play the rôle of a cutoff factor, which may allow us to calculate the function $Z_3(G^2)$ with arbitrary precision).

We notice, however, that as illustrated in the case of a potential, the convergence of the integral defining Z_3 implies that $\left|\Gamma(s)\right|_{(s\rightarrow\infty)} \longrightarrow 0$, and consequently, if the properties of the non-relativistic vertex can be extended to the relativistic case, we would have $Z_1 = 0$) . If we admit such conditions, the matrix $S_Y(G^2, \mu^2, m)$ can be expressed as in chapter 2 in terms of the constant g_F defined by $g_F = G^2\Delta'_F(0)$ and of Z_3, instead of being expressed in terms of the parameters G^2 and μ^2. The "G^2 propagator" can then be written [10]

$$G^2\Delta'_F = \frac{g_F}{1 - g_F(Z_1^2/Z_2^2)\left[B_o(p^2) - B_o(0)\right] + p^2(Z_3/G^2)g_F}$$

with

$$B_o(p) = \int d^4k \, \mathrm{Tr}\left(S'_o(k)\Gamma^o_5(p, p-k)S'_o(p-k)\gamma_5\right)$$

where S'_o and Γ^o_5 are the unrenormalized dressed propagator of the fermions and the unrenormalized vertex, respectively. They are functionally expressed in terms of

$$Y(p^2) = (Z_1/Z_2)^2 \, G^2 \Delta'_F$$

For instance,

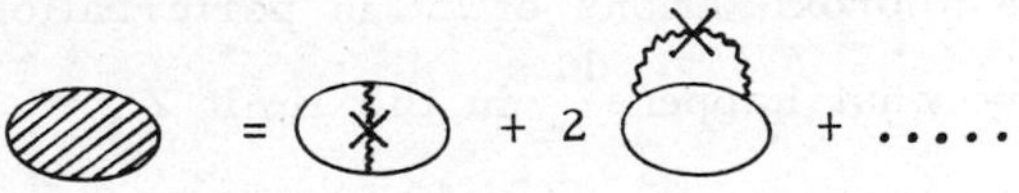

where  $= Y(p^2)$.

From the assumption that Z_3 is finite,

$$B_{RX}(s) \equiv (Z_1^2/Z_2^2)\left[B_o(s) - B_o(0)\right]$$

can be written as

$$s\int \frac{\sigma(s')\,ds'}{s'(s' - s + i\varepsilon)} \quad , \quad \text{with} \quad \int \frac{\sigma(s')ds'}{(s' - \mu^2)^2} < \infty \quad ,$$

$B_{RX}(s)$ is therefore convergent and when $s \longrightarrow \infty$ its absolute value remains smaller than s. Consequently $G^2\Delta'_F$ behaves as G^2/sZ_3 at infinity.

The Yukawa theory being, by assumption, renormalizable in perturbation theory (the series of divergences in perturbation theory of Z_3 is supposed to sum up to a finite function), it is clear that such a theory, if it exists, is still renormalizable in powers of the propagator $(G^2\Delta'_F)$ which has the same asymptotic behavior as Δ_F, i.e. the counterterms $\delta\nu^2$, δm, Z_1, Z_2, calculated in perturbation theory or as a functional series in $G^2\Delta'_F$, are enough to suppress all divergences in the observable matrix elements (the series for Z_3 sums up conveniently). Notice that Dyson's sufficient criterion for renormalizability in perturbation theory is still valid if the propagator $G^2\Delta'_F$ is asymptotically more divergent than the free propagator by powers of logarithms, as is the case for the approximations of Δ' in perturbation theory.

Let us now study what happens[11] in the limit $Z_3 \to 0$. One has

$$X(p^2) \equiv G^2\Delta'_F \Big|_{Z_3 = 0} = \frac{g_F}{1 - g_F B_{RX}(s)}$$

Then, either

$$\int \frac{\sigma(s')ds'}{s'} < \infty \quad \text{and} \quad B_{RX}(\infty) = \text{constant}$$

and the limit theory becomes as catastrophic as the Fermi theory in perturbation theory because $G^2\Delta'_F \to$ constant when $s \to \infty$; or

$$\int \frac{\sigma(s')ds'}{s'} = \infty$$

(then $\delta\nu^2 = \infty$), and in this last case, although

$$\lim_{s\to\infty} \frac{B_{RX}(s)}{s} = 0 \quad ,$$

we can have

$$B_{RX}(s)\Big|_{s \to \infty} \longrightarrow \infty$$

so that $\lim_{s \to \infty} X(s) = 0$, and the difficulty related to the Born expansion in g_F is not so serious at infinity.

However the question is now to know whether the renormalizability still exists in the limit $Z_3 = 0$ since in that case

$$G^2 \Delta'_F \Big|_{Z=0} = X(s)$$

is more singular at infinity than the free or the dressed propagator of the Yukawa theory. The only thing we can say is that there may exist propagators X(s) for which the Fermi theory is renormalizable. For instance if we have

$$B_{RX}(s)\Big|_{s \to \infty} \sim \frac{s}{\mathrm{Log}\, s}$$

(which corresponds to have $\sigma(s') \sim \frac{s'}{\mathrm{Log}^2\, s'}$), which is compatible with $Z_3 < \infty$ and $\delta\nu^2 = \infty$, then $X(s) \sim \mathrm{Log}\, s/s$, and although the propagator is more divergent than a Yukawa propagator, it is still sufficiently convergent for the sufficient criterion of renormalizability of Dyson to apply; it is possible in this case to include all the divergences of the S_x matrix, appearing in a functional perturbation theory in X(s), into the counterterms $\delta\nu^2$ (or the renormalization constant Z of g_o), δm, Z_1 and Z_2. Clearly if

X(s) has such a form it has at least one pole. Moreover, one has

$$g_o = \frac{g_F(Z_1/Z_2)^2}{1 - g_F\int\frac{\sigma(s')ds'}{s'}} = 0$$

Conversely, the preceding argument shows that if we have a Fermi theory determined by the observed quantities m and g_F and its couplings are such that the equivalent Yukawa theory, if it exists, is renormalizable for $Z_3 \neq 0$, then it may well be that this theory is renormalizable in the whole, without occurrence of unitarity violations. If this happens, then X(s) always has a pole for real s (or on the second sheet) and the theory is acceptable only if this pole appears for $s > 0$ (this implies $g_F > 0$). Let us finally remark that the fact that

$$S_X[X(s)] \equiv S_Y\left[\lim_{Z\to 0} G^2\Delta'_F(s)\right]$$

defines a matrix S_X by its functional expansion in X(s) does not prove that[12]

$$S_Y(G, m)\Big|_{Z\to 0} = S_Y(\lim_{Z\to 0} G^2\Delta'_F(s))$$

The preceding results can be generalized in principle to the couplings (S, S), (pS, pS) or (V, V) (with conserved currents, and also to some cases where the currents contain different types of fermions).

3. We shall now state some points with more precision and

indicate some other points which have to be clarified.

a. <u>The $\lambda\varphi^4$ term of the Y theory.</u> In the (pS, pS) case it is known that the Yukawa theory is renormalizable if one adds a coupling $\lambda_o(\varphi_o G_o)^4$ which permits the elimination of the divergence of the four point bubble. One could think, because of the simple argument of the limit

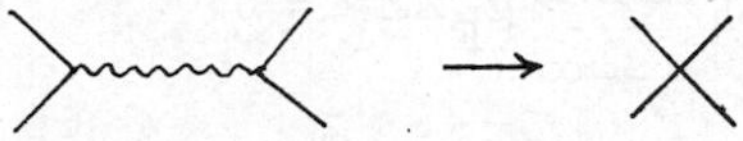

in the graphs representing the S matrix, that the addition of a term $\lambda_o g_o^4 (J_5)^4$ to the X theory would permit the renormalization and that the Lagrangian equivalence would then be easily deduced. In fact this is not so, and the elimination of the field φ_c solution of

$$\delta\nu^2 \varphi_c + 3\lambda_o \varphi_c^3 G_c^4 = G J_5$$

leads to a complicated non linear[13] Lagrangian in the current J_5. Another solution is to put $\lambda_o = 0$, which is equivalent to assume that, as for G^2, the observable constant λ_{obs} would be determined by the condition[10]

$$\lambda_o = \lambda_{obs} Z_4(\lambda_{obs}) = 0$$

b. <u>The mass equation in the X theory.</u> We have seen that when this theory is renormalizable

$$X(s)\Big|_{s \to \infty} \sim 0\left[s^{-1} (\text{Log } s)^N\right]$$

and then we have necessarily

$$g_o = 0$$

This last result is a consequence of the fact that this bare constant is given by the asymptotic limit

$$\Gamma_R(s)^2 X(s)\Big|_{s \to \infty} \longrightarrow g_F Z Z_1^2 = 0$$

From these results we conclude that the mass of the composite meson is determined only by the observable constant g_F, and it is then equivalent to fix the physical mass a priori and then deduce g_F. We see that an experimental parameter must anyway be introduced into the theory. Nevertheless, one can ask for the origin of the mass of particles of this type, if they exist. For instance when the fundamental fermions have masses equal to zero it would be necessary to have a finite g_o to fix the mass scale. While in the elastic case we always have[11]

$$g_o = g_F Z Z_1^2 = 0$$

because, even if $Z \neq 0$ Z_1 should be zero, we see that in the relativistic case there exists a possibility that

$$g_o = g_F (Z Z_1^2 / Z_2^2) \neq 0$$

and this possibility is $Z \neq 0$ (which implies $Z_1 = 0$) and $Z_2 = 0$ with $Z_1/Z_2 \neq 0$. The convergence of the S_X matrix and its renormalizability would then result from the convergence of the form factors (and not of the propagator $X \rightarrow g_F Z \neq 0$). The Dyson's sufficient conditions for renormalization do not apply here, but nothing prevents us from thinking that a renormalizable process of successive approximations can exist in which the vertex introduces convergent form factors (this is not the case studied by Dyson). The essential difficulties which appear when studying this type of renormalization come from the fact that although it is possible for the vertex functions to play the role of a cutoff in the expansions in intermediate states, as it has been shown by Salam and Delbourgo[14], the convergence of this kind of approach is a priori doubtful because i) the fermion propagator must be more singular than the free propagator ($Z_2 = 0$) and in consequence high energy states with half integral spins can destruct the good results obtained by approaching the propagators by poles (the calculation of the electromagnetic self energy is a good example of this phenomenon), and ii) if

$$X(s)\Big|_{s \to \infty} \longrightarrow g_F Z \longrightarrow \text{constant} \quad ,$$

then high mass states of the propagator X(s) can also play a critical role in an expansion in intermediate states. Moreover the constant term in the spectral form for the propagator X(s) can be at the origin of a number of difficulties in limits (se chapter 3), and as it also appears in the calculation of the vertex function, this constant term can change the L. S. Z. analysis for the convergence conditions of form factors[15].

C. Comparison of relativistic particles of type X and type H. The paradox of Fierz transformations. We shall now discuss the question of the equivalence of the bootstrap theory with the theory of fields with contact couplings.[4] Let us call bootstrap solutions the H-type solutions (and all the known illustrations of bootstrap are of that type). Now, it has been shown in the preceding chapters that when the interaction in the t channel is given, the H solution is different, both, in the physical content and in the mathematical behavior, from the X solution, which suppose a contact interaction. However, such a distiction does not necessarily survive when one considers the fully relativistic case, for, on the one side, the internal consistency of the various channels may introduce a constraint which determines the masses, and, on the other, the singularity of the potential produced by the exchange of a composite propagator weakens the difference between the X and H solutions. We shall now give an argument in favor of this possibility.

Let us suppose that we have been able to prove in the relativistic case the identity

$$S_X(g_F Z_1^2 J_5 J_5) = S_Y(G Z_1 J_5 \varphi_c)$$

and that we have constructed in this way the π^o meson as a bound state of a neutron and an antineutron ($J_5 = \bar{n}\gamma_5 n$). In such a system the π meson is by construction a particle of type X. But in the S_X matrix of the theory there may exist one or various bound states or resonances (dineutron (n n) in the singlet state, etc.) which would be then particles of type H having their origin in the exchange of composite pions between the neutrons. Nevertheless nothing forbids us to write in L_x:

$$g_5^o \bar{\psi} \gamma_5 \psi \cdot \bar{\psi} \gamma_5 \psi = -(\bar{\psi} \gamma_5 C^{-1} \bar{\psi}^c)(\psi^c C \gamma_5 \psi) g_5^o$$

and to make then a Fierz transformation[16] leading to a sum of couplings

$$\sum_{i = SVTAP} g_i^o (\bar{\psi} \theta_i \psi^c)(\bar{\psi}^c \theta_i \psi)$$

Graphically this process is

This way of considering the coupling is in fact equivalent to suppose that the contact interactions defined by L_x occur in the channel n+n → n+n instead of occurring in the channel n+n̄ → n+n̄: we are then in the presence of a theory with Fermi couplings which is the same as the preceding one and if the S matrix corresponding to the first theory exists it is reasonable to suppose that the second one should also exist. But in this last S matrix we would construct first the bound state dineutron (n n), and perhaps some other states, which would then be X particles. Now, reversing the preceding argument, the π^o would be constructed by the non local exchange of (n n) between the nucleons and would be then a particle of type H. This discussion leads us to think that the generalization of the objective differences between particles of type X and of type H established in chapter 5 to the relativistic case is not possible. The following possibilities may arise: i) consistency conditions can imply the existence of only one solution X $\rightarrow$ H ; ii) on the contrary, an arbitrary situation exists for at least one particle which is of type X and fixes the scale of the whole system.

The existence of Fierz invariance leads us to face the possibility of studying the interesting cases where one can obtain an acceptable solution corresponding to the renormalizable case in a given channel s:

$$X_{[S]}(s)\Big|_{s \to \infty} \sim \frac{1}{s} \operatorname{Log}^n s$$

and where the same situation does not occur in the transverse channel t,

$$X_{[T]}(t)\Big|_{t \to \infty} \neq 0$$

We would have then

$$Z_S (Z_1^2)_S = Z_T (Z_1^2)_T$$

and

$$X_{[S]}(s)\Gamma(s)^2\Big|_{s^2 \sim \Lambda^2} \approx X_{[T]}(t)\Gamma(t)^2\Big|_{t^2 \sim \Lambda^2} \quad \text{when } \Lambda^2 \to \infty$$

A case of this type could be useful for the purpose of understanding the problem of renormalizability in the cases for which Dyson's sufficient criterion cannot be used.

2. <u>Convergence of $Z_3(G^2)$.</u> The most delicate point of this chapter is to know whether in a theory with local coupling and physically valid, in particular in electrodynamics where we have already seen in chapter 3 that the leptons play a dominat rôle, it is possible for a solution of the equation $Z_3(\alpha) = 0$ to exist. We remark here that $Z_3(\alpha) = 0$ is at the present time the only proposed equation which would permit, if it has a solution, to fix theoretically the value of the fine structure constant.

Let us remark here the evident distinction between the possibility that $Z_3 \equiv 0$ for all α (as it is the case for instance with the calculation of $1/Z_3$ in perturbation theory

$$\frac{1}{Z_3} = 1 + \frac{\alpha}{3\pi} \text{Log} \frac{\infty}{m^2} + \ldots\ldots),$$

and the fact that $Z_3(\alpha)$ can vanish for a certain (and perhaps correct) value α_c of α. The problem of $Z_3(\alpha)$ being identically null or of the possible of solutions of $Z_3(\alpha) = 0$ for a particular value α_c of α has been extensively discussed, and although it is true that the problems to be solved are clear it is also true that their solutions have not progressed much.

The limit $Z_3 \rightarrow 0$ when $\alpha \rightarrow \alpha_c$ leading to the class of delicate problems we have explained before, one may first ask the question whether it is at all possible for $Z_3(\alpha)$ to be <u>finite and different from zero</u> for certain values of $\alpha < \alpha_c$. In such a case ($\alpha < \alpha_c$) the two definitions of Z_3 coincide.

It has been shown that in a particular gauge one has[17]

$$\frac{1}{Z_3} = \sum_{\xi} \sum_{p^2} \rho(\xi, p^2) = \sum_{\xi} \sum_{p^2} |<0| A_\mu | \xi, p^2 >|^2$$

where $|\xi, p^2>$ are the physical N particles states of total momentum p and total energy $E = \sqrt{p^2}$. Each term $\rho(\xi, p^2)$ is positive semi definite. If the physical states are a basis of a Hilbert space, then the series in the right-hand side converges uniformly, and limiting this series to the electron-positron states one obtains

$$\frac{1}{Z_3} > \sum_{p^2} |<0| A_\mu | (e\bar{e}), p^2>|^2$$

It can be shown that

$$<0| A_\mu | e\bar{e}, (0, E)> = e\Delta'_F(s)\Gamma_R(s)$$

where $E = \sqrt{s}$. Now, if Z_3 is finite and different from zero, then

$$\Delta'_F(s) \Big|_{s\to\infty} \longrightarrow \frac{1}{s Z_3}$$

and if it is true that

$$\Gamma_R(s) \Big|_{s\to\infty} \longrightarrow Z_1$$

then we have

$$\frac{1}{Z_3} > (Z_1^2/Z_3^2)\int_{c>0}^{\infty} \frac{ds}{s}$$

which is impossible, except if Z_1 is null. In this argument which has a general good aspect some points are doubtful and it would be important to make them clear:

1) Although in potential theory we have seen that $\Gamma_R(\infty) = Z_1$, and the equality is valid in a global sense and also at each order of perturbation theory, the proof of the same statement in relativistic theory is not so clear [18]. Indeed, in perturbation theory we have

$$\Gamma_R(s) \sim 1 + \frac{\alpha}{2\pi} \mathrm{Log}^2 s$$

whereas

$$Z_1 \sim 1 + \frac{\alpha}{2\pi} \mathrm{Log}(\Lambda^2/m^2)\Big|_{\Lambda^2 \to \infty}$$

and the introduction of a cutoff in the photon propagator, which makes the expressions convergent, does not make them equal [19]. The reason for this difficulty which appears with the vectorial relativistic case is probably related to gauge problems but this is not clear at the moment;

2) The expansion in intermediate states

$$|\xi\rangle = |e\bar{e}\rangle\ ,\ |e\bar{e}\gamma\rangle\ ,\ \ldots\ldots$$

introduces, for each term of the series $\frac{1}{Z_3} = \sum_{\xi} \frac{1}{Z_3(\xi)}$, infrared divergences [10]; for instance the squared matrix element $|\langle 0|A_\mu|e\bar{e}\gamma\rangle|^2$ gives rise to an infrared divergent integral at the limit when the momentum k_γ of the photon tends to zero (according to the correspondence principle the contribution of the pole of the virtual electron is infrared divergent, as is the corresponding term in perturbation theory which must coincide with the global calculation when $k_\gamma \rightarrow 0$). Moreover it is known that the infrared divergences cancel out in Z_3 and in consequence the terms of the series $\frac{1}{Z_3(\xi)} = \sum_{p^2} \rho(\xi, p^2)$, $\xi \neq (e\bar{e}\gamma)$, must cancel the infrared divergences having their origin in the state $|\xi_1> = |e\bar{e}\gamma>$. But since each term of the series $\rho(\xi, p^2)$ is positive or null the cancellation is possible if either i) each ρ is zero, or ii) the series is divergent (in this case the formal sum $\sum_{\xi \neq \xi_1} \sum_{p^2} \rho$ can have any sign. Furthermore it is also known that these infrared divergences generally cancel correctly when one sums up the cross sections integrated in only a finite energy domain (for instance in the physical expression

$$d\sigma\left[\gamma \rightarrow e\bar{e}\right] + \int_{(\Delta E)} \sum_N d\sigma\left[\gamma \rightarrow e\bar{e} + N\gamma\right] \Pi dE_\gamma$$

the infrared divergences corresponding to the dressing of the vertex and to the production of N photons cancel each other and the dependence in the photon mass is replaced by a dependence in ΔE).

To see the implication of this last property, let us look how it occurs in the infrared divergences cancellation of the second order terms in α of $Z_3(\alpha)$, represented by the graphs

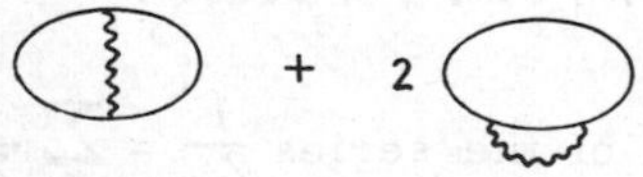

Let us separate the contributions of the intermediate states $(e\bar{e})$ and $(e\bar{e}\gamma)$:

$$Z_3 \sim \int \frac{da}{a^2}$$ 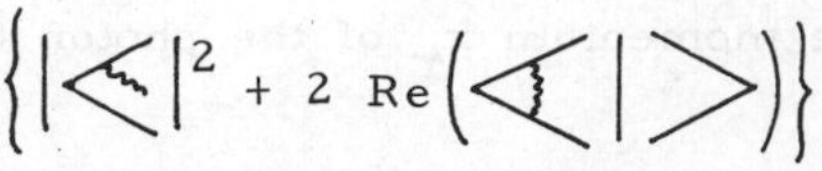

The first contribution is infrared divergent (it is proportional to

$$d\sigma\left[\gamma \longrightarrow e\,\bar{e}\,\gamma\right]).$$

The second contribution, which is negative, contains the infrared divergence of the vertex and has its origin only in a part of the positive definite term representing the contribution of the state $(e\bar{e})$ to Z_3:

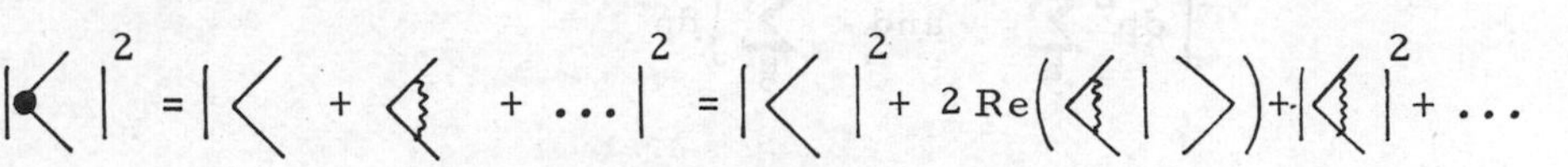

In the case we are discussing the cancellation of the infrared divergences occurs for the small values of $a \sim 4m^2$, and then the definition

$$\frac{1}{Z_3(\Lambda^2)} = \int^{\Lambda^2} dp^2 \left[\sum_{\xi}^{\infty} \left| <0 \,|\, A \,|\, \xi, p> \right|^2\right]$$

can be correct and not infrared divergent, but this is not the case for the definition

$$\frac{1}{Z_3(N)} = \sum_{\xi}^{N} \int^{\infty} dp^2 \left| <0 \,|\, A \,|\, \xi, p> \right|^2 , \quad N \text{ finite}$$

The series

$$\sum_{p^2} \sum_{\xi} \rho(\xi, p^2)$$

would be then a non uniformly convergent series which cannot be minorized and whose order of summation must be explicitly defined if the series is to have any sense whatsoever. This is in evident contradiction with the postulate of the existence of a Hilbert space for the physical states of electrodynamics. The same type of difficulties arise when one deals with the photon in dispersion relations. The fact that such anomalies appear in the case of the photon with zero mass leads us to ask how these problems arise in theories with finite mass μ^2, because it is quite clear that in the limit $\mu^2 \rightarrow 0$ the series

$$\int dp^2 \sum_{\xi} \quad \text{and} \quad \sum_{\xi} \int dp^2$$

should have the same difficulties. Nevertheless this limit is quite difficult to study because one has

$$\frac{1}{Z_3(\Lambda)} = \int^{\Lambda^2} dp^2 \sum_{\xi}^{N(\Lambda)} \rho(\xi, p^2)$$

with

$$N(\Lambda) \Big|_{\mu^2 \rightarrow 0} \longrightarrow \infty$$

Let us now look at the various attempts which have been made to calculate practically $Z_3(\alpha)$. Some progress has been achieved in the last years but we still do not have a satisfactory solution to the problem. The reader can find in this book the interesting results recently obtained by K. Johnson and collaborators. From our side we have obtained, using the method we explain in the Seminar published in this same book, some other informations which we shall now briefly summarize[20]. It can be shown that the equation for the weight function of the unrenormalized propagator deduced from the relation

$$\frac{\partial \lambda^{o}}{\partial A_{\mu}\, \partial A^{\mu}} \sim \mu_{o}^{2}$$

can be deduced, in a simpler way, by the following method: one has

$$\underline{\mu_{o}^{2}} = \int \rho_{1}^{o}\, a\, da = \pi^{o}(0)$$

where $\pi^{o}(0)$ is the coefficient of the term in $\delta_{\mu\nu}$ of the vacuum polarization tensor. If we write the unrenormalized propagator of the electron in the form

$$S_{F}^{\prime o}(p) = \int_{o}^{\infty} \frac{\sigma_{1}^{o}(b)\, i\, \gamma \cdot p + \sigma_{2}^{o}(b)}{p^{2} + b - i\varepsilon}\, db$$

then we obtain for $\pi^{o}(0)$, using Ward's theorem, the expression*

---

* This formula is proved in reference 20 directly from a formulation of gauge invariance with non zero photon bare mass. Actually, since in our formalism we have added to the usual Maxwell-Dirac Lagrangian the terms

$$\underline{\mu_{o}^{2}} : \varphi_{\mu} \varphi^{\mu} : + \underline{\lambda_{4}} : (\varphi_{\mu} \varphi^{\mu})^{2} :$$

(the vacuum energy λ_{o} plays no rôle here) the gauge invariant and renormalized vacuum polarization function which is such that $\pi_{ren}(0) = 0$ is given by

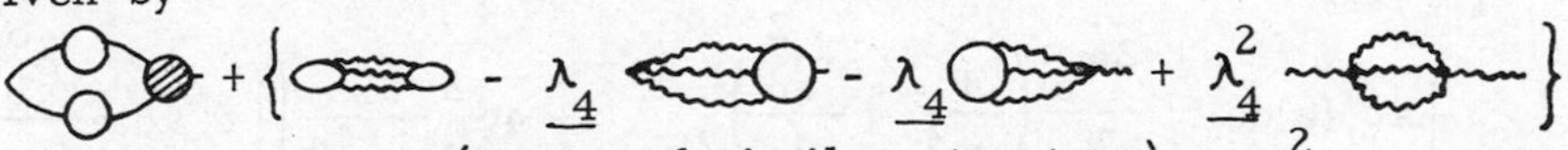

+ (terms of similar structure) - $\underline{\mu_{o}^{2}}$

The $\underline{\lambda_{4}}$ constants are such that they cancel the part of the four photons interaction term which is not gauge invariant (in a similar way as this term cancels the Matthews type divergences in (p s) meson theory). The series in the bracket $\{\ \}$ has therefore a gauge invariant form proportional to p^{2} and one has

$\underline{\mu_{o}^{2}}$ = 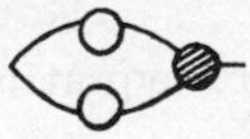

$$\Pi^{o}(0) = -2\pi\alpha_{o}\int_{o}^{\infty}\sigma_{1}^{o}(b)\,\xi_{\mu}\frac{\partial}{\partial\xi_{\mu}}\,\Delta_{1}(\xi, b)\,db\Big|_{\xi^{2}\to+0}$$

$=$ 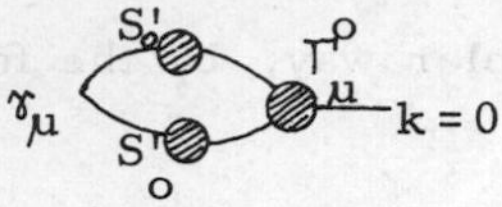

which gives (performing first the limit $\xi \to 0$)

$$\Pi^{o}(0) = \left[\frac{2\alpha_{o}}{\pi}\frac{1}{\xi^{2}}\int\sigma_{1}^{o}\,db - \frac{2\alpha_{o}}{\pi}\int\frac{\sigma_{1}^{o}b}{4}\,db + 0(\xi^{2})\right]_{\xi^{2}\to 0}$$

Using the canonical relations one can show that

$$\int\sigma_{1}^{o}(b)db = 1 \quad , \quad \int b\sigma_{1}^{o}(b)db = m_{o}^{2} + \frac{1}{2}e_{o}^{2} < 0|\varphi_{\mu}^{o}\varphi^{o\mu}|0> ,$$

where

$$< 0|\varphi_{\mu}^{o}\varphi^{o\mu}|0> = -\frac{i}{(2\pi)^{4}}\int\frac{4\rho_{1}^{o}(a)}{k^{2} + a - i\varepsilon}\,da\,d^{4}k$$

and finally one gets the equation for the $\rho_{1}^{o}(a)$ function

$$\int a\rho_{1}^{o}(a)da = \frac{2\alpha_{o}}{\pi}\left(\frac{1}{\xi^{2}} - \frac{m_{o}^{2}}{4}\right)_{\xi^{2}\to+0} + 4\alpha_{o}^{2}\frac{i}{(2\pi)^{4}}\iint d^{4}k\,da\frac{\rho_{1}^{o}(a)}{k^{2} + a - i\varepsilon}$$

This equation is a relation between different quadratically divergent quantities (in perturbation theory) and has no definite meaning from a pure mathematical point of view. However, precisely because the integrals are divergent, this equation implies relations between the asymptotic behavior of the three quantities. Nevertheless it is not possible to use such relations in a consistent mathematical way (at least with the mathematics existing to-day).

We shall take the point of view that the relation is a "sentence" written in the "language of distribution products" which is well-known to be non associative, and to depend on the context in which it occurs, as the usual language. For instance for a field theoretist

$$\frac{P}{x} \times \delta(x) \quad \text{means} \quad \frac{1}{2}\,\delta(x)$$

when this expression occurs in the renormalization of an external line. Therefore, as for a language, we have first to recognize the "meaning" of each of the three "objects" of the sentence and then "translate" each object of the sentence to a common language; one may then see that the equation we try to translate "means", graphically,

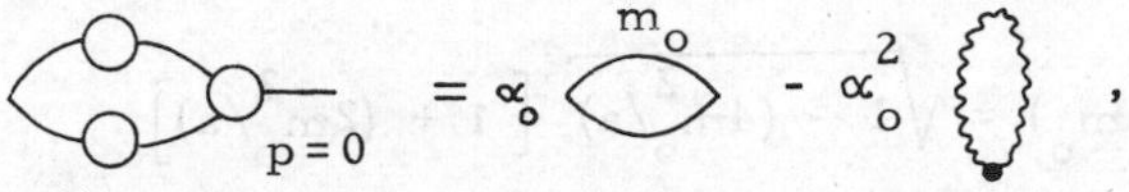

a language which for a field theoretist has a well defined meaning. The closed loop in the second member is the closed loop to the first order in α_o calculated with bare electron propagators, the second graph is $\langle 0 \,|\, \varphi^{o}_{\mu} \varphi^{o\mu} \,|\, 0 \rangle$ and we see then that this equation is simply a consequence of the fact that only the four photons interaction term involves a finite non gauge invariant term $\lambda_4(\varphi_\mu \varphi_\mu)^2$. Let us remark here that the photon self-energy does not contain any graph of the type

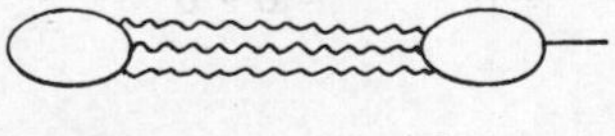

because the vertex functions involved in this case are proportional to p_μ according to gauge invariance after a subtraction due to the λ_4 contact coupling included in the Lagrangian. Returning to our "sentence" we see then that we can translate it into various common "languages" expressing each of the three graphs in terms of integrals over the <u>same</u> variable, and if we use the same cutoff for the integration domain of the chosen variable we obtain an integral equation. In the language of the unrenormalized weight function of the photon expressed in terms of α_o one gets for instance the equation

$$\int_0^A \rho_1^o(a, \alpha_o, m_o) a\,da = \frac{\alpha_o}{3\pi}\int_0^A \phi(a, m_o) da$$

$$- \frac{\alpha_o^2}{4\pi^2}\int_0^A \frac{1}{a}\int_0^a\int_0^b \rho_1^o(c)\,dc\,db\,da$$

where

$$\phi(a, m_o) = \sqrt{1 - (4m_o^2/a)}\left[1 + (2m_o^2/a)\right]$$

In the language of the spectral weight function of the vacuum polarization tensor expressed in terms of the renormalized coupling constant α one gets

$$\int_0^A \frac{\mathbf{K}(a, \alpha, m_o)}{a}\,da = \frac{\alpha}{3\pi}\int_0^A \phi(a, m_o) da$$

$$- \frac{\alpha^2}{4\pi}\int_0^A \frac{da}{a}\int_0^a\int_0^b \rho_1(c)\,dc\,db$$

with

$$\rho_1(c,\alpha,m_o) = \delta(c) + \mathbf{K}(c,\alpha,m_o)\left|\frac{1}{c\left(1 - c\displaystyle\int\frac{\mathbf{K}(z,\alpha,m_o)dz}{z^2(z+c-i\varepsilon)}\right)}\right|^2$$

and similarly in terms of the momentum of the photon propagator one has

$$\int d^4k\left[\frac{\partial^2}{(\partial k^2)^2}\left(\Delta_F'^{-1}(k^2)\right) + \frac{\alpha}{3\pi}\frac{\partial^2}{(\partial k^2)^2}\left(k^2\,\mathrm{Log}\frac{k^2}{4m^2}\right) - \frac{\alpha^2}{4\pi}\Delta_F'(k^2)\right] = 0$$

In perturbation theory one deduces from these equations the expression

$$Z_3(\alpha,m_o,\Lambda) = 1 - \int\frac{\mathbf{K}(a,m_o^2,\alpha)}{a}$$

$$= 1 - \frac{\alpha}{3\pi}L_o + \frac{\alpha^2}{4\pi^2}L_o + \frac{\alpha^3}{12\pi^2}\left(\frac{1}{2}L_o^2 - L_o\right) + \ldots$$

where

$$L_o = \mathrm{Log}\frac{\Lambda^2}{m_o^2}$$

and using the known expression of

$$\frac{m_o}{m} = f\left(\alpha,\ \mathrm{Log}\frac{\Lambda^2}{m^2}\right)$$

to the lowest orders in α one can check that the preceding formula gives the right result for $Z_3(\alpha, m, \Lambda)$ up to the order α^3. Furthermore from the absence in the self-energy of chains of loops connected by many photons one can deduce that such graphs can only contribute to Z_3 with finite terms. This also shows that even if the series of positive terms

$\sum_n \Big|$ 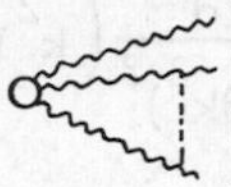 $\Big\}_n \Big|^2$

gives in $\int \rho(a)da$ a divergent contribution, there exists other contributions which are of equal importance and which cancel out these terms; therefore one cannot conclude from such a selective choice of intermediate states that $Z_3 \equiv 0$. However, if one takes seriously the equation given above, and supposing m_o finite, calculates $Z_3(\alpha, m_o)$ at all order in perturbation theory one gets that $Z_3 = 3\alpha/4\pi$ (i.e. α_o is only determined in agrement with the renormalization group) and that the function $\rho(a)$ is not positive definite. But many points of this "vigorous" approach need a more careful investigation that an exact computation of m_o and Z_3 to the order α^3 might help to realize. In particular the hypothesis of considering m_o as a finite quantity is an essential point in the result we have obtained and if one requires that the ghost should go to infinity this implies $m_o \to \infty$ and our result is no longer valid.

REFERENCES

1. G. Chew and S. Frautschi, Phys. Rev. Letters 7, 349 (1961).
2. Basseto Pacanoni, Nuovo Cimento 44, 1139 (1966).
   A. P. Contogouris, B. Diu, M. Pusterla, Nuovo Cimento 48A, 412 (1967).
3. M. Bander and G. L. Schaw, Phys. Rev. 135 B, 267 (1964).
4. W. Guttinger, Nuovo Cimento 36, 968 (1965).
   M. A. Braun, Nuclear Physics B1, 277 (1967).
5. The example of a relativistic theory in a space with a smaller number of dimensions modifies the properties of convergence and renormalizability.
6. E. G. P. Rowe, Nuovo Cimento 45, 593 (1963).
7. B. Jouvet, Nuovo Cimento 3, 1133 (1956).
   D. Lurie and A. Macfarlane, Phys. Rev. 136 B, 816 (1964).
8. W. Guttinger, Phys. Rev. 89, 1012 (1953).
9. B. Jouvet, Nuovo Cimento Supp. 2, 941 (1955); Nuovo Cimento Supp. 4, (1956); Journ. Math. 33, 201 (1954).
   J. G. Taylor, Nuovo Cimento Supp. 1, 857, 1036 (1963).
10. B. Jouvet, Nuovo Cimento 5, 1 (1957).
11. A. Jacquemin and B. Jouvet, Ref.1 in chapter 5.
12. This property has only been proved in the very particular inelastic case of the sector Nθθ of the Lee model (see J. C. Houard, Thèse, Paris 1965).
13. R. L. Zimmerman, Phys. Rev. 146, 955 (1966).
14. A. Salam and R. Delbourgo, Phys. Rev. 135 B, 1398 (1964).
15. E. Tirapegui, Nuovo Cimento 47 A, 400 (1967).
16. For an explicit illustration see Ref. 6.
17. G. Källen, Helv. Phys. Acta 25, 417 (1952), Acta Phys. Austriaca, Supp. 2 (1965).

18. S. G. Gasiorowicz, D. R. Yennie and H. Suura, Phys. Rev. Letters 2, 153 (1959).

19. O. Fleichmann, Nuovo Cimento 29, 1098 (1963).

20. B. Jouvet, Nuovo Cimento 25, 135 (1962).

M. Astaud and B. Jouvet, Comptes Rendues Acad. Sc. Paris 263, 107 (1966).

7. THEORY OF AUTOCOMPOSITE FIELDS

All the problems we have considered so far concern the case of particles composed of particles different from themselves. These last particles were in fact supposed to be elementary.

We shall now study some of the curious problems appearing in the two autocomposite cases corresponding to the two notions of heterodivisibility and of homodivisibility.

1. The case that occurs when we find among the constituents of the composite particle the composite particle itself together with at least one elementary particle. It is the "oedipic case" *. The "father" particle is identical to the "son" particle, and a "mother" particle ensures the transition "father → son": A → M + A.

2. The case where the particle is only composed of itself, or, in other words, by divisibility we can only reproduce the original particle in any number of samples as in the Russian dolls called in French "gigognes" (A → A + A → A + A + A → ...).

While in the allocomposite case we had some exactly soluble models which make it possible to illustrate in a precise way the

---

* "Cas oedipien" in the French original.

difficulties due to the vanishing of the renormalization constant, in the case we shall study now it is very difficult to construct non trivial and soluble models and we shall then take the risk of studying the problems from a formal point of view to at least see where a theory of this kind may lead us to. The study in soluble cases of the interesting points should be done later to confirm the present explotations, which, as we shall see, are proceeding in different directions which are not necessarily con vergent.

7.1. "Oedipien" case.

A. An example of such a case would be a theory of composite electrons interacting with the photon which is assumed to be elementary, or a theory of nucleons when the pion is supposed to be an elementary and a priori given particle. Clearly the programme for this case has been already sketched:

- to extend to this case what has been done for the allo-composite case.
- to find the particular properties of autocomposite particles in comparison with allocomposite particles.

But the extension of the case "allo" to the case "auto" has some difficulties.

Let us suppose for instance a model of a "scalar electron" ψ coupled with the field of a "scalar photon" φ. When $Z_2 \neq 0$ the theory is super-renormalizable, which implies that the Z's are finite functions of G^2 in perturbation theory. Defining the composite character of that electron by the constraint equation $Z_2(G^2) = 0$, we obtain the following equation for the autocomposite field of the electron $\psi_c = \lim\limits_{Z_2 \to 0} \psi$:

$$(GZ_1\varphi - \delta\nu)\psi_c = 0 \tag{7.1}$$

Writing (assuming $Z_3 \neq 0$)

$$\lambda_o = \frac{GZ_1}{\delta\nu\sqrt{Z_3}}$$

we get

$$(\lambda_o\varphi_o - 1)\psi_c = 0 \tag{7.2}$$

The last relation clearly expresses the "oedipien" character $\psi_c = \lambda_o\psi_c\varphi_o$, but it does not allow, contrary to the allocomposite case, to express in an evident way (and even classically) ψ_c as a function of φ_o, and in consequence to eliminate ψ_c from L and to obtain in this way at least a theory in which the field ψ_c does not appear, providing then the heuristic basis for an eventual equivalence theorem.

A way to arrive at such a goal is, as suggested by R. L. Zimmerman[1], to use the following method: to eliminate first by the method of Matthews and Salam, when one knows how to apply it, the elementary ψ field, and afterwards to take the limit $Z_2 \rightarrow 0$ for the bare propagator and coupling constants of the field ψ; the limit towards the contact coupling is now obtained by

$$\left.\frac{G_o}{p^2 + m_o^2}\right|_{Z_2\rightarrow 0} \longrightarrow \lambda_o \tag{7.3}$$

because

$$G_o = \frac{GZ_1}{Z_2\sqrt{Z_3}}, \qquad m^2 = m_o^2 + \frac{\delta\nu}{Z_2}, \tag{7.4}$$

(and not by $G_o^2/(p^2+\mu_o^2)$ as in the allocomposite case).

The elimination of the ψ field is in fact equivalent to calculate $L(\varphi) \sim \langle 0_\psi | L_{int} | 0_\psi \rangle$, for an unquantized field φ, and the resulting Lagrangian is given by the series of graphs

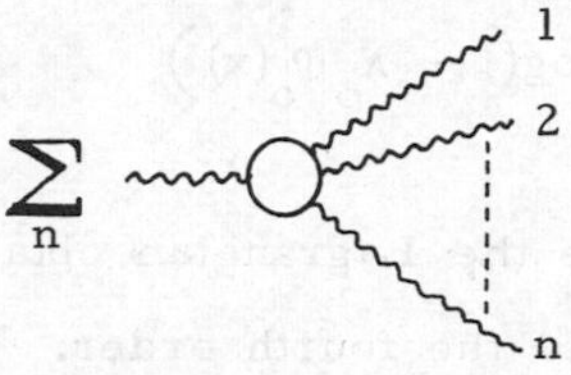

and various anomalies appear at the limit $Z_2 \rightarrow 0$.

a) The graphs are real before the limit $Z_2 \rightarrow 0$ is taken, because in them we find the integral of the closed loop

$$L(\varphi) \sim \sum i \int d^4k \begin{bmatrix} \text{product of propagators} \\ \text{of } \psi \text{ fields} \end{bmatrix} \varphi(p_1)\varphi(p_2)\ldots\varphi(p_n)$$

which contains propagators of the field ψ. By a rotation of the integration contour in k we obtain in the integral a factor i and the final integration is now over a four dimensional real space with euclidean metric and we obtain then a real value for $L(\varphi)$ (for momentum of the φ particles not greater than $4m_o^2$).

b) If we take the limit

$$(G_o S_o) \longrightarrow \lambda_o$$

directly in L, we obtain an imaginary expression; it is therefore necessary to rotate the integration contour before taking the limit $Z_2 \rightarrow 0$.

c) But there is still an ambiguity according to whether we take the limit before or after the integration in k space, the integral being divergent in this limit. In the first case we obtain the local and non linear Lagrangian

$$L \sim \delta^{(4)}(0)\mathrm{Log}\left(1 - \lambda_o \varphi_o(x)\right) \tag{7.5}$$

while in the second case the Lagrangian obtained contains derivatives of the field φ up to the fourth order.

With the local Lagrangian we have then

$$G_o S'_o(p) = < 0 \mid \lambda_o (1 - \lambda_o \varphi_o)^{-1} \mid 0 > \tag{7.6}$$

Expanding this expression in perturbation theory we get

$\lambda_o + 3\lambda_o^2$  $+ 5 \cdot 3\lambda_o^3$  $+ \ldots$

where the φ field propagator must be taken bare and uncoupled (free); then we have

$$G_o S'_o(p^2) = \sum \lambda_o^n (2n - 1)!! \left[\int \Delta_o(k) d^4k\right]^n \tag{7.7}$$

which is a divergent series independent of p.

In order to investigate better the meaning of such anomaly we shall consider the model in which S'(p) is constructed in the approximation of neglecting the dressing of the vertices. This leads, when $Z_2 = 0$, to the following integral equation, for the renormalized propagator:

$$GS'^{(1)}_R = \left[G\Sigma_R(-m^2) - G\Sigma_R(p^2)\right]^{-1}, \tag{7.8}$$

$$\Sigma_R(p^2) = -i(2\pi)^3 \int d^4k\Delta(p+k)S'^{(1)}_R(k)$$

Graphically this equation is represented by

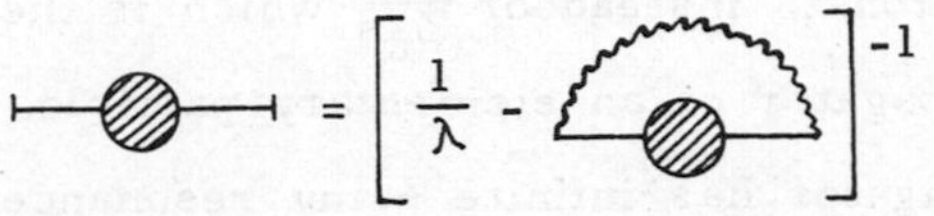

where we have written

$$\lambda = \frac{G}{\delta\nu}$$

If we expand the propagator in powers of λ, we get the following constant series:

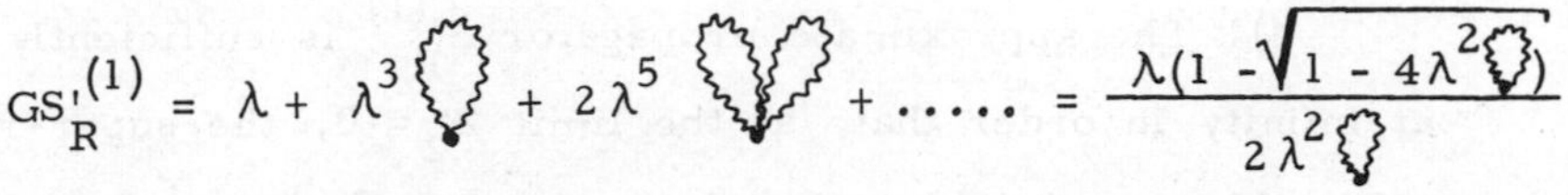

This corresponds, up to some factors due to the fact that we have neglected the vertex effects of the propagator, to the series (7.7).

However, the integral equation (7.8) has also a very consistent solution from both the mathematical and the physical point of view, which can be determined in detail in the case when the mass of the φ_o particle vanishes and which has the following satisfactory properties:

1) The residue condition (residue = 1) for $S'^{(1)}_R$ determines (except for the infrared divergence ambiguity) the coupling constant G^2, by means of a relation which is equivalent to the equation

$Z_2(G^2) = 0$ imposed on the elementary particle in the same type of approximation.

2) We have the asymptotic behavior

$$S'^{(1)}_R(s) \xrightarrow[s\to\infty]{} \frac{1}{\sqrt{s}} F(s)$$

where $F(s) \xrightarrow[s\to\infty]{}$ const. instead of $\frac{1}{Z_2 s}$ which is the asymptotic behavior of the propagator of an elementary particle.

3) This propagator has infinite many resonances, which are located at exponentially increasing distances, whereas if $Z_2 \neq 0$ the resonances occur in a finite number and are located at finite distances. This phenomenon is similar to the one which occurs in the allo-composite case, where the characteristic asymptotic behavior is determined by a resonance which goes to infinity with $1/Z_3$.

4) The approximate propagator $S'^{(1)}_R$ is sufficiently convergent at infinity in order that, at the limit $Z_2 = 0$, the super-renormalizable theory we study, though more singular when $Z_2 = 0$, is still renormalizable. This occurs because the corrections due to the vertices and to the vacuum polarization of the elementary φ field can be renormalized at any functional order in $S'^{(1)}_R$.

5) The propagator $S'^{(1)}_R$ is very different from the one which we would obtain by approximating in Σ_R the propagator of the composite particle by its pole term (which would be equivalent to write

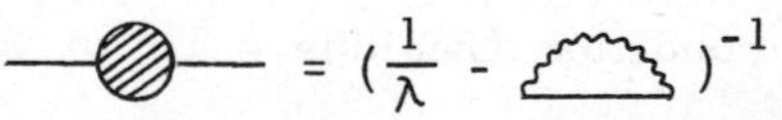

and would lead to a propagator which would behave asymptotically as 1/log s and would be in consequence useless for a functional expansion of the matrix elements leading to a renormalizable theory). An interesting feature of this model is the fact that it clearly illustrates the points we discussed in the allo-composite relativistic case:

i. The theory is very singular when expressed in powers of g_F (i.e. of λ).

ii. However, if we develop it in functional powers of a convenient first approximation of the composite propagator, it can be acceptable and renormalizable at all orders (however, this fact does not prove that this series of finite matrix elements converges).

iii. The fact of neglecting the compositeness of a particle in virtual processes may lead to solutions very different from more exact ones.

In addition to the dynamical properties (and difficulties) so illustrated, we can deduce an interesting property which is typical of autocomposite particles, and which will be largely extended in the "gigogne" case. The field equation (7.1) {from which, if we have, as in chapter 2, $< 0 \mid \psi_c(x) \mid c(p) > \sim e^{ipx}$, results the mass equation

$$< 0 \mid \psi_c \mid c > \; = \; \lambda_o < 0 \mid \psi_c \varphi_o \mid c > \quad \text{i.e.}$$

(•— = λ_o 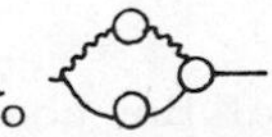) $\Longrightarrow 1 = \lambda_o \Sigma(-m^2)$ }

and the integral equation for the composite propagator, expressed in terms of an observable constant $\lambda_R = GS'_R(p^2 = 0)$, namely

$$GS'_R(p^2) = \lambda_R\left[1 - \lambda_R\left[\int d^4k(-i)(2\pi)^4\Delta'_R(p+k)GS'_R(k)\right.\right.$$

$$\left.\left.\Gamma_o(p+k,\ k,\ p)\Gamma_o^{-2}(\mu,0,0) - (\text{id. for } p = 0)\right]\right]^{-1} \tag{7.9}$$

can a priori have solutions for any postulated value of the spin of ψ. In fact, contrary to the allo-composite case in which the spin of φ is determined by the spin of its constituents and their angular momentum, here the spin of ψ depends on the spins of φ and ψ, so that it can take both integer and half-integer values.

If there exist such solutions for some set of values of J_ψ (integer or half-integer), the equations (7.1) or (7.9) determine in principle mass equations for series of particles of integer or half-integer spin.

Such a phenomenon is manifestly different from that of the Regge recurrences, and one can ask what generalization of this notion it requires. The possibility of the autocomposite equations of having solutions of arbitrary spin comes from the vanishing of the dynamical term of the field in L. Thus, although in the "oedipien" case the φ field still fixes the space-time frame of reference, the spin of ψ must however be determined in a self-consistent way, as a violation of the group which leaves the Lagrangian invariant; this is analogous to the determination of the mass in the models of Nambu and Jona-Lasinio.

B. The fact of having no proof of the convergence of the above indicated series of finite approximations of the S matrix, and the difficulties we found in eliminating the autocomposite field (which in such a way has no classical correspondence) can legitimately lead us to adopt a priori, and for exploratory purposes, the classical point of view for the field equations and to investigate for which class of theories these equations have at least non-trivial classical solutions; we have to do so, since no soluble model allows one as yet to know exactly the relation between the S matrix and the field equations.

For mathematical reasons Broido and Taylor[2] conclude that it is legitimate "to divide by ψ" the equations for the autocomposite field whenever it is possible, which is then equivalent to consider them as classical equations.

In particular, for Eq. (7.1) it results the constraint $GZ_1\varphi = \delta\nu$ for the field φ, which could mean that $G = \delta\nu = 0$; in such a case the field φ should be a free field and the S matrix equal to unity.

This could mean either that the approximate series we obtained above was identically convergent to zero, or that we may have different solutions for the field equations (we have already seen that Eq. (7.8) has two solutions, and one should also remember that the N/D and Schrödinger equations have no unique solution for weakly singular potentials (see chapter 5)). The just mentioned authors give as an example of autocomposite equations whose solution should be non trivial, the equations of the type

$$(1 - \lambda\theta^{\mu}(\varphi)\gamma_{\mu}) = 0 \quad , \quad \text{with} \quad \theta^{\mu} = \varphi^{\mu},\ \partial^{\mu}\varphi, \ldots$$

where the matrix applied to ψ is not diagonalizable in the spinorial space, so that it is not possible to divide by ψ.

Since it is obviously strange to try to use the classical point of view for the problem of compositeness which involves the high energy domain for which the celebrated correspondence principle fails, this situation requires some comments. The classical point of view can be used in a consistent way in the case of the allo-composite fields where the classical Lagrangian containing a non linear (Fermi) coupling can be interpreted as a classical Yukawa Lagrangian involving a meson of infinite mass coupled with an infinite coupling constant. In such a case the correspondence principle between the classical non linear theory and the quantum field theory consists in replacing the classical quantities by quantum bare quantities; furthermore the critical (infinite) values of the bare constants (mass and coupling constant) of the classical quantities are interpreted as quantum constraints on the renormalization constants of the quantum fields. It follows from this that the quantum field theory keeps track of the classical theory which arises at very high energies or at very small distances: namely, the quantization of a theory with contact coupling or of a theory with infinite mass and coupling constant gives the same asymptotic constraints in the quantum scattering amplitudes. Therefore it is possible to understand that a study of the classical equations of composite fields can be a valid approach in order to try to explain the observable properties of the existing particles if they are composite.

From this point of view Le Guillou[3] has shown the important modifications and the selection of some physical theories which appear when one takes into account the Hadronic group (working only with SU(2) in his case) in the equations for the autocomposite fields.

Let us consider for instance the case where the nucleon and the pion are scalar particles, but are respectively an isospinor and an isovector. If the nucleons are composite one has the constraint relation

$$GZ_1(\boldsymbol{\tau}\cdot\boldsymbol{\varphi})\psi = \delta\nu_2\psi \tag{7.10}$$

while the pions satisfy the equation

$$Z_3(\Box + \mu^2)\boldsymbol{\varphi} = -\delta\nu_3\boldsymbol{\varphi} + GZ_1(\bar{\psi}\boldsymbol{\tau}\psi) \tag{7.11}$$

Relation (7.10) can only be satisfied if the three pion fields satisfy the constraint

$$\boldsymbol{\varphi}^2 = \Sigma\varphi_i\varphi^i = \left[\frac{\delta\nu_2}{GZ_1}\right]^2 \tag{7.12}$$

which is a large enough condition for the fields to conserve non trivial dynamics. From Eqs. (7.10) and (7.12) we deduce

$$GZ_1(\bar{\psi}\boldsymbol{\tau}\psi) = \left(\frac{G^2Z_1^2}{\delta\nu_2}\right)(\bar{\psi}\psi)\boldsymbol{\varphi} \tag{7.13}$$

The coupling $\bar{\psi}\boldsymbol{\tau}\psi\cdot\boldsymbol{\varphi}$ is replaced by the coupling $\bar{\psi}\psi(\boldsymbol{\varphi})^2$ which results, as in the allocomposite case, of the "contraction" of the composite ψ propagator in the simpler graph for the scattering:

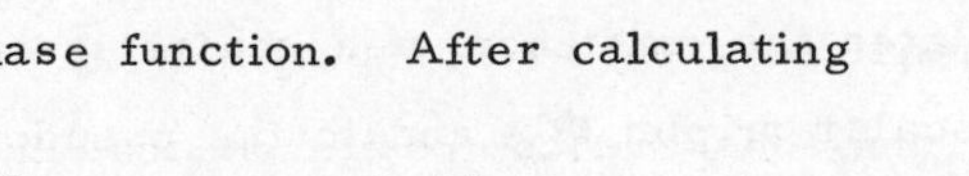

From Eqs. (7.10) and (7.11) we also see that it is possible to express the composite field ψ as an explicit function of the fields φ and of a phase function. After calculating

$$\bar{\psi}\psi = C_1 + C_2\partial_\mu\varphi\partial_\mu\varphi \quad , \quad C_i = \text{constant} \,, \tag{7.14}$$

it is possible to completely eliminate ψ from Eq. (7.11) to obtain the non linear equation for φ:

$$Z_3\left[\Box\boldsymbol{\varphi} + \frac{G^2 Z_1^2}{\delta\nu_2^2}(\partial_\mu\boldsymbol{\varphi}\cdot\partial_\mu\boldsymbol{\varphi})\boldsymbol{\varphi}\right] = 0 \qquad (7.15)$$

Starting now from Eqs. (7.15) and (7.12), which we can now quantize, and from the fact that Z_3 appears only as a factor in the equation for φ, we may think that the limit $Z_3 \to 0$ (taken after $Z_2 = 0$) could be an approach to the study of the "gigogne" fields. For the same reasons we have discussed in section A, the preceding conclusions are not modified if the field ψ is a Dirac spinor instead of being a scalar field while the nature of the "mother" field of pions is not changed. On the contrary if the nature of the "mother" field of pions is modified the structure of the equations is completely changed. For instance if the pions are pseudoscalars, ψ cannot be any more a scalar, but it can be a spinor, a vector, etc. In the case when ψ is a spinor the γ_5 matrix leads to the constraint relation

$$f^2\boldsymbol{\phi}^2 = -(\delta\nu_2)^2 \qquad (7.16)$$

which is impossible or trivial ($f = \delta\nu_2 = 0$).

The addition of a pseudoscalar isosinglet ϕ permits a solution but now the equation for $\boldsymbol{\phi}$ contains non linear terms $(\boldsymbol{\phi}^2)^{-1}$ not very acceptable. Nevertheless this new difficulty may be avoided if one postulates the existence of a scalar isotriplet $\boldsymbol{\varphi}$ added to the pseudoscalar triplet $\boldsymbol{\phi}_\pi$ and to the pseudoscalar singlet ϕ_η. The field equation for φ taking into account the different constraints is a non linear free field equation, similar to Eq. (7.15). Only the equations for the fields ϕ_π and ϕ_η contain currents $(\partial_\mu \varphi \cdot \partial_\mu \varphi)\phi_\pi$ and $(\partial_\mu \varphi \cdot \partial_\mu \varphi)\phi_\eta$, which, using a relation analogous to (7.14), are equivalent (apart from a mass term) to the currents $\phi_\pi \bar{\psi}\psi$ and $\phi_\eta \bar{\psi}\psi$. In this way the field φ which is a matter field in terms of which the nucleons are constructed, does not necessarily correspond to an observable field because it satisfies a free field equation (which is non linear). The question one asks now is whether this curious phenomenon might have some relation with a fundamental property of non observability of quarks?

7.2. "Gigogne" fields. Let us consider the simplest example of the field of a scalar meson in self interaction by the coupling $\lambda\phi^3$. If we impose the condition that the field should be autocomposite we obtain the constraint

$$g\phi^2 = \delta m^2 \phi \qquad (7.17)$$

This relation has only the trivial solution

$$\phi = \text{constant} \qquad (7.18)$$

If we treat the quantum problem in the usual canonical way we obtain (because the conjugate momentum of ϕ is null) that $P_i = 0$, $H \sim \phi$ and then $\dot{\phi}(x, t) \sim i\int dx' \left[\phi(x', t), \phi(x, t)\right] = 0$, which means that the field ϕ does not change with time (as in the classical theory).

But, is it still legitimate to use that formalism in this case? Let us consider independently of the way we obtain it the equation

$\phi^2 \sim \phi$. This equation does not give any information about the space-time structure in which the field is supposed to evolve and the degeneracy we find here is much more fundamental than the one we found in the "oedipien" case where the spin was already arbitrary. One would also like to answer the question of what dynamics can be constructed compatible with the field equation which can be written (by a rescaling) $\phi^2 = 2\phi$ or

$$\psi^2 = (\phi - 1)^2 = 1 \tag{7.19}$$

We shall investigate here the case of only one dimension [4], the time [5], i.e. we shall try to construct the most general time displacement operator H compatible with Eq. (7.19) and defined by

$$\dot{\psi} = i\left[H, \psi\right] \tag{7.20}$$

If such operator exists, then we obtain from Eq. (7.1)

$$\left\{\dot{\psi}, \psi\right\}_+ = 0 \tag{7.21}$$

From this last equation we obtain

$$\left\{\dot{\psi}\psi, \psi\right\}_+ = \left\{\dot{\psi}\psi, \dot{\psi}\right\}_+ = 0 \tag{7.22}$$

From Eq. (7.19) we obtain

$$\left[\dot{\psi}, \psi\right]_- = 2\dot{\psi}\psi$$

$$\left[\dot{\psi}\psi, \dot{\psi}\right]_- = -2\dot{\psi}^2\psi$$

$$\left[\dot{\psi}\psi, \psi\right]_- = 2\dot{\psi}$$

The last of these relations gives then

$$H = -\frac{i}{2}\psi\dot{\psi} + C \ , \quad \text{where} \quad \left[C,\psi\right] = 0 \ , \tag{7.23}$$

Postulating that $H = H(\psi, \dot{\psi})$, which is equivalent to postulate that

$$\psi(t) = e^{iHt}\psi(0)\,e^{-iHt}$$

can be calculated in an unique way when $\psi(0)$ and $\dot{\psi}(0)$ are given, one gets that

$$C = A(\dot{\psi}^2)\psi + B(\dot{\psi}^2) \tag{7.24}$$

where A and B are arbitrary functions of $\dot{\psi}^2$. Then

$$(H - B)^2 = \frac{\dot{\psi}^2}{4} + \left[A(\dot{\psi}^2)\right]^2 = \frac{\left[m(\dot{\psi}^2)\right]^2}{4} \tag{7.25}$$

Since $\left[\dot{\psi}^2, H\right] = 0$ we shall restrict ourselves to a given eigen-space of $\dot{\psi}^2$ in which $\dot{\psi}^2$ is a c-number, and furthermore we shall put $B = 0$ which is equivalent to add a constant to H. Then H has two eigenvalues $\pm \frac{m}{2}$. The lowest one may conventionally be called the "vacuum" and the highest one a particle state of mass m.

The general solution can then be obtained. It is of the form

$$\psi(t) = \sqrt{2m}\ \varphi(t)\cos\theta + \gamma\sin\theta \tag{7.26}$$

where

$$\dot{\psi}^2 = m^2\cos^2\theta$$

$$A = \frac{m}{2}\sin\theta$$

and

$$\varphi(t) = \frac{1}{\sqrt{2m}}(a_+ e^{imt} + a_- e^{-imt}) \tag{7.27}$$

$$\gamma = -2i\dot{\varphi}\varphi = \frac{2}{m} H$$

The general solution $\psi(t)$ is then a superposition of the field φ and its conserved current γ. These last two separately satisfy Eq. (7.19) and are such that $\{\varphi , \gamma\}_+ = 0$. We also have

$$\{a_+ , a_-\}_+ = 1 \quad \text{and} \quad a_+^2 = a_-^2 = 0 \ ,$$

i.e. the φ field follows Fermi statistics, which explains why we have only one particle state (since we have no space dimension).

When trying to construct a Lagrangian from which these equations and the constraints on φ and γ can be deduced, one must first note that the relations $\dot{\varphi} = i[H, \varphi]$ and $H = -2i\dot{\varphi}\varphi$ are invariant under any transformation of coordinates $t = f(t')$ and therefore the Lagrangian must be invariant under this group (which implies the introduction of a "metric" tensor in zero dimension). Furthermore, the field equations being of the Klein-Gordon type, we shall start with the action (written in a covariant form according to our previous discussion)

$$W = \int L \, dx^o \tag{7.28}$$

$$L = L_\varphi + L_G = \frac{e_o}{2}(g^{oo} \varphi_o^2 - m^2 \varphi^2) + \lambda e_o \tag{7.29}$$

where

$$g_{oo} = e_o^2 \ , \quad g^{oo} = (g_{oo})^{-1} \ , \quad \varphi_o = \frac{\partial \varphi}{\partial x^o} \tag{7.30}$$

and $e_o(t)$ is the basic vector operator of the one-dimensional manifold; $L_g = \lambda e_o$ is the metric field Lagrangian and λ an arbitrary constant. Treated classically this Lagrangian leads to

$$H = H_\varphi + H_G \tag{7.31}$$

which is null according to the field equations; this means that the total system (matter + metric) does not change in time, although each component separately changes. In order to observe the manifestations of the evolution of the matter field one has to fix a macroscopic frame and therefore one distinguishes between the microscopic quantum metric field e_o and its macroscopic mean value which we may define as $< 0 | e_o | 0 >$, the normalized vacuum state vector $| 0 >$ being an eigenvector of H. We replace therefore in L the metric part λe_o by $\lambda < 0 | e_o | 0 >$, and treat L as a quantum operator. Nothing is changed in the deduction of the field equations, but then

$$H = \lambda e_o - \lambda < 0 | e_o | 0 >, \quad \text{so that} \quad < 0 | H | 0 > = 0 \tag{7.32}$$

As the classical fields φ and e_o are independent, one may quantize by supposing that either $[\varphi, e_o]_- = 0$ or $\{\varphi, e_o\}_+ = 0$. But the existence of a dynamics for φ implies that $[H, \varphi]_- \neq 0$ and this implies the choice $\{\varphi, e_o\}_+ = 0$. In this way, and provided $\lambda = \frac{m}{2}$ we obtain the desired quantum relations:

$$\varphi^2 = \frac{1}{2m} \tag{7.33}$$

$$\varphi_o^2 = \frac{m}{2} g_{oo} \qquad e_o = -2i \varphi_o \varphi = \gamma$$

We see then that the conserved current of the field φ is also the "current" of time, this last one being then constructed from the field φ. One may furthermore restrict g_{oo} to be a number (as we did for $\dot{\psi}^2$ to which it is proportional) and choose

$$e_o^2 = g_{oo} = 1 \tag{7.34}$$

This example, which is very restricted and unrealistic, shows how "gigogne" field theory might perhaps allow one, when generalized to a larger group, to set the problem of determining why our Universe has the dimensions it has, i.e. if some consistency requirements permits the selection of the Lorentz group (or Lorentz + hadrons group) among all the possible groups.

Although in the case we discussed the scalar field violates the usual spin and statistics relation one should notice that the field itself is not necessarily an observable of our world, but that it could be the matter field out of which are built the composite observable fields (like g_{oo}) which have the correct statistical property. The case discussed in the preceding section gives an example of a mechanism which may explain how this non-observability works.

REFERENCES

1. B. Jouvet and J. C. Le Guillou, Nuovo Cimento 49, 677 (1967). R. L. Zimmerman, Phys. Rev. 141, 1554 (1966).
2. M. Broido and J. C. Taylor, Phys. Rev. 147, 993 (1966).
3. J. C. Le Guillou, Preprint Institut Henri Poincaré, Paris

(June 1967), to be published in Nuovo Cimento.

4. G. Clement and B. Jouvet, Preprint PAM 6703, Paris (June 1967), to be published in Annales de l'Institut Henri Poincaré.

5. For Feynmann rules for models in $L^{o}T^{l}$ see B. Jouvet and E. Tirapegui, Ref. 12 of chapter 3.

EPILOGUE

A PARTICLE THEOCRACY ?

We have seen that the field theoretical approach to composite particles allows one to express in a simple mathematical way the concept that each particle is composed of other particles as well as of itself, no particle being therefore more elementary than the others ("Particle Democracy"). However, it emerges from this approach the possibility that some fields, although being also composite, may play a more fundamental role in the construction of the discrete states of matter, in agreement with the "Aristocratic" concept. Furthermore, it appears that these basic composite fields, with which even the space-time might also have to be constructed (since it would no longer be given a priori by the field equations), are not necessarily directly associated to observable particles. Thus the hierarchy of matter states would be endowed with what one may perhaps call a "Theocratic" structure.

3

SEMINAR

GAUGE INVARIANCE WITH NON ZERO PHOTON BARE MASS+

Bernard Jouvet, Collège de France, Paris

+ Translated into (bad) English from the original French by Dr. Enrique Tirapegui.

1. It has been known for a long time that the expression for the photon vacuum polarization tensor $\langle 0 | T(j_\mu j'_\mu) | 0 \rangle$ calculated in perturbation theory by Feynmann's method is not gauge invariant; it is not even covariant if the T product is explicitly calculated in the form

$$T(\varphi\varphi') = \{\varphi, \varphi'\} + \varepsilon(t - t')[\varphi, \varphi']$$

The first difficulty introduces a self-energy $\delta\mu^2$ (infinite in perturbation theory) of the photon and leads to the following paradox : the self-energy term is a violation in the S matrix of the gauge group which is an invariance group of the Maxwell-Dirac Lagrangian, and if one wants to get rid of that term by a renormalization such that the S matrix is gauge invariant, the counterterm $\delta\mu^2 \varphi_\mu \varphi^\mu$, which violates gauge invariance, should be added to the Lagrangian which ceases then to be invariant under the gauge group. The currently accepted solution of this paradox consists on saying, against all evidence, that $\delta\mu^2$ must be zero. A possible explanation of the non zero value obtained for this term is the ambiguity (∞) of perturbation theory calculations, and indeed regularization makes it vanish. There exists also a "global proof"[1] which states that the bare mass is related to the bare spectral function of the $\delta_{\mu\nu}$ part of the bare propagator of the photon

$$\Delta'(p) = \int \frac{\rho_1^o(a)da}{p^2 + a - i\varepsilon} \qquad (1)$$

by

$$\frac{1}{\mu_o^2} = \int \frac{\rho_1^o(a)}{a} da$$

Since

$$\rho_1^o(a) = Z_3 \delta(a - \mu^2) + \ldots\ldots$$

we have

$$\frac{1}{\mu_o^2} \longrightarrow \frac{Z_3}{\mu^2} + \ldots\ldots \longrightarrow \infty ,$$

if the observable photon mass $\mu^2 \rightarrow 0$.

We do not agree with this point of view, i) because of simple reasons of mathematical coherence which do not seem to us satisfactory; and ii) because of the physical interest presented by the self mass of the photon. In the theory of the composite photon this quantity appears when one expresses the composite electromagnetic potential in terms of the currents of the electrons; furthermore, this quantity can provide, in a way we shall now explain, interesting information about the asymptotic behavior of the photon propagator in view of an exact calculation of the function $Z_3(\alpha)$.

All the methods that have been proposed to calculate the propagators or their asymptotic behavior (i.e. the renormalization constants, in particular Z_3) finally reduce to systems of antirecurrent relations. For instance the two points function is expressed in terms of the three points function (Dyson-Schwinger equations), or in terms of the four points function (Johnson's formalism); but the calculation of these last two quantities needs the calculation of functions of higher order (the same problem appears in the dispersion relations approach). To our knowledge there exists one exception to that kind of method, and it is the following: it is known that the vacuum energy density can be written [2] in the form of an integral over the coupling constant

$$\lambda_o(\alpha) - \lambda_o(\alpha = 0) \sim \int_o^{\alpha} \frac{d\alpha'}{\alpha'} \pi(p^2, \alpha')\, \Delta'(p', \alpha') d^4p \qquad (2)$$

where

$$\Delta' = \frac{\Delta}{1 - \Delta \cdot \pi(p^2, \alpha)}$$

is the dressed unrenormalized propagator of the photon, Δ is the free bare propagator of the photon, and π the vacuum polarization function (for notational convenience we restrict ourselves to the $\delta_{\mu\nu}$ part of these expressions).

The corresponding series of graphs is

$\lambda_o \sim$ 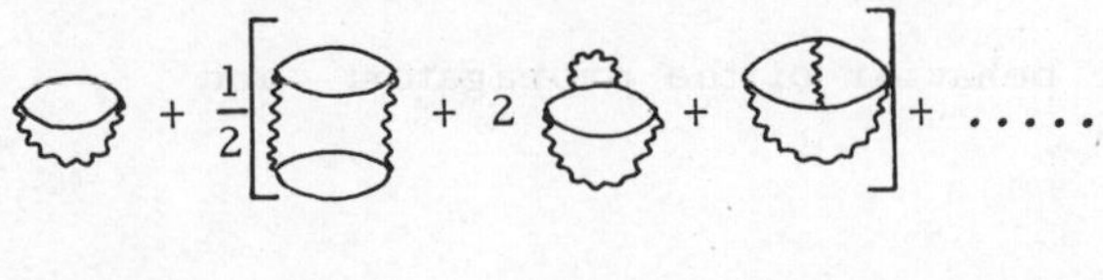

Let us suppose that the system is put in a constant and uniform external potential A_μ; then

$$\pi \longrightarrow \pi(p,\ eA,\ \alpha)$$

and

$$\lambda_o \longrightarrow \lambda_o(eA,\ \alpha)$$

It is then easy to verify that the following relation holds:

$$\left[\frac{\partial \lambda_o(eA,\alpha)}{\partial eA_\mu \partial eA^\mu} - \frac{\partial \lambda_o(eA,0)}{\partial eA_\mu \partial eA^\mu}\right]_{A=0} \sim 2\left(2 \ \text{[diagram]}\right.$$

$$+ \ \text{[diagram]} + 2 \ \text{[diagram]} + \ \text{[diagram]} +$$

$$+ 2 \ \text{[diagram]} + \ \cdots \cdots \bigg)$$

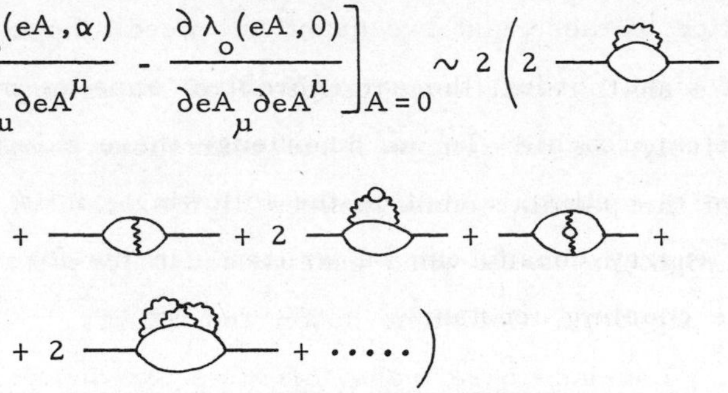

$$= 2\left(\frac{\delta\mu^2(\alpha)}{\alpha} - \left[\frac{\delta\mu^2(\alpha)}{\alpha}\right]_{\alpha=0}\right) \tag{3}$$

Now, if it is possible to justify or prove the following two statements:

i. $\delta\mu^2$ can be expressed by a Lehmann relation,

$$\delta\mu^2 \sim \int \rho(a)a\,da \tag{4}$$

which ensures that it is different from zero (in agreement with perturbation theory) and allows us to relate it to the observable asymptotic behavior of the propagator; and

ii. even though $\delta\mu^2 \neq 0$ the theory is still gauge invariant and in particular there exists a Ward theorem implying that

$$\frac{\partial}{\partial(ieA_\mu)} \sim \frac{\partial}{\partial k_\mu(\text{electron})} , \qquad (5)$$

then, it is easy to see that from relations (2) to (5) it follows a relation, at least formal, between the function $\rho(a,\alpha)$ and its derivative $\frac{\partial\rho(a,\alpha)}{\partial\alpha}$. This relation conduces then to an iterative method of calculation of the asymptotic behavior of $\rho(a,\alpha)$ (Refs. 5, 6).

We shall recall here the proof of statements i. and ii. given, respectively, in references 3 and references 2 and 4, and discuss some of the peculiar consequences of the proof of statement i. which might be useful when generalized to present problems of current algebras, Goldstone boson and PCAC.

I. Lehmann bare mass formulae for the photon[3]. We start from the Lagrangian

$$L = L^o_{\text{Dirac}}(\psi) + L^o_{\text{Maxwell}}(\varphi) + ie\varphi_\mu\bar{\psi}\gamma_\mu\psi - \frac{\mu_o^2}{2}\varphi_\mu\varphi^\mu$$

where the fields and currents are unrenormalized. The field equation is

$$\left[(\Box - \mu_o^2)\delta_{\mu\nu} - \partial_\mu\partial_\nu\right]\varphi_\nu = j_\mu = -ie\bar{\psi}\gamma_\mu\psi$$

$$\partial_\mu j^\mu = 0 \Longrightarrow \mu_o^2\partial_\mu\varphi^\mu = 0$$

A. We first admit covariance for the vacuum expectation values of commutators of φ and J. For instance

$$<0|[\varphi_\mu, \varphi'_\nu]|0> = i\int_0^\infty [\rho_1(a)\delta_{\mu\nu} + \rho_2(a)\partial_\mu\partial_\nu]\Delta(x-x';a)$$

Only the ρ_1 function can be observed with conserved currents, the ρ_2 part not being involved in any observable processes. From $\partial_\mu \varphi_\mu = 0$ we obtain $\rho_1 + a\rho_2 = 0$ which implies $\rho_2 = (-\rho_1/a) + A\delta(a)$ where A is an arbitrary constant which we are not allowed to drop without an explicit physical statement. Its significance is the eventual presence of some zero mass and zero spin boson which, as stated above, cannot be observed. We only know a physical constraint on the $\rho_1(a)$ function which should contain the photon contribution proportional to $\delta(a - \mu_\gamma^2)$, then

$$<0|[\varphi_\mu, \varphi'_\nu]|0> = i\int[\Box^1_{\mu\nu}\frac{\rho_1}{a} - A\delta(a)\partial_\mu\partial_\nu]\Delta$$

$$\Box^1_{\mu\nu} \equiv \Box\delta_{\mu\nu} - \partial_\mu\partial_\nu$$

Similarly one sets

$$<0|[j_\mu, \varphi'_\nu]|0> = i\int\left[\Box^1_{\mu\nu}\left(\frac{\rho_1(a-\mu_o^2)}{a}\right) + A\mu_o^2\delta(a)\partial_\mu\partial_\nu\right]\Delta$$

$$<0|[j_\mu, j'_\nu]|0> = i\int\left[\Box^1_{\mu\nu}\left(\frac{\rho_1}{a}(a-u_o^2)^2\right) - \mu_o^4 A\delta(a)\partial_\mu\partial_\nu\right]\Delta$$

B. We admit now the <u>canonical equal time commutation relations</u> between φ_i, ψ and their conjugate fields ($\pi_i = \partial_4\varphi_i - \partial_i\varphi_4$, and ψ^+) respectively. There follows among the other usual relations the two relations

a) $[j_\mu, \varphi'_j] = 0$

b) $[j_\mu, \pi'_j] = 0$

One also has the identity

$$\text{c)} \quad \partial_i \pi_i = -\left[j_4 + \mu_o^2 \varphi_4 \right]$$

From a) and c) it follows that

$$\text{a')} \quad \left[\varphi_4 , \varphi_j' \right] = \frac{1}{\mu_o^2} \partial_j \delta(\mathbf{x} - \mathbf{x}')$$

From c) and b) it follows

$$< 0 | \left[j_i , \varphi_4' \right] | 0 > = - \frac{1}{\mu_o^2} < 0 | \left[j_i , j_4' \right] | 0 >$$

whereas from a) we get

$$< 0 | \left[j_4 , \varphi_i' \right] | 0 > = 0$$

But as $< 0 | \left[j_\mu , \varphi_\nu' \right] | 0 >$ is symmetric in μ and ν , these last relations can only be true if

$$\text{b')} \quad < 0 | \left[j_\nu , j_4' \right] | 0 > = 0$$

providing μ_o^2 is finite. From b) and c) also results that

$$< 0 | \left[\partial_4 \varphi_i , j_j' \right] | 0 > = - \frac{1}{\mu_o^2} \partial_i < 0 | \left[j_4 , j_j' \right] | 0 > = 0$$

C. The canonical rule implies the following sum rules on the spectral functions ρ_1, ρ_2 (i.e. on ρ_1 and A):

from (a'): $\int \rho_2 da = -1/\mu_o^2$ i.e. $1/\mu_o^2 = A + \int (\rho_1/a)da$

from (b): $\mu_o^2 = \int \rho_1 a da$, i.e. Lehmann's relation,

and it can be checked from these expressions that b') is indeed fulfilled (one has $A\mu_o^4 = - \int (\rho_1/a)(a - \mu_o^2)^2 da$). The constant A is then determined only by a consistency requirement to be satisfied between the field equations and canonical quantization (this result is also consistent with the fact that the physical world cannot give any value for A because this constant is not observable). If A is taken null a priori one gets for μ_o^2 the Johnson sum rule which leads to $\mu_o^2 \rightarrow 0$ when $\mu_\gamma^2 \rightarrow 0$. But such a relation follows only from the constraint A = 0 imposed to the unobservable ρ_2 function.

D. If <u>unitarity</u> is to be imposed this should be done on observable processes: i.e. $\rho_1 \geqslant 0$. Then $A < 0$ and the zero mass, zero spin boson of the theory is an unobservable ghost acting like a gauge field. This explains why one may have $< 0 | j_o H j_o | 0 > = 0$, $(ij_o = j_4)$, which follows from (b'). An explicit calculation shows furthermore that the relation (b') for $\nu = 1$ can be written as

$$(b') \sim e^2 \delta(x - x') < 0 | \bar{\psi}\gamma_i \psi' - \bar{\psi}'\gamma_i \psi | 0 > = 0$$

This is not an identity since $< 0 | \bar{\psi}\gamma_i \psi' | 0 >$ contain odd and singular functions of $(x - x')$; it is rather a condition which reads, in terms of observable quantities,

$$\frac{\alpha_{obs} Z_1^2}{Z_2 Z_3} \partial_i \delta(x) \int \sigma_1^{ren}(a) \Delta_1(x, a) da = 0 \ ,$$

$\sigma_1(a)$ being the $\gamma\delta$ part of the weight function of the electron propagator. If unitarity is to be fulfilled such a condition leads necessarily to $Z_1 = 0$. We do not know whether this is an identity (perhaps depending on the particular gauge selected by the A gauge field) or a condition (for instance of compositeness of the electron) that has to be imposed to make quantum electrodynamics consistent.

E. From the expression of the commutators of the φ_μ field one can construct the photon propagator, and if we admit that the unsubtracted <u>vacuum polarization tensor</u> $\pi_{\mu\nu}(p)$ can be deduced from the propagator by Dyson's equation we get the surprising result

$$\pi_{\mu\nu}(p) = \left(\delta_{\mu\nu} - \frac{p_\mu p_\nu}{p^2 - i\varepsilon}\right) U(p^2)$$

where

$$U(0) = \mu_o^2 - \frac{1}{\int(\rho_1/a)da} \neq 0$$

We see that $\pi_{\mu\nu}(p)$ has formally a gauge invariant form, contains the pole of the ghost scalar particle, and is then different from the perturbation theory expression.

In perturbation theory we get to first order the expression (which is not gauge invariant and not covariant):

$$\pi_{\mu\nu}^{(pert)} = -(p^2\delta_{\mu\nu} - p_\mu p_\nu)\int\frac{K^{(pert)}}{p^2 + a - i\varepsilon}da$$

$$+ (\delta_{\mu\nu} - \delta_{\mu 4}\delta_{\nu 4})\int K_1^{(pert)} da$$

To the same order we get from the global result given above

$$\pi_{\mu\nu} = -(p^2\delta_{\mu\nu} - p_\mu p_\nu)\int \frac{K^{(pert)}}{p^2 + a - i\varepsilon} da + (\delta_{\mu\nu} - \frac{p_\mu p_\nu}{p^2 - i\varepsilon})\int K_1^{(pert)} da$$

We see then that the $\delta_{\mu 4}\delta_{\nu 4}$ term of perturbation theory is replaced by $p_\mu p_\nu/(p^2 - i\varepsilon)$. We believe that the inconsistency of perturbation theory comes precisely from the fact that condition (b'), which ensures Lorentz covariance and implies $Z_1 = 0$, is obviously violated in each order of perturbation theory.

2. <u>A formulation of gauge invariance for Electrodynamics with non zero photon bare mass.</u>[4,5] Without overlooking the photon self energy problem we would like to construct a "good" photon Lagrangian such that the resulting S matrix is the "good" one, namely: the observed photon mass is null and the Ward relations are valid.

It is known that Ward relations can be demonstrated formally from the existence of the gauge invariance group [(1) + (2)] of the field equations

$$\begin{cases} (1) \quad \varphi_\mu \longrightarrow \varphi_\mu + \partial_\mu \phi = \boldsymbol{\varphi}_\mu \\ (2) \quad \psi(x) \longrightarrow \psi(x) e^{ie\phi(x)} = \boldsymbol{\psi}(x) \end{cases}$$

This invariance group means physically that the S matrix of a system in a gauge field $\partial_\mu \phi$ can be obtained from the S matrix corresponding to the system in vacuum (in absence of a gauge field) if one modifies the phase of Fermions according to the group [(1) + (2)] , i.e.

$$S(\psi, \ldots\ldots; \varphi_\mu + \partial_\mu \phi) = S(\psi e^{-ie\phi}, \ldots\ldots; \varphi)$$

The usual Maxwell-Dirac Lagrangian $L_{M.D.}$ is invariant under this group but the addition of a photon mass term to $L_{M.D.}$ destroys this invariance. Without worrying for the moment about this obvious difficulty let us first construct the explicit "good" Lagrangian defined above in the case when $\phi = A_\mu x^\mu$, and see later why this "good" Lagrangian is gauge invariant in agreement with the general theorem stated above.

Looking first to lowest order perturbation theory (i. e. using the bare propagator of the electron) we find successively in the S matrix various terms which violate gauge invariance which can be eliminated by adding suitable counterterms in L. They are

1. The vacuum expectation value $< j_\mu >_o$ which is usually not null and requires a counterterm of the form $\lambda_1^{(0)\mu} \varphi_\mu$,

2. The photon self-energy term which requires a counterterm of the form $\lambda_2^{(0)\mu\nu} \varphi_\mu \varphi_\nu$,

3. The photon-photon interaction term which is not gauge invariant in spite of the fact that it is finite (to lowest order in α_o the counterterm $\lambda_4^{(0)} (\varphi_\mu \varphi^\mu)^2$ with $\lambda_4^{(0)} = \frac{1}{3!} \alpha_o^2$ is necessary to render the photon-photon scattering amplitude gauge invariant). Note that if this counterterm is not included the Ward identity $Z_1 = Z_2$ would not be satisfied (due to the graph 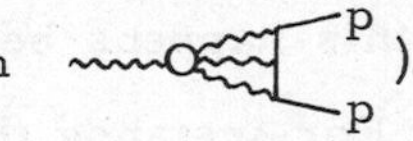).

The three constants we have introduced can easily be obtained computing the expression

$$< 0 | j_\mu^\phi | 0 > \; = \; i e \lim_{\xi \to 0} \; Tr < 0 | \bar{\psi}(x) \gamma_\mu \psi(x+\xi) | 0 >$$

$$< 0 | j_\mu^\phi | 0 > \; = \; i e \lim_{\xi \to 0} \; Tr < 0 | \bar{\psi} \gamma_\mu \psi(x+\xi) | 0 >$$

where $\bar{\psi}$ is given by (2). In the computation it is necessary to use

$$<0|\,\mathrm{Tr}\left[\bar{\Psi}(0)\gamma_\mu \psi(\xi)\right]|\,0> = 4\frac{\partial}{\partial \xi}\Delta_1(\xi^2)$$

and do the appropriate average over the space-time angles (i.e. $\xi_\mu \xi_\nu f(\xi^2) = \frac{i}{4}\delta_{\mu\nu}\xi^2 f(\xi^2)$) as it is usually done in Feynmann symmetrical integration.

The interaction terms involving more than four external photon fields are gauge invariant without subtractions (the parts which are not gauge invariant go to zero when $\xi^2 \to 0$). The non gauge invariant parts of the N photons interaction term can be suppressed eliminating the only non gauge invariant term coming from the bare electron propagator closed loop, because after this subtraction the closure of external lines does not affect the gauge invariance of the tensor. Therefore the "good" Lagrangian we are looking for takes the form (after subtraction of the vacuum energy density λ_o):

$$L = L_{\mathrm{M.D.}} + \sum_{i=0} \lambda^i [\varphi]^i$$

Let us now explain why this "good" Lagrangian is invariant under the group $[(1) + (2)]$. Although each term in $\sum_{i=0} \lambda^i [\varphi]^i$ violates separately the group (1) + (2), the sum $\sum_i \lambda_i [\varphi]^i$ is invariant under the group, and this happens because the "constants" λ_i depend on the spinor gauge. For instance the "constant"

$$\lambda_2^{\mu\nu} \sim \int d^4p\, \gamma_\mu S(p)\gamma^\mu S(p) \sim$$ 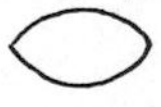

takes the new value

$$\boldsymbol{\lambda}_2^{\mu\nu} \sim \int d^4p\, \gamma_\mu \boldsymbol{S}_A(p)\gamma^\mu \boldsymbol{S}_A(p)$$

with $\mathbf{S}_A(p) = S(p+ieA)$ when we make the change $\psi \rightarrow \boldsymbol{\psi}_A = e^{ieA_\mu x^\mu}\psi$, and this displacement of variables in a quadratically divergent integral gives $\boldsymbol{\lambda}_2(A) = \lambda_2 + cA_\mu A^\mu$, where c = finite constant. The gauge invariance of L is then expressed by

$$\sum_i \lambda_i [\varphi]^i = \sum_i \boldsymbol{\lambda}_i(A)\,[\varphi + A]^i$$

and from this expression one can easily check that indeed

$$\boldsymbol{\lambda}_2(A) - \lambda_2 \sim \lambda_4 A_\mu A^\mu$$

By a similar argument it is also possible to deduce in general all the "constants" λ_i, $i \geqslant 1$, from the expressions of $\boldsymbol{\lambda}_o(A)$ or $\boldsymbol{\lambda}_1(A)$ and in particular the relation

$$\mu_o^2 \sim \left.\frac{\delta \boldsymbol{\lambda}_o(A)}{\delta A_\mu\, \delta A^\mu}\right|_{A=0} \sim \left.\frac{\delta}{\delta A_\mu}\boldsymbol{\lambda}_1^\mu(A)\right|_{A=0}$$

Going back to a previous relation obtained from $\left[j_i, \partial_4 \varphi_i\right] = 0$ one may define the gauge invariant true bare mass

$$\underline{\mu_o^2} = \int \rho_1 \, a da = -\left(\lambda^\mu_{2\mu} - \frac{1}{2!}\frac{4!}{3}\lambda^{\mu\nu}_{4\mu}\, \rho < 0|\varphi_\nu \varphi_o|0> + \ldots\right)$$

We can now rewrite

$$L_{int} = -ie\bar{\psi}\gamma_\mu \psi \varphi_\mu + \sum \lambda_i [\varphi_i]$$

using Wick products in the form

$$L_{int} = -ie : \bar{\psi}\gamma_\mu \psi \varphi_\mu : -\underline{\mu}_o^2 : \varphi_\mu \varphi_\mu : - \underline{\lambda}_4 : \varphi_\mu \varphi^\mu \varphi_\nu \varphi_\nu : - \ldots$$

where the constants $\underline{\mu}_o^2$ and $\underline{\lambda}_4$ are gauge invariant constants. Due to the fact that $\lambda_6 \sim \xi^2$ and $(\varphi^2)_o - \Delta_F(0) \sim (1/\xi^2)_o$ the constant $\underline{\lambda}_4 = \lambda_4 + (\sim \lambda_6(\varphi^2)_o) + \ldots$ can be different from the first order value $\alpha_o^2/3!$; on the contrary the constant $\underline{\lambda}_6 = \lambda_6 + (\sim \lambda_8(\varphi^2)_o) + \ldots$ remains of the order of $\xi^2 \to 0$. Furthermore the renormalizability of the photon S matrix (which is precisely the S matrix resulting exactly from our "good" Lagrangian) implies that the constants of the type λ_{2n}, $n \geqslant 3$, which have dimension M^{-2n+4} are null.

REFERENCES

1. K. Johnson, Nucl. Phys. 25, 433 (1961).
2. See list of references in Ref. 4a.
3. B. Jouvet, Nuovo Cimento 26, 283 (1962).

4a. B. Jouvet, Comptes Rendus Acad. Sc. Paris 251, 1116 (1960).

4b. B. Jouvet, Nuovo Cimento 20, 28 (1961).

5. B. Jouvet, Nuovo Cimento 25, 135 (1962).
6. M. Astaud and B. Jouvet, Comptes Rendus Acad. Sc. Paris 263B, 107 (1966).

4

ALGEBRAS IN HADRON PHYSICS[+]

Yuval Ne'eman, Tel-Aviv University, Israel[++]

+ Preliminary notes of these lectures were taken by Messrs. C. A. López and Hernán Quintana.

++ Sponsored in part by the Air Force Office of Scientific Research under Grant AF EOAR 66-39 through the European Office of Aerospace Research (OAR) United States Air Forces.

The algebraic approach to high-energy Physics has undergone a rapid development since 1961. The remarkable successes achieved so far have shown the predictive powers of this method and supplied a coherent picture, which enables us to say that these ideas will indeed be a part of the final future theory.

Two essentially different toolkits are currently used in Elementary Particles Theory, one analytic and the other one algebraic. The former claims that it is possible to get all the physical information out of the analytical structure of the S-matrix. On the other hand, the algebraic approach emphasizes the symmetries of the interactions as a clue towards the establishment of a dynamical theory. As a matter of fact this point of view is not new as we recall that the original formulation of Quantum Mechanics by Heisenberg was a matrix-algebra formalism. The little attention that was further paid to this method might perhaps be explained as a conservative attitude of physicists against the introduction of new techniques: after all, classical mechanics and electrodynamics were mainly based upon differential equations.

1. UNITARY SYMMETRY. SU(3)

1.1. THE THEORY.[1,2] Between the forties and the sixties our understanding of the strongly interacting particles (hadrons) evolved mainly through the discovery of an appropriate set of dynamical variables (observables). Starting from them, an algebraic scheme suitable for the description of hadron interactions was established, without attempting to give any "fundamental" explanation for their origin. From this scheme the following basic results were obtained:

a) Classification of particles. The host of new particles or resonances that emerged by 1961 provided an experimental basis for the identification of the algebraic pattern which fitted them. They could be assigned to irreducible representations of a symmetry group. An analogous situation was the discovery by Mendeleyev of the periodic table of the elements. This became possible after a large amount of experimental facts about the chemical properties of many substances has been accumulated. In both cases the classification permitted the correct prediction of some missing particles with specified properties. In fact, we had one complete octet and an incomplete one (7/8) when we identified the group. We now have at least six complete multiplets!

b) Conservation laws. They were established starting from a set of selection rules observed in a lot of reactions. These conservation laws need not be exact. Consider for instance the situation in Chemistry where we can talk of the existence of 92 conservation laws which are exact as far as chemical reactions are concerned. These laws are no longer valid in Nuclear Physics where we deal with energies a thousand times larger.

In Quantum Mechanics a conservation law is expressed by

$$\dot{Q} = i\left[H , Q\right] = 0$$

This equation tells us also that the Hamiltonian is invariant under the transformation generated by the hermitian operator Q. The set of all these Q_i operators defines under commutation a Lie Algebra and by exponentiation the associated Lie Group or Symmetry.

c) Intensity rules. They come out from the comparison of two processes related by a transformation of the group. Their cross sections are then compared by means of Clebsch-Gordan coefficients. An example of this situation is given by the baryon-pseudoscalar meson vertices. In Lagrangian form, these used to be expressed as (see any pre 1962 textbook) as

$$L = g_1 \bar{N}\boldsymbol{\tau} \cdot \boldsymbol{\pi} N + g_2 \bar{\boldsymbol{\Sigma}} \Lambda \cdot \boldsymbol{\pi} + \ldots + g_8 \ldots$$

We used to have eight independent coupling constants since the η wasn't yet known. We would now need twelve such g_i. Unitary Symmetry reduces these constants to two.

d) Non-strong interactions. Electromagnetic and Weak Interactions violate the symmetry in a definite and simple way allowing us to make statements also about them.

e) Mass-spectrum. This is also accounted for assuming a definite transformation law for the mass splitting interaction.

f) Universality properties. It is possible in some cases to make absolute calculations. To see how this can be done consider the case of forward Coulomb scattering, where the complete strength at zero momentum transfer is essentially determined by the charge.

Similarly, the assumption of a local SU(3) gauge yields universal couplings for the strong interactions, in the limit of zero-mass vector-meson mediators. This picture can be replaced by one in which the physical (massive) vector mesons have approximately universal couplings, with a derivation based upon dispersion relations. There is also some more recent hope of an exactly universal coupling --to Regge trajectories instead of just to the spin-one mesons.

The Mass-Spectrum shows that SU(3) is a badly violated symmetry. Nevertheless it is still possible to define in a precise way the exact symmetry limit. This is done by specifying that the generators of SU(3) commute with the space-time generators (Poincaré group) in the limit of zero breaking

$$[SU(3), P]_{(H_8 \to 0)} \longrightarrow 0$$

where H_8 is the breaking term. Beyond SU(3) this idealized limit no longer exists. In the case of "spin-unitary spin" SU(6) for instance, the spin generators belong to both SU(6) and P. Therefore SU(3) is the largest "internal" symmetry.

Recent experiments have shown that SU(3) is not so badly broken as was originally thought. The two couplings $(\overline{N}K\Lambda)$ and $(\overline{N}\pi N)$ now appear to be of the same order of magnitude and correctly related by the group[3] in contradiction with previous experimental evidence. A similar situation is presented with the decay of $Y_1^*(1385)$, where both the $\Lambda\pi$ and $\Sigma\pi$ modes have now been observed with a branching ratio in fairly good agreement[4] with the predictions of SU(3).

Moreover, recent fits to high-energy meson-baryon and baryon-baryon elastic scattering also display "exact" SU(3) symmetry[5].

1.2. THE ABSTRACT ALGEBRA. The group SU(3) is the set of all unitary unimodular 3 x 3 matrices.

For the corresponding Lie Algebra we use the following set of 8 traceless hermitian matrices, with the notation first introduced by Gell-Mann:

$$\lambda_1 = \begin{bmatrix} 0 & 1 & 0 \\ 1 & 0 & 0 \\ 0 & 0 & 0 \end{bmatrix} \qquad \lambda_2 = \begin{bmatrix} 0 & -i & 0 \\ i & 0 & 0 \\ 0 & 0 & 0 \end{bmatrix}$$

$$\lambda_3 = \begin{bmatrix} 1 & 0 & 0 \\ 0 & -1 & 0 \\ 0 & 0 & 0 \end{bmatrix} \qquad \lambda_4 = \begin{bmatrix} 0 & 0 & 1 \\ 0 & 0 & 0 \\ 1 & 0 & 0 \end{bmatrix}$$

$$\lambda_5 = \begin{bmatrix} 0 & 0 & -i \\ 0 & 0 & 0 \\ i & 0 & 0 \end{bmatrix} \qquad \lambda_6 = \begin{bmatrix} 0 & 0 & 0 \\ 0 & 0 & 1 \\ 0 & 1 & 0 \end{bmatrix}$$

$$\lambda_7 = \begin{bmatrix} 0 & 0 & 0 \\ 0 & 0 & -i \\ 0 & i & 0 \end{bmatrix} \qquad \lambda_8 = \frac{1}{\sqrt{3}}\begin{bmatrix} 1 & 0 & 0 \\ 0 & 1 & 0 \\ 0 & 0 & -2 \end{bmatrix} \tag{1.1}$$

From (1.1) by explicit calculation one gets:

$$\mathrm{Tr}(\lambda_i \lambda_j) = 2\delta_{ij} \tag{1.2}$$

$$\left[\lambda_i , \lambda_j\right] = 2 i f_{ijk} \lambda_k \tag{1.3}$$

The normalization (1.2) used in (1.1) has now become traditional, although it implies remembering that the abstract or physical group generators (for <u>any</u> representation) is then taken as $F_i \sim \frac{1}{2}\lambda_i$ [Compare (1.3) with (3.1)].

The structure constants f_{ijk} are real and totally antisymmetric as can be seen from the equality

$$T_r \lambda_k [\lambda_i , \lambda_j] = 4if_{ijk} \tag{1.4}$$

which is obtained directly from Eqs. (1.2) and (1.3).

Beside the commutation relations (1.3) among the λ's which define the algebra and are independent of the representation, one can also write the anticommutation relations

$$\{\lambda_i , \lambda_j\} = 2d_{ijk}\lambda_k + \frac{4}{3}\delta_{ij} \tag{1.5}$$

Here the real constants d_{ijk} are not algebraic coefficients because the anticommutator does not belong to the Lie Algebra. Therefore Eq. (1.5) is only true for the particular choice (1.1) of the λ-matrices rather than for any SU(3) representation. The d_{ijk} are symmetric in all three indices on account of the relation

$$T_r \lambda_k \{\lambda_i , \lambda_j\} = 4d_{ijk} \tag{1.6}$$

obtained from Eqs. (1.2) and (1.5).

It is of great importance to notice that Eqs. (1.4) and (1.6) are the only two scalar products which can be formed with three λ-matrices. Later on we shall see that this fact corresponds to the two possible couplings "F" and "D" among three octets.

The matrices λ_1, λ_2, λ_3 define the isotopic-spin SU(2) subgroup. In fact one has

$$I_x = \frac{1}{2}\lambda_1 \quad , \quad I_y = \frac{1}{2}\lambda_2 \quad , \quad I_z = \frac{1}{2}\lambda_3 \tag{1.7}$$

with the diagonal matrix λ_3 standing for the conserved z-component of the isotopic spin. The matrix λ_8 is also diagonal and commutes with the isotopic spin matrices. It represents an observable which is identified with the hypercharge,

$$Y = \frac{1}{\sqrt{3}}\lambda_8 = \begin{bmatrix} 1/3 & 0 & 0 \\ 0 & 1/3 & 0 \\ 0 & 0 & -2/3 \end{bmatrix} \tag{1.8}$$

The factor $1/\sqrt{3}$ will be explained later on. The charge states are obtained by substituting in the formula of Gell-Mann and Nishijima:

$$Q = e(I_z + \frac{1}{2}Y) \quad , \tag{1.9}$$

I_z by $\frac{1}{2}\lambda_3$ and Y by $\frac{1}{\sqrt{3}}\lambda_8$. The result is the charge matrix Q

$$Q = \frac{1}{2}e(\lambda_3 + \frac{1}{\sqrt{3}}\lambda_8) = e\begin{bmatrix} 2/3 & 0 & 0 \\ 0 & -1/3 & 0 \\ 0 & 0 & -1/3 \end{bmatrix} \tag{1.10}$$

Although no known elementary particle belongs to the fundamental representation of SU(3) given by (1.1), (1.8) and (1.10) the physical content of the Lie Algebra is best presented by introducing three hypothetical particles ("quarks") which may or may not exist.

They belong to the eigenstates of the matrices Y and Q which have been normalized in a convenient way in order to get the correct physical values for the known particles that are accommodated in higher order representations. The three quark states will be designated by the symbols u, d, s. Their hypercharge y and charge q are then

$$u\left(y=\frac{1}{3},\ q=\frac{2}{3}e\right),\quad d\left(y=\frac{1}{3},\ q=-\frac{1}{3}e\right),$$

$$s\left(y=-\frac{2}{3},\ q=-\frac{1}{3}e\right) \tag{1.11}$$

The baryonic number is given by the unit matrix λ_o which does not belong to SU(3) but to U(3). Normalizing λ_o to the same length as the other λ's (see Eq. 1.2), one gets

$$\lambda_o = \sqrt{\frac{2}{3}}\begin{bmatrix} 1 & 0 & 0 \\ 0 & 1 & 0 \\ 0 & 0 & 1 \end{bmatrix} \tag{1.12}$$

and the baryonic number turns out to be

$$B = \frac{1}{\sqrt{6}}\lambda_o = \begin{bmatrix} 1/3 & 0 & 0 \\ 0 & 1/3 & 0 \\ 0 & 0 & 1/3 \end{bmatrix} \tag{1.13}$$

where the factor $\frac{1}{\sqrt{6}}$ has been inserted in order to get the correct physical values for the known particles. All three quarks have therefore the baryonic number 1/3, i.e. we shall regard the physical baryons as three-quark products.

<u>Rank, root and weight diagrams.</u> In any semisimple Lie Algebra it is possible to select as a basis a set of commuting operators ω_i and raising and lowering operators ω_ξ which satisfy the commutation relations

$$\left[\omega_i , \omega_\xi\right] = \Delta_i(\xi)\omega_\xi = \left[\boldsymbol{\Delta}_i \cdot \boldsymbol{\omega}(\xi)\right]\omega_\xi \qquad (1.14)$$

where the number $\Delta_i(\xi)$ is the i-component of the root vector $\boldsymbol{\omega}(\xi)$, $\boldsymbol{\Delta}_i$ being a unit vector in the i-direction.

The number ℓ of commuting operators is called the rank of the algebra. The root vectors span an ℓ-dimensional space, which for SU(3) becomes a plane because we have two commuting operators Y and I_z. These vectors can always be represented by diagonal matrices in a certain basis. The operators ω_ξ for SU(3) are linear combinations of the λ's.

The corresponding matrices are

$$I^+ = \begin{bmatrix} 0 & 1 & 0 \\ 0 & 0 & 0 \\ 0 & 0 & 0 \end{bmatrix}, \quad I^- = \begin{bmatrix} 0 & 0 & 0 \\ 1 & 0 & 0 \\ 0 & 0 & 0 \end{bmatrix},$$

$$U^+ = \begin{bmatrix} 0 & 0 & 0 \\ 0 & 0 & 1 \\ 0 & 0 & 0 \end{bmatrix}, \quad U^- = \begin{bmatrix} 0 & 0 & 0 \\ 0 & 0 & 0 \\ 0 & 1 & 0 \end{bmatrix},$$

$$V^+ = \begin{bmatrix} 0 & 0 & 0 \\ 0 & 0 & 0 \\ 1 & 0 & 0 \end{bmatrix}, \quad V^- = \begin{bmatrix} 0 & 0 & 1 \\ 0 & 0 & 0 \\ 0 & 0 & 0 \end{bmatrix} \qquad (1.15)$$

and their commutations relations with Y and I_z (see Eqs. 1.7 and 1.8) are

$$\left[I_z, I^{\pm}\right] = \pm I^{\pm} \quad , \quad \left[Y, I^{\pm}\right] = 0$$

$$\left[I_z, U^{\pm}\right] = \mp \frac{1}{2} U^{\pm} \quad , \quad \left[Y, U^{\pm}\right] = \pm U^{\pm} \qquad (1.16)$$

$$\left[I_z, V^{\pm}\right] = \mp \frac{1}{2} V^{\pm} \quad , \quad \left[Y, V^{\pm}\right] = \mp V^{\pm}$$

These relations are graphically represented in the root diagram of Fig. 1

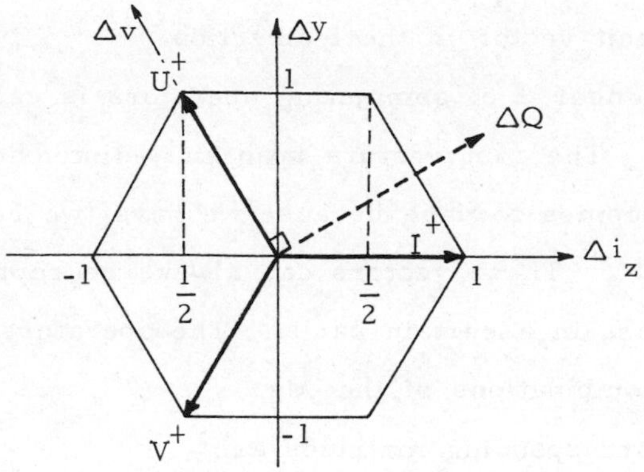

Fig. 1

This diagram shows that there are three SU(2) subgroups whose raising operators are separated by angles of 120°. They define three spins, i.e. the I-spin, the U-spin and the V-spin. The axis of electric charge is also shown in Fig. 1 at a right angle from the U-axis.

The root diagram characterizes completely the algebra considered. In a given representation the basis vectors $|\omega_1' \ldots \omega_\ell'\rangle$ become eigenvectors of the commuting operators ω_i

$$\omega_i \,|\, \omega_1' \ldots \omega_\ell' \rangle = \omega_i' \,|\, \omega_1' \ldots \omega_\ell' \rangle \,, \qquad (1.17)$$

the ℓ eigenvalues ω_i' can be considered as components of a vector in an ℓ-dimensional space. This vector is referred to as the weight of the state $|\omega_1' \ldots \omega_\ell'>$. The heads of all weight vectors correspond to the eigenstates of the system. These points build the so-called weight diagram of the representation and their number is equal to the dimension of the representation.

A weight is said to be greater than another if the first non-vanishing difference of their components is positive. In every representation there is one weight $\mathbf{\Lambda}$ which is the highest and characterizes it completely. Cartan showed that there are ℓ fundamental representations defining ℓ fundamental weights $\mathbf{\Lambda}_i$. The highest weight of any other irreducible representation is given as a linear combination of the ℓ fundamental weights with non-negative integer coefficients

$$\mathbf{\Lambda} = \sum_{i=1}^{\ell} \lambda_i \mathbf{\Lambda}_i \tag{1.18}$$

One designates every irreducible representation of SU(3) as $D^d(\lambda, \mu)$ where d is the dimension and λ, μ are the coefficients of the highest weight in the above expansion, namely

$$\mathbf{\Lambda} = \lambda \mathbf{\Lambda}_1 + \mu \mathbf{\Lambda}_2 \tag{1.19}$$

and the dimension d is given by

$$d = \frac{1}{2}(\lambda + 1)(\mu + 1)(\lambda + \mu + 2) \tag{1.20}$$

With the notation of U(3) one has

$$\lambda = h_1 - h_2 \qquad \mu = h_2 - h_3 \tag{1.21}$$

the fundamental weights being linear combinations of I_z, Y, B and given by

$$H_1 = I_Z + \frac{1}{2}Y + B$$

$$H_2 = -I_Z + \frac{1}{2}Y + B \qquad (1.22)$$

$$H_3 = -Y + B$$

whence the baryonic number becomes

$$B = \frac{1}{3}\sum h_i \qquad (1.23)$$

and the coefficients of the highest weight are

$$\lambda = 2\, i_Z \qquad \mu = 2\, u_Z \qquad (1.24)$$

<u>Fundamental representations of SU(3).</u> The set (1.1) of λ-matrices which define the SU(3) algebra gives us one of the fundamental representations of dimension three, namely the quark representation $D^{(3)}(1,0) \equiv 3$. The basis vector are the quark states u, d, s and the corresponding weight diagram, obtained by means of the relations

$$I_Z\,|\,u> = \frac{1}{2}\,|\,u> \quad , \quad Y\,|\,u> = \frac{1}{3}\,|u>$$

$$I_Z\,|\,d> = -\frac{1}{2}\,|\,d> \quad , \quad Y\,|\,d> = \frac{1}{3}\,|\,d> \qquad (1.25)$$

$$I_Z\,|\,s> = 0 \quad , \quad Y\,|\,s> = -\frac{2}{3}\,|\,s>$$

is plotted in Fig. 2.

$D^{(3)}(1,0) \equiv 3$

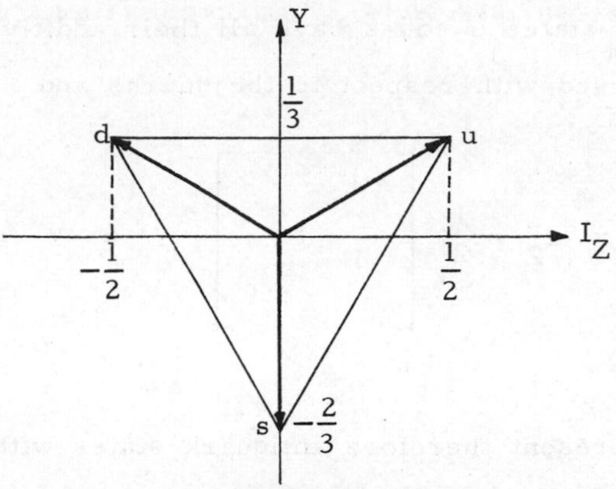

Fig. 2

The highest weight is $\Lambda(\frac{1}{2}, \frac{1}{3}) = (1,0) = u$.

The other fundamental representation $D^{(3)}(0,1)$ is the conjugate or contragradient $\bar{3}$. This representation is defined by taking the transpose of the λ-matrices with minus sign

$$\lambda_i' = -\tilde{\lambda}_i \tag{1.26}$$

whence the weight diagram becomes

$D^{(3)}(0,1) \equiv \bar{3}$

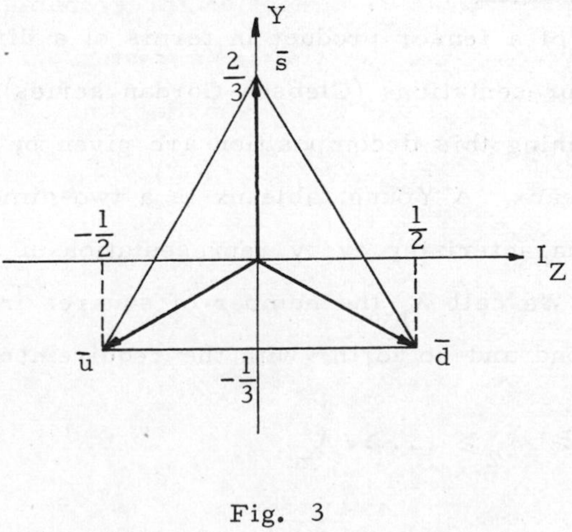

Fig. 3

where the new states $\bar{u}$, $\bar{d}$, $\bar{s}$ have all their additive quantum numbers reversed with respect to the quarks and

$$I'_Z = -I^{\sim}_Z = \frac{1}{2}\begin{bmatrix} -1 & & \\ & 1 & \\ & & 0 \end{bmatrix} \qquad Y' = -Y^{\sim} = \begin{bmatrix} -\frac{1}{3} & & \\ & -\frac{1}{3} & \\ & & \frac{2}{3} \end{bmatrix}$$

(1.27)

They represent therefore antiquark states with a highest weight $\bar{S} = (0, 1)$.

This representation can also be defined as the antisymmetric part of the tensor product of the quark representation by itself. This is due to the fact that the complete antisymmetric part of three quark states is a scalar, so that the antisymmetric product of two quarks cancels a quarks. Explicitly

$$3 \otimes 3 = \underset{s}{6} \oplus \underset{a.s.}{\bar{3}} \tag{1.28}$$

Young tableaux. Equation (1.28) is a particular case of the decomposition of a tensor product in terms of a direct sum of irreducible representations (Clebsch-Gordan series). The general rules for obtaining this decomposition are given by the techniques of Young tableaux. A Young tableaux is a two-dimensional array of squares, characterizing every representation of a particular group SU(n). We call λ_1 the number of squares in the first line, λ_2 in the second and so forth, with the requirement

$$\lambda_1 \geqslant \lambda_2 \geqslant \ldots \geqslant \lambda_n \tag{1.29}$$

as shown in Fig. 4:

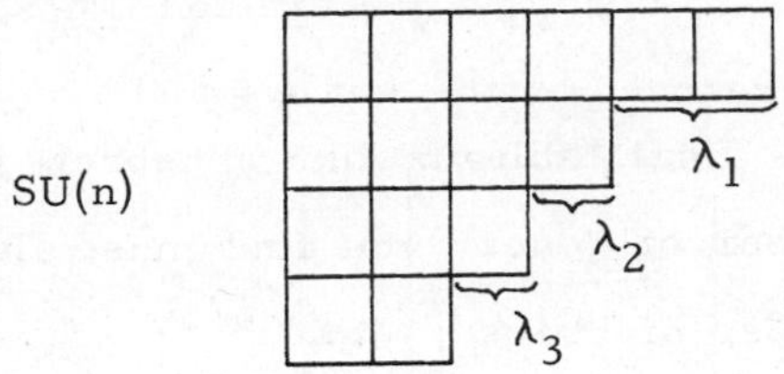

Fig. 4

Every square stands for one index of the tensor defining the representation. This tensor is completely symmetric in all indices lying in a row, completely antisymmetric in all indices within a column. The fundamental representation 3 of SU(3) is characterized by only one square □ and $\overline{3}$ by a column of two squares ⊟. A column with n squares in SU(n) is equivalent to the identical representation $(0, 0, \ldots, 0) \equiv 1$, and can be suppressed. Therefore in the case of SU(3) all Young tableaux have only two lines with λ_1 and λ_2 squares, where

$$\lambda_1 = \lambda + \mu \qquad \lambda_2 = \mu \tag{1.30}$$

with λ and μ defined in Eq. (1.24).

Rules for multiplying tableaux. To obtain the Clebsch-Gordan series of the tensor product of two representations the procedure is as follows: take the first tableau and add to it as many squares as are contained in the second one. Label all squares of the first line of the second tableau with a "1", the corresponding ones of the second line with a "2" and so forth. There are many different ways of inserting the blocks, one at a time. Some of them are eliminated according to the following rules:

1) No row of the final tableaux should be shorter than the lower ones.

2) If you read the final tableaux like a hebrew journal (from right to left), the number of "ones" you find must always be at least equal to the number of "twos", etc.

$$n_1 \geqslant n_2 \geqslant \cdots \tag{1.31}$$

all along the entire path.

3) Reading each row separately in a latin order, the value of the indices you find must not disminish.

4) If you finally read each column separately in a chinese way (top to bottom) you should not find the same index more than once, and the indices should increase.

The remaining tableaux give us the required decomposition.

To see how these rules work let us calculate again the decomposition of $3 \otimes 3$ (see Eq. 1.28)

$$(1,0) \otimes (1,0) \qquad (2,0) \oplus (0,1)$$

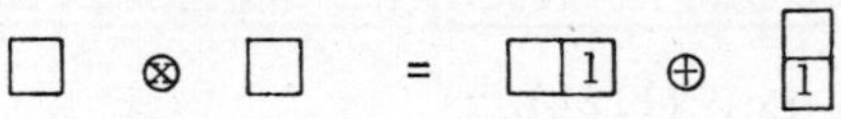

$$3 \otimes 3 = 6 \oplus \bar{3} \tag{1.32}$$

Another example is given by the product $\bar{3} \otimes 3$

$$(0,1) \quad (1,0) \qquad (0,0) \quad (1,1)$$

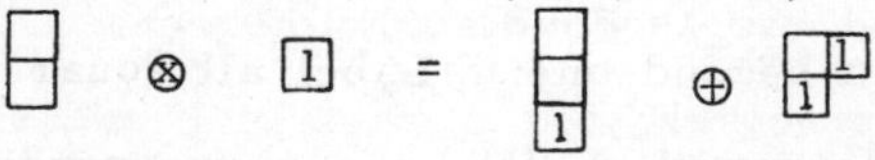

$$\bar{3} \otimes 3 = 1 \oplus 8 \tag{1.33}$$

The tableau 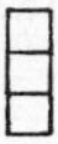 $\equiv (0,0) \equiv 1$ is the identity in SU(3).

The remaining representation 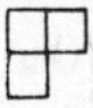 has dimension 8 and is self-conjugate ($\bar{8}$ = 8 ; this is true whenever $\lambda = \mu$). This is the regular or adjoint representation and can also be obtained by means of the structure constants. To see this let us rewrite the commutation relations between the λ-matrices

$$\left[\lambda_i , \lambda_j\right] = -2\, F_{i}{}^{(j}{}_{k)}\, \lambda_k \tag{1.34}$$

with $F_{i}{}^{(j}{}_{k)} = -i\, f_{ijk}$

Written in this form it is clear that the structure constants $F_{i}{}^{(j}{}_{k)}$ can be considered as a set of 8 x 8 matrices $(F_i)^j_k$, where j and k designate the rows and columns of the matrix F_i.

The highest weight of this representation is (1 , 1) and its weight diagram is identical with the root diagram of SU(3) (Fig. 1), having in addition two zero weights.

2. UNITARY SYMMETRY. PHYSICAL APPLICATIONS.

2.1. ASSIGNEMENTS. The isospin-hypercharge content of the regular representation can be obtained according to Eq. (1.33) as the traceless part of the tensor product of a quark and an anti-quark representation. It consists of an isosinglet and an isotriplet with zero hypercharge, and two isodoublets with hypercharges equal to +1 and -1. This is precisely the pattern of pseudoscalar mesons which we fit in the weight diagram of Fig. 5 which is a regular hexagon

$D^{(8)}(1,1) \equiv 8$

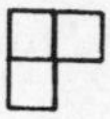

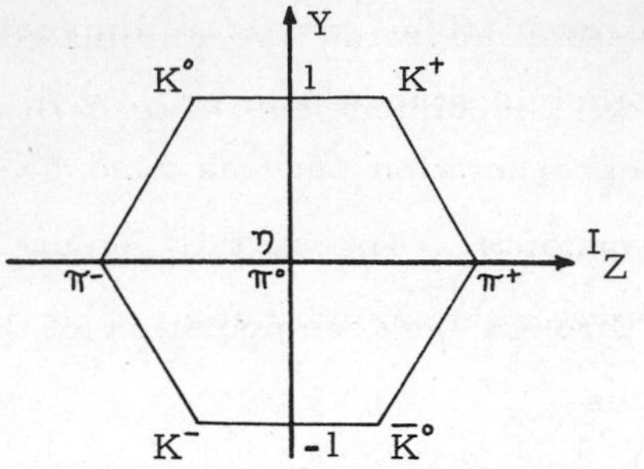

Fig. 5

The eight spin (1/2) baryons also belong to an octet as is shown below

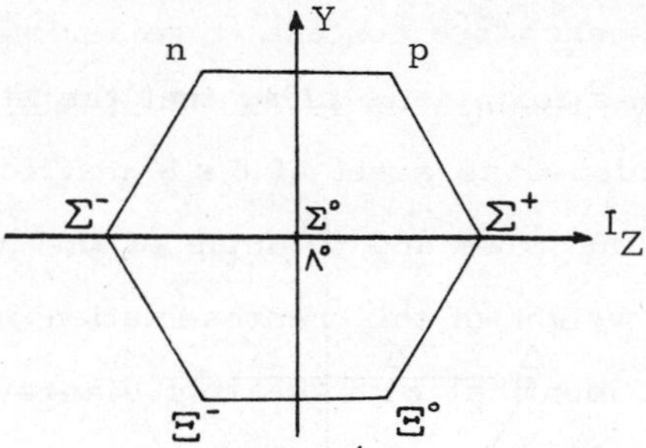

Fig. 6

To obtain the representations where the baryon and meson resonances lay we must calculate the decomposition of the product of two octets. Using Young tableaux we get the following sum

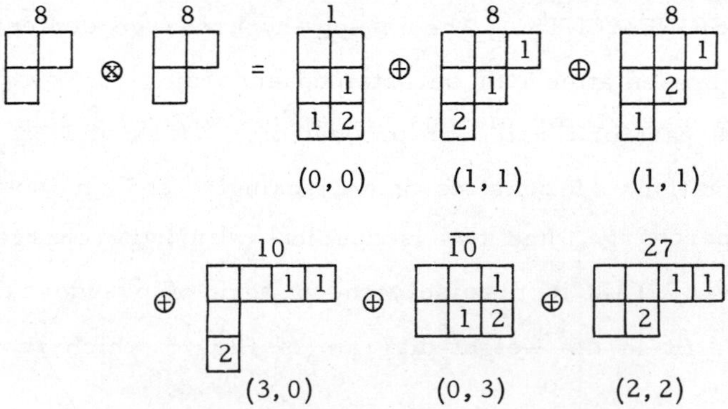

$$8 \times 8 = 1 + 8 + 8 + 10 + \overline{10} + 27 \qquad (2.1)$$

All other possible diagrams are eliminated by applying the multiplication rules. The dimensions have been calculated using formula (1.20).

The physical content of the representation $10 \equiv D^{(10)}(3,0)$ can easily be obtained through the decomposition of the direct product of three quark states

$$3 \otimes 3 \otimes 3 = (6 \oplus \bar{3}) \otimes 3 = 1 \oplus 8 \oplus 8 \oplus 10 \qquad (2.2)$$

because everything else in Eq. (2.2) is known. Its weight diagram with the isospin-hypercharge content, together with the assignment of the $(3/2)^+$ baryon resonances is shown in Fig. 7.

$D^{(10)}(3,0) \equiv 10$

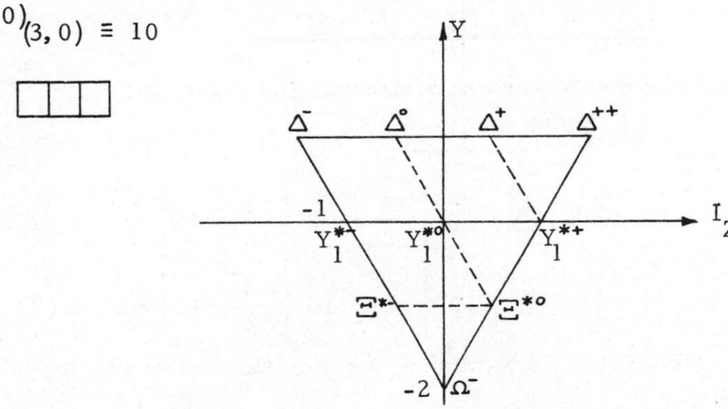

Fig. 7

The nine vector mesons are accommodated inside an octet and a singlet

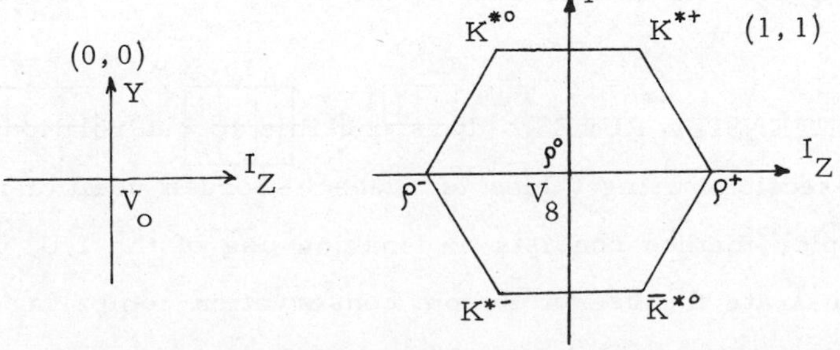

Fig. 8

This is also a consequence of the Yang-Mills theory because the currents i.e. the generators, or λ_i matrices have the same quantum numbers as the vector mesons. An interesting situation occurs here: the eighth vector meson of the octet turns out to be mixed with the singlet representation (0, 0), to give the observed ϕ and ω mesons. This strange phenomenon will be made clearer when we consider the mass formula.

At this stage we can make a survey of the present knowledge of the classification of known particles and resonances by means of SU(3) multiplets. They are sketched in table I adding a question mark to those which are still uncertain:

TABLE I

Classification of known particles and resonances

a) Baryons

$J^P =$	$\frac{1}{2}^+$ 8	$\frac{5}{2}^+$ 8	$\frac{1}{2}^-$ 1	$\frac{5}{2}^-$ 8 or 10
	$\frac{3}{2}^+$ 10	$\frac{7}{2}^+$ 10	$\frac{3}{2}^-$ 8+1	$\frac{1}{2}^+$ 8 (?)

b) Mesons

$$1 + 8 \quad \text{for} \quad 0^-, 1^-, 1^+, 2^+, 1^{+-} (?)$$

(The second sign in 1^{+-} stands for η_U, the charge-parity of the 3rd. and 8th components of the 8).

2.2. INTENSITY RULES. It is possible to get relations between cross-sections using tables of Clebsch-Gordan coefficients for SU(3). A simpler method consists in making use of the I, U, and V-spins. We illustrate the use of U-spin conservation comparing two reactions where a proton is bombarded with a negative π-meson to produce a positive meson and a negative resonance

$$\pi^- + p \rightarrow \Delta^- + \rho^+ \qquad (2.3)$$

$$\pi^- + p \rightarrow Y_1^{*-} + K^{*+} \qquad (2.4)$$

$$\begin{array}{lcccc} U & \frac{1}{2} & \frac{1}{2} & \frac{3}{2} & \frac{1}{2} \\ U_{total} & \multicolumn{2}{c}{0,1} & \multicolumn{2}{c}{1,2} \end{array}$$

Conservation of total U-spin leaves only the U = 1 channel open. Therefore the cross-sections for both reactions can be expressed in terms of only one parameter by means of SU(2) Clebsch-Gordan coefficients. The ratio of both cross-sections is therefore parameter independent and is equal to $-\sqrt{3}$.

2.3. BREAKING SU(3). Mass formula. The symmetry breaking interaction responsible for the large mass splittings between I-spin multiplets is assumed to transform like λ_8. This contains both U = 0 and U = 1, $U_Z = 0$ pieces. Since U = 0 would yield m(p) = $m(\Sigma^+)$, Δm has to transform as the third component of a U-spin vector. It then behaves like the operator U_Z giving equal spacing for Δ^-, Y^{*-}, Ξ^{*-} and Ω^- in the decuplet, for instance, in remarkable agreement with the experimental values. For the octet we get equal spacing[6] between the U-spin members of the multiplet formed by the three states:

$$\begin{array}{lll} 1) & N & U_Z = 1 \\ 2) & -\frac{\sqrt{3}}{2}\Lambda + \frac{1}{2}\Sigma & U_Z = 0 \\ 3) & \Xi & U_Z = -1 \end{array} \qquad (2.5)$$

The $U_Z = 0$ state is given as a combination of Λ and Σ. The coefficients can be calculated by means of the algebraic relations, but we already know them because they also appear in the charge matrix $Q = e(\frac{\sqrt{3}}{2}\lambda_3 + \frac{1}{2}\lambda_8)$ which represents the orthogonal U = 0 combination. From (2.5) we get

$$m_N + m_\Xi = \frac{3}{2}m_\Lambda + \frac{1}{2}m_\Xi \quad (2.6)$$

in fairly good agreement with experiment. Okubo worked out a general expression valid for any baryon multiplet:

$$M = a + bY + c\left[I(I+1) - \frac{Y^2}{4}\right] \quad (2.7)$$

For mesons we use Eq. (2.7) for the masses squared and get better agreement with the experimental values. One argument to justify this procedure is the fact that in the field equations for mesons the masses appear always squared. More recently, Fubini and Furlan have shown that m fits rest-states, whereas m^2 would be correct for states with $\mathbf{p} \longrightarrow \infty$.

The mixing between the two vector mesons φ and ω is another manifestation of this mass-splitting interaction. They are mixtures of the octet $I_Z = 0$, $Y = 0$ state V_8, which is the one satisfying the mass formula (2.7), and the singlet state V_o. We can express this mixture by means of a parameter

$$\left.\begin{aligned} |\phi> &= V_8 \cos\alpha + V_o \sin\alpha \\ |\omega> &= V_o \cos\alpha - V_8 \sin\alpha \end{aligned}\right\} \quad (2.8)$$

Introducing the measured values for the ϕ and ω masses and the calculated value for the V_8 mass we obtain the mixing parameter

$\cos\alpha \sim 0.78$

In the quark model there is a simple explanation for the equal spacing rule in U-space. It is assumed that the s-quark is heavier than the other two, which are degenerate. The mass differences are then proportional to the difference in the number of s-quarks in the corresponding states. We illustrate this result considering the resonance decuplet

state	quark content	Number of s-quarks
Δ^{++}	u u u	0
Y_1^{*+}	u u s	1
Ξ^{*o}	u s s	2
Ω^-	s s s	3

whence

$$m_{\Omega^-} - m_{\Xi^{*o}} = m_{\Xi^{*o}} - m_{Y_1^{*+}} = m_{Y_1^{*+}} - m_{\Delta^{++}} = m_s - m_u \tag{2.9}$$

Electromagnetic transitions. The electromagnetic interaction conserves U-spin. It transforms like the electric charge operator Q, which belongs to an octet. Therefore it is possible to get relations among magnetic moments. For instance the proton and Σ^+ should have the same magnetic moment because they are eigenstates of the same U-spin multiplet. We list below the complete set of relations obtained by Coleman and Glashow $\left(\mu(\Sigma^+) + \mu(\Sigma^-) = 2\mu(\Sigma^o)\right.$ was known previously from I-spin$\left.\right)$:

$$\mu(\Sigma^+) = \mu(p)$$

$$\mu(\Lambda) = \frac{1}{2}\mu(n)$$

$$\mu(\Xi^o) = \mu(n)$$

$$\mu(\Xi^-) = \mu(\Sigma^-) = -\left[\mu(p) + \mu(n)\right]$$

$$\mu(\Sigma^o) = -\frac{1}{2}\mu(n) \qquad (2.10)$$

$\mu(\Sigma^+)$ has just been measured[7] and fits beautifully. So does $\mu(\Lambda)$.

The same transformation properties are valid for the electromagnetic mass differences. They are of course superposed to the splittings given by the Gell-Mann-Okubo mass formula. If we call δ^-, δ^o, δ^+ the electromagnetic mass differences of the three charge states, we get for the baryon octet,

p	n	Σ^+	Σ^-	Ξ^o	Ξ^-
$m_N + \delta^+$	$m_N + \delta^o$	$m_\Sigma + \delta^+$	$m_\Sigma + \delta^-$	$m_\Xi + \delta^o$	$m_\Xi + \delta^-$

and by eliminating the three unknowns δ^+, δ^-, δ^o we obtain

$$m_{\Xi^-} - m_{\Xi^o} = m_{\Sigma^-} - m_{\Sigma^+} + m_p - m_n \qquad (2.11)$$

The formula holds within 0.5 MeV according to the latest data.

Weak interactions.

a) Leptonic: Cabibbo suggested that the leptonic weak transitions are given by a non-diagonal operator, a linear combination of I^+ and V^-. It is normalized to unit length in order to account for the experimentally observed universality of weak interactions

$$J_\mu = \cos\theta \, I^+ + \sin\theta \, V^- \qquad (2.12)$$

This assumption is in excellent agreement with the experimental data if the angle $\theta \approx 0,26$.

b) Non-leptonic: This interaction is assumed to be of the current-current type. Therefore it should transform as the product of two octets. The CP properties (for the CP-conserving part, at least) of the resulting expansion leaves us with only the representations 1, 8 and 27. The experimentally observed $\Delta I = 1/2$ rule shows that the contribution of 27 is negligible. So far there is no fully satisfactory explanation for this "octet enhancement by strong interactions" mechanism. This situation reminds us of the success of the Gell-Mann-Okubo mass formula where a similar octet dominance is at work. Alternatively, the 8 may be unenhanced, with unobserved neutral currents cancelling out the 27. At present the experimental evidence is not conclusive, and we cannot rule out the 27 entirely, to fit such a theory[8].

3. CURRENT-GENERATED ALGEBRAS, SU(6) STRUCTURES AND SUPERCONVERGENCE

3.1. THE CHIRAL $[U(3) \times U(3)]_{\gamma_5}$. Although SU(3) started out --and still is primarily a symmetry of strong interactions, it can be observed in weak transitions. Gell-Mann suggested that it be indeed defined through equal-time commutation of weak and electromagnetic currents. Starting from this algebraic structure it is possible to get correct results even if the underlying symmetry is badly violated. Gell-Mann defined the SU(3) algebra using commutation relations between charges

$$\left[F_i, F_j\right] = i f_{ijk} F_k \tag{3.1}$$

where the

$$F_i = \int F_{io} \, d^3x \tag{3.2}$$

are space integrals of the densities, which are local field operators whose matrix elements are correctly measured through perturbation theory.

This algebra accounts only for the conserved vector current component V of the complex weak current. But we know there also exists a non-conserved axial part A. The most interesting property of these two components is universality, i.e. the presence of only one coefficient G in the combined current in the $j_\mu^w (j_\mu^w)^+$ Hamiltonian,

$$j_\mu^w = G \overline{\psi}(1 + \gamma_5)\gamma_\mu \psi \tag{3.3}$$

which can be written in this form for the leptons, and more generally as $(v_\mu + a_\mu)$ for hadrons.

The axial vector weak current also transforms like an octet. These considerations allow us to enlarge the SU(3) algebra to include both the V and A components (these are all space-integrals)

$$\left[V_i , V_j\right] = i f_{ijk} V_k \tag{3.4}$$

$$\left[V_i , A_j\right] = i f_{ijk} A_k \tag{3.5}$$

$$\left[A_i , A_j\right] = i f_{ijk} V_k \tag{3.6}$$

Eq. (3.5) expresses the fact that A_j transforms like a vector under SU(3). The last equation, at first simply postulated by Gell-Mann (Salam and Ward had suggested it for the Sakata model), closes the system upon the "chiral" algebra SU(3) x SU(3). Assuming a universal coupling for the entire weak current, we have supplied[9] a proof of (3.6). This is achieved by examining the SU(2) isospin subgroup and is equivalent to saying that in the whole expansion

$$\left[A_i , A_j\right] = a\, 8 + b\, 10 + c\, \overline{10} \tag{3.7}$$

the coefficients b and c are zero. These coefficients can be calculated inside SU(2) because the Cabibbo currents already close upon such an algebra, and we can turn this into the I-spin SU(2) via a U-spin rotation.

If we add to these scalar and pseudoscalar octet and singlet generators of $\left[U(3) \times U(3)\right]_{\gamma_5}$ an additional set of six "nonets" representing[10] the space integrals of all <u>space-components</u> of vector and axial-vector current densities we get the Feynman-Gell-Mann-Zweig chiral algebra $\left[U(6) \times U(6)\right]_{\gamma_5}$. Including in addition $\sigma^{\mu\nu}$ tensor densities integrated generators, the whole U(12) algebra is obtained.

3.2. SU(6), RELATIVITY AND UNITARITY. From $\left[U(6) \times U(6)\right]_{\gamma_5}$ the following interesting results are derived

$$\frac{\mu(n)}{\mu(p)} = -\frac{2}{3} \;, \qquad \frac{G_A}{G_V} = -\frac{5}{3} \;, \qquad \frac{F}{D} = \frac{2}{3} \tag{3.8}$$

which depend upon the assignment of the $j = \frac{1}{2}^+$ octet and $j = \frac{3}{2}^+$ decuplet to representation 56 (□□□) of the U(6) product-subgroup. Mesons are assigned to 35. This SU(6) has as generators the integrals V_i of the v_i^o SU(3) charge-densities, and the

$$A_i^r = \int d^3x \, a_i^r \tag{3.9}$$

constructed from the space-components of the axial-vector currents. In a quark-model, the latter are just (r = 1, 2, 3, a space index ; i = 0, 1, ... 8, a unitary spin index)

$$a_i^r = \psi^+ \sigma^r \lambda_i \psi \tag{3.10}$$

and coincide for i = 0 with quark-spin. This is why the results (3.8) were first derived from a non-relativistic ansatz, i.e. the suggested[10] approximate "spin and unitary-spin independence" of strong interactions, put forward by Gursey and Radicati, by Zweig and by Sakita. The similarity between (3.9) and physical spin at the quark level led many of us to believe at first that a "relativistic" symmetry could be constructed by adjoining to (3.9) a set of generators $\overline{V}_i^r$ which would be pure Lorentz transformations for i = 0, and otherwise just U(3) rotated analogs. The commutation relations would then be

$$\left[\bar{V}_i^r, \bar{V}_j^s\right] = -i(\varepsilon^{rst} d_{ijk} A_k^t + \delta^{rs} f_{ijk} V_k) \qquad (3.11)$$

$$\left[\bar{A}_i, \bar{A}_j\right] = -i f_{ijk} V_k \qquad (3.12)$$

where the A_i are necessary for closure since

$$\left[\bar{V}_i^r, A_j^s\right] = i(\varepsilon^{rst} d_{ijk} \bar{V}_k^t + \delta^{rs} f_{ijk} \bar{A}_k) \qquad (3.13)$$

Note that the $\bar{V}_i^r \sim i V_i^r$ and $\bar{A}_i \sim i A_i$ as far as the commutation relations go. The barred generators close with the V_i and A_i^r on the non-compact algebra of $SL(6, C)_{\gamma_5}$, which will be discussed in this school by Profs. Fronsdal and White. The difference between this and $\left[U(6) \times U(6)\right]_{\gamma_5}$ is in a minus sign in the commutation relations [compare (3.12) and (3.6), (3.14) and (3.11)]

$$\left[V_i^r, V_j^s\right] = i(\varepsilon^{rst} d_{ijk} A_k^t + \delta^{rs} f_{ijk} V_k) \qquad (3.14)$$

$$\left[V_i^r, A_k^s\right] = i(\varepsilon^{rst} d_{ijk} V_k^t + \delta^{rs} f_{ijk} A_k) \qquad (3.15)$$

If nature should indeed want the strong interactions to be spin- and unitary-spin invariant, it should obey the non-compact $SL(6, C)_{\gamma_5}$, or the larger $\left[U(6, 6)\right]_\beta$ which is the non-compact analog of U(12) which leaves invariant β (i.e. the representative of the Minkowsky metric in a 12-spinor representation, a diagonal matrix with six +1 and six -1 eigenvalues). This $\left[U(6, 6)\right]_\beta$ was suggested by Dothan, Gell-Mann and Ne'eman as a classification scheme (a "spectrum generating algebra") which could only be used as a symmetry in an extremely degenerate limit. It should be distinguished from other schemes [also denoted U(6, 6) or $\tilde{U}(12)$]

which represented the same group in the abstract but had a different physical connotation. However, a non-compact algebra (in quantum mechanics we really discuss algebras, which are observable and have real eigenvalues upon diagonalization) can only have hermitian infinite-dimensional representations. Multiplication by an $i = \sqrt{-1}$, which gives the correct commutation relations by taking (3.6) $\longrightarrow$ (3.12) etc... is meaningless physically. It could have happened that the current-generated algebra of V_i^r and A_i etc... should require a minus sign and obey SL(6, C). This would have implied the abandon of the quark representation for the description of weak and electromagnetic currents. It is an experimental question, and we shall see that it was answered negatively by the success of the Adler-Weisberger sum rule.

For some time, there was somehow an illusion of being able to keep finite representations and at the same time have the minus sign of non-compactness as required by the identification of $\bar{V}_o^r$ with a pure Lorentz transformation Λ^r, and of A_o^r with total angular momentum at rest J^r,

$$\left[\Lambda^r , \Lambda^s\right] = -i\, \varepsilon^{rst}\, J^t \tag{3.16}$$

It would seem (and it seemed to many) that for a quark spinor field this Λ^r would indeed be given by a non-hermitian bilinear density $i\,\bar{\psi}[\gamma^r , \gamma^o]\psi$. However, if you try to calculate Λ^r from the Noether theorem, you will find that although the six generators of the homogeneous Lorentz group $M^{\mu\nu}$ can be written as

$$M^{\mu\nu} = S^{\mu\nu} + L^{\mu\nu} \tag{3.17}$$

with spin and orbital parts, the $S^{\mu\nu}$ vanishes for either μ or $\nu = 0$, so that $\Lambda^{r} \equiv M^{ro} = L^{ro}$ and the Lorentz transformation is entirely orbital (i.e. infinite-dimensional, in momentum space). To reproduce such a situation for U(6, 6) one would have to adjoin 144 "momenta", translation-generators in the internal space.

In further work with current algebra, one tends to work mainly with either the charges, $[U(3) \times U(3)]_{\gamma_5}^{+}$, or with the $[U(3) \times U(3)]_{\sigma_z}$ of just the V_i and A_i^z. All the results (3.8) can be recovered with just this small algebra, provided we keep the same assignments as in the larger SU(6). This puts the baryon octet and the $\sigma_z = \pm\frac{1}{2}$ components of the decuplet (or a 10 with $j = \frac{1}{2}^{+}$) in (6, 3) $\dot{+}$ (3, 6). The above subgroup is also contained in $U(6)_w$, another subgroup (λ_i, $\sigma_z\lambda_i$, $\beta\sigma_x\lambda_i$, $\beta\sigma_y\lambda_i$) of the $[U(6) \times U(6)]_\beta$ of all even-parity density generators. This $U(6)_w$ would remain a symmetry of 3-particle vertices, provided the $[U(6) \times U(6)]_\beta$ classifies rest-states.

<u>The non-compact group program.</u> Following our introduction of $U(6,6)_\beta$, the smaller SL(6, C) or even just $[U(6) \times U(6)]_\beta \otimes SL(2,C)_L$ have been suggested as classification schemes. The latter uses a rest-classification $[U(6) \times U(6)]_\beta$ in which a quark is (6, 1), an anti-quark $(1, \bar{6})$, and (1, 6) would either create a pseudo-quark (a quark with odd relative parity) or just destroy an antiquark, and $(\bar{6}, 1)$ would destroy a quark or generate an "anti-pseudo-quark". "Ordinary" SU(6) is in the product of the two U(6) commuting subgroups, transforming like $(1 \pm \beta)\sigma^r \lambda_i$, with r = 0, 1, 2, 3 and $\sigma^o = 1$. The baryons are thus in $(56, 1)^+$ and the mesons in $(6, \bar{6})^-$ which reduces to 35^- and 1^- (the χ meson at 959 MeV, probably) of SU(6).

$SL(2, C)_L$ is a non-compact spectrum-generating algebra whose representations would be infinite sequences of rotational excitations such as $L = 0^-, 1^+, 2^-, 3^+, \ldots$ This L is defined[10] as just the difference between J^t and the spin-simulating algebra of A_o^r.

$$L^r + A_o^r = J^r \tag{3.18}$$

We have suggested[10] an alternative $SL(3, R)_L$, which gives $\Delta L = 2$ levels 0^+, 2^+, 4^+, etc. which could fit better the sequences of Regge-recurrences if these are split by exchange-forces.

Present work in non-compact groups is aimed at one of the following physical targets (other than sheer mathematical delight),

a) Classification. The recent discovery[11] of five new resonances with positive strangeness (Y = 2, such as the Z^+ at 1860 MeV etc.) seem to point to the existence of $\left[U(6,6)\right]_\beta$ -like towers, where the various levels are built up by adjoining one more quark-antiquark pair each time. It is impossible to make a Z^+ from just 3 quarks. The $SL(2, C)_L$ or $SL(3, R)_L$ must in addition be superimposed upon such a scheme.

b) Study of the degenerate symmetry limit, as will be discussed in this school.

c) Problems relating to the introduction of appropriate field theories (spin-statistics, wave equations, etc.). Nambu, Barut, Fronsdal and others are studying these issues.

d) Classifications relating to Regge-pole dynamics. Some of the recent advances in that field are extremely simple to understand in an algebraic picture (such as Toller's $O(4)_L$).

e) Saturation of current algebra and superconvergence sum rules by such representations. Indeed, Fubini has shown that the only possibility of saturating superconvergence sum rules with discrete levels is to use infinite-component structures.

3.3. SUM RULES[10].

Fubini-Furlan method. This method provided the first real tool for the derivation of sum rules from commutators. It consists in the use of the commutation relations of a given current algebra to obtain physical predictions, taking into account that a symmetry generator would connect only one-particle states, whereas a broken symmetry would lead in addition to many-particle states. For example, I^- acting on the proton yields a neutron only; but U^- would lead to Σ^+ only 90 % of the time, leading also to $p\bar{K}^o$, $\Sigma^+\pi^o$ etc. If we have a set of charges G^i defining under commutation a certain algebra

$$\left[G^i , G^j\right] = c^{ijk} G^k \tag{3.19}$$

and if the Hamiltonian is not invariant with respect to some of the G^i's we can write

$$\left[G^i , H\right] = R^i , \quad R^i = i\int r^i d^3x \tag{3.20}$$

where

$$r^i \equiv \partial_\mu j^{\mu i} \tag{3.21}$$

The commutator (3.19) sandwiched between one-particle states provides sum rules if it is expanded in terms of a complete set of intermediate states. Explicitly from Eq. (3.19) one gets for the transition between the states a and b:

$$< a\,|\left[G^i , G^j\right]|\,b > = c^{ijk} < a\,|G^k|\,b > \tag{3.22}$$

Now projecting out over a complete set of intermediate states we have ("m" are the one-particle states, belonging to the same representations as a and b; n are the "leakage" many-particle states

$$\sum_m \left\{ < a | G^i | m > < m | G^j | b > - < a | G^j | m > < m | G^i | b > \right\}$$

$$- \sum_n \left\{ < a | G^i | n > < n | G^j | b > - < a | G^j | n > < n | G^i | b > \right\}$$

$$= c^{ijk} < a | G^k | b > \tag{3.23}$$

where we can use

$$< a | G^i | n > = \frac{< a | R^i | n >}{E_n - E_a} \tag{3.24}$$

to estimate the leakage. For many-particles intermediate states $E_n \gg E_a$. We also observe that taking $a \equiv b$ and G^k diagonal, G^i and G^j a raising-lowering pair such as U^+ and U^-, we get from (3.23),

$$(g_{iam}^{\text{Renormalized}})^2 = 1 + \sum_n (\Delta E_{na})^2 r_{ian}^2 \tag{3.25}$$

and since $r_i \sim \left[H_{\text{sym. breaking}}, j_\mu \right]$ we get as a just sum rule the Ademollo-Gatto theorem which states that the symmetry-breaking acts only in second order.

The correction terms that account for the breaking of the symmetry actually depend on the choice of the common momentum **p** of a and b, because the separation in single and multiple particle contributions is not covariant. In fact, the correction part includes the kinematical factor C

$$C = \frac{(E_n + E_a)^2}{|4E_n E_a|} \tag{3.26}$$

which reaches its minimum value 1 for $\mathbf{p} \rightarrow \infty$ and its maximum value for $\mathbf{p} \rightarrow 0$,

$$C \xrightarrow[\mathbf{p} \rightarrow 0]{} \frac{(m_n + m_a)^2}{4 m_n m_a} \quad . \tag{3.27}$$

<u>Adler-Weisberger sum rule.</u> I shall not go through the variety of sum rules which have been derived from the algebra. These form the contents of Prof. Nauenberg's lectures in this school. However let us just see the best known example.

Starting from the commutator of two axial charges and making some approximations Adler and Weisberger calculated the weak axial vector renormalization constant as in (3.25), where $(g^{\text{renormalized}}_{iam} / g_{iam})$ is given by the r_{iam}. These become here measurable quantities via the Goldberger-Treiman relation

$$\partial_\mu a_\mu = \frac{2 m_N m_\pi^2}{g_{\bar{N}N\pi}} \frac{G_A}{G_V} \phi_\pi \tag{3.28}$$

which brings in ϕ_π, the pion field. The result is

$$\left[\frac{G_V}{G_A}\right]^2 = 1 + \frac{2}{\pi} \left[\frac{m_N}{g_{\bar{N}\pi N}}\right]^2 \int_{m_\pi}^{\infty} \frac{k d\nu}{\nu^2} \left[\sigma_{tot}^{\pi^- p}(\nu) - \sigma_{tot}^{\pi^+ p}(\nu)\right] \tag{3.29}$$

Introducing the experimental values for the cross-sections one gets

$$\left|\frac{G_A}{G_V}\right| \sim 1,2$$

while the experimental value is $\frac{G_A}{G_V} = -1,18 \pm 0,02$

The success of this sum rule also proves the correctness of the plus sign in (3.6), rather than the minus in (3.12) --as far as the current-generated algebra goes.

<u>Fubini, Bjðrken, Weisberger algorithm.</u> Using the reduction formula for the retarded commutator taken between two particles states of momenta p_A and p_B, treating the densities as fake particles with momenta $q, \bar{q}$

$$t^{\mu\nu} = i \int d^4x\, e^{iqx} < p_A | \left[g^{\mu a}(x),\ g^{\nu b}(0) \right] | p_B > \theta(x^\circ) \tag{3.30}$$

where

$$T^{\mu\nu} = (2\pi)^4\, \delta^4(p_A - q - p_B + \bar{q})\, t^{\mu\nu} \tag{3.31}$$

and contracting with q^μ and integrating by parts one gets

$$q_\mu t^{\mu\nu} = - \int d^4x\, e^{iqx} < p_A | \left[\partial_\mu g^{\mu a}(x),\ g^{\nu b}(0) \right] | p_B > \theta(x^\circ)$$

$$+ i \int d^4x\, i^{iqx} < p_A | \left[g^{oa}(x),\ g^{\nu b}(0) \right] | p_B > \delta(x^\circ) \tag{3.32}$$

Introducing the value for the equal time commutator given by the current algebra and expanding in terms of Lorentz invariants, Fubini's sum rule is finally obtained

$$\frac{1}{\pi} \int_0^\infty a(\nu,\ q^2,\ \bar{q}^2,\ t)\, d\nu = F(t) \tag{3.33}$$

Symbollically this relation can be written in terms of Hilbert transforms h of the components of $t^{\mu\nu}$

$$(q_\mu h - h q_\mu) u^{\mu\nu} = F^\nu(t) \tag{3.34}$$

where $u^{\mu\nu}$ is the tensor $t^{\mu\nu}$ without the $\theta(x^\circ)$ function.

A remarkable feature of Eq. (3.34) is the fact that it expresses the "off-mass-shell" form factor F(t) as a difference of two "on-mass-shell" amplitudes. The algorithm (3.32) or (3.34) is an extremely useful tool in deriving sum rules.

<u>Superconvergence.</u> The integral in Eq. (3.33) is independent of the values of q^2 and $\bar{q}^2$. Taking the limits $q^2 \to 0$ and $\bar{q}^2 \to 0$ the following sum rule is obtained

$$\int \text{Im}\, A(\nu, t) d\nu = 0 \tag{3.35}$$

with

$$A = \frac{1}{\pi} \int \frac{a}{\nu' - \nu} d\nu'$$

This is a strong interaction sum rule connected with the high-energy limit. This kind of superconvergent integrals yields relations like

$$(g^2_{\omega\rho\pi} + g^2_{\phi\rho\pi}) m^2_\rho - 4 g^2_{\rho\pi\pi} = 0 \tag{3.36}$$

The integral (3.34) is actually independent of the detailed structure of the current-current commutators and could have been deduced directly from the combined use of analyticity, unitarity and the high-energy behavior

$$|A(\nu)| < \nu^\beta \tag{3.37}$$

with $\beta < -1$.

This limit is forced by unitarity in the case of high-spin particles scattering.

Gell-Mann's program. Fubini introduced the method of putting the outside momenta $\mathbf{p} \to \infty$. This has the following advantages:

1) it yields better sum rules [Eq. (3.27)] ;

2) it allows us to write dispersion relations in ν and t, fixing $q_1^2 \to 0$ and $q_2^2 \to 0$;

3) it allows the use of the Goldberger-Treiman and similar relations, replacing densities by mesons, which is only correct at $\Delta E_{na} \to 0$;

4) we can neglect resonance-transitions to "leakage" intermediate states contributions. The $\langle a | R^i | n \rangle$ of Eq. (3.24) are like form factors and may resonate at $\Delta E_{na} \sim m_\pi$ for instance;

5) we do not have to consider independent-loop or Z type diagrams representing for instance the creation of a pair, or of a meson, in addition to any one-particle state. Field theory shows that we would otherwise get together with a neutron, for instance, n + pairs or $n + \eta$, $n + \pi^\circ$ etc... These vanish at $\mathbf{p} \to \infty$.

These considerations made Gell-Mann and Dashen suggest the use of an algebra of the densities with commutation relations similar to those of their integrated generators. One is then led to an infinite algebra of the Fourier transforms, since

$$\left[F_i(k), F_j(k')\right] = i f_{ij\ell} F_\ell(k + k') \qquad (3.38)$$

Working between states at $\mathbf{p} \to \infty$ allows one to use such an algebra, without relying upon field-theory and the reduction formula. The hope is that (3.38) would have simple representations which would perhaps reproduce the rotational levels of the quark-antiquark system for instance. A seemingly naive approach emulating the methods of dealing with nuclei led Dalitz and others to predict such levels. They could appear here as representations of the algebra.

The problem contains mathematical difficulties and the only known working solution to date is a "one-quark" model.

This represents the most ambitious and still hypothetical attempt to extend the applications of the algebra of weak currents. Other than that you will find the literature full of new sum rules, low energy theorems, transition-renormalization estimates etc.

Another program suggested by Gell-Mann has consisted in reproducing the correct G_A/G_V in (3.29) from (3.6) directly from saturation by one particle states via representation-mixing. One would like to keep $\mu(n)/\mu(p) = -2/3$ of Eq. (3.8) and get $|G_A/G_V| = 1.2$ at the same time. Such a mixing has been found[14] by Harari and others, in terms of representations of the $[U(3) \times U(3)]_{\gamma_5}$ which coincides between rest-states with $[U(3) \times U(3)]_{\sigma_z}$ of (3.8) between states at $\mathbf{p} \to \infty$.

The superconvergence program has yielded several interesting sum rules and a beautiful analysis[12] by Harari of the electromagnetic mass splittings.

4. THE DYNAMICAL HIGH ENERGY ALGEBRA $[U(3) \times U(3)]_\beta$

Strong interactions couplings at low energy. We have seen how SU(3), which started out as a strong interaction symmetry, has been treated in our previous section as a system generated from space-integrals (and perhaps even directly from densities) of currents measured in weak and electromagnetic interactions. How is it then that the strong Hamiltonian, which forms the main part of

$$H = -\int d^3x \, \theta^{00} \tag{4.1}$$

is somehow approximately symmetric under SU(3)? Somehow, strong interactions seem to preserve SU(3) couplings; moreover, the vector mesons even seem to obey "universal-SU(3)" couplings, i.e. f_{ijk} type coefficients exclusively.

One way of understanding this situation can be made to work for the low-energy couplings. This is the method of approximate-universality, based upon a dispersion analysis of the weak and electromagnetic form factors, in which one assumes dominance for a meson pole. This is a generalization of the original Nambu (and later Frazer-Fulco more elaborate) prediction of $J = 1^-$ mesons from the shape of electromagnetic form factors, and of the original Goldberger-Treiman derivation of their relation for the coupling to a 0^- meson. The Dirac form factor is written as [I(t) is our integral over a cut]

$$F_e(t) = \frac{gm^2}{m^2 - t} + I(t) \qquad (4.2)$$

where m^2 is the mass of the ρ for the isovector part, or for the ω for the isoscalar piece. For t = 0, $F_e(0) = Q$, the charge, or its corresponding SU(3) coefficient in Eq. (1.10), or even better in terms of the F_i of (3.1) and (1.34). We thus get for $< A | j_e^\mu | B >$

$$\begin{aligned} f_{3\bar{A}B} &= g_{\rho\bar{A}B} + I(0) \\ f_{8\bar{A}B} &= \sqrt{3}\, g_{\omega\bar{A}B} + I(0) \end{aligned} \qquad (4.3)$$

where ω stands for the V_8 of Fig. 8 and Eq. (2.8). Similarly, from $< A | \partial^\mu a_i^\mu | A >$ we find for the ith. unitary component,

$$(m_A + m_B) F_A(t) + t F_P(t) = \frac{g_{\bar{A}B\phi} m_\phi^2}{m_\phi^2 - t} + I_\phi(t) \qquad (4.4)$$

leading at t = 0 to

$$(m_A + m_B) \left[-\frac{G_A}{G_V} \right]_{\bar{A}B} = g_{\bar{A}B\phi} + I_\phi(0) \qquad (4.5)$$

where we could take G_A/G_V from the algebraic structure [Eq. (3.8), for instance; or the 1.2 of the mixings in Ref. 14]. Usually, of course, one takes G_A/G_V from experiment, but we now observe how this could now be regarded as a universal coupling prescribed by the algebra for pions and 0^- mesons. Note that we always get only an approximate universality, since I(0) and $I_\phi(0)$ do not vanish, but can be considered as "small".

Another way of getting universality for low energy couplings is based upon the bootstrap, or upon superconvergence relations, such as the results in Eq. (3.36).

In high-energy scattering, some surprising results had been derived from a nuclear-like quark model by Levin and Frankfurt, Lipkin and Scheck, Kokkedee and Van Hove, Freund. By assuming an "impulse approximation" --which is bad even in nuclei-- they got relations between meson-baryon and baryon-baryon total cross-sections. Some of these fitted experiments, others didn't. This focused our attention, leading to the so-called CHN algebra.

The CHN algebra of factorized Regge residues.[15] In the Regge pole model of scattering[16] with a single pole, the amplitude is assumed to have the following dependence on the energy s and the momentum transfer t

$$T = \beta(t) s^{\alpha(t)} \qquad (4.6)$$

where $\beta(t)$ is the residue and $\alpha(t)$ the complex angular momentum of the pole which is exchanged in the t-channel. It can be further shown[16] that $\beta(t)$ is factorizable into two $\gamma(t)$ vertex-strengths.

We have suggested, together with Cabibbo and Horwitz, that high-energy scattering be described in terms of the t-channel exchange of two unitary spin nonets of meson trajectories, coupled <u>universally</u> to scalar (s) and vector (v) "high-energy currents" respectively.

The S^i and V^i in a quark model are given by

$$S^i = \frac{1}{2}\int d^3x\, q^+ \beta \lambda^i q \tag{4.7}$$

$$V^i = \frac{1}{2}\int d^3x\, q^+ \lambda^i q \tag{4.8}$$

and generate $\left[U(3) \times U(3)\right]_\beta$,

$$\left[S^i, S^j\right] = i f^{ij}_k V^k \tag{4.9}$$

$$\left[V^i, S^j\right] = i f^{ij}_k S^k \tag{4.10}$$

We postulate

$$\delta^3(\mathbf{p}_A - \mathbf{p}_B)\, \gamma^{AB}_{s(i)}(0) = \langle A | S_i | B \rangle \tag{4.11}$$

$$\delta^3(\mathbf{p}_A - \mathbf{p}_B)\, \gamma^{AB}_{v(i)}(0) = \langle A | V_i | B \rangle \tag{4.12}$$

for a factorized strength at the AB vertex of $A + X \rightarrow B + Y$. Since $\beta(q) = 1$, and $\beta(\bar{q}) = -1$, the sign in Eq. (1.26) for λ_0, λ_3, λ_8 is inverted and $\beta\lambda_i$ has identical eigenvalues for q and $\bar{q}$.

Thus, for example, the presence of β makes the eigenvalues of S^o proportional to the number of quarks plus antiquarks, while V^o is proportional to the number of quarks minus antiquarks, i.e. baryon number. With this model we can make an estimate of the asymptotic ratio between $\sigma_{\pi+p}$ and σ_{pp} (see Fig. 9). This limit corresponds to the t-channel exchange of a Pomeranchuk trajectory (our S^o)

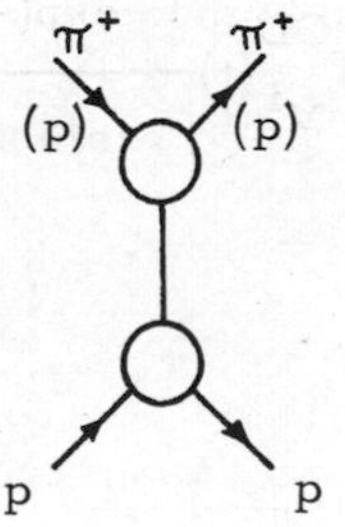

Fig. 9

Assuming that this trajectory dominates the high-energy behavior we get

$$\frac{\sigma_{\pi p}}{\sigma_{pp}} = \frac{\gamma_{S^o}^{\pi\pi}(0)\gamma_{S^o}^{pp}(0)}{\gamma_{S^o}^{pp}(0)\gamma_{S^o}^{pp}(0)} \approx \frac{2}{3} \tag{4.13}$$

since S^o counts 2 for a pion and 3 for a nucleon.

We assume that the scattering amplitude is given by

$$T_{AC\rightarrow BD}(\nu, t) = - \sum_{i=0}^{8} \left\{ \gamma^{AB}_{S^i}(t)\, \gamma^{CD}_{S^i}(t) \times \right.$$

$$\times \frac{1 + \exp(-i\pi\alpha^s_i)}{\sin \pi\alpha^s_i} \, \frac{\Gamma(\alpha^s_i + \frac{3}{2})}{\Gamma(\alpha^s_i + 1)} \left(\frac{\nu}{\nu_{S^i}}\right)^{\alpha^s_i(t)}$$

$$\left. + \gamma^{AB}_{V^i}(t)\, \gamma^{CD}_{V^i}(t) \frac{1 - \exp(-i\pi\alpha^v_i)}{\sin \pi\alpha^v_i} \, \frac{\Gamma(\alpha^v_i + \frac{3}{2})}{\Gamma(\alpha^v_i + 1)} \left(\frac{\nu}{\nu_{v^i}}\right)^{\alpha^v_i(t)} \right\} \tag{4.14}$$

where

$$\nu = (\text{total energy in C.M.}) + \frac{1}{2} t - m_A^2 - m_B^2 \tag{4.15}$$

From Eq. (4.14) we can calculate total cross-sections for nucleon-nucleon and meson-nucleon scattering in the case of elastic scattering $(i = 0, 3, 8)$ since we can use the optical theorem. In table 2 the normalization $T_r \lambda_i^2 = 2$ has been used, and the t_i^s or t_i^v represent everything in (4.14) other than the product $\gamma^{AB}(0)\gamma^{CD}(0)$.

TABLE 2

Total cross-sections

$$\bar{P}N = 6t_o^s + 3t_8^s - t_3^s + 6t_o^v + 3t_8^v - t_3^v$$

$$PN = 6t_o^s + 3t_8^s - t_3^s - 6t_o^v - 3t_8^v + t_3^v$$

$$PP = 6t_o^s + 3t_8^s + t_3^s - 6t_o^v - 3t_8^v - t_3^v$$

$$\bar{P}P = 6t_o^s + 3t_8^s + t_3^s + 6t_o^v + 3t_8^v + t_3^v$$

$$\pi^+ P = 4t_o^s + 2t_8^s - 2t_3^v$$

$$\pi^- P = 4t_o^s + 2t_8^s + 2t_3^v$$

$$K^+ P = 4t_o^s - t_8^s + t_3^s - 3t_8^v - t_3^v$$

$$K^- P = 4t_o^s - t_8^s + t_3^s + 3t_8^v + t_3^v$$

$$K^+ P = 4t_o^s - t_8^s - t_3^s - 3t_8^v + t_3^v$$

$$K^- N = 4t_o^s - t_8^s - t_3^s + 3t_8^v - t_3^v$$

For baryon-meson scattering the following relations are derived from table 2 (since all $t_s^i, t_v^i \geqslant 0$)

$$\begin{aligned} K^-P &> K^-N \\ \pi^-P &> \pi^+P \\ K^-P &> K^+P \\ K^-P &> K^+N \\ K^-P - K^-N &> |K^+P - K^+N| \\ K^+P + K^-P &> K^+N + K^-N \end{aligned} \qquad (4.16)$$

These relations are remarkably good. Also for baryon-baryon scattering we get

$$\begin{aligned} \bar{P}P &> PP \\ \bar{P}P &> PN \\ \bar{P}P &> \bar{P}N \\ \bar{P}P - PP &> \bar{P}N - PN \\ \bar{P}P + PP &> \bar{P}N + PN \end{aligned} \qquad (4.17)$$

and the four Lipkin identities

$$\begin{aligned} K^+P - K^+N &= PP - NP \\ K^-P - K^-N &= \bar{P}P - \bar{P}N \\ 3(\pi^+P + \pi^-P) &= \bar{P}N + PN + PP + \bar{P}P \\ K^+P + \pi^-P + K^-N &= K^-P + \pi^+P + K^+N \end{aligned} \qquad (4.18)$$

There is however one important correction which is essential. The S^i generators are not Lorentz-scalars. For anything but rest-matrix elements, they will be renormalized. This has only one effect: in table 2, the V^i couplings are all F-type SU(3) coefficients, the S^i are D-type for mesons (from charge-conjugation considerations) and F-type for baryons. This is because β is irrelevant if the states are made of quarks only, e.g. qqq, and we have universal SU(3) couplings. The above renormalization will now allow a D-type admixture to occur, and the t_8^s column is thereby modified. This changes only one relation, the third in (4.18) which becomes an inequality

$$3(\pi^+P + \pi^-P) < \bar{P}N + PN + PP + \bar{P}P \qquad (4.19)$$

The Johnson-Treiman relations are obtained when SU(3) symmetry is assumed ($t_3^v = t_8^v$; $t_3^s = t_8^s$)

$$K^-P - K^+P = 2(\pi^-P - \pi^-P) = 2(K^-N - K^+N) \qquad (4.20)$$

Assuming U(3) for the vector trajectories ($t_o^v = t_3^v = t_8^v$) we get Freund's relation

$$\bar{P}P - PP = \frac{5}{4}(\bar{P}N - PN) = 5(\pi^-P - \pi^+P) \qquad (4.21)$$

which fits experiments only to within some 20 %.

If we assume Arnold's exchange-degeneracy of SU(2) x SU(2) ($t_s^3 = t_v^3$) we get

$$\begin{aligned} K^+P &= K^+N \\ K^-N &= \frac{1}{2}(K^-P + K^+P) \end{aligned} \qquad (4.22)$$

A satisfactory over all fit[15] to the total cross-sections and to the ratio of real to imaginary parts of the elastic amplitudes has been demonstrated for the available region 6 GeV $\lesssim E_{\ell ab} \lesssim$ 20 GeV. Actually this seems to require $\alpha_o^s(0) = 0.925$ rather than the usually assumed value of one, reaching the Froissart bound. All cross-sections then go like $\nu^{-0.075}$, vanishing at $\nu \rightarrow \infty$. The results also seem to indicate that SU(3) is unbroken to first order.

The method has been used to predict[17] charge-exchange and associated-production $d\sigma/dt$, rather than σ_T, since the optical theorem is not available. The only discrepancy in these results seem to occur when one compares $p + \bar{p} \rightarrow n + \bar{n}$ with $p + K^- \rightarrow n + \bar{K}^o$

and is probably due to the effect of the pseudoscalar and axial vector trajectories, or double spin flip contributions, in the $p + \bar{p}$ case. These are not included in Eq. (4.14) and require a larger algebra. More recently we have been able to understand[17] the connection between the S^i densities and θ^{oo}. Also, it seems that the CHN postulate imposes very stringent conditions[18] on cuts in the complex L plane. In the forward direction, the cuts would simply vanish. This turns out to be essential for many super-convergence results, such as Harari's[12]. It should now provide a useful tool for the understanding of the role of cuts in general.

Summing up, we see that we may now possess the foundations for an exact algebraic theory of the strong interactions. The densities of V^i and S^i are connected with the usual (weak and electromagnetic) vector currents and with θ^{oo}, the gravitational current. However, they differ mainly in that they represent couplings to the 1^- or 2^+ poles of the above non-strong form factors, and do not have the pole of Eq. (4.2) for instance. This is an algebra of a generalized-Reggeized $g_{\rho\bar{A}B}$ of Eqs. (4.2) - (4.3).

AKNOWLEDGEMENTS

I would like to thank Prof. E. Friedmann of the Chilean Atomic Energy Commission and Prof. I. Saavedra of the University of Chile for their kind invitation. I would also like to thank Messrs. C. A. López and H. Quintana who took notes and provided me with a draft of these lectures.

REFERENCES

1. I have just published a lecture-note volume "Algebraic Theory of Particle Physics", W.A. Benjamin pub. (1967) containing what is probably the fullest account to date of our subject-matter. There is one textbook, by P. Carruthers, "Unitary Symmetry" which deals with the earlier phases of SU(3) theory. Lipkin ("Lie Groups for Pedestrians"), Frazer ("Elementary Particles") and Gasiorowitz ("Elementary Particles") have chapters about Unitary Symmetry.
2. The main papers related to SU(3) are contained in "The Eightfold Way", a reprint volume edited by M. Gell-Mann and myself, published by W.A. Benjamin, New York (1964). To these should be added H. Goldberg and Y. Ne'eman, Nuovo Cimento 27, 1 (1963).
3. J. K. Kim, Argonne Conference on Unitary Symmetry (June 1967)
4. A. H. Rosenfeld et al, Rev. Mod. Phys. 39, 1, (1967).
5. See for example S. Meshkov and Y. B. Yodh, to be published. Similarly, the fit in N. Cabibbo, L. Horwitz, J.J.J. Kokkedee and Y. Ne'eman, Nuovo Cimento 45, 275 (1966) also displays SU(3) symmetry, with $t_3^v \sim t_8^v$ and $t_3^s \sim t_8^s$.
6. This derivation is due to H.J. Lipkin.
7. C.R. Sullivan, A.D. McInturff, D. Kotelchuck and C.E. Roos, Phys. Rev. Letters 18, 1163 (1967).
   D. Kotelchuck et al, Phys. Rev. Letters 18, 1166 (1967).
8. See the discussion in "Algebraic Theory" p. 122 or in paper 23 of "The Eightfold Way".
9. "Alg. Th." p. 134, and M. Gell-Mann and Y. Ne'eman, Annals of Physics 30, 360 (1965), republished in preprint form in Ref. 2.

10. These ideas are discussed in "Algebraic Theory", chapters VII, VIII, X. The main papers are reprinted in F. Dyson's "Symmetry Groups", W.A. Benjamin. An important omission is M. Gell-Mann, Phys. Rev. Letters 14, 72 (1965).

11. A.H. Rosenfeld et al, Rev. Mod. Phys. 39, 9 (1967) for Z_o^* (1865); the new Z^{++} (1860), (2125), (2280) are in J. Tyson et al, Phys. Rev. Letters 19, 255 (1967); see also R.J. Abrams et al, Phys. Rev. Letters 19, 259 (1967).

12. See "Algebraic Theory" p. 183, and H. Harari, Phys. Rev. Letters 17, 1303 (1966). The basic paper is V. de Alfaro et al, Phys. Letters 21, 576 (1966).

13. See "Algebraic Theory" p. 239. The basic paper is R.E. Dashen and M. Gell-Mann, Phys. Rev. Letters 17, 340 (1966).

14. See "Algebraic Theory" p. 236. The main papers are H. Harari, Phys. Rev. Letters 16, 964 (1966) and 17, 56 (1966); R. Gatto, L. Maiani and G. Preparata, Phys. Rev. Letters 16, 377 (1966) and Physics Letters 21, 459 (1966); I.S. Gerstein and B.W. Lee, Phys. Rev. Letters 16, 1060 (1966).

15. See chapter IX of "Algebraic Theory". The basic papers are N. Cabibbo, L. Horwitz and Y. Ne'eman, Physics Letters 22, 336 (1966), and N. Cabibbo, L. Horwitz, J.J.J. Kokkedee and Y. Ne'eman, Nuovo Cimento 45, 275 (1966).

16. See for example R. Omnes and M. Froissart, "Mandelstam Theory and Regge Poles", W.A. Benjamin, N.Y. (1963).

17. C. Frahm, Y. Ne'eman and J. Yellin, Proceedings of the Fourth (1967) Coral Gables Conference on Symmetry at High Energy, p. 2. There is an error in that paper. The erratum is available in the Tel-Aviv Un. preprint TAUP-18-67.

18. L. Horwitz and Y. Ne'eman, to be published. The suggestion is first presented in Y. Ne'eman, Racah Memorial Volume, to be published. (Available as TAUP 26-67).

5

INTRODUCTION TO CURRENT ALGEBRA[+]

Michael Nauenberg, Division of Natural Sciences, University of California, Santa Cruz, California

+ Work supported in part by a grant of the National Science Foundation.

INTRODUCTION

In 1962 Gell-Mann published an article entitled "Symmetries of Baryons and Mesons" which contains some of the most fundamental and fruitful ideas on the physics of the strongly interacting particles. In these lectures we will assume that you are familiar with the development of SU(3) symmetry, suggested independently by Ne'eman[2], and we will concentrate on the ideas now commonly known as current algebra[3].

One of the fundamental concepts in current algebra is the notion of a partially conserved axial vector current, P. C. A. C., which has been developed by several people[4,5] in the wake of the success of the Goldberger-Treiman relation. Nambu and his collaborators[6,7] went further to explore the consequences of an exact axial vector current conservation and obtained soft pion theorems which were later rediscovered by the methods of current algebra. We shall discuss later on the connections between these two approaches[+]. Other interesting consequences of P. C. A. C. for

---

+ The material on Nambu's technique contained in here is based on lectures given by Professor Marshall Baker.

strong interaction were obtained by Adler[8]. In his paper and in subsequent work[3], Gell-Mann emphasized the importance of the equal time commutation relation for vector and axial vector currents, but it took several years before methods were developed to deduce from these relations useful consequences for physical amplitudes. In 1965 Fubini and Furlan[9] developed a technique which was promptly applied by Adler[10] and independently by Weisberger[11] to calculate the renormalization of the axial coupling constant in β-decay in terms of the pion nucleon total cross-sections. Their success led to intensive theoretical activity to apply these methods to other problems connected with strong interaction and to solve some of the difficulties which had become apparent in earlier work.

We shall discuss in these lectures the Adler-Weisberger relation and select other applications to illustrate the scope of current algebra and some of its problems and limitations.

1. CURRENTS, CHARGES AND EQUAL TIME COMMUTATORS

We begin by considering general properties of the vector current $j_\mu^{V,\alpha}(x)$ and axial current $j_\mu^{A,\alpha}(x)$ of the hadrons. For orientation we define these currents in terms of spin one-half quark fields $\psi(x)$ which play no essential role here except to help us establish some notation and convention.

Let

$$j_\mu^{V,\alpha}(x) = \bar{\psi}(x)\gamma_\mu \frac{\lambda^\alpha}{2} \psi(x) \qquad (1.1)$$

and

$$j_\mu^{A,\alpha}(x) = \bar{\psi}(x)\gamma_\mu \gamma_5 \frac{\lambda^\alpha}{2} \psi(x) \tag{1.2}$$

where we adopt the Dirac γ-matrices

$$\gamma_o = \begin{bmatrix} 1 & 0 \\ 0 & -1 \end{bmatrix} , \quad \gamma_i = \begin{bmatrix} 0 & \sigma_i \\ -\sigma_i & 0 \end{bmatrix} \quad i = 1, 2, 3$$

and

$$\gamma_5 = i\gamma_0\gamma_1\gamma_2\gamma_3 = \begin{bmatrix} 0 & 1 \\ 1 & 0 \end{bmatrix} \tag{1.3}$$

The matrices λ^α are the generators of the internal symmetry, i.e. SU(2) or SU(3), for which we use Gell-Mann's convention[1, 3]. (See also Ne'eman's lectures). With this convention, the currents defined by Eqs. (1.1) and (1.2) are hermitian

$$j_\mu^{\alpha+}(x) = j_\mu^\alpha(x) \tag{1.4}$$

We will often drop the superscript V or A when we are dealing with properties common to the vector and axial currents.

The great importance of the hadron currents is due to the fact that they appear explicitly in the electromagnetic and in the weak interactions. For the electromagnetic interactions of the hadrons we have the Hamiltonian density

$$e\, j_\mu^{em}(x)\, A^\mu(x) \tag{1.5}$$

where the electromagnetic current j_μ^{em} takes the form

$$j_\mu^{em} = j_\mu^{v,3} + \frac{1}{\sqrt{3}} j_\mu^{v,8} \tag{1.6}$$

Only vector currents appear in the electromagnetic current. For the leptonic weak interaction of the hadrons we have the interaction

$$\frac{G}{\sqrt{2}} j_\mu^{w}(x)\, \ell^{\mu}(x) + \text{h.c.} \tag{1.7}$$

where the hadron weak current j_μ^w is given by

$$j_\mu^{w} = \left\{\cos\theta\,(j_\mu^{v,1} + ij_\mu^{v,2}) + \sin\theta\,(j_\mu^{v,4} + ij_\mu^{v,5})\right\}$$

$$-\left\{\cos\theta\,(j_\mu^{A,1} + ij_\mu^{A,2}) + \sin\theta\,(j_\mu^{A,4} + ij_\mu^{A,5})\right\} \tag{1.8}$$

and the corresponding lepton current ℓ_λ is

$$\ell_\lambda = \bar{\psi}_e \gamma_\lambda (1 - \gamma_5) \psi_{\nu e} + \bar{\psi}_\mu \gamma_\lambda (1 - \gamma_5) \psi_{\nu\mu} \tag{1.9}$$

Associated with the hadron current j_μ^α we define the charge

$$J^\alpha(t) = \int d^3x\, j_o^\alpha(\mathbf{x}, t) \tag{1.10}$$

which may be time dependent; we have

$$\frac{dJ^\alpha(t)}{dt} = i\left[H, J^\alpha(t)\right] \tag{1.11}$$

where H is the hadron Hamiltonian. Since the space integral of the three-divergence of the current vanishes, we also have

$$\frac{dJ^{\alpha}(t)}{dt} = \int d^3x \, \partial^{\mu} j_{\mu}^{\alpha}(\mathbf{x}, t) \tag{1.12}$$

A case of spacial interest occurs when a current j_{μ}^{α} is conserved, i.e.

$$\partial^{\mu} j_{\mu}^{\alpha}(x) = 0 \tag{1.13}$$

According to Eq. (1.12) the corresponding charge J^{α} is time independent and hence commutes with the Hamiltonian, Eq. (1.11). An example are the vector currents with components $\alpha = 1, 2, 3$ corresponding to isotopic spin conservation, and $\alpha = 8$ for hypercharge. These charges satisfy commutation relations

$$\left[J^{v, \alpha}, J^{v, \beta} \right] = i \epsilon_{\alpha \beta \gamma} J^{v, \gamma} \tag{1.14}$$

and

$$\left[J^{v, \alpha}, J^{v, 8} \right] = 0 \tag{1.15}$$

Equation (1.14) is the Lie algebra for SU(2), or isospin, which is an exact symmetry of the strong interaction Hamiltonian.

Gell-Mann[1,3] generalized these commutation relations to time dependent charges, including axial charges, by considering these commutators at equal times, and made the fundamental assumption that the commutator of two axial charges is proportional to the vector charges. This leads to a closed algebra under commutation:

$$\left[J^{v, \alpha}(t), J^{v, \beta}(t) \right] = i f_{\alpha \beta \gamma} J^{v, \gamma}(t) \tag{1.16}$$

$$\left[J^{v, \alpha}(t), J^{A, \beta}(t) \right] = i f_{\alpha \beta \gamma} J^{A, \gamma}(t) \tag{1.17}$$

$$\left[J^{A,\alpha}(t),\ J^{A,\beta}(t)\right] = i f_{\alpha\beta\gamma} J^{V,\gamma}(t) \qquad (1.18)$$

where $f_{\alpha\beta\gamma}$ are the structure constants for SU(3), defined by

$$\left[\lambda^{\alpha},\ \lambda^{\beta}\right] = i f_{\alpha\beta\gamma} \lambda^{\beta} \qquad (1.19)$$

These equal time commutation relations can be deduced directly from the definition of the currents in terms of the quark field, Eqs. (1.1) and (1.2). From the canonical commutation relations for the quark fields we obtain

$$\left[j_0^{V,\alpha}(x),\ j_\mu^{V,\beta}(y)\right]_{x_0=y_0} = i f_{\alpha\beta\gamma} j_\mu^{V,\gamma}(x)\delta^3(\mathbf{x}-\mathbf{y}) \qquad (1.20)$$

$$\left[j_0^{V,\alpha}(x),\ j_\mu^{A,\beta}(y)\right]_{x_0=y_0} = i f_{\alpha\beta\gamma} j_\mu^{A,\gamma}(x)\delta^3(\mathbf{x}-\mathbf{y}) \qquad (1.21)$$

$$\left[j_0^{A,\alpha}(x),\ j_\mu^{A,\beta}(y)\right]_{x_0=y_0} = i f_{\alpha\beta\gamma} j_\mu^{V,\gamma}(x)\delta^3(\mathbf{x}-\mathbf{y}) \qquad (1.22)$$

The equal time commutation relations for current densities, Eqs. (1.20) - (1.22) are assumed to be valid irrespective of the existence of quark fields and constitute the fundamental equations in current algebra. Integrating over space coordinates we get back Eqs. (1.16) - (1.18) for the charges. We postpone the discussion of additional terms proportional to gradients of the $\delta^3(\mathbf{x}-\mathbf{y})$ function [12] which must be present in Eqs. (1.20) - (1.22) for the space components, $\mu = 1, 2$, or 3. (See section 7).

It is important to note that while the equal time commutators between two vector charges, and between vector and axial charges,

Eqs. (1.16) and (1.17), are quite general and model independent, the validity of the axial-axial equal time commutator, Eq. (1.18) is an assumption. However, it has been confirmed by the success of the Adler-Weisberger relation (see section 5).

The two linear combinations $J^{V,\alpha} + J^{A,\alpha}$ and $J^{V,\alpha} - J^{A,\alpha}$ commute with each other and satisfy separately the SU(3) commutation relations, Eq. (1.19). Thus, we refer to the algebra of the vector and axial charges as SU(3) x SU(3).

2. FORM FACTORS AND CURRENT CONSERVATION

An important consequence of the non-linearity of the current-current equal time commutators, Eqs. (1.20) - (1.22), is that the magnitude or normalization of the currents is fixed. This important fact was stressed by Gell-Mann[1], who pointed out that Eq. (1.22) could be used to calculate the renormalization of the axial vector coupling constant. We shall go in detail into this calculation first carried out by Adler[10] and Weisberger[11]. First, let us see how this comes about in the case of a conserved vector current. For simplicity we consider the matrix elements of $j_\mu^{V,\alpha}$, $\alpha = 1, 2, 3$ between spin-zero single particle states ($\mathbf{p}$ a), where $\mathbf{p}$ is the momentum and a labels the third component of the isospin. By Lorentz covariance we have

$$\sqrt{2p_o' 2p_o}\,(\mathbf{p}'a'|\, j_\mu^{V,\alpha}\,|\,\mathbf{p}\, a) = \left\{ f_+(p' + p)_\mu + f_-(p' - p)_\mu \right\} t^\alpha_{a'a} \tag{2.1}$$

where $f_\pm$ are form factors which depend only on the invariant momentum transfer $q^2 = (p' - p)^2$, and $t^{\alpha}_{a'a}$ are the appropriate Clebsch-Gordan coefficients to couple a and a' into isospin one.

The conservation of isospin implies the vanishing of the divergence of the vector current

$$(\mathbf{p}'a' \,|\, \partial^{\mu} j^{\alpha}_{\mu} \,|\, \mathbf{p}\, a) = iq^{\mu} (\mathbf{p}'a \,|\, j^{\alpha}_{\mu} \,|\, \mathbf{p}\, a) = 0 \tag{2.2}$$

Substituting Eq. (2.1) in Eq. (2.2) we get

$$f_+(m'^2 - m^2) + q^2 f_- = 0 \tag{2.3}$$

where m and m' are the particle masses. For equal masses current conservation simply implies

$$f_-(q^2) = 0 \tag{2.4}$$

Now consider the matrix element of the charge $J^{v,\alpha}$ between the one particle states. From Eq. (1.10) and translation invariance we get

$$\begin{aligned}(\mathbf{p}'a' \,|\, J^{v,\alpha} \,|\, \mathbf{p}\, a) &= \int d^3\mathbf{x}\, e^{i(p'-p)x} (\mathbf{p}'a' \,|\, j_o^{v,\alpha} \,|\, \mathbf{p}\, a) \\ &= (2\pi)^3 \delta^3(\mathbf{p}' - \mathbf{p}) e^{i(p_o' - p_o)t} (\mathbf{p}'a' \,|\, j_o^{v,\alpha} \,|\, \mathbf{p}\, a)\end{aligned} \tag{2.5}$$

Time independence of the charges $J^{v,\alpha}$ then implies

$$(\mathbf{p}'a' \,|\, j_o^{v,\alpha} \,|\, \mathbf{p}\, a) = 0 \quad \text{for} \quad m' \neq m \tag{2.6}$$

In other words, $J^{v,\alpha}$ has only diagonal matrix elements between states of the same energy and momentum, and according to Eqs. (2.1), (2.4) and (2.5)

$$\sqrt{2p_o' 2p_o}\, (\mathbf{p}'a'|\, J^{v,\alpha}\,|\,\mathbf{p}a) = (2\pi)^3 \delta^3(\mathbf{p}' - \mathbf{p}) 2p_o f_+(0) t^\alpha_{a'a}$$

$$(2.7)$$

To determine $f_+(0)$ we insert a complete set of intermediate states in the corresponding matrix element of the commutation relation between vector charges, Eq. (1.14)

$$\sum_n \left[(\mathbf{p}'a'|\, J^{v,\alpha}\,|\, n)(n|\, J^{v,\beta}\,|\,\mathbf{p}a) - (\mathbf{p}'a'|\, J^{v,\beta}\,|\, n)(n|\, J^{v,\alpha}\,|\,\mathbf{p}a) \right]$$

$$= i\varepsilon_{\alpha\beta\gamma}\,(\mathbf{p}'a'|\, J^{v,\gamma}\,|\,\mathbf{p}a) \qquad (2.8)$$

and observing that only the single particle intermediate states can contribute, in virtue of Eq. (2.6), we obtain

$$f_+^2(0)\left[t^\alpha,\, t^\beta \right] = i\varepsilon_{\alpha\beta\gamma}\, t^\gamma f_+(0) \qquad (2.9)$$

Since t^α is a matrix representation of the algebra of SU(2),

$$f_+(0) = 1 \qquad (2.10)$$

Thus, we see how the commutation relations normalize charges in the simple case that the current is conserved. The more complicated case of a non-conserved current, e.g., the axial current, will be treated in section 5.

3. PARITY, CHARGE CONJUGATION AND TIME REVERSAL

We want to discuss briefly the transformation properties of the currents under parity P, charge conjugation C and time reversal T, and the restrictions which these impose on the current matrix elements. These properties can readily be deduced from the expression for the currents in terms of the quark field ψ, Eqs. (1.1) and (1.2), by considering the conventional transformation of ψ under P, C and T. We leave this as an elementary exercise and quote here only the results:

$$P j_\mu^\alpha(\mathbf{x},t) P^+ = \eta_P(\mu) j_\mu^\alpha(-\mathbf{x},t)\,; \quad \eta_P^V(0) = 1 \quad \eta_P^V(i) = -1 \quad i = 1,2,3$$
$$\eta_P^A(0) = -1 \quad \eta_P(i) = +1 \tag{3.1}$$

$$C j_\mu^\alpha(\mathbf{x},t) C^+ = \eta_C(\mu)\delta_\alpha j_\mu^\alpha(\mathbf{x},t)\,; \quad \eta_C^V = -1 \quad \delta_\alpha = 1\,,\ \lambda_\alpha \text{ real}$$
$$\eta_C^A = 1 \quad \delta_\alpha = -1\,,\ \lambda_\alpha \text{ imaginary} \tag{3.2}$$

$$T j_\mu^\alpha(\mathbf{x},t) T^{-1} = \eta_T(\mu)\delta_\alpha j_\mu^\alpha(\mathbf{x},-t)\,; \quad \eta_T(0) = 1 \quad \eta_T(i) = -1 \tag{3.3}$$

It is important to note that P and C are unitary operators while T is anti-unitary, i.e., $(a|T^+T|b) = (a|b)^*$.

For an application of Eqs. (3.1) to (3.3) let us return to our previous example of the matrix elements of a current between spinless single particle states, Eq. (2.1). Under parity, we have

$$P\,|\,\mathbf{p}\,a) = \xi_p\,|-\mathbf{p}\,a) \tag{3.4}$$

where ξ_p = +(-) for scalar (pseudoscalar) particles; hence

$$(\mathbf{p}'a'|\, j_\mu^\alpha \,|\mathbf{p}a) = (\mathbf{p}'a'|\, P^+ P j_\mu^\alpha P^+ P \,|\mathbf{p}\, a)$$

$$= \eta_P(\mu)\xi_{P'}\xi_P(-\mathbf{p}'a'|\, j_\mu^\alpha \,|-\mathbf{p}\, a) \qquad (3.5)$$

Substituting Eq. (2.1) in Eq. (3.5), we see that the vector (axial) current matrix elements vanishes if the states labeled by a and a' have opposite (equal) intrinsic parity. Under time reversal

$$T\,|\,\mathbf{p}\, a) = |-\mathbf{p}\, a) \qquad (3.6)$$

and

$$(\mathbf{p}'a'|\, j_\mu^\alpha \,|\mathbf{p}\, a)^* = (\mathbf{p}'a'|\, T^+ T j_\mu^\alpha T^{-1} T\,|\mathbf{p}\, a)$$

$$= \eta_T(\mu)\delta_\alpha(-\mathbf{p}'a'\,|\, j_\mu^\alpha \,|-\mathbf{p}\, a) \qquad (3.7)$$

To satisfy Eq. (3.7), the form factors f_+ and f_- in Eq. (2.1) must be real. Charge conjugation does not lead to any further restriction in this case.

For matrix elements of the vector and axial currents between single particle states of spin one-half, Lorentz covariance and parity imply that the non-vanishing terms are

$$\sqrt{2p_o' 2p_o}\;(p'|\, j_\mu^{v,\alpha} \,|p) = \bar{u}(p')\Big\{F_1^v \gamma_\mu$$

$$+ F_2^v[\gamma_\mu, \not{q}] + iF_3^v q_\mu\Big\}\frac{\lambda^\alpha}{2}\, u(p) \qquad (3.8)$$

$$\sqrt{2p_o' 2p_o}\,(p' \mid j_\mu^{A,\alpha} \mid p) = \bar{u}(p') \Big\{ F_1^A \gamma_\mu + F_2^A q_\mu$$

$$+ iF_3(p' + p)_\mu \Big\} \gamma_5 \frac{\lambda^\alpha}{2} \mu(p) \qquad (3.9)$$

where the form factors F_i are functions of $q^2 = (p' - p)^2$. In Eqs. (3.8) and (3.9) we have supressed the spin and SU(3) indeces of the particle states.

Conservation of the vector current leads to the condition

$$F_1^v(m' - m) + iF_3^v q^2 = 0 \qquad (3.10)$$

Time reversal requires that the form factors F_i be real. In the special case that we are dealing with matrix elements between different components of the same single particle states, we obtain a further restriction from hermiticity and time reversal properties of the currents:

$$F_3 = 0 \qquad (3.11)$$

This condition is also implied by charge conjugation. Note that in the case of conserved vector currents this condition is already satisfied, i.e., Eq. (3.10) for m = m'. Incidentally, this is the reason why it is not possible to test charge conjugation or time reversal violation of the electromagnetic current by measuring the electromagnetic form factors.

Further examples of the restrictions imposed by P, C and T will be given later.

4. POLE DOMINANCE OF THE DIVERGENCE OF THE AXIAL VECTOR CURRENT

In this section we discuss a fundamental hypothesis which is the cornerstone in the applications of current algebra. It is sometimes referred to as P.C.A.C. which stands for partially conserved axial current, but perhaps more properly it should be called P.D.D.A.C. for pion pole dominance of the divergence of the axial current.

Let us consider the matrix elements of the axial current between the vacuum and a pion state with momentum q and isospin β. It has the form

$$\sqrt{2q_o}\,(0\,|\,j_\mu^{A,\alpha}\,|\,\pi^\beta, q) = i\,\frac{f_\pi}{\sqrt{2}}\,q_\mu\,\delta_{\alpha\beta} \tag{4.1}$$

where f_π is real by time reversal. We have introduced a factor $\sqrt{2}$ in order that it does not appear in the corresponding matrix element for charged pions, i.e.,

$$\sqrt{2q_o}\,(0\,|\,j_\mu^{A,\mp}\,|\,\pi^\pm, q) = \mp\, i f_\pi q_\mu$$

where $j_\mu^{A,\pm} = j_\mu^{A,1} \pm i j_\mu^{A,2}$ and $|\,\pi^\pm q) = \mp \frac{1}{\sqrt{2}} \left\{|\,\pi^1, q) + i\,|\,\pi^2, q)\right\}$

(under charge conjugation $C\,|\,\pi^\pm q) = -\,|\,\pi^\mp q)$)

The decay rate of the charged pion is directly determined by f_π. According to Eq. (4.1), the corresponding matrix element of the divergence of the axial current $\partial^\mu j_\mu^{A,\alpha}$ is given by

$$\sqrt{2q_o}\,(0\,|\,\partial^\mu j_\mu^{A,\alpha}\,|\,\pi^\beta q) = \frac{i f_\pi}{\sqrt{2}}\, m_\pi^2\, \delta_{\alpha\beta} \tag{4.2}$$

Since the matrix element of $\partial^\mu j_\mu^{A,\beta}$ between the vacuum and the single pion state does not vanish, it can be used as an interpolating field ϕ^α by the requirement

$$\sqrt{2q_o}\,(0\,|\,\phi^\alpha\,|\,\pi^\beta q) = \delta_{\alpha\beta} \tag{4.3}$$

Hence, we set $\partial^\mu j_\mu^{A,\alpha} = C_\pi \phi^\alpha$ (4.4)

where $C_\pi = \dfrac{f_\pi m_\pi^2}{\sqrt{2}}$

Equation (4.4) is sometimes referred to as P.C.A.C., but it should be understood that it is just a definition of an interpolating field for the pion[13]. We shall make this clear by proving the following theorem:

$$\lim_{q^2 \to m_\pi^2} (q^2 - m_\pi^2)(a\text{ out}\,|\,j_\mu^{A,\alpha}\,|\,b\text{ in}) = \frac{if_\pi}{\sqrt{2}}\, q_\mu (a\text{ out}\,|\,j^\alpha\,|\,b\text{ in}) \tag{4.5}$$

where $|a\text{ out})$ and $|b\text{ in})$ are hadronic states with four momentum p_a and p_b respectively, $q = p_b - p_a$, and j^α is the source function of the pion with isospin α. In the case that the limit $q^2 \to m_\pi^2$ implies unphysical values of p_a and p_b, Eq. (4.5) is understood to be valid for an appropriately continued matrix element.

To prove Eq. (4.5), we will make use of the L.S.Z. formalism.

We consider for simplicity the case that the state $|a\ \text{out})$ consists of a single spin zero meson with momentum k and mass m. Removing this meson from the out state, we get

$$\sqrt{2k_o}\,(a\ \text{out}\,|\, j_\mu^{A,\alpha}\,|\, b\ \text{in}) =$$

$$= i\int d^4x e^{ikx}(0\,|\left[j(x), j_\mu^{A,\alpha}(0)\right]|\, b\ \text{in})\,\theta(x_o) \qquad (4.6)$$

where j(x) is the source function of the meson. We have neglected the possible contribution of equal time commutators in Eq. (4.6), because these do not contribute to Eq. (4.5). The only contributions which we need to consider are the singularities of Eq. (4.6) where $q^2 \longrightarrow m_\pi^2$. These can be obtained by examining the absorptive part A_μ of Eq. (4.6) which is simply obtained by dropping the step function and replacing i by 1/2.

$$A_\mu = \frac{1}{2}\int d^4x e^{ikx}(0\,|\left[j(x), j_\mu^{A,\alpha}(0)\right]|\, b\ \text{in}) \qquad (4.7)$$

Introducing a complete set of intermediate states $|n)$ and using translational invariance, we can integrate over the space-time coordinate x

$$A_\mu = \frac{1}{2}\sum_n (2\pi)^4\Big\{\delta^4(k-p_n)(0\,|\,j\,|\,n)(n\,|\,j_\mu^{A,\alpha}\,|\,b\ \text{in})$$

$$-\ \delta^4(q-p_n)(0\,|\,j_\mu^{A,\alpha}\,|\,n)(n\,|\,j\,|\,b\ \text{in})\Big\} \qquad (4.8)$$

The first sum in Eq. (4.8) must vanish because $(0\,|\,j\,|\,n) = 0$ for $p_n^2 = k^2 = m^2$. To get the contributions of A_μ for $q^2 = m_\pi^2$, we need to consider only intermediate states $|n)$ in the second sum for which $p_n^2 = m_\pi^2$, i.e., single pion states. Substituting Eq. (4.1) in Eq. (4.8) we obtain

$$A_\mu^\pi = -\pi\delta(q^2 - m_\pi^2)\, i \frac{f_\pi}{\sqrt{2}}\, q_\mu\, (\pi^\alpha q\,|\, j \,|\, b \text{ in}) \qquad (4.9)$$

To get the corresponding contribution to Eq. (4.6) we just replace $\pi\delta(q^2 - m_\pi^2)$ by the pole $\frac{1}{(m_\pi^2 - q^2)}$. Observing that

$$(\pi^\alpha q\,|\, j \,|\, b \text{ in}) = (a \text{ out}\,|\, j^\alpha \,|\, b \text{ in}) \qquad (4.10)$$

we obtain the pole contribution

$$(a \text{ out}\,|\, j_\mu^{A,\alpha} \,|\, b \text{ in})\Big|_{\text{pole}} =$$

$$= +i\, \frac{f_\pi q_\mu}{\sqrt{2}}\, \frac{1}{(q^2 - m_\pi^2)}\, (a \text{ out}\,|\, j^\alpha \,|\, b \text{ in}) \qquad (4.11)$$

which in the limit $q^2 \rightarrow m_\pi^2$ gives the exact theorem Eq. (4.5). From Eq. (4.5) we find in particular that

$$\lim_{q^2 \rightarrow m_\pi^2} (q^2 - m_\pi^2)(a \text{ out}\,|\, \partial^\mu j_\mu^{A,\alpha} \,|\, b \text{ in}) =$$

$$= -\frac{f_\pi m_\pi^2}{\sqrt{2}}\, (a \text{ out}\,|\, j^\alpha \,|\, b \text{ in}) \qquad (4.12)$$

Equation (4.12) shows explicitly that

$$\phi^{\alpha} = \frac{\sqrt{2}}{f_{\pi} m_{\pi}^{2}} \partial^{\mu} j_{\mu}^{A,\alpha}$$

is an interpolating field of the pion, where the pion source function is defined in the usual manner by the equation

$$(\Box + m_{\pi}^{2}) \phi^{\alpha} = j^{\alpha}$$

The fundamental hypothesis of P. D. D. A. C. is that Eq. (4.12) remains approximately valid for q^2 in the neighborhood of m_{π}^{2},

$$(q^{2} - m_{\pi}^{2})(\text{a out} \mid \partial^{\mu} j_{\mu}^{A,\alpha} \mid \text{b in}) \cong - \frac{f_{\pi}}{\sqrt{2}} m_{\pi}^{2} (\text{a out} \mid j^{\alpha} \mid \text{b in}) \tag{4.13}$$

This assumption of smoothness is used to approximate the right-hand side of Eq. (4.12), which correponds to a physical process involving a pion, to the matrix element of the left-hand side which, in the limit $q \rightarrow 0$, can in certain cases be evaluated in terms of observable quantities. However, P. D. D. A. C. has no meaning until we specify how to continue both sides of Eq. (4.13) to unphysical values of the momentum q. This is usually done by means of the L. S. Z. reduction formula.

The first application that was made of P. D. D. A. C. is the famous Goldberger-Treiman relation[14]. In this case |a out) and |b in) correspond to single nucleon states, the left-hand side of Eqs. (4.5) and (4.13) can be expressed in terms of the axial form factors, Eq. (3.9), while the right-hand side defines the renormalized pion nucleon coupling constant $g_{\pi n}$,

$$\lim_{q^2 \to m_\pi^2} \sqrt{2p_a^o 2p_b^o}\,(p_a | j_\pi^\alpha | p_b) = g_{\pi n}\, \bar{u}(p_a) i\gamma_5 \tau^\alpha u(p_b) \quad (4.14)$$

Substituting Eq. (3.9) in Eq. (4.5) we find the exact relations

$$\lim_{q^2 \to m_\pi^2} (q^2 - m_\pi^2) F_1^A(q^2) = 0 \quad (4.15)$$

and

$$\lim_{q^2 \to m_\pi^2} (q^2 - m_\pi^2) F_2^A(q^2) = -\sqrt{2}\, f_\pi g_{\pi n} \quad (4.16)$$

Observe that only F_2^A has a pole at $q^2 = m_\pi^2$.

Now let us apply P.D.D.A.C. Eq. (4.13) which implies in this case

$$(q^2 - m_\pi^2)\left\{2M_n F_1^A(q^2) + q^2 F_2^A(q^2)\right\} \cong -\sqrt{2}\, f_\pi g_{\pi n} m_\pi^2 \quad (4.17)$$

provided $q^2 \sim m_\pi^2$. In particular, for $q^2 = 0$, Eq. (4.17) leads to the Goldberger - Treiman relation

$$f_\pi \cong \sqrt{2}\, \frac{M_n F_1^A(0)}{g_{\pi n}} \quad (4.18)$$

Substituting on the right-hand side the measured values $F_1^A(0) = 1.18$ and $g_{\pi n} = 13.6$ we obtain $f_\pi^{th} = .82\, m_\pi$ in fair agreement with the value $f_\pi = .93\, m_\pi$ from the observed π decay rate $\Gamma(\pi \to \mu + \nu) = 3.8 \times 10^7\ sec^{-1}$.

The hipothesis of P.D.D.A.C. is a bold assumption whose

validity rests on the agreement obtained with its prediction and experiments. Nambu[5,6,7] has considered a theory in which the divergence of the axial current vanishes identically

$$\partial^{\mu} j_{\mu}^{A,\alpha} = 0 \tag{4.19}$$

It is clear in this case that according to Eq. (4.2), the pion mass must vanish, and from Eq. (3.9) we observe that

$$F_2^A(q^2) = -\frac{2M_n F_1^A(p^2)}{q^2} \tag{4.20}$$

must be satisfied for all q^2. We note that F_2^A now has a pole at $q^2 = 0$, and Eq. (4.5) or Eq. (4.16) gives the residue

$$\lim_{q^2 \to 0} q^2 F_2^A(q^2) = -\sqrt{2}\, f_\pi g_{\pi n} \tag{4.21}$$

Eqs. (4.20) and (4.21) then lead to the Goldberger-Treiman relation, Eq. (4.18), as an exact relation.

We shall see that all the approximate relations obtained from the P.D.D.A.C. hypothesis are exact in the limit of vanishing divergence of the axial current. This is a very attractive theory which puts the axial current and the vector current on a similar footing but the main problem, in this case, is to explain the origin of the pion mass.

5. RENORMALIZATION OF THE AXIAL VECTOR COUPLING CONSTANT: THE ADLER-WEISBERGER RELATION AND THE PION NUCLEON SCATTERING LENGTHS

In his fundamental paper of 1962,[1] Gell-Mann pointed out that the axial current-current commutation relation Eq. (1.21) would fix the value of the renormalization of the axial coupling constant in weak interactions, i.e., the magnitude of $F_1^A(q^2)$ at $q^2 = 0$. The calculation of $F_1^A(0)$ in terms of pion nucleon parameters, however, was not carried out until several years later by Adler[10] and independently by Weisberger[11] using a technique developed by Fubini and Furlan[9]. In this section we discuss the Adler-Weisberger relation for $F_1^A(0)$ in terms of pion-proton total cross-sections and also in terms of the pion-proton scattering lengths[15].

We start with the fundamental P.D.D.A.C. hypothesis Eq. (4.13) for the matrix element of the divergence of the axial current $\partial^\mu j_\mu^{A,\beta}$ between the state $|\mathbf{p}, \mathbf{q}\, \alpha \text{ out})$ of a nucleon with momentum $\mathbf{p}$ and a pion with momentum $\mathbf{q}$ and isospin α, and the state $|p)$ of a single nucleon with momentum $\mathbf{p}$. The spin and isospin labels of the nucleon do not need to be considered explicitly. Applying the L.S.Z. reduction to the pion in the out state we get

$$\sqrt{2q_o}\,(pq\alpha\,|\,\partial^\mu j_\mu^{A,\beta}\,|\,p) = \frac{i}{C_\pi}\int d^4x e^{iqx}(\Box + m_\pi^2)$$

$$(p\,|\left[\partial^\mu j_\mu^{A,\alpha}(x),\, \partial^\nu j_\nu^{A,\beta}(0)\right]|\,p)\,\theta(x_o) \qquad (5.1)$$

where we have substituted $\frac{1}{C_\pi}\partial^\mu j_\mu^{A,\alpha}$ as an interpolating field for the pion (see section 4). Equation (5.1) can also be written in the form

$$\sqrt{2q_o}\,(p\,q\,\alpha\,|\,\partial^{\mu} j_{\mu}^{A,\beta}\,|\,p) = -\lim_{q^2 \to m_\pi^2} (q^2 - m_\pi^2)$$

$$\cdot \frac{i}{C_\pi} \int d^4x e^{iqx} (p\,|\,[\partial^{\mu} j_{\mu}^{A,\alpha}(x), \partial^{\nu} j^{A,\beta}(0)]\,|\,p)\theta(x_o)$$

(5.2)

as can be shown by integration by parts, neglecting surface terms. The latter can be justified by letting q_o have a small positive imaginary part. The P.D.D.A.C. hypothesis, Eq. (4.13), now gives us an expression for the off-mass shell forward pion nucleon scattering amplitude

$$(p\,q\,\alpha\,|\,j^{\beta}\,|\,p) = \frac{(q^2 - m_\pi^2)^2}{C_\pi^2}\, i \int d^4x e^{iqx}$$

$$\cdot\,(p\,|\,[\partial^{\mu} j_{\mu}^{A,\alpha}(x), \partial^{\nu} j_{\nu}^{A,\beta}(0)]\,|\,p)\,\theta(x_o) \qquad (5.3)$$

To proceed further, it is convenient to introduce the tensor $T_{\mu\nu}^{\alpha\beta}(q)$ defined as the Fourier transform of the retarded commutator of two axial currents

$$T_{\mu\nu}^{\alpha\beta}(q) = 2p_o\, i \int d^4x e^{iqx} (p\,|\,[j_{\mu}^{A,\alpha}(x), j_{\nu}^{A,\beta}(0)]\,|\,p)\,\theta(x_o)$$

(5.4)

We now evaluate $q^{\mu} q^{\nu} T_{\mu\nu}^{\alpha\beta}$ by observing that multiplication by q_{μ} in Eq. (5.4) corresponds to the substitution

$$q_{\mu} e^{iqx} = -i \frac{\partial e^{iqx}}{\partial x^{\mu}}$$

under the integral. Integrating by parts, again dropping the surface term we obtain

$$q^{\mu} T^{\alpha\beta}_{\mu\nu} = -2p_o \int d^4x e^{iqx} \Big\{ (p| \big[\partial^{\mu} j^{A,\alpha}_{\mu}(x),\ j^{A,\beta}_{\nu}(0) \big] | p) \theta(x_o)$$

$$+ (p| \big[j^{A,\alpha}_{o}(x),\ j^{A,\beta}_{\nu}(0) \big] | p) \delta(x_o) \Big\} \qquad (5.5)$$

and repeating this operation we get

$$q^{\mu} q^{\nu} T^{\alpha\beta}_{\mu\nu} = 2p_o i \int d^4x e^{iqx} \Big\{ (p| \big[\partial^{\mu} j^{A,\alpha}_{\mu}(x),\ \partial^{\nu} j^{A,\beta}_{\nu}(0) \big] | p) \theta(x_o)$$

$$- (p| \big[\partial^{\mu} j^{A,\alpha}_{\mu}(x),\ j^{A,\beta}_{o}(0) \big] | p) \delta(x_o)$$

$$+ iq^{\nu} (p| \big[j^{A,\alpha}_{o}(x),\ j^{A,\beta}_{\nu}(0) \big] | p) \delta(x_o) \qquad (5.6)$$

The first term on the right-hand side of Eq. (5.6) is the desired expression for off-mass shell-forward pion nucleon scattering, Eq. (5.3), while the last term contains the equal-time commutator between two axial currents, whose form has been conjectured by Gell-Mann, Eq. (1.22). It can be readily shown by differentiating Eq. (1.22), that the equal-time commutator appearing in the second term on the right-hand side of Eq. (5.6) must be symmetric in α and β; therefore we set

$$\big[\partial^{\mu} j^{A,\alpha}_{\mu}(x),\ j^{A,\beta}_{o}(y) \big]_{x_o = y_o} = \delta_{\alpha\beta} \sigma(x) \delta^3(\mathbf{x} - \mathbf{y}) \qquad (5.7)$$

where $\sigma(x)$ is a scalar operator.

Collecting these results, we obtain

$$q^{\mu} q^{\nu} T^{\alpha\beta}_{\mu\nu}(q) = \frac{C_{\pi}^{2} M^{\alpha\beta}(q)}{(q^{2} - m_{\pi}^{2})} - i\epsilon_{\alpha\beta\gamma} 2p_{o} q^{\nu} (p \mid j_{\nu}^{v,\gamma} \mid p)$$

$$- i\delta_{\alpha\beta} 2p_{o} (p \mid \sigma \mid p) \qquad (5.8)$$

where $M^{\alpha\beta}(q)$ is the forward pion-nucleon amplitude

$$M^{\alpha\beta} = \sqrt{2q_{o}}\, 2p_{o} (\mathbf{p}\, \mathbf{q}\, \alpha \mid j_{\pi}^{\beta} \mid p)$$

which can be decomposed according to isospin into the form

$$M^{\alpha\beta} = \bar{u}(p) \Big\{ M_{+} \delta_{\alpha\beta} + M_{-} \frac{1}{2} [\tau_{\alpha}, \tau_{\beta}] \Big\} u(p) \qquad (5.9)$$

For arbitrary values of q, the tensor $T^{\alpha\beta}_{\mu\nu}(q)$ appearing in Eq. (5.8) is not known, but we can achieve an essential simplification by taken the limit $q \to 0$, because in this case, only singular terms in $T^{\alpha\beta}_{\mu\nu}$ can contribute to $q^{\mu} q^{\nu} T^{\alpha\beta}_{\mu\nu}$. These correspond to the nucleon pole terms shown in Fig. 1,

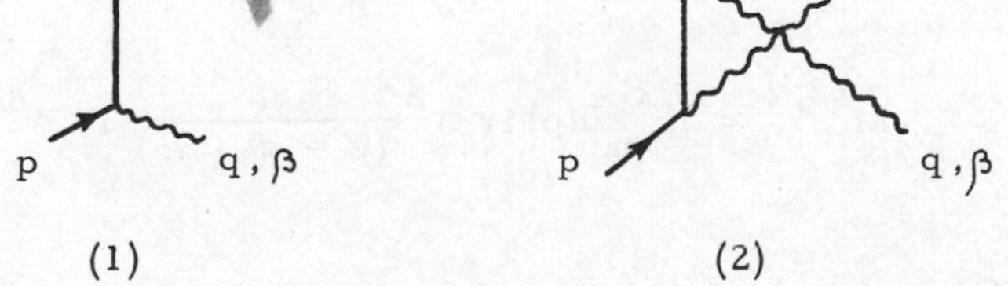

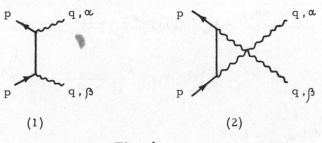

Fig. 1

and are given by

$$T^{\alpha\beta,1}_{\mu\nu} = i(F^A_1)^2 \bar{u}(p)\gamma_\mu\gamma_5 \frac{\tau^\alpha}{2} \frac{i}{(\not{p} + \not{q} - m)} \gamma_\nu\gamma_5 \frac{\tau^\beta}{2} u(p) \tag{5.10}$$

$$T^{\alpha\beta,2}_{\mu\nu} = i(F^A_1)^2 \bar{u}(p)\gamma_\nu\gamma_5 \frac{\tau^\beta}{2} \frac{i}{(\not{p} - \not{q} - m)} \gamma_\mu\gamma_5 \frac{\tau^\alpha}{2} u(p) \tag{5.11}$$

Note that the denominator in Eqs. (5.10) and (5.11) vanishes as $q \to 0$. We have dropped the contribution from F^A_2, since it does not lead to any singularities as $q \to 0$. Hence

$$q^\mu q^\nu (T^{\alpha\beta,1}_{\mu\nu} + T^{\alpha\beta,2}_{\mu\nu}) = -(F^A_1)^2 \bar{u}(p)\Big\{\frac{\not{q}}{4}\left[\tau^\alpha, \tau^\beta\right] - \frac{Mq^2 \tau^\alpha\tau^\beta}{2(q^2 + 2q p)} - \frac{Mq^2 \tau^\beta\tau^\alpha}{2(q^2 - 2q p)}\Big\} u(p) \tag{5.12}$$

There appears to be a complication with Eq. (5.12), because the limit $q \to 0$ of the last two terms is ambiguous. However, note that the corresponding pole terms in forward π-N scattering are given by

$$M^{\alpha\beta,1} = ig^2_{\pi n} \bar{u}(p)\, i\gamma_5\tau^\alpha \frac{i}{(\not{p} + \not{q} - m)} i\gamma_5\tau^\beta u(p) \tag{5.13}$$

$$M^{\alpha\beta,2} = ig^2_{\pi n} \bar{u}(p)\, i\gamma_5\tau^\beta \frac{i}{(\not{p} - \not{q} - m)} i\gamma_5\tau^\alpha u(p) \tag{5.14}$$

Simplifying, we have

$$M^{\alpha\beta,1} + M^{\alpha\beta,2} = - g_{\pi n}^2 \bar{u}(p) \not{q} \left[\frac{\tau^\alpha \tau^\beta}{q^2 + 2qp} - \frac{\tau^\beta \tau^\alpha}{q^2 - 2qp} \right] u(p) \tag{5.15}$$

Substituting these pole terms in Eq. (5.8) we see that in virtue of the Goldberger-Treiman relation, Eq. (4.18), and the definition $C_\pi = f_\pi m_\pi^2 / \sqrt{2}$, Eq. (4.4), the last two pole terms in Eq. (5.12) cancel with the πN poles, Eq. (5.15). Hence we obtain from Eq. (5.8) the following two relations in the limit $q = 0$

$$M_+^{N.P.}(\nu, q^2)\Big|_{\substack{\nu = 0 \\ q^2 = 0}} = \left(\frac{\sqrt{2}}{f_\pi}\right)^2 \sigma \tag{5.16}$$

$$\left[\frac{M_N}{g_{\pi n}}\right]^2 \frac{\partial M_-^{N.P.}}{\partial \nu}(\nu, q^2)\Big|_{\substack{\nu = 0 \\ q^2 = 0}} = \frac{1}{\left[F_1^A(0)\right]^2} - 1 \tag{5.17}$$

where we have put the superscript N. P. on M_+ and M_- to indicate that these are the amplitudes without the nucleon pole terms.

Equation (5.16) was first obtained by Adler[8] with $\sigma = 0$ by a somewhat different procedure, in which he started with P. D. D. A. C., Eq. (4.13), and then proceeded to take the limit $q \to 0$ without reducing the outgoing pion. For forward π-N scattering it is not possible to take this limit without first taking both pions off the mass-shell, a procedure which we have seen gives rise to the σ-commutator. Experimentally, however, it turns out that σ is small in this case. We can see this by comparing Eq. (5.16) with the corresponding value of $M_+^{N.P.}$ at the nearest physical point, the π-N threshold energy, because we have assumed that the continuation to unphysical values of pion momentum is smooth. At threshold, M_+ can be expressed in terms of the $\pi^\pm$ - p scattering lengths $a_{\pi^\pm p}$, and from Eq. (5.16) we obtain

$$\frac{\sigma}{2\pi f_\pi^2} = (M_N + m_\pi)(a_{\pi^- p} + a_{\pi^+ p}) + \frac{1}{2}\frac{g_{\pi n}^2}{4\pi}\left[\frac{m_\pi}{M_N}\right]^2 \qquad (5.18)$$

Experimentally we have,

$$a_{\pi^- p} = .085 \pm .003\, m_\pi^{-}$$

and

$$a_{\pi^+ p} = -.088 \pm .004\, m_\pi^{-1} \quad ,$$

justifying the approximation $\sigma \cong 0$.

From Eq. (5.17), we obtain the famous Adler-Weisberger relation for the renormalization of the axial vector current coupling constant $F_1^A(0)$ in terms of total $\pi^\pm$-proton cross-sections $\sigma_{tot}^{\pi^\pm p}$ by means of the forward pion nucleon dispersion relation for M_-

$$M_-^{N.P.}(\nu, q^2) = \frac{2\nu}{\pi}\int^{\infty} \frac{d\nu'\sqrt{\nu'^2 - M_N^2 m_\pi^2}}{\nu'^2 - \nu^2}\left\{\sigma_{tot}^{\pi^- p}(\nu') - \sigma_{tot}^{\pi^+ p}(\nu')\right\}$$

(5.19)

We approximate $\frac{\partial}{\partial\nu} M_-^{N.P.}(\nu, q^2)$ at $\nu = q^2 = 0$ in Eqs. (5.17) for its corresponding value at the physical pion mass $q^2 = \mu^2$, but unphysical energy $\nu = 0$, and obtain[10,11]

$$\frac{1}{\left[F_1^A(0)\right]^2} = 1 + \left[\frac{M_N}{g_{\pi n}}\right]^2 \frac{2}{\pi}\int_{m_\pi}^{\infty} \frac{d\omega'\sqrt{\omega'^2 - m_\pi^2}}{\omega'^2}\left\{\sigma_{tot}^{\pi^- p}(\omega') - \sigma_{tot}^{\pi^+ p}(\omega')\right\}$$

(5.20)

The integration variable $\omega = \frac{\nu}{M}$ corresponds to the laboratory energy of the pion. We can compare Eq. (5.20) with experiments by substituting on the righ-hand side the measured value of the difference of π^+ and π^- proton total cross-sections up to the highest presently available pion energy, ω = 30 BeV. Assuming different extrapolated forms, Adler[10] obtained $F_1^A(0) = 1.24$, while Weisberger[11] obtained $F_1^A(0) = 1.15$, in good agreement with the experimentally measured value of $F_1^A(0) = 1.18 \pm .02$.

Alternatively, we can test Eq. (5.17) by expanding $M_-^{N.P.}$ to first order in m_π

$$M_-^{N.P.}(m_\pi M_N, m_\pi^2) = \frac{\partial M_-}{\partial \nu}(\nu', q^2)\Big|_{\substack{\nu = 0 \\ q^2 = 0}} m_\pi M_N \qquad (5.21)$$

and evaluating the threshold value of M_- in terms of the observed $\pi^{\pm}p$ scattering lengths,

$$M_-^{N.P.}(m_\pi M_N, m_\pi^2) = 4\pi(M_N + m_\pi)(a_{\pi^- p} - a_{\pi^+ p}) - g_{\pi n}^2\left[\frac{m_\pi}{M_N}\right] \qquad (5.22)$$

Substituting Eq. (5.21) in Eq. (5.17) and applying Eq. (5.22) we obtain[15]

$$\frac{1}{\left[F_1^A(0)\right]^2} = \frac{4\pi}{g_{\pi n}^2}(M_N + m_\pi)\left[\frac{M_N}{m_\pi}\right](a_{\pi^- p} - a_{\pi^+ p}) \qquad (5.23)$$

Substituting the experimental values for $a_{\pi^{\pm} p}$, we obtain $F_1^A(0) = 1.27$. This alternative form of the Adler-Weisberger relation does not require the assumption of unsubtracted dispersion relations for M_- as does Eq. (5.20); however, the validity of this assumption was demonstrated a long time ago by the success of the Goldberger-Miyazawa-Oehme relation[16] for the difference of $\pi^+ p$ and $\pi^- p$ scattering lengths. [Eq. (5.20) minus Eq. (5.23)].

It is of interest to consider the corresponding derivation of the Adler-Weisberger formula in Nambu's theory in which $\partial^\mu j_\mu^{A,\alpha} = 0$, and consequently $m_\pi = 0$ (see section 4). In this case, instead of Eq. (5.8), we have the relation

$$q^\mu q^\nu T_{\mu\nu}^{\alpha\beta} = -i\,\varepsilon_{\alpha\beta\gamma}\, q^\mu (p|\, j_\mu^{V,\gamma} \,|\, p) \tag{5.24}$$

which we can obtain directly from the defining equation for $T_{\mu\nu}^{\alpha\beta}$ Eq. (5.4). However, we must be careful to observe that the theory with $\partial^\mu j_\mu^{A,\alpha} = 0$ does not imply vanishing pion nucleon scattering. Let us consider the limit $q \to 0$ of Eq. (5.24), which now corresponds to the threshold energy. For this purpose, it is convenient to separate from $T_{\mu\nu}^{\alpha\beta}$ the various pole terms due to the coupling of the conserved axial current to the zero mass psudoscalar pion. There are four terms corresponding to the possibility of a double pole, single poles and no poles at $q^2 = 0$, which are identified in Fig. 1.

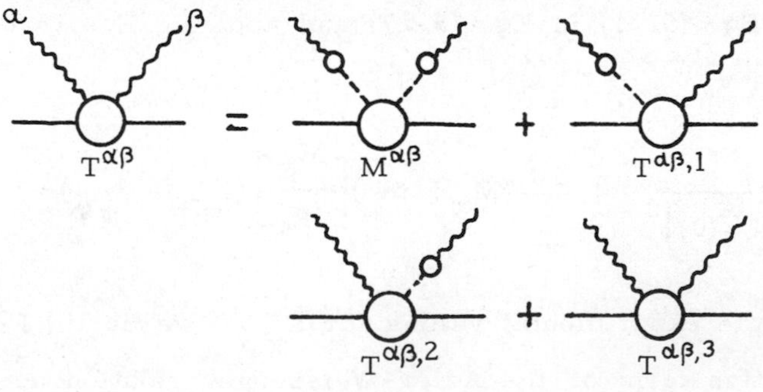

Fig. 2

Hence

$$T^{\alpha\beta}_{\mu\nu}(q) = \frac{M^{\alpha\beta}(q)}{(q^2)^2}\,\frac{f_\pi^2}{2}\,q_\mu q_\nu + i\,\frac{T^{\alpha\beta,1}_\nu}{q^2}\,i\,\frac{f_\pi}{\sqrt{2}}\,q_\mu$$

$$+\, i\,\frac{T^{\alpha\beta,2}_\mu}{q^2}\,i\,\frac{f_\pi}{\sqrt{2}}\,q_\nu + T^{\alpha\beta,3}_\mu(q) \tag{5.25}$$

where $M^{\alpha\beta}$ is the forward pion nucleon amplitude, Eq. (5.9),

$$T^{\alpha\beta,1}_\nu = (\mathbf{p}\,\mathbf{q}\,\alpha\ \text{out}\,|\,j^{A,\beta}_\nu\,|\,p) - i\,\frac{M^{\alpha\beta}}{q^2}\,i\,\frac{f_\pi q_\nu}{\sqrt{2}} \tag{5.26}$$

$$T^{\alpha\beta,2}_\mu = (p\,|\,j^{A,\alpha}_\mu\,|\,\mathbf{p}\,\mathbf{q}\,\beta,\ \text{in}) - i\,\frac{M^{\alpha\beta}}{q^2}\,i\,\frac{f_\pi q_\mu}{\sqrt{2}} \tag{5.27}$$

are matrix elements of the axial current between a nucleon and a pion-nucleon state, minus the single pion pole term, and $T^{\alpha\beta,3}_{\mu\nu}$ is the remaining contribution to $T^{\alpha\beta}_{\mu\nu}$ containing no pion pole terms. From Eqs. (5.23) - (5.25) and axial current conservation it follows that

$$q^\mu q^\nu T^{\alpha\beta}_{\mu\nu} = -\frac{1}{2}f_\pi^2 M^{\alpha\beta} + q^\mu q^\nu T^{\alpha\beta,3}_{\mu\nu} \tag{5.28}$$

Substituting Eq. (5.28) in Eq. (5.24) we get

$$q^\mu q^\nu T^{\alpha\beta,3}_{\mu\nu}(q) = \frac{1}{2}\,f_\pi^2\,M^{\alpha\beta}(q) - i\varepsilon_{\alpha\beta\gamma}(p\,|\,j^\gamma_\nu\,|\,p) \tag{5.29}$$

which is similar to Eq. (5.8) with $\sigma = 0$. In the limit $q \rightarrow 0$ only the nucleon pole terms of $T^{\alpha\beta,3}_{\mu\nu}$ contribute, which are given by

Eq. (5.11). Note that the reason for not including the contribution of F_2^A in this case is that it has a pion pole at $q^2 = 0$ [see Eq. (4.20)] and therefore is excluded from $T_{\mu\nu}^{\alpha\beta, 3}$ by definition. Hence, we obtain again Eq. (5.16) with $\sigma = 0$, and Eq. (5.17), which are in this case exact relations applying to threshold scattering of zero mass pseudoscalar pions.

6. SEMI-LEPTONIC K-DECAYS

In order to discuss an elementary application of current algebra which involves the equal-time commutator of an axial and a vector current, we consider now the semi-leptonic K-decays[17,18]. According to the form of the weak interaction, Eq. (1.7), the decay $K^{\pm} \rightarrow \pi^{o} + \ell^{\pm} + \nu$ depends on the matrix element of the weak hadronic current between the π and the K-meson; by parity (see section 3) only the vector current contributes, and we have

$$\sqrt{2q_o 2k_o}\,(q, \pi_o | j_{\lambda}^{v,-} | K^+, k) = f_+(k+q)_{\lambda} + f_-(k-q)_{\lambda} \qquad (6.1)$$

where $j_{\lambda}^{v} = j_{\lambda}^{v,4} - i j_{\lambda}^{v,5}$ lowers charge and hypercharge by one unit. Applying the L.S.Z. reduction formula to the π^{o}, and using the P.D.D.A.C. hypothesis we get for $q^2 \quad m^2$

$$\sqrt{2q_o}\,(q, \pi^o | j_{\lambda}^{v,-} | K^+, k) \cong -(q^2 \sim m_{\pi}^2)$$

$$\times \frac{i}{C_{\pi}} \int d^4x e^{iqx} (0 | [\partial^{\mu} j_{\mu}^{A,3}(x), j_{\lambda}^{v,-}(0)] | K^+ k) \theta(x_o) \qquad (6.2)$$

Following our previous procedure, we introduce the tensor

$$T_{\mu\lambda} = i\sqrt{2k_o}\int d^4xe^{iqx}(0|\left[j_\mu^{A,3}(x), j_\lambda^v(0)\right]|K^+, k)\theta(x_o) \tag{6.3}$$

and obtain after integration by parts

$$q^\mu T_{\mu\lambda} = -\sqrt{2k_o}\int d^4xe^{iqx}\Big\{(0|\left[\partial^\mu j_\mu^{A,3}(x), j_\lambda^v(0)\right]|K^+,k)\theta(x_o)$$

$$+ (0|\left[j_o^{A,3}(x), j_\lambda^v(0)\right]|K^+,k)\delta(x_o)\Big\} \tag{6.4}$$

The equal-time axial-vector current commutator which appears in Eq. (6.4) is given by Eq. (1.23); hence we can write Eq. (6.2) in the form

$$\sqrt{2q_o 2k_o}\,(q,\pi^0|j_\lambda^v|K^+,k) \cong (q^2 - m_\pi^2)\frac{i}{C_\pi}\Big\{q^\mu T_{\mu\lambda}$$

$$+ \frac{1}{2}(0|j_\lambda^A|K^+,k)\Big\} \tag{6.5}$$

where $j_\lambda^A = j_\lambda^{A,4} - i j_\lambda^{A,5}$. The axial current matrix element appearing in Eq. (6.5) has the form

$$\sqrt{2k_o}\,(0|j_\lambda^A|K^+,k) = if_K k_\lambda \tag{6.6}$$

where f_K determines the decay $K^\pm \rightarrow \ell^\pm + \nu$ in analogy with the corresponding π-decay, Eq. (4.2). Substituting Eqs. (6.1) and (6.6) in Eq. (6.5) we obtain a relation first derived by Callan and Treiman[17] and by Mathur, Okubo and Pandit[18],

$$f_+ + f_- \cong \frac{f_K}{\sqrt{2}\, f_\pi} \tag{6.7}$$

with f_+ and f_- evaluated at the unphysical momentum transfer $(k - q)^2 = M_K^2$.

An interesting problem is to apply P.D.D.A.C. to the K^+ instead of the π^o meson, and consider the corresponding limit $k \to 0$. We obtain instead of Eq. (6.7)

$$f_+ - f_- \cong \frac{f_K}{\sqrt{2}\, f_K} \tag{6.8}$$

where f_+ and f_- are now evaluated at the momentum transfer m_π^2. If the form factors f_+ and f_- are nearly constants, Eqs. (6.7) and (6.8) are compatible if $f_- = 0$, $f_\pi = f_K$ and $f_+ = 1/\sqrt{2}$. This, of course, is just the prediction in the exact SU(3) limit when the strangeness changing vector current is conserved and $m_\pi = m_K$.

From the experimental decay rates $\Gamma(\pi \to \mu + \nu) = 3.8 \times 10^7\ \text{sec}^{-1}$, and $\Gamma(K \to \mu + \nu) = 5.1 \times 10^7\ \text{sec}^{-1}$, we obtain $\cos\theta\, f_\pi = .93\, m_\pi$ and $\sin\theta\, f_K = .07\, m_K$, respectively. The decay rate $\Gamma(K \to \pi^o + e + \nu) = 3.9 \times 10^6\ \text{sec}^{-1}$ is insensitive to f_- and gives $\sin\theta\, f_+ = .16$. If we assume for f_+ its theoretical value $f_+ = 1/\sqrt{2}$, we obtain $\sin\theta = .22$ for the Cabibbo angle, in good agreement with estimates from other decays, and $f_K/f_\pi = 1.27$. Then Eq. (6.7) requires that the ratio $\xi = f_-/f_+ = 0.27$. Experimentally, the value of ξ is quite controversial[19]. The observed ratio

$\Gamma(K\mu_3)/\Gamma(Ke_3)$ implies a solution $\xi = +.46 \pm .27$ while the polarization of the μ in $K\mu_3$ leads to $\xi \cong -1$. This conflict in different estimates of ξ may be due to the fact that the form factors f_+ and f_- are not constant, in which case we should substitute the appropriate extrapolated values at the momentum transfer M_K^2 in Eq. (6.7).

A subtle problem arises when we extend the application of current algebra to the decay $K^\pm \to \pi^+ + \pi^- + \ell^\pm + \nu$, which depends on the axial current matrix element

$$\sqrt{2q_o^+ 2q_o^- 2k_o}\,(\pi^+\pi^- \text{out}\,|\,j_\lambda^A\,|\,K^+) = i\Big\{f_1(q_+ + q_-)_\lambda + f_2(q_+ - q_-)_\lambda + f_3(k - q_+ - q_-)_\lambda\Big\} \tag{6.9}$$

where the f_i's are real form factors which may depend on the invariants $q_+ \cdot k$, $q_- \cdot k$ and $q_+ \cdot q_-$.

We begin by removing either the π^+ or the π^- from the out state, applying P. D. D. A. C. and then taking the limit of zero pion momentum. Let us see what happens. If we reduce the π^- and set $q^- = 0$ we obtain

$$(f_1 + f_2)q_\lambda^+ + f_3(k - q^+)_\lambda = \frac{\sqrt{2}}{f_\pi}\Big\{f_+(k + q^+)_\lambda + f_-(k - q^+)_\lambda\Big\} \tag{6.10}$$

while if we reduce the π^+ and set $q^+ = 0$ we find instead

$$(f_1 - f_2)q_\lambda^- + f_3(k - q^-)_\lambda = 0 \tag{6.11}$$

Eq. (6.10) implies

$$f_3 = \frac{\sqrt{2}}{f_\pi}(f_+ + f_-)\,, \qquad f_1 + f_2 = \frac{2\sqrt{2}}{f_\pi} f_+ \tag{6.12}$$

while Eq. (6.11) implies[17]

$$f_3 = 0 \qquad f_1 = f_2 \tag{6.13}$$

Observe that Eqs. (6.12) and (6.13) clearly contradict our previous result, Eq. (6.7).

To resolve this dilemma, let us consider carefully what happens if we reduce both the π^+ and the π^- meson, as has been stressed by Weinberg[20], and consider the case where <u>both</u> q^+ and q^- become small. We have

$$\sqrt{2q_o^+ 2q_o^-}\,(\pi^+\pi^- \text{out}\,|\, j_\lambda^A \,|\, K^+) = -\lim_{q^{\pm 2} \to m_\pi^2} (q^{+2} - m_\pi^2)(q^{-2} - m_\pi^2)$$

$$\cdot \frac{1}{2C_\pi^2} \int d^4 x e^{iq^+ x} \int d^4 y e^{iq^- y} \; (0\,|\, T \partial^\mu j_\mu^{A,-}(x)$$

$$\cdot\, \partial^\nu j_\nu^{A,+}(y) j_\lambda^A(0) \,|\, K^+) \tag{6.14}$$

which suggests that we introduce the tensor

$$T_{\mu\nu\lambda} = \sqrt{2k_o} \int d^4 x e^{iq^+ x} \int d^4 y e^{iq^- y} (0\,|\, T j_\mu^{A,-}(x) j_\nu^{A,+}(y) j_\lambda^A(0) \,|\, K^+) \tag{6.15}$$

and proceed to evaluate $q_+^\mu q_-^\nu T_{\mu\nu\lambda}$.

We leave it as an exercise to show that $\Big\{$ hint: use the identity

$$\partial^\mu T A_\mu(x)B(y)C(z) = T\partial^\mu A_\mu(x)B(y)C(z) + T[A_o(x), B(y)] \cdot C(z)\delta(x_o - y_o) + T[A_o(x), C(z)]B(y)\delta(x_o - z_o) \Big\}$$

$$q_+^\mu q_-^\nu T_{\mu\nu\lambda} = -\sqrt{2k_o}\int d^4xe^{iq^+x}\int d^4ye^{iq^-y}(0|T\partial^\mu j_\mu^{A-}(x) \cdot \partial^\nu j_\nu^{A+}(y)j_\Lambda^A(0)|K^+) - 2q_-^\mu T_{\mu\lambda}(q^+ + q^-) - iT_\lambda(q^+) \tag{6.16}$$

where

$$T_{\mu\lambda}(q) = i\sqrt{2}k_o\int d^4xe^{iqx}(0|Tj_\mu^{\nu,3}(x)j_\lambda^A(0)|K^+) \tag{6.17}$$

and

$$T_\lambda(q) = i\sqrt{2k}_o\int d^4xe^{iqx}(0|T\partial^\mu j_\mu^{A,-}(x)\ j_\lambda^\nu(0)|K^+) \tag{6.18}$$

The currents j_λ^A and j_λ^ν in Eqs. (6.17) and (6.18) stand for the linear combinations $j_\lambda^A = j_\Lambda^{A,4} - ij_\Lambda^{A,5}$ and $j_\Lambda^\nu = j_\Lambda^{\nu,6} \rightarrow j_\Lambda^{\nu,7}$ respectively.

It can be readily verified that in the two previous limits $q^- = 0$ and $q^+ = 0$, Eq. (6.16) leads back to Eqs. (6.11) and (6.12), respectively. We now expand both sides of Eq. (6.16) up to first order in q^+ and q^-. For this purpose we must evaluate $T_{\mu\lambda}(q)$, Eq. (6.17) up to first order in q, a task which can be performed because we know that:

1) The vector current $j_\mu^{\nu,3}$ is conserved, and the equal time vector and axial vector current commutators, Eq. (1.21) gives

$$q^\mu T_{\mu\lambda}(q) = \frac{1}{2}\sqrt{2}k_o(0|j_\lambda^A|K^+, k) \tag{6.19}$$

2) The pole contribution $T^p_{\mu\nu}(q)$ from the single K meson intermediate state is

$$T^p_{\mu\lambda}(q) = \frac{1}{2}(0|j_\lambda^A|K, k-q)\frac{k_\mu}{qk} \tag{6.20}$$

To satisfy Eqs. (6.19) and (6.20) up to first order in q, $T_{\mu\lambda}(q)$ must have the form

$$T_{\mu\lambda} = \frac{if_K}{2}\left\{\frac{k_\mu}{kq}(k-q)_\lambda + g_{\mu\lambda}\right\} \tag{6.21}$$

Substituting Eq. (6.21) for the second term on the righ-hand side of Eq. (6.16) and applying P.D.D.A.C. to replace the first and third terms by Eqs. (6.14) and (6.2), respectively, we obtain

$$-f_\pi^2\left\{f_1(q^+ + q^-)_\lambda + f_2(q^+ - q^-)_\lambda + f_3(k - q^+ - q^-)_\lambda\right.$$

$$= f_K\left\{\frac{q^- k}{(q^+ + q^-)k}(k - q_+ - q_-)_\lambda + q^-_\lambda\right\}$$

$$- \sqrt{f_\pi}\left\{f_+(k+q^+)_\lambda + f_-(k-q^+)_\lambda\right\} \tag{6.22}$$

From Eqs. (6.22) together with Eq. (6.7) it follows that[20,21]

$$f_3 = \frac{f_K}{f_\pi^2}\frac{q_+ k}{(q^+ + q^-)k} \tag{6.23}$$

and

$$f_1 = f_2 = \sqrt{2}\,\frac{f_+}{f_\pi} \tag{6.24}$$

We can now understand that the apparent contradiction that arose with Eqs. (6.12), (6.13) and (6.17) is due to the fact that f_3 is a rapidly varying form factor and not a constant, as we had previously assumed, based on a naive application of P.D.D.A.C.

Similar considerations for the decay $K^\pm \to 2\pi^o + \ell^\pm + \nu$ do not give rise to this problem because of the absence of the K-meson pole term, and we obtain

$$f_1' = \sqrt{2}\,\frac{f_+}{f_\pi}\ , \qquad f_2' = 0 \quad \text{and} \quad f_3' = \frac{f_K}{2f_\pi^2} \tag{6.25}$$

The ratio of the phase space average of f_1 and f_2 have been measured for

$$K^+ \to \pi^+ + \pi^- + e^+ + \nu \quad ,$$

and found to be[22]

$$\frac{\langle f_1 \rangle}{\langle f_2 \rangle} = .8 \pm .3 \quad ,$$

and from the decay rate we obtain $\sin\theta \langle f_1 \rangle = 1.2\ m_K^{-1}$ in qualitative agreement with Eq. (6.24), which predicts $\sin\theta\, f_1 = .86\, m_K^{-1}$. An evaluation of f_3 has to await a careful measurement of the $K_{\mu 4}$ decay spectrum.

7. DISPERSION RELATION TECHNIQUES. GRADIENT OF THE δ-FUNCTION IN THE EQUAL TIME CURRENT-CURRENT COMMUTATORS

We have seen that in applications of current algebra it was useful to introduce a tensor $T^{\alpha\beta}_{\mu\nu}(q)$, which is the Fourier transform of the matrix element of a retarded commutator of two currents,

$$T^{\alpha\beta}_{\mu\nu}(q) = 2p_o\, i \int d^4x e^{iqx} (p|\left[j^{\alpha}_{\mu}(x), j^{\beta}_{\nu}(0)\right]|p)\theta(x_o) \tag{7.1}$$

The tensor character of $T^{\alpha\beta}_{\mu\nu}$ depends on the vanishing of the current-current commutator for space-like separation, i.e., causality,

$$\left[j^{\alpha}_{\mu}(x), j^{\beta}_{\nu}(y)\right] = 0 \quad \text{for} \quad (x-y)^2 < 0 \tag{7.2}$$

and on a not too singular behavior on the light cone, $(x-y)^2 = 0$. As we shall see in this section this latter property is not satisfied, so that $T^{\alpha\beta}_{\mu\nu}$ contains non-covariant terms. From causality one deduces also analyticity properties of $T^{\alpha\beta}_{\mu\nu}$ which, together with suitable assumptions about its asymptotic behavior, lead to dispersion relations.

We would like to examine here what additional information can be obtained in current algebra by applying the techniques of dispersion relations, following a procedure developed by Fubini[23].

If we ignore, for the time being, possible non-covariant terms in $T^{\alpha\beta}_{\mu\nu}$, Eq. (7.1), and assume that the single particle states $|p)$ have spin zero (or have averaged over spin) we can expand it in the form

$$T^{\alpha\beta}_{\mu\nu} = A^{\alpha\beta}_1 p_\mu p_\nu + A^{\alpha\beta}_2 p_\mu q_\nu + A^{\alpha\beta}_3 q_\mu p_\nu + A^{\alpha\beta}_4 q_\mu q_\nu + A^{\alpha\beta}_5 g_{\mu\nu} \tag{7.3}$$

where $A^{\alpha\beta}_i$ are scalar functions of the invariants $\nu = q \cdot p$ and q^2. Fubini[23] assumed that these functions satisfy unsubtracted dispersion relations in the variable ν for fixed q^2

$$A^{\alpha\beta}_i(\nu, q^2) = \frac{1}{\pi} \int_{-\infty}^{\infty} \frac{a^{\alpha\beta}_i(\nu', q^2)}{\nu' - \nu} d\nu' \tag{7.4}$$

The absorptive parts $a(\nu, q^2)$ are obtained from the Fourier transform of the current-current commutator

$$t^{\alpha\beta}_{\mu\nu} = p_o \int d^4x e^{iqx} (p|[j^\alpha_\mu(x), j^\beta_\nu(0)]|p) \tag{7.5}$$

which has the corresponding expansion

$$t^{\alpha\beta}_{\mu\nu} = a^{\alpha\beta}_1 p_\mu p_\nu + a^{\alpha\beta}_2 p_\mu q_\nu + a^{\alpha\beta}_3 q_\mu p_\nu + a^{\alpha\beta}_4 q_\mu q_\nu + a_5 g_{\mu\nu} \tag{7.6}$$

It can be readily seen from Eq. (7.5) that in the case where j^α_μ and j^β_ν are both either vector or axial currents, the components of $a^{\alpha\beta}_i$ which are symmetric or antisymmetric under the intercharge $\alpha \leftrightarrow \beta$ satisfy simple symmetry properties when $\nu \rightarrow -\nu$. By translation invariance we see from Eq. (7.5) that

$$t^{\alpha\beta}_{\mu\nu}(-q) = -t^{\beta\alpha}_{\nu\mu}(q) \tag{7.7}$$

Hence, the linear combination $t^{\alpha\beta}_{\mu\nu} + t^{\beta\alpha}_{\mu\nu} \pm t^{\alpha\beta}_{\nu\mu} \pm t^{\beta\alpha}_{\nu u}$ is $\begin{bmatrix}\text{odd}\\ \text{even}\end{bmatrix}$ when

$q \rightarrow -q$, and therefore $a_i^{\alpha\beta} + a_i^{\beta\alpha}$ is odd when $\nu \rightarrow -\nu$ for i = 1, 4 and 5, while $a_2^{\alpha\beta} + a_2^{\beta\alpha} \pm a_3^{\alpha\beta} \pm a_3^{\beta\alpha}$ must be $\begin{bmatrix}\text{even}\\ \text{odd}\end{bmatrix}$. On the other hand, the linear combination $t_{\mu\nu}^{\alpha\beta} - t_{\mu\nu}^{\beta\alpha} \pm t_{\nu\mu}^{\alpha\beta} \mp t_{\nu\mu}^{\beta\alpha}$ is $\begin{bmatrix}\text{even}\\ \text{odd}\end{bmatrix}$ under $q \rightarrow -q$, and $a_i^{\alpha\beta} - a_i^{\beta\alpha}$ is even when $\nu \rightarrow -\nu$ for i = 1, 4 and 5, while $a_2^{\alpha\beta} - a_2^{\beta\alpha} \pm a_3^{\alpha\beta} \mp a_3^{\beta\alpha}$ is $\begin{bmatrix}\text{odd}\\ \text{even}\end{bmatrix}$.

Now let us consider $q^\mu T_{\mu\nu}^{\alpha\beta}$, which after integration by parts, takes the form

$$q^\mu T_{\mu\nu}^{\alpha\beta} = -2p_o \int d^4x e^{iqx} \Big\{ (p|[\partial^\mu j_\mu^\alpha(x), j_\nu^\beta(0)]|p)\theta(x_o)$$

$$+ (p|[j_o^\alpha(x), j_\nu^\beta(0)]|p)\delta(x_o) \qquad (7.8)$$

Introducing the vector $U_\nu^{\alpha\beta}(q)$

$$U_\nu^{\alpha\beta}(q) = 2p_o \int d^4x e^{iqx} (p|[\partial^\mu j_\mu^\alpha(x), j_\nu^\beta(0)]|p)\theta(x_o) \qquad (7.9)$$

and substituting for the equal time current-current commutator which appears in Eq. (7.8) the expression given in Eqs. (1.20) or (1.22) we have

$$q^\mu T_{\mu\nu}^{\alpha\beta} + U_\nu^{\alpha\beta} = -if_{\alpha\beta\gamma}\, 2p_o (p|j_\nu^\gamma|p) \qquad (7.10)$$

We expand $U_\nu^{\alpha\beta}$

$$U_\nu^{\alpha\beta} = U_1^{\alpha\beta} p_\nu + U_2^{\alpha\beta} q_\nu \qquad (7.11)$$

where $U_i^{\alpha\beta} = U_i^{\alpha\beta}(\nu, q^2)$ are also assumed to satisfy unsubtracted dispersion relations in ν for fixed q^2

$$U_i^{\alpha\beta}(\nu, q^2) = \frac{1}{\pi}\int_{-\infty}^{\infty} \frac{u_i^{\alpha\beta}(\nu', q^2)}{\nu' - \nu} d\nu' \tag{7.12}$$

The absorptive parts $u_i^{\alpha\beta}$ in Eq. (7.12) are the expansion coefficients of $q^\mu t_{\mu\nu}^{\alpha\beta}$ and can be readily obtained from Eq. (7.6)

$$\begin{aligned} u_1 &= \nu a_1 + q^2 a_3 \\ u_2 &= \nu a_2 + q^2 a_4 + a_5 \end{aligned} \tag{7.13}$$

Substituting Eqs. (7.3), (7.4), (7.12) and (7.13) in Eq. (7.10) we get the relations

$$\frac{1}{2\pi}\int_{-\infty}^{\infty} d\nu \, a_1^{\alpha\beta}(\nu, q^2) = i f_{\alpha\beta\gamma} \lambda^{\gamma} \tag{7.14}$$

$$\int_{-\infty}^{\infty} d\nu \, a_2^{\alpha\beta}(\nu, q^2) = 0 \tag{7.15}$$

Similar considerations on $q^\nu T_{\mu\nu}^{\alpha\beta}$ lead to the additional requirement

$$\int_{-\infty}^{\infty} d\nu \, a_3^{\alpha\beta}(\nu, q^2) = 0 \tag{7.16}$$

An alternative procedure which leads to equation (7.14) has been given by Dashen and Gell-Mann[24] who evaluated the equal time current-current commutator in the limit $p \rightarrow \infty$. Consider the integral of $t_{o\mu}^{\alpha\beta}(q)$ over q_o for fixed values of $\mathbf{q}$. Interchanging orders of integration, it can be expressed in terms of the equal time current-current commutators, e.g.

$$\frac{1}{\pi}\int_{-\infty}^{\infty} dq_o\, t_{o\mu}^{\alpha\beta}(q_o, \mathbf{q}) = 2p_o \int d^4x e^{iqx}\delta(x_o)(p|[j_o^{\alpha}(x), j_{\mu}^{\beta}(0)]|p)$$

$$= i f_{\alpha\beta\gamma} 2p_o (p|j_{\mu}^{\gamma}|p) \qquad (7.17)$$

If we now substitute for $t_{o\mu}^{\alpha\beta}$ its covariant expression Eq. (7.6) we are led to the conditions

$$\frac{1}{2\pi}\int_{-\infty}^{\infty} dq_o \left\{a_1^{\alpha\beta}(\nu, q^2)p_o + a_3^{\alpha\beta}(\nu, q^2)q_o\right\} = i f_{\alpha\beta\gamma}\lambda^{\gamma} \qquad (7.18)$$

$$\int_{-\infty}^{\infty} dq_o \left\{a_2^{\alpha\beta}(\nu, q^2)p_o + a_4^{\alpha\beta}(\nu, q^2)q_o\right\} = 0 \qquad (7.19)$$

$$\int_{-\infty}^{\infty} dq_o \left\{a_2^{\alpha\beta}(\nu, q^2)p_o q_o + a_4^{\alpha\beta}(\nu, q^2)q_o^2 + a_5^{\alpha\beta}(\nu, q^2)\right\} = 0$$

$$(7.20)$$

where $\nu = q_o p_o - \mathbf{q}\cdot\mathbf{p}$ and $q^2 = q_o^2 - \mathbf{q}^2$, and the integrals are evaluated for fixed $\mathbf{q}$. In order to consider the limit $p \to \infty$ of Eqs. (7.18) through (7.20) we change the variable of integration to ν and set $q^2 = (1/p_o^2)(\nu + \mathbf{q}\cdot\mathbf{p})^2 - \mathbf{q}^2$. Then in the limit $p_o \to \infty$, $q^2 = -q_{\perp}^2$ is independent of ν where $q_{\perp}$ is the component of $\mathbf{q}$ transverse to $\mathbf{p}$. Provided we can interchange the orders of limit and integration, and the conditions

$$\lim_{p_o\to\infty} \frac{1}{p_o}\int_{-\infty}^{\infty} d\nu\, a_i^{\alpha\beta}(\nu, q^2) = 0 \qquad (7.21)$$

$$\lim_{p_0 \to \infty} \frac{1}{p_0^2} \int d\nu \, \nu a_i^{\alpha\beta}(\nu, q^2) = 0 \tag{7.22}$$

are satisfied for i = 3, 4 , we obtain again Eqs. (7.14) and (7.15). These assumptions are equivalent to the existence of unsubtracted dispersion relations required by Fubini.

If we apply crossing symmetry, Eq. (7.7), we have, furthermore,

$$\frac{1}{2\pi} \int_{-\infty}^{\infty} d\nu a_1^{\alpha\beta}(\nu, q^2) = \frac{1}{2\pi} \int_0^{\infty} d\nu \left\{ a_1^{\alpha\beta}(\nu, q^2) - a_1^{\beta\alpha}(\nu, q^2) \right\} \tag{7.23}$$

which is antisymmetric under $\alpha \leftrightarrow \beta$ as required by Eq. (7.14), while Eqs. (7.15) and (7.16) lead to the condition

$$\int_0^{\infty} d\nu \left\{ a_2^{\alpha\beta}(\nu, q^2) \pm a_2^{\beta\alpha}(\nu, q^2) \pm a_3^{\alpha\beta}(\nu, q^2) + a_3^{\beta\alpha}(\nu, q^2) \right\} = 0 \tag{7.24}$$

We note in particular that the value of the integral in Eq. (7.14) is independent of the invariant q^2, for values of q^2 for which the dispersion integrals are valid. This is a direct consequence of causality as can be shown, for example, by using the Jost-Lehman-Dyson representation.

As an example of the application of Eq. (7.14) let us rederive the Adler-Weisberger relation, Eq. (5.20). Observe that the function $a^{\alpha\beta} = q^\mu q^\nu t_{\mu\nu}^{\alpha\beta}$ given by

$$a^{\alpha\beta} = \nu^2 a_1^{\alpha\beta} + \nu q^2 (a_2^{\alpha\beta} + a_3^{\alpha\beta}) + (q^2)^2 a_4^{\alpha\beta} + q^2 a_5^{\alpha\beta} \tag{7.25}$$

is proportional to the absorptive part for off-mass shell forward pion-nucleon scattering. In particular, we see from Eq. (7.25) that in the limit $q^2 = 0$

$$a_1^{\alpha\beta} = \frac{a^{\alpha\beta}}{\nu^2} \tag{7.26}$$

However, some care has to be taken before substituting Eq. (7.26) in Eq. (7.14), because of the single nucleon contributions. The simplest procedure is to evaluate these contributions to $a_1^{\alpha\beta}$ directly, and then substitute Eq. (7.26) for the remainder. We find

$$a_1^{\alpha\beta,\,P}(\nu, q^2) = \pi\left[F_1^A(q^2)\right]^2 \Big\{\delta(q^2 + 2\nu)\theta(\nu + M_N^2)$$

$$+ \delta(q^2 - 2\nu)\theta(-\nu + M_N^2)\Big\}\frac{1}{2}\left[\tau^\alpha, \tau^\beta\right] \tag{7.27}$$

where we have left out the contribution of F_2^A, because it drops out in the limit $q^2 \rightarrow 0$. Substituting Eqs. (7.26) and (7.27) in Eq. (7.14) and applying crossing symmetry, Eq. (7.11), we obtain

$$\frac{1}{\pi}\int_0^\infty \frac{d\nu}{\nu^2}\, a_-^{NP}(\nu, 0) = 1 - \left[F_1^A(0)\right]^2 \tag{7.28}$$

Finally, using P.D.D.A.C. to relate a_-^{NP} to pion-nucleon total cross-sections we recover the Adler-Weisberger relation.

We end this section by considering briefly the existence of terms in the equal time current-current commutators proportional to gradients of the δ-function[12] and their non-covariant contributions to $T^{\alpha\beta}_{\mu\nu}$. For this purpose we introduce the Fourier transform $t^{\alpha\beta}_{\mu\nu}$ of the vacuum expectation value of the commutator of two currents

$$t^{\alpha\beta}_{\mu\nu}(q) = \int d^4x e^{iqx} (0|[j^\alpha_\mu(x), j^\beta_\nu(0)]|0) \tag{7.29}$$

Summing over a complete set of intermediate states $|n)$ and applying translational invariance, we can perform the space-time integration in Eq. (7.29), and obtain

$$t^{\alpha\beta}_{\mu\nu}(q) = \sum_n (2\pi)^4 \{\delta^4(q - p_n)(0|j^\alpha_\mu|n)(n|j^\beta_\nu|0)$$

$$- \delta^4(q + p_n)(0|j^\beta_\nu|n)(n|j^\alpha_\mu|0)\} \tag{7.30}$$

According to Lorentz covariance and the positive definitness of the energy spectrum,

$$t^{\alpha\beta}_{\mu\nu}(q) = \{\rho^{\alpha\beta}_1(q^2)g_{\mu\nu} + \rho^{\alpha\beta}_2(q^2)q_\mu q_\nu\}\epsilon(q_o) \tag{7.31}$$

From Eq. (7.31) and (7.29) we get

$$(0|[j^\alpha_\mu(x), j^\beta_\nu(0)]|0) = \int_0^\infty \frac{dm^2}{2\pi}\{\rho^{\alpha\beta}_1(m^2)$$

$$+ \rho^{\alpha\beta}_2(m^2)\partial_\mu\partial_\nu\}\Delta(x, m^2) \tag{7.32}$$

where

$$\Delta(x, m^2) = \int \frac{d^4q}{(2\pi)^4} 2\pi\delta(q^2 - m^2)\epsilon(q_o)e^{iqx} \tag{7.33}$$

In particular for the equal time commutator of a space and a time component of the current, Eq. (7.32) becomes

$$(0|\left[j_o^{\alpha}(x), j_i^{\beta}(0)\right]|0)\Big|_{x_o = 0} = -i\frac{\partial}{\partial x^i}\,\delta^3(\mathbf{x})\int_0^{\infty}\frac{dm^2}{(2\pi)}\,\rho_2^{\alpha\beta}(m^2) \tag{7.34}$$

where i = 1, 2, 3. It can be readily seen from Eqs. (7.30) and (7.31) that in the case that both j_μ^α and j_ν^β are vector or axial vector currents $\rho_2^{\alpha\beta}$ is positive definite, and therefore the coefficient of the gradients of the δ-function cannot vanish.

If we look at the Fourier transform of the retarded commutator of these two currents,

$$T_{\mu\nu}^{\alpha\beta}(q) = i\int d^4x e^{iqx}(0|\left[j_\mu^\alpha(x), j_\nu^\beta(0)\right]|0)\theta(x_o) \tag{7.35}$$

we obtain

$$T_{\mu\nu}^{\alpha\beta}(q) = \int_0^\infty \frac{\rho_1^{\alpha\beta}(m^2)}{(m^2 - q^2)}\,\frac{dm^2}{2\pi}\,g_{\mu\nu} + \int \frac{\rho_2^{\alpha\beta}(m^2)}{(m^2 - q^2)}\,\frac{dm^2}{2\pi}\,q_\mu q_\nu$$

$$+\, g_{\mu o}g_{\nu o}\int_0^\infty \frac{dm^2}{2\pi}\,\rho_2^{\alpha\beta}(m^2) \tag{7.36}$$

The non-covariant term in Eq. (7.36) has precisely the same coefficient as the gradient of the δ-function in the equal time current-current commutator , Eq. (7.34). We can therefore justify our neglect of these gradient terms because they are compensated by leaving out the non-covariant terms in $T_{\mu\nu}$. An alternative way of demonstrating this cancellation is to apply the divergence equations for the currents including electromagnetic and weak interactions. For a discussion of this approach we refer you to the literature[26] and some lectures given elsewhere[27].

8. TESTS OF EQUAL TIME CURRENT-CURRENT COMMUTATION RELATIONS

After the success of the initial applications of current algebra, Adler[28] suggested a test of the equal time current-current commutation relations based on the measurement of neutrino and anti-neutrino proton cross-sections at high energy and fixed invariant momentum transfer. Adler's relation is a direct application of the Fubini-Dashen-Gell-Mann[23,24] sum rule, Eq. (7.14), and we shall discuss its derivation in this section.

According to the weak interactions, Eq. (1.7), the amplitude for the neutrino process $\nu + p^+ \to \ell^- + n^{++}$ (ν = neutrino, p^+ = proton, ℓ^- = lepton, and n^{++} = hadronic state, see Fig. 3)

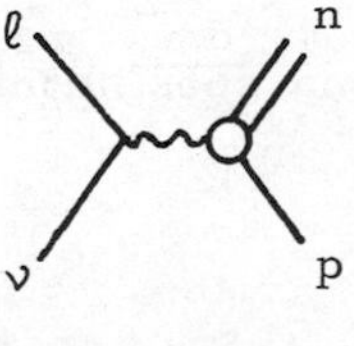

Fig. 3

is given by

$$\frac{G}{\sqrt{2}} \cos\theta \, (n^{++} \text{ out} \,|\, j^{w}_{\mu} \,|\, p^{+}) \, \bar{u}(k') \gamma^{\mu} (1 - \gamma_5) \, u(k) \qquad (8.1)$$

for strangeness conserving transitions, where k and k' are the neutrino and lepton momentum, respectively.

The corresponding differential cross-section averaged over the lepton spins and neglecting the lepton mass is then

$$d\sigma = \frac{1}{2k_o} \frac{G^2}{2} \cos^2\theta \sum_n (p| j_\mu^{w+} | n)(n| j_\nu^{w} | p) \mathrm{Tr}\, \not{k}\gamma^\mu (1-\gamma_5)$$

$$\cdot \not{k}'\gamma^\nu (1-\gamma_5)(2\pi)^4 \delta^4(k+p-k'-p_n) \frac{d^4k'}{(2\pi)^4} 2\pi\delta(k'^2)$$

(8.2)

Eq. (8.2) suggests that we introduce the tensor $m_{\mu\nu}(q)$

$$m_{\mu\nu}(q) \equiv 2p_o \sum_n (p| j_\mu^{w+} | n)(n| j_\nu^{w} | p)(2\pi)^4 \delta^4(q+p-p_n)$$

(8.3)

which by Lorentz covariance has the expansion

$$m_{\mu\nu}(q) = b_1 p_\mu p_\nu + b_2 p_\mu q_\nu + b_3 q_\mu p_\nu + b_4 q_\mu q_\nu + b_5 g_{\mu\nu}$$

(8.4)

where $q = k - k'$, and the scalar functions b_i depend only on the invariants $q \cdot p$ and q^2.

Evaluating the trace and substituting Eq. (8.4) in Eq. (8.2) we obtain

$$d\sigma = \frac{G^2}{p_o k_o} \cos^2\theta \left\{ b_1 \left[2(k\cdot p)(k'\cdot p) + M_N^2 \frac{q^2}{2} \right] + b_5 q^2 \right\} \frac{d^3k'}{(2\pi)^3 2k'_o}$$

(8.5)

Replacing $\frac{d^3k'}{2k'_o}$ by $\frac{\pi d\nu}{2} \frac{dq^2}{\omega M}$ and integrating the differential cross-section, Eq. (8.5), over lepton energies for fixed invariant momentum transfer q^2, in the lab. system,

$$\mathbf{p} = 0 \quad , \quad p_o = M \ , \quad \text{and} \quad k_o = \omega \ , \ \text{we get}$$

$$\frac{d\sigma}{dq^2} = \frac{G^2 \cos^2\theta}{16\pi^2(\omega M)^2} \int_0^{\omega M(1 - q^2/4\omega^2)} d\nu \Big\{ b_1(\nu, q^2)$$

$$\Big[2\omega M(\omega M - \nu) + M^2 \frac{q^2}{2}\Big] + b_5(\nu, q^2) q^2 \Big\} \qquad (8.6)$$

Correspondingly, for the anti-neutrino process $\bar{\nu} + p^+ \rightarrow \ell^+ + n^o$ the differential cross-section is given by Eq. (8.6) with b_i replaced by $\bar{b}_i$ defined by the analog of Eqs. (8.3) and (8.4):

$$\bar{m}_{\mu\nu}(q) \equiv 2p_o \sum_n (p| j_\mu^w | n)(n| j_\nu^{w+} | p)(2\pi)^4 \delta^4(q + p - p_n) \qquad (8.7)$$

and

$$\bar{m}_{\mu\nu}(q) = \bar{b}_1 p_\mu p_\nu + \bar{b}_2 p_\mu q_\nu + \bar{b}_3 q_\mu p_\nu + \bar{b}_4 q_\mu q_\nu + \bar{b}_5 g_{\mu\nu} \qquad (8.8)$$

respectively.

Note that the Fourier transform $t_{\mu\nu}(q)$ of the matrix element between nucleon states of the commutator between the weak interaction current j_μ^w and its hermitian conjugate j_μ^{w+}

$$t_{\mu\nu}(q) = 2p_o \int d^4x e^{iqx} (p| [j_\mu^{w+}(x), j_\nu^w(0)] | p) \qquad (8.9)$$

is related to $m_{\mu\nu}(q)$ and $\overline{m}_{\mu\nu}(q)$ by

$$t_{\mu\nu}(q) = m_{\mu\nu}(q) - \overline{m}_{\mu\nu}(-q) \tag{8.10}$$

The corresponding invariant functions a_i defined by

$$t_{\mu\nu} = a_1 p_\mu p_\nu + a_2 p_\mu q_\nu + a_3 q_\mu p_\nu + a_4 q_\mu q_\nu + a_5 g_{\mu\nu} \tag{8.11}$$

are related to b_i and $\overline{b}_i$ appearing in the ν and $\overline{\nu}$ differential cross-sections, Eq. (8.6), by

$$a_i(\nu q^2) = b_i(\nu q^2) - \overline{b}_i(-\nu, q^2) \tag{8.12}$$

For $q^2 < 0$, b_i and $\overline{b}_i$ vanish below a threshold $\nu_{th} > 0$ and therefore

$$\int_{-\infty}^{\infty} a_i(\nu, q^2) d\nu = \int_{-\infty}^{\infty} d\nu \left\{ b_i(\nu q^2) - \overline{b}_i(\nu, q^2) \right\} \tag{8.13}$$

For i = 1, the left-hand side of Eq. (8.13) is given by the Fubini-Dashen-Gell-Mann sum rule, Eq. (7.14) which takes the form

$$\frac{1}{2\pi} \int_{-\infty}^{\infty} d\nu\, a_1(\nu, q^2) = 4 \tag{8.14}$$

where the factor 4 comes from the equal contribution of the vector-vector and axial-axial terms in Eq. (8.9) (vector-axial terms do not contribute) and the additional coefficient 2 in Eq. (8.9). To proceed further, we must assume the following asymptotic conditions

$$\lim_{\omega \to \infty} \frac{1}{\omega} \int_0^{\omega M} d\nu \left\{ b_1(\nu, q^2) - \bar{b}_1(\nu, q^2) \right\} \nu = 0 \qquad (8.15)$$

and

$$\lim_{\omega \to \infty} \frac{1}{\omega^2} \int_0^{\omega M} d\nu \left\{ b_5(\nu, q^2) - \bar{b}_5(\nu, q^2) \right\} = 0 \qquad (8.16)$$

Then we obtain from Eqs. (8.6), (8.13) and (8.14) Adler's relation

$$\lim_{\omega \to \infty} \frac{d\sigma}{dq^2} - \frac{d\bar{\sigma}}{dq^2} = \frac{G^2}{\pi} \cos^2\theta \qquad (8.17)$$

Observe that the right-hand side of Eq. (8.17) is independent of q^2. The practical question naturally arises for what finite energies we can expect such a relation to become approximately valid. For $q^2 = 0$ this question has been answered by Adler and Gilman[29]. As we have seen in section 7, the amplitude $a_1(\nu,0)$ can be evaluated in terms of π-N total cross-sections by means of P. D. D. A. C. They find that Eq. (8.17) is satisfied for $q^2 = 0$ when $\omega \sim 5$ BeV. The corresponding relation for the strangeness changing transitions is

$$\lim_{\omega \to \infty} \frac{d\sigma}{dq^2} - \frac{d\bar{\sigma}}{dq^2} = \frac{2G^2}{\pi} \sin^2\theta \qquad (8.18)$$

Another interesting test of the equal time commutation relations has been proposed by Bjorken[30], who derived the following inequality for the differential cross-section for inelastic electron or muon nucleon scattering at high energies, by an isotopic spin rotation of Adler's relation,

$$\lim_{\omega \to \infty} \frac{d\sigma_p}{dq^2} + \frac{d\sigma_n}{dq^2} > \frac{2\pi\alpha^2}{q^4}$$

Experiments are under way to check this inequality at the highest electron energy available at SLAC, $\omega = 20$ BeV.

We have covered in these lectures only a small sample of the many interesting applications of current algebra, but we hope that these will stimulate your interest, help you to read the current literature, and hopefully lead you to participate in further developments.

ACKNOWLEDGEMENTS

I am indebted to my colleagues and to many students at the IX Latin Americal School of Physics for discussions which helped clarify some of the ideas presented here. In particular I like to thank Dr. Alex Maksymowicz for help in preparing the bibliography and for corrections in a preliminary version of the manuscript, and Dr. C. A. Savoy for his notes of some of the lectures.

REFERENCES

1. M. Gell-Mann, Phys. Rev. 125, 1067 (1962).
2. Y. Ne'eman, Nuclear Physics 26, 222 (1961).
3. M. Gell-Mann, Physics 1, 63 (1964).
4. M. Gell-Mann and M. Levy, Nuovo Cimento 16, 705 (1960).
5. Y. Nambu, Phys. Rev. Letters 4, 380 (1960).
6. Y. Nambu and D. Lurie, Phys. Rev. 125, 1429 (1962).
7. Y. Nambu and E. Shrauner, Phys. Rev. 128, 862 (1962).
8. S. Adler, Phys. Rev. 137 B, 1022 (1965).
9. S. Fubini and G. Furlan, Physics 1, 229 (1965).
10. S. Adler, Phys. Rev. Letters 143, 1051 (1965).
    Phys. Rev. 140 B, 736 (1965).
11. W. Weisberger, Phys. Rev. Letters 14, 1047 (1965).
    Phys. Rev. 143, 1302 (1966).
12. T. Goto and T. Imanura, Progress of Theoretical Physics 14, 396 (1955).
    J. Schwinger, Phys. Rev. Letters 3, 296 (1959).
    K. Johnson, Nuclear Physics 25, 431 (1961).
13. R. Haag, Phys. Rev. 112, 669 (1958)
    H. Araki and R. Haag, Comm. of Math. Physics 4, 77 (1967).
    See also comments by Nishijima, Proceedings of the International Conference on Weak Interactions at Argonne, Oct. 1965, pg. 418.
14. M. L. Goldberger and S. Treiman, Phys. Rev. 110, 1178 (1958).
15. S. Weinberg, Phys. Rev. Letters 17, 616 (1966).
16. M. L. Goldberger, H. Miyazawa and R. Oehme, Phys. Rev. 99, 986 (1955).

17. G. G. Callan and S. B. Treiman, Phys. Rev. Letters 16, 153 (1966).

18. V. S. Mathur, S. Okubo and L. K. Pandit, Phys. Rev. Letters 16, 376 (1966).

19. See, for example, Cabibbo's report in the Proceedings of the XIII International Conference on High Energy Physics, pg. 32 (Univ. of California Press 1967).

20. S. Weinberg, Phys. Rev. Letters 17, 336 (1966). See also an erratum in Phys. Rev. Letters 18, 1178 (1967).

21. The importance of the K-pole terms was noted earlier in K-3π decay by C. Bouchiat and P. Meyer.

22. R. W. Birge et al, Phys. Rev. 139 B, 1600 (1965).

23. S. Fubini, Nuovo Cimento 43, 475 (1966).

24. R. F. Dashen and M. Gell-Mann, Proceedings of the Third Coral Gable Conference, pg. 147 (1966).

25. J. D. Bjorken, Phys. Rev. 148, 1467 (1966).

26. M. Veltman, Phys. Rev. Letters 17, 553 (1966).

27. M. Nauenberg, Phys. Rev. 154, 1455 (1967), and Proceedings of the VI International School on High Energy Physics, Schladming, Austria, 1967 (to be published).

28. S. Adler, Phys. Rev. 143, 1144 (1966).

29. S. Adler and F. Gilman, Phys. Rev. 156, 1598 (1967).

30. J. D. Bjorken, Phys. Rev. Letters 16, 408 (1966).

6

K_{e4} DECAY AND π-π SCATTERING[+] (Seminar)

Alexander Maksymowicz, Division of Natural Sciences, University of California, Santa Cruz, California, and Department of Physics, University of Pittsburgh, Pittsburgh, Pennsylvania

---

+ Work supported in part by the National Science Foundation, and in part by the U. S. Atomic Energy Commission under Contract AT(30-1)-3829.

The lectures of Professor Nauenberg contain a detailed calculation of current algebra predictions for the decay $K \to (2\pi) l\nu$, known as K_{l4} decay. It is pointed out in these lectures that these predictions are in reasonable agreement with the early experimental data[1] for this decay mode. The above calculation contains the implicit assumption that any final state interaction between the pions may be neglected. The qualitative agreement with experiment is then taken as evidence that the low-energy π-π interaction is indeed weak. This is in accord with and, in fact, provides the chief support for a prediction by Weinberg[2] of small π-π scattering lengths, based on an explicit current algebra calculation.

Prior to the publication of this last calculation it appeared very likely on the basis of the so-called ABC experiment[3] that the S-wave π-π interaction near threshold is quite strong. K_{e4} decay was proposed as a very suitable process for determining the parameters of this interaction, since the only hadrons in the final state of this reaction are two pions[4]. How this might be accomplished in a relatively "clean" manner was shown in a paper by Cabibbo and Maksymowicz.[5]

The present talk is devoted chiefly to outlining the analysis of this last paper, paying special attention to the assumptions involved. Such an undertaking presupposes, of course, that current algebra has not said the last word about the low-energy π-π interaction, and that the problem of its experimental determination is still of interest.

In his calculation Weinberg had assumed a priori that the π-π interaction was weak by neglecting the unitarity cut starting at threshold. The fact that he ended up with small scattering lengths as his final result merely showed that his calculation was self-consistent. The only "experimental" support for this result was the success of the current algebra predictions for K_{e4} decay under the same assumption that the π-π interaction could be ignored. However, a recent elaborate data-fitting analysis of more than 300 K_{e4} events by Berends, Donnachie, and Oades[6] seems to indicate that these predictions are rather insensitive to the strength of a nonresonant low-energy π-π interaction. Thus, on the basis of available data, current algebra results for K_{e4} decay are not at all incompatible with a strong π-π interaction near threshold. Since the results of the ABC experiment are yet to be explained, we here take the viewpoint that such an interaction quite likely might exist.

We restrict our discussion to the decay mode $K^+ \rightarrow \pi^+\pi^- e^+ \nu$, since this is the reaction of principal experimental interest. We let p_K, p_+, p_-, p_e, and p_ν denote the four-momenta of the particles involved. We now make the following four generally accepted assumptions:

1. The interaction Lagrangian for semi-leptonic processes has the current x current form

$$L_{int} = \frac{G}{\sqrt{2}}\left\{ j^{\lambda}_{lep} J^{+}_{\lambda} + \text{hermitian conjugate} \right\}, \qquad (1)$$

where the lepton current is given by the explicit V-A form

$$j^{\lambda}_{lep} = \bar{\Psi}_{\nu} \gamma^{\lambda} (1 - \gamma_5) \Psi_l \qquad (2)$$

Thus, to first order in this interaction the matrix element for K_{e4} decay is given by

$$< \pi^+ \pi^- e^+ \nu | L_{int} | K^+ > = \frac{G}{\sqrt{2}} \left[\bar{u}_{\nu} \gamma^{\lambda} (1 - \gamma_5) u_e \right] \left[< \pi^+ \pi^- | V_{\lambda} | K^+ > \right.$$

$$\left. + < \pi^+ \pi^- | A_{\lambda} | K^+ > \right] \qquad (3)$$

where V_{λ} and A_{λ} are vector and axial currents respectively, and we have neglected some kinematic factors.

2. Lorentz invariance requires the following forms for the matrix elements of V_{λ} and A_{λ}.

$$< \pi^+ \pi^- | V_{\lambda} | K^+ > = \frac{i f_4(s, t, u)}{M_K^3} \varepsilon_{\lambda\mu\nu\sigma} p_k^{\mu} p_+^{\nu} p_-^{\sigma} \qquad (4)$$

$$< \pi^+ \pi^- | A_{\lambda} | K^+ > = \frac{1}{M_K} \left\{ f_1(s, t, u)(p_+ + p_-)_{\lambda} + f_2(s, t, u) \right.$$

$$\left. \times (p_+ - p_-)_{\lambda} + f_3(s, t, u)(p_K - p_+ - p_-)_{\lambda} \right\} \qquad (5)$$

with

$$s = (p_+ + p_-)^2$$
$$t = (p_K - p_+)^2 \qquad (6)$$
$$u = (p_K - p_-)^2$$

3. Only the f_1 and f_2 terms contribute significantly to the decay rate.

This assumption may seem confusing, since current algebra predicts a very definite behavior for the form factor f_3. However, noting that $p_K - p_+ - p_- = p_e + p_\nu$ by four-momentum conservation, after contraction with the lepton current and use of the Dirac equation one finds the f_3 term to be proportional to m_e, the mass of the electron, whereas the f_1 and f_2 terms are, roughly speaking, proportional to the pion mass, m_π. Therefore, in order to study the behavior of f_3 one must turn to $K_{\mu 4}$ decay, since here the mass of the muon is close to that of the pion.

The contribution of the f_4 term is simply shot down by phase space, due to the presence in it of the product of three momenta.

The above kinematical arguments are valid only if f_3 and f_4 are of the same order of magnitude as or smaller than f_1 and f_2. Should they in fact be much larger, they would give rise to observable effects and could be taken into account.

4. The weak current of the hadrons, J_λ, is identical to the Cabibbo current[7]. In particular,

$$A_\lambda = \cos\theta\, A_\lambda^{\Delta S=0} + \sin\theta\, A_\lambda^{\Delta S=1} , \tag{7}$$

where $A_\lambda^{\Delta S=0}$ and $A_\lambda^{\Delta S=1}$ transform as members of the same octet representation under SU(3). K_{e4} decay involves the strangeness-changing current $A_\lambda^{\Delta S=1}$, which has the same SU(3) transformation properties as the K^- meson and thus change isotopic spin by only half a unit. This means that the two pions emitted in K_{e4} decay can be only in relative I = 0 or 1 isotopic spin states. We now have to make two crucial but more dubious additional assumptions.

5. The form factors f_1 and f_2 depend strongly only on the variable s; their dependence on t and u may be neglected.

In order to justify this assumption one usually argues that the singularities in t and u are far from the region of interest in the sense of dispersion theory. That this, in fact, is quite likely to be the case is made plausible in the detailed dispersion theoretic analysis of K_{e4} decay by Kacser, Singer and Truong[8].

With this assumption we can write

$$< \pi^+ \pi^- | A_\lambda | K^+ > \simeq \frac{1}{M_K} \left\{ f_1(s)(p_+ + p_-)_\lambda + f_2(s)(p_+ - p_-)_\lambda \right\} \tag{8}$$

Notice that the f_1 term is even under the interchange $p_+ \leftrightarrow p_-$, whereas the f_2 term is odd. In the center of mass system (c.m.s.) of the two pions, the last equation is given by

$$< \pi^+ \pi^- | A_\lambda | K^+ > \simeq \frac{1}{M_K} \left\{ f_1(s) \sqrt{s} + f_2(s) \sqrt{s - 4m^2}\, \hat{p}_+ \right\} ,$$

where $\hat{p}_+$ is a unit vector along the direction of the π^+ momentum. We see that the f_1 term is a scalar under rotations, the f_2 term a vector. Combining these results with Bose statistics for the pions, we obtain the very simple result that the f_1 term represents the amplitude for emission of the two pions in an $l = 0$, $I = 0$ state, and the f_2 term that for emission in an $l = 1$, $I = 1$ state.

6. Time-reversal invariance is valid for the decay in question. This assumption leads to the following forms for f_1 and f_2:

$$f_1(s) = \tilde{f}_1(s) e^{i\delta_0(s)} \qquad f_2(s) = \tilde{f}_2(s) e^{i\delta_1(s)} \tag{9}$$

where $\tilde{f}_1$ and $\tilde{f}_2$ are real numbers, and δ_o and δ_1 are the π-π scattering phase shifts in the $l = 0$, $I = 0$ and $l = 1$, $I = 1$ states, respectively. This result is a special case of the Watson Theorem.[9]

Figure 1 illustrates some of the kinematics for the process $K^+ \rightarrow \pi^+\pi^- e^+ \nu$. We have indicated two angular variables in the figure: θ, the angle of the π^+ in the c.m.s. of the pions with respect to the direction of flight of the K^+ in that system; and ϕ, the angle between the plane containing the pion momenta and that containing the lepton momenta in the K^+ rest system. The angle θ is polar, ϕ azimuthal.

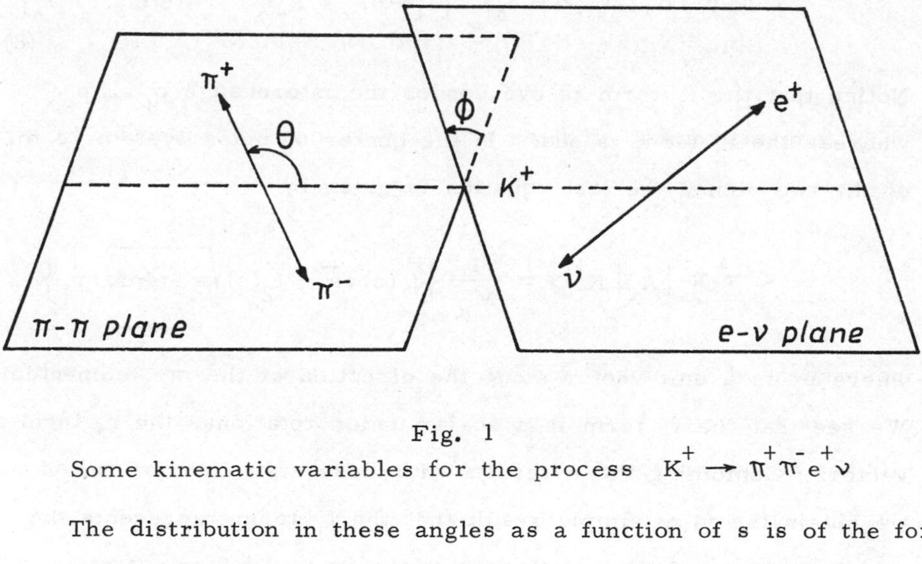

Fig. 1
Some kinematic variables for the process $K^+ \rightarrow \pi^+\pi^- e^+ \nu$

The distribution in these angles as a function of s is of the form

$$\frac{d\Gamma}{ds\, d\cos\theta\, d\phi} \sim \tilde{f}_1^2(s)A(s) + \tilde{f}_2^2(s)\left[B(s) + C(s)\cos^2\theta + D(s)\sin^2\theta \sin^2\phi\right] + \tilde{f}_1(s)\tilde{f}_2(s)E(s)\cos(\delta_o - \delta_1)\cos\theta + \tilde{f}_1(s)\tilde{f}_2(s)F(s)\sin(\delta_o - \delta_1)\sin\theta \sin\phi \qquad (10)$$

where A, B, C, D, E, F are known functions. From this expression one can easily calculate the following two angular correlations. First, the forward-backward asymmetry of the π^+, which is just the number of events N_F with $0 < \theta < \frac{\pi}{2}$ minus the number N_B with $\frac{\pi}{2} < \theta < \pi$:

$$\alpha(s) \equiv N_F(s) - N_B(s) \sim \tilde{f}_1(s)\tilde{f}_2(s)E(s)\cos(\delta_o - \delta_1) \tag{11}$$

Second, the up-down asymmetry of the e^+ with respect to the plane of the pions, which is the number of events N_U with $0 < \phi < \pi$ minus the number N_D with $\pi < \phi < 2\pi$:

$$\beta(s) \equiv N_U(s) - N_B(s) \sim \tilde{f}_1(s)\tilde{f}_2(s)F(s)\sin(\delta_o - \delta_1) \tag{12}$$

A measurement of these two correlations as a function of s then yields the quantity

$$\tan(\delta_o - \delta_1) = \frac{\beta(s)}{\alpha(s)} \frac{E(s)}{F(s)} \tag{13}$$

independent of the unknown form factors $\tilde{f}_1$ and $\tilde{f}_2$. Even though one does not yet have sufficient data to make a statistically significant determination of $\tan(\delta_o - \delta_1)$ as a function of s, one can obtain some indication of the nature of the low energy π-π interaction from the value of this quantity suitably averaged over s.

The up-down asymmetry is the expectation value of $\sin \phi$, which is essentially $\mathbf{p}_e \cdot (\mathbf{p}_+ \times \mathbf{p}_-)$. This latter quantity and hence $\sin \phi$ are odd under time-reversal. We thus seem to have an apparent contradiction with our assumption of T invariance. If we look at the angular distribution, Eq. (10), we see that $\sin \phi$ enters into the F(s) term, and that another factor in this term is the quantity $\sin(\delta_o - \delta_1)$. Since partial-wave phase shifts change sign under time-reversal, we find that the F(s) term is actually even under this operation if the final state interaction is taken into account. Nevertheless, we have come up against a real difficulty. If the observed violation of CP invariance in neutral K meson decay is a property of all weak interactions and is not, in general, a small effect, it would be exceedingly hard to separate its effects from those due to a final state π-π interaction. Thus, a significant violation of T invariance in K_{e4} decay would render impractical the scheme of analysis outlined above.

REFERENCES

1. R. W. Birge et al., Phys. Rev. Letters 11, 35 (1963).
2. S. Weinberg, Phys. Rev. Letters 17, 616 (1966).
3. N. E. Booth, A. Abashian and K. M. Crowe, Phys. Rev. Letters 7, 35 (1961); N. E. Booth and A. Abashian, Phys. Rev. 132, 2314 (1963).
4. E. P. Shabalin, Zh. Eksperim. i Teor. Fiz. 44, 765 (1963). [translation: Soviet Physics -- JETP 17, 517 (1963)].
5. N. Cabibbo and A. Maksymowicz, Phys. Rev. 137, B 438 (1965).
6. F. A. Berends, A. Donnachie, and G. C. Oades, CERN report TH 792, 1967 .
7. N. Cabibbo, Phys. Rev. Letters 10, 531 (1963).
8. C. Kacser, P. Singer and T. N. Truong, Phys. Rev. 137, B 1605 (1965).
9. K. M. Watson, Phys. Rev. 95, 228 (1954).

7

INFINITE COMPONENT FIELD THEORIES

Christian Fronsdal, University of California, Los Angeles, U.S.A.

1. REVIEW OF THE BASIC IDEAS AND SUCCESSES OF SU(6)

1.1. INTRODUCTION. The invention of SU(6) symmetry was a natural application of a very simple idea that had already scored some notable triumphs. Consider Heisenberg's introduction of isotopic spin; let ψ_1 and ψ_2 be the states of a single proton and a single neutron, neglect the mass difference and the spin, and look at the free lagrangian

$$\mathcal{L}_o = \psi_1^* (p^2 + m^2)\psi_1 + \psi_2^* (p^2 + m^2)\psi_2$$

This is an example of a hermitian form:

$$a_1 |\psi_1|^2 + a_2 |\psi_2|^2$$

with $a_1 = a_2$. Now there is something very special about hermitian forms with equal coefficients: invariance. Not only do ψ_1 and ψ_2 enter on an equal footing, but any transformation

$$\psi_i \longrightarrow \sum_{j=1}^{2} U_{ij} \psi_j \quad , \quad i = 1 , 2 \qquad (1.1)$$

leaves the form invariant, provided only that U_{ij} are the elements of a unitary matrix. The appearance of hermitian forms, invariant under unitary transformations, is inevitable, due to the common practice of normalizing similar states in the same way. Thus $|\psi_1|^2$ and $|\psi_2|^2$ have the same coefficients in $\mathcal{L}_o$ simply because both ψ_1 and ψ_2 are normalized to, say, one particle per unit volume. Now Heisenberg suggested that perhaps the transformation (1.1) leaves invariant the entire Lagrangian, not just the free part. Thus was born SU(2) (isospin), the group of unitary transformations on a state space of two independent states.

Although isospin was not very popular at first, it became very important when the strange particles began to be discovered. So many particles were discovered, in fact, that some people started to look for a larger symmetry group.

Sakata proceeded to generalize Heisenberg's idea in the most direct way. Suppose, said Sakata, that the Λ is as fundamental as the two nucleons, and let us ignore the mass-differences and the spins. Then the free Lagrangian is of the form

$$a_1|\psi_1|^2 + a_2|\psi_2|^2 + a_3|\psi_3|^2 ,$$

with $a_1 = a_2 = a_3$. This hermitian form is invariant under

$$\psi_i \longrightarrow \sum_{j=1}^{3} U_{ij}\,\psi_j \quad , \quad i = 1, 2, 3 \qquad (1.2)$$

provided U_{ij} are the elements of a unitary 3 x 3 matrix. Thus was born SU(3), and the suggestion that the whole Lagrangian might be invariant under this group. This idea came to play a very important role in elementary particle physics, but only after Gell-Mann and Ne'eman made a very essential modification of it.

Long before SU(3), and in fact just a short time after the introduction of isospin, Wigner took another look at Heisenberg's invariant Lagrangian and decided to include the spin. If ψ_1 and ψ_2 are proton states with spin up and spin down, and ψ_3 and ψ_4 are the two neutron states, then the free Lagrangian is a hermitian form with four, rather than two, terms with equal coefficients:

$$\sum_{i=1}^{4} a_i |\psi_i|^2 , \tag{1.3}$$

Rotational invariance is invariance under the SU(2) transformation

$$\left.\begin{aligned} \psi_i &\rightarrow \sum_{j=1,2} U_{ij} \psi_j , \quad i = 1, 2 \\ \psi_i &\rightarrow \sum_{j=3,4} U_{ij} \psi_j , \quad i = 3, 4 \end{aligned}\right\} \tag{1.4}$$

and requires that $a_1 = a_2$, $a_3 = a_4$. Isospin invariance is invariance under

$$\left.\begin{aligned} \psi_i &= \sum_{j=1,3} U_{ij} \psi_j , \quad i = 1, 3 \\ \psi_i &= \sum_{j=2,4} U_{ij} \psi_j , \quad i = 2, 4 \end{aligned}\right\} \tag{1.5}$$

and requires $a_1 = a_3$, $a_2 = a_4$. Wigner noticed the obvious: that (1.3), with all a_i equal, is invariant under

$$\psi_i = \sum_{j=1,2,3,4} U_{ij} \psi_j , \quad i = 1, 2, 3, 4 \tag{1.6}$$

and suggested that this SU(4) invariance could be extended to the complete Lagrangian.

The introduction of SU(6) would now be quite obvious, except for the unhappy fact that Sakata's triplet did not exist. This was solved, not by the discovery of an SU(3) triplet, but by inventing it. Suppose that all known particles are made up of several quarks, these latter forming the missing SU(3) triplet. Then these must have spin 1/2; so there actually 6 states; ergo: SU(6). Thus we see that SU(2), SU(3), SU(4) ánd SU(6) are all manifestations of our preoccupation with the invariance properties of hermitian forms with equal coefficients.

Note that the hermitian forms in question are free Lagrangians, and that the coefficients are equal only if the masses are equal, hence mass degeneracy is an essential ingredient. In non relativistic quantum mechanics we know of examples where the degeneracy is very nearly exact, and where this fact can be traced to invariance of the Hamiltonian under simple transformation groups. The well known case of the SU(4) symmetry of the hydrogen atom is of particular interest because of the close analogy to SU(6). We shall return to this later.

1.2. TENSOR REPRESENTATIONS OF SU(6). Let χ_A, $A = 1, 2, \ldots 6$ be the six quarks states; since they have not been observed we consider states of two or three quarks. Before SU(6) was suggested, it had already been pointed out that the most economical use of the quarks was as follows. Each member of the SU(3) octet and decuplet contains three quarks, and each member of the two SU(3) octets of mesons contains one quark and one antiquark. The 216 threequark states may be labeled ψ_{ABC}, and the 36 quark-antiquark states may be labeled ψ_A^B.

Let the SU(6) transformations of χ_A be written

$$\chi_A \rightarrow (U\chi)_A = U_A^B \chi_B$$

where U is a unitary 6 by 6 matrix. Similarly, the antiquarks transform as follows

$$\chi^{*A} \rightarrow (\chi^* U^+)^A$$

Why? Consider infinitesimal transformations,

$$U = 1 + i\varepsilon^k L_k \qquad (1.7)$$

where ε^k are infinitesimal real parameters and L_k are a set of 35 hermitian 6 by 6 matrices. Among these matrices are some that are to be identified with charge, hypercharge and so on; each L_k corresponds to a physical quantum number. By anti-quarks is meant a set of states whose quantum numbers are the negatives of the quantum numbers of the quarks. Hence, when transforming the antiquarks, we must use the same rule as for quarks, except that L_k is to be replaced by $-L_k$. Actually we should use $-L_k^T$, the negative transpose. This is seen as follows. Consider the hermitian form

$$\sum_A \chi^{*A} \chi_A$$

This is "neutral", for if $\varepsilon^k L_k$ is diagonal, then the transformation induced by (1.1) is

$$\sum_A \chi^{*A} \chi_A \rightarrow \sum_A [\chi^*(1 - i\varepsilon^k L_k)]^A \, [(1 + i\varepsilon^k L_k)\chi]_A =$$

$$= \sum_A \chi^{*A} \chi_A$$

In a different basis, where $\varepsilon^k L_k$ is not necessarily diagonal, the cancellation still persists, because we have placed the operator acting on χ^* on the right. Thus χ^{*A} is multiplied by $-L_k$ on the right, or by $-L_k^T$ on the left. Another point is that the matrices $-L_k^T$ satisfy the same commutation relationships as the L_k; in high-brow language this means that the transformation $L_k \rightarrow -L_k^T$ is an algebra isomorphism.

The tensors ψ_{ABC} and φ_A^B transform like products of quarks:

$$\psi_{ABC} \rightarrow U_A^{A'} U_B^{B'} U_C^{C'} \psi_{A'B'C'} \tag{1.8}$$

$$\varphi_A^B \rightarrow U_A^{A'} U^{+B}_{B'} \varphi_{A'}^{B'} = (U\varphi U^+)_A^B$$

Not all 216 components of ψ_{ABC} get mixed up with each other under these transformations. Thus it is obvious that, if ψ_{ABC} is symmetric, then the symmetry remains, so that symmetric components get mixed up with symmetric components only. We say that ψ_{ABC} is the basis for a reducible representation of SU(6). However, the symmetric components form the basis for an irreducible representation; that is, every symmetric component gets mixed up with every other symmetric component. The complete reduction into symmetry classes will not be discussed, we just mention that the components of ψ_{ABC} breaks up into a symmetry class, corresponding to the Young tableaux

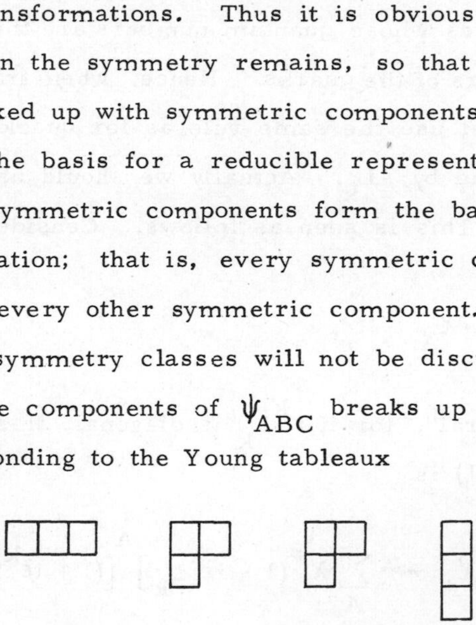

with 56, 70, 70, 20 components, respectively. The number 56 of components in the completely symmetric part is arrived at as follows.

Since the order of the indices is irrelevant, the only thing that matters is how many indices are equal to 1, how many equal to 2, and so on. The problem is thus to count the number of ways 3 objects can be placed in 6 boxes, namely $\frac{6 \cdot 7 \cdot 8}{1 \cdot 2 \cdot 3} = 56$.

The components of φ_A^B cannot be arranged in symmetry classes, because the two indices transform differently. Still φ_A^B is not reducible, for if φ_A^B is traceless, then it remains traceless:

$$(U \varphi U^+)_A^A = (\varphi U^+ U)_A^A = \varphi_A^A$$

Hence φ_A^B can be split into a traceless part with 35 components and a single component proportional to δ_A^B:

$$\varphi_A^B = (\delta_A^{A'} \delta_{B'}^B - \frac{1}{6} \delta_A^B \delta_{B'}^{A'}) \varphi_{A'}^{B'} + \frac{1}{6} \delta_A^B (\delta_{B'}^{A'} \varphi_{A'}^{B'})$$

The multiplets that the early SU(6) papers associated with known particles were the 56-dimensional one represented by a symmetric tensor ψ_{ABC} and the 35-dimensional one represented by a traceless tensor φ_A^B. We shall henceforth assume the symmetry and the tracelessness, without introducing new symbols.

1.3. THE TWO PHYSICAL MULTIPLETS. To understand what are the physical particles that make the 56 and 35 dimensional multiplets we reduce them into submultiplets that have fixed spin and fixed unitary spin. That is, we reduce the irreducible SU(6) representations into a sum of irreducible representations of the group

$$\underset{\text{(spin)}}{SU(2)} \otimes \underset{\text{(unitary spin)}}{SU(3)}$$

Let X_1 and X_2 be the two spin states of the proton-quark, X_3 and X_4 the two spin states of the neutron-quark, and X_5, X_6 the states of the Λ-quark, and introduce the new notation

$$\left.\begin{array}{l}\left.\begin{array}{l}X_1\\X_2\end{array}\right\} X_{1\alpha}\\ \left.\begin{array}{l}X_3\\X_4\end{array}\right\} X_{2\alpha}\\ \left.\begin{array}{l}X_5\\X_6\end{array}\right\} X_{3\alpha}\end{array}\right\} X_{a\alpha}\ , \quad \begin{array}{l}a = 1, 2, 3\\ \alpha = 1, 2\end{array}$$

Then SU(2) (spin) transformations act on the Greek index, and SU(3) acts on the latin index. Our symmetric tensor ψ_{ABC} is now written

$$\psi_{ABC} \rightarrow \psi_{abc,\alpha\beta\gamma} \qquad \begin{array}{l}a, b, c, = 1, 2, 3\\ \alpha, \beta, \gamma, = 1, 2\end{array}$$

This object is symmetric with respect to simultaneous application of the same permutation to the latin indices and the Greek indices, but it is not symmetric with respect to separate permutations of each group of indices.

The reduction of $\psi_{abc,\alpha\beta\gamma}$ into parts that transform irreducibly with respect to SU(2) ⊗ SU(3) is given by the formula

$$\psi_{abc,\alpha\beta\gamma} = \tilde{\psi}_{abc,\alpha\beta\gamma} + 18^{-1/2}\Big[\varepsilon_{abd}\,\varepsilon_{\alpha\beta}\,\psi_{c,\gamma}^{\ d} + \varepsilon_{bcd}\,\varepsilon_{\beta\gamma}\,\psi_{a,\alpha}^{\ d} + \varepsilon_{cad}\,\varepsilon_{\gamma\alpha}\,\psi_{b,\beta}^{\ d}\Big] \qquad (1.9)$$

Why? The first term is simply the part that is completely symmetric in each group of indices. It accounts for 4 x 10 = 40 of the 56 independent components. The spin is 3/2 (quadruplet) and the SU(3) characteristics are those of the wellknown decuplet. This leaves only 16 components to be accounted for. The Young tableaux, for both groups of indices must be those of intermediate symmetry, since the completely symmetric part has been used up and the antisymmetric part doesn't exist due to the fact that the Greek indices take only 2 values. The dimension of the multiplet

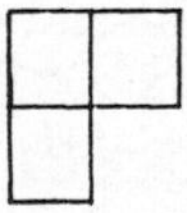

is 8 for SU(3) and 2 for SU(2); hence the components that are yet to be accounted for consist of a single multiplet, octet with respect to SU(3) and doublet (spin 1/2) with respect to SU(2). Having thus determined the symmetry properties of the 16 remaining components we can easily write down a general tensor that possesses this symmetry. There remains only to determine the expression for $\psi_{a,\alpha}^{\;\;b}$ in terms of $\psi_{abc,\alpha\beta\gamma}$. This is simple, just multiply both sides of (1.9) by $\varepsilon^{abc}\cdot\varepsilon^{\alpha\beta}$, to obtain

$$\varepsilon^{abe}\varepsilon^{\alpha\beta}\psi_{abc,\alpha\beta\gamma} = 18^{-1/2}\Big[4\psi_{c,\gamma}^{\;\;e}\;\; 2\delta^{c}_{e}\,\psi_{d,\gamma}^{\;\;d}$$

$$+\, 2\psi_{c,\gamma}^{\;\;e}\Big]$$

Contracting over c, e, the left-hand side vanishes, hence $\psi_{a,\alpha}^{\;\;b}$ is traceless, as required of an octet, and

$$\psi_{a,\alpha}^{\;\;b} = \sqrt{1/2}\,\varepsilon^{abe}\varepsilon^{\alpha\beta}\psi_{abc,\alpha\beta\gamma}$$

The factor $18^{-1/2}$ in (1.9) is chosen as follows. From (1.9) it follows that

$$\psi^{*abc,\alpha\beta\gamma}\psi_{abc,\alpha\beta\gamma} = \tilde{\psi}^{*abc,\alpha\beta\gamma}\psi_{abc,\alpha\beta\gamma}$$

$$+ \psi_{b}^{*a,\alpha}\psi_{a,\alpha}^{b} \qquad (1.10)$$

Hence the choice $18^{-1/2}$ in (1.9) means that we have chosen the most convenient normalization for all the tensors involved, namely:

$$\left|\psi_{abc,\alpha\beta\gamma}\right|^2 = 1$$

$$\left|\frac{1}{\sqrt{n}} S\,\tilde{\psi}_{abc,\alpha\beta\gamma}\right|^2 = 1$$

where S is a symmetrization operator and where n is the number of terms needed to symmetrize; e.g.

$$\left|\psi_{111,222}\right|^2 = 1$$

$$\left|\frac{\psi_{111,122} + \psi_{111,212} + \psi_{111,221}}{\sqrt{3}}\right|^2 = 1$$

and

$$\left|\frac{1}{\sqrt{n}} T\psi_{a,\alpha}^{b}\right|^2 = 1$$

where T is an operator that makes traceless, and where n is the sum of the squares of the coefficients needed to make traceless, e.g.,

$$\left|\psi_{1,\alpha}^{2}\right|^2 = 1$$

$$\left| \frac{\psi_{1,\alpha}^{1} - \frac{1}{3} \sum \psi_{a,\alpha}^{a}}{\sqrt{2/3}} \right|^2 = 1$$

The easiest way to establish the correct coefficient to use in (1.9), in order to obtain this standard and convenient normalization, is to calculate the norm (1.10) for arbitrary coefficient, and adjust the coefficient in (1.9) so that the coefficient of the second term in (1.10) becomes 1.

The meson multiplet is treated similarly:

$$\varphi_A^B \rightarrow \varphi_{a,\alpha}^{b,\beta} \quad \text{with} \quad \varphi_{a,\alpha}^{a,\alpha} = 0$$

$$\varphi_{a,\alpha}^{b,\beta} = \tilde{\varphi}_{a,\alpha}^{b,\beta} + C_1 \delta_a^b \tilde{\varphi}_\alpha^\beta + C_2 \delta_\alpha^\beta \tilde{\varphi}_a^b \tag{1.11}$$

where $\tilde{\varphi}_{a,\alpha}^{b,\beta}$ is traceless in both kinds of indices, and $\tilde{\varphi}_\alpha^\beta$, $\tilde{\varphi}_a^b$ are also traceless.

$$\varphi_{a,\alpha}^{a,\beta} = 3C_1 \tilde{\varphi}_\alpha^\beta$$

$$\varphi_{a,\alpha}^{b,\alpha} = 2C_2 \tilde{\varphi}_a^b$$

Determine C_1, C_2 (No cross terms!)

$$\varphi_{b,\beta}^{a,\alpha} \varphi_{a,\alpha}^{b,\beta} = \tilde{\varphi}_{b,\beta}^{a,\alpha} \tilde{\varphi}_{a,\alpha}^{b,\beta} + 9|C_1|^2 |\varphi_\alpha^\beta|^2 + 4|C_2|^2 |\tilde{\varphi}_a^b|^2$$

hence $C_1 = 1/3$, $C_2 = 1/2$. The three terms in (1.11) are: spin 1 - octet, spin 1 - singlet and spin 0 - octet.

2. EXPERIMENTAL PREDICTIONS OF SU(6)

2.1. MASS RELATIONS. Ambitious attempts to predict the masses within the framework of SU(6) have not been very successful. This is in striking contrast to the situation with SU(3), where the Gell-Mann Okubo mass formula constitutes one of the main successes of the theory. The most complete discussion was given by Beg and Singh, who proceeded in close analogy with Gell-Mann and Okubo.

The Gell-Mann Okubo formula, which will surely be discussed in Professor Ne'eman's lectures, may be written

$$M \text{ (or } M^2) = a + bY + c\left[I(I+1) - \frac{Y^2}{4}\right] \qquad (2.1)$$

where I and Y are the isotopic spin and the hypercharge, and a, b, c are numerical constants to be fitted to experiment. The formula gives M or M^2 according to your taste; the most conventional form of the relation is that which writes M for fermions and M^2 for bosons. For bosons b vanishes.

Eq. (2.1) works very well for the baryon octet and the baryon decuplet. It is a curious fact that b and c turn out to be the same in these two cases. [Actually this is not a double coincidence, but only a single one, for in the case of the decuplet $I(I+1) - Y^2/4 = 2 - (3/2)Y$]. A more sophisticated way of expressing this fact is to say that the masses of all the 56 baryons fit the formula

$$M = a_1 + a_2 s(s+1) + bY + c\left[I(I+1) - Y^2/4\right]$$

where s is the spin. This formula is a result of SU(6) in the following sense. The mass operator is a linear combination of neutral components of SU(6) tensors. All these SU(6) tensors must be constructed from the product $\psi^{ABC}\psi_{DEF}$, which means that they must have dimension 1, 35, 405 or 2695. The above operator has no term that belongs to the 2695 dimensional representation. In other words, if the phenomenological mass operator is analyzed with respect to its SU(6) transformation properties, then the most complicated terms do not occur.

Incidentally, the reduction of the product 56 x 56 is trivial:

1° There is a singlet, namely $\overline{\psi}^{ABC}\ \psi_{ABC}$

2° There is a 35-plet, namely $\overline{\psi}^{ABC}\ \psi_{ABD}$ which has 36-components less the singlet.

3° There is a 405-plet, namely $\overline{\psi}^{ABC}\ \psi_{ADE}$ which has 21 x 21 components ($21 = \frac{6 \cdot 7}{1 \cdot 2}$) less 36 already counted.

4° Finally the remainder is $56^2 - 21^2 = 77 \times 35 = 2695$.

The fact that one of the four parts does not contribute is support for SU(6), but real significance could have been assigned to this result only if the mass operator would have been, say, pure 1 and 35.

Turning to mesons we find a worse situation, all possible transformation properties are represented in the mass operator. There are some successful mass formulae, but their justifications are so weak that I don't want to discuss them here. The only notable success of SU(6) in connection with meson masses is the "prediction" of a good value for the mixing angle; see Professor Ne'eman's lectures.

Let me add some general statements about the meaning of mass formulae. Sometimes the Gell-Mann Okubo relation and related formulae are referred to as perturbation theory results, and there was at one time a lot of discussion of how to understand why perturbation theory gives a correct answer. Another approach has been to attempt to prove that the mass formulae (and related results) are the results of the dynamics. I think very little additional understanding has resulted from either approach, and I should prefer to think of the mass formulae as simple summaries of experimental results. The usefulness of SU(6) in this context is then a function of the basic simplicity of the mass phenomenology when it is expressed in SU(6) language. From this point of view SU(6) has not been a spectacular success.

Finally a question. Usually SU(6) is called a static symmetry. Are masses really static properties? Certainly so in an obvious sense; but in the language of perturbation theory and potential theory, the values of the masses are related to that part of the interaction that becomes important only at very high energy. Add to this the hypothesis that mass differences become irrelevant at very high energies, and you have a jumble of apparently contradictory points of view. To unify them all and to justify them without contradicting yourselves is a nontrivial sophistic exercise.

2.2 INVARIANT VERTICES. Traditionally, the first application of symmetry groups has always been to the Yukawa vertex; the baryon-antibaryon-meson vertex. Here SU(6) fails completely.

Let $\overline{\psi}^{ABC}$ be the antibaryon tensor. It transforms like the product of three antiquarks. The problem is to write down an invariant coupling between $\overline{\psi}^{ABC}$, ψ_{ABC} and φ^{B}_{A}. Invariance requirements are trivial to apply; it amounts simply to saturating the indices. In fact there is only one invariant: $\overline{\psi}^{ABC}\,\psi_{ABC'}\varphi^{c'}_{c}$, but this is not a satisfactory Yukawa vertex. In fact, in SU(3) ⊗ SU(2) notation,

$$\overline{\psi}^{abc,\alpha\beta\gamma}\,\psi_{abc',\alpha\beta\gamma'}\,\varphi^{C'\gamma'}_{C\gamma} \qquad (2.2)$$

Consider the part of this vertex that involves pseudoscalar mesons: that is, replace $\varphi^{c'\gamma'}_{c\gamma}$ by $\delta^{\gamma'}_{\gamma}\varphi^{c'}_{c}$. Then all spin indices become summed out from $\bar{\psi}$ to ψ, so that the two baryons form a scalar. Hence this vertex is odd under space reflection. There is no SU(6) invariant Yukawa vertex!

The literature is full of references to the SU(6) - predicted BBM vertex. What is meant is different in each case, but common to all the predictions, is that they go beyond static SU(6) to introduce non-zero momenta in some way or other. I repeat that SU(6) makes no prediction whatever about this vertex, except that it vanishes in the static limit.

There is a related vertex, which though highly artificial is consistent with SU(6) invariance, and that is the annihilation of a baryon-antibaryon pair into a single meson. What makes this unrealistic is that SU(6) is hardly reliable when the meson (or the baryons) is so far off the mass shell; in other words, the process is highly virtual so that comparison with experiment is very difficult. However, in this case (2.2) does not violate parity conservation.

2.3. CURRENTS AND GENERATORS. One of the most popular methods for extracting experimental predictions from symmetry theories is to assume that observable charges, and more generally, observable currents, are strongly related to the generators of the symmetry algebra. The identification of static charge and hypercharge with generators is of course basic to the definitions of isospin, as well as SU(3), SU(4) and SU(6). The identification of weak currents with generators of internal symmetry groups has been popular for a long time. Gravitational currents have also been considered.

Magnetic moments. One of the most spectacular consequences of SU(6) is the prediction of the correct ratio of the proton and neutron magnetic moments. First let us consider the fact that the neutron magnetic moment is non-zero. To achieve this with a simple universal coupling is really remarkable. In some of the early versions of relativistic SU(6) this feature was retained; in fact the universal coupling took the form of a minimal electromagnetic coupling. This is a spectacular achievement of these theories. It cannot mitigate their many unsavory features, but it is something to try to emulate. The prediction $\mu_N/\mu_P = -2/3$ is obtained by postulating that the magnetic moment transforms like an SU(6) generator, whose SU(3) transformation properties are the same as that of the charge. The spin properties are, of course, those of a vector. Hence, for baryons

$$< \mu > = \bar{\psi}^{ABC} \mu_{ABC}^{DEF} \psi_{DEF}$$

$$= \bar{\psi}^{ABC} \mu_{C}^{C'} \psi_{ABC'}$$

$$= \bar{\psi}^{abc,\alpha\beta\gamma} \mu_{c\gamma}^{c'\gamma'} \psi_{abc'\alpha\beta\gamma'}$$

$$\sim \bar{\psi}^{abc,\alpha\beta\gamma} Q_{c}^{c'} \sigma_{\gamma}^{\gamma'} \psi_{abc'\alpha\beta\gamma'}$$

$$\xrightarrow[\text{decouplet}]{\text{ignore}} \bar{\psi}^{abc,\alpha\beta\gamma} Q_{c}^{c'} \sigma_{\gamma}^{\gamma'} \left[\varepsilon_{abd}\, \varepsilon_{\alpha\beta}\, \psi_{c',\gamma'}^{d} + \ldots\right]$$

$$\sim \left[5 \bar{\psi}_{a}^{b,\alpha} Q_{b}^{c} \sigma_{\alpha}^{\beta} \psi_{c,\beta}^{a} + \bar{\psi}_{a}^{b,\alpha} Q_{d}^{a} \sigma_{\alpha}^{\beta} \psi_{b,\beta}^{d}\right]$$

Here, ignore strange particles by taking $a = d = 3$ and $b, c \neq 3$:

$$\langle \mu \rangle = 5\bar{\psi} Q \,\boldsymbol{\sigma}\, \psi + \bar{\psi} Q_3^3 \,\boldsymbol{\sigma}\, \psi \qquad (2.3)$$

Remember that $Q = \begin{bmatrix} 2/3 & & \\ & -1/3 & \\ & & -1/3 \end{bmatrix}$

and $P = \psi_1^3$, $N = \psi_2^3$; hence

$$\left.\begin{array}{l} \mu_P \sim 5 \cdot \frac{2}{3} - \frac{1}{3} = 3 \\ \mu_N \sim 5 \cdot (-\frac{1}{3}) - \frac{1}{3} = -2 \end{array}\right\} \frac{\mu_N}{\mu_P} = -\frac{2}{3}$$

Weak interactions. By similar assumptions and calculations one finds that SU(6) predicts $G_A/G_V = 5/3$. The experimental value is 1.18. This is one case where current algebra does very much better. Another prediction is $D/F = 3/2$ for semileptonic vertex. This seems to agree with experiment.

2.4. NON-STATIC SU(6). We end our short review of static SU(6) here, perhaps without giving it its due. The outstanding successes of the theory are:

1) The grouping of many observed particles and resonances into multiplets in a very economical way.

2) One relation each for baryon and meson masses.

3) $\mu_N/\mu_P = -2/3$.

The reason for the paucity of reliable predictions is easy to understand: the field of application is limited to particles at rest. From the very beginning it was realized that momenta had, somehow, to be introduced.

It became a very popular game to find wider applications of SU(6) by lifting it up from the purely static domain. The obvious way to do this seemed to be to make the theory relativistic, and many attempts were made in this direction. In fact, the rush to publish became so extreme that some of the suggestions were less than completely reasonable. This brought "relativistic SU(6)" into disrepute, and it soon became fashionable to believe that such theories could not be constructed.

I think this pessimistic conclusion is unwarranted. There is no doubt that a relativistic SU(6) can be constructed. The predictions of auch a theory are extremely rich; for example, one can predict entire form factors rather that just the static moments. Not only that, but the predictions are basically sound. The trouble is that the mass degeneracy of the multiplets is really quite imperfect. Up to now there exists a theory of relativistic SU(6) in a world where SU(6) is an exact symmetry, but very little has been done to take the mass breaking into account.

3. THE REPRESENTATIONS OF THE POINCARE GROUP

3.1. INTRODUCTION. Current developments in high energy physics may be characterized by a gradual convergence of three separate developments. One originates in SU(6), and the efforts to make it relativistic. Another is current algebra and superconvergences and the third is recently renewed interest in the kinematical structure of the S-matrix (generalized phase-shift analysis). Clearly all these ideas rely heavily on the theory of representations of the Poincaré group. It therefore seems appropriate to review that theory.

3.2. THE STRUCTURE OF THE POINCARE GROUP. The Poincaré group is defined as a set of transformations of 4 real variables x_o, x_1, x_2, x_3 :

$$\chi_\mu \rightarrow \Lambda_\mu^\nu \chi_\nu + a_\mu$$

where Λ_μ^ν and a_ν are real numbers with

$$\Lambda_\mu^\nu \Lambda_\sigma^\rho g_{\nu\rho} = g_{\mu\sigma}$$

The algebra consists of all real linear combinations of 10 generators:

$$P_\mu : \chi_\mu \rightarrow (1 + ia^\nu P_\nu)\chi_\mu = \chi_\mu + a_\mu \quad \therefore \quad P_\mu = i\frac{\partial}{\partial \chi^\mu}$$

$$L_{\mu\nu} : \chi_\mu \rightarrow (1 + \theta^{\nu\lambda} L_{\nu\lambda})\chi_\mu = \chi_\mu + \theta_\mu^\nu$$

$$\therefore \quad L_{\mu\nu} = (\chi_\mu \frac{\partial}{\partial \chi^\nu} - \chi_\nu \frac{\partial}{\partial \chi^\mu})$$

The structure of this algebra is

$$\mathcal{P} = \{L_{\mu\nu}\} \cdot \{P_\mu\} \qquad (3.1)$$

In words: the Poincaré algebra is the semidirect sum of the algebra of homogeneous Lorentz transformations called SO(3, 1) or SL(2, c) and the algebra of the four translations. The meaning of the term "semidirect product" is that the commutator of an element of the first factor with an element of the second factor is an element of the second factor. In our case:

$$\left[L_{\mu\nu}, P_\lambda\right] = -ig_{\mu\lambda} P_\nu + ig_{\nu\lambda} P_\mu$$

The other commutation relations are

$$\left[P_\mu , P_\nu\right] = 0$$

$$\left[L_{\mu\nu} , L_{\lambda\rho}\right] = -i(g_{\mu\lambda} L_{\nu\rho} + g_{\nu\rho} L_{\mu\lambda} - g_{\mu\lambda} L_{\nu\rho} - g_{\nu\rho} L_{\mu\lambda})$$

The Poincaré group has two types of representations; we shall call them the irreducible representations and the local representations. The former are useful in phenomenology, the latter in field theory.

3.3. IRREDUCIBLE REPRESENTATIONS. I shall limit this review of the irreducible representations to those that are of the most immediate physical applications. Also, I shall leave out the proofs, and give only the construction of the representations.

The algebra has two invariant operators (Casimir operators), namely

$$m^2 = P_\mu P^\mu$$

$$W^2 = W_\mu W^\mu$$

where

$$W_\mu = \varepsilon_{\mu\nu\lambda\rho} L^{\nu\lambda} P^\rho$$

and this must be fixed in an irreducible representation. We shall first consider the case when m is a real number different from zero.

One introduces a basis in which the P_u are diagonal:

$$P_\mu \mid p_\mu , \alpha > = p_\mu \mid p_\mu , \alpha >$$

where α stands for whatever quantum numbers are needed to distinguish between states with the same momentum. Since only homogeneous Lorentz transformation operators contain off-diagonal matrix elements, there follows that every state can be constructed from any arbitrarily chosen state by means of such transformations, provided the representation is irreducible.

We consider first the states with

$$p_\mu = \hat{p}_\mu = (m, \mathbf{0})$$

and construct all other states by means of Lorents transformations:

$$e^{i\theta^{\mu\nu} L_{\mu\nu}} | \hat{p}_\mu, \alpha > = \sum_{\alpha'} M_\alpha^{\alpha'} | p_\mu, \alpha' > \tag{3.2}$$

where p_μ and the matrix $M_\alpha^{\alpha'}$ depend on $\theta^{\mu\nu}$. If $\theta^{oi} = 0$, that is, if the transformation is a pure rotation, then $p_\mu = \hat{p}_\mu$:

$$e^{i\theta^{ij} L_{ij}} | \hat{p}_\mu, \alpha > = \sum_{\alpha'} M_\alpha^{\alpha'} | \hat{p}_\mu, \alpha' > \tag{3.3}$$

Thus the rest-system states provide a representation of the rotation subgroup. This representation is irreducible. I won't prove that here, but an indication that this may be true is given by the fact that

$$W^2 | \hat{p}_\mu, \alpha > = m^2 L_{ij}^2 | p_\mu, \alpha >$$

Hence W^2 is essentially the Casimir operator for the rotation group, so that irreducibility of the L_{ij} on these states is sufficient for irreducibility of the representation of the whole group. In fact it is also necessary.

An irreducible representation of the rotation group is given by the positive number j defined by

$$L_{ij}^2 \mid \hat{p}_\mu , \alpha > = j(j+1) \mid \hat{p}_\mu , \alpha >$$

and the states may be labeled completely by the eigenvalue of one of the three generators, L_{12} say. Hence the rest system states may be labeled as follows

$$|\hat{p}_\mu , j_z > , \quad \hat{p}_\mu = (m, 0, 0, 0) , \quad j_z = -j, -j+1, \ldots j$$

The quantization axis is, of course, entirely arbitrary.

Next let $\theta^{\mu\nu} = 0$ except θ^{03} and θ^{30}. Then

$$e^{i\theta^{\mu\nu} L_{\mu\nu}} \mid \hat{p}_\mu , j_z > = \sum_{j'_z} M_{j_z}^{j'_z} \mid p_\mu , j'_z >$$

where p_μ is of the form $(p_o , 0, 0, p_3)$.

Note that the j_z has been defined for rest-system states only. Hence we are free to <u>define</u> j_z for moving states such that

$$e^{i\theta^{03} L_{03}} \mid \hat{p}_\mu , j_z > = \mid p_\mu , j_z >$$

That is, the boost acts only on the momentum. This can easily be generalized. Let **a** be a unit vector parallel to **p**, and choose **a** as the quantization axis for the rest-system states:

$$\mathbf{a} \cdot \mathbf{L} \mid \hat{p}_\mu , \lambda > = \lambda \mid \hat{p}_\mu , \lambda >$$

Then define λ for moving states by

$$e^{i\theta a_i L_{io}} | \hat{p}_\mu , \lambda > = | p_\mu , \lambda >$$

With this definition λ is the helicity. The operators of arbitrary Lorentz transformations are now completely determined, but we shall not need to calculate them.

These representations, with $P_\mu P^\mu > 0$, are the most important ones, but we shall need some others too.

If $P_\mu P^\mu = -m^2 < 0$, then $\hat{p}_\mu = (m, \mathbf{0})$ is not one of the possible sets of eigenvalues of P_u, and the above breaks down. Instead we may take

$$\hat{p}_\mu = (0, 0, 0, m) \tag{3.4}$$

Let $| p_\mu , \alpha >$ denote all states with this momentum, and consider the Lorentz transformation (3.2). Again we specialize to the subset of Lorentz transformations that leave $\hat{p}_\mu$ invariant, in this case it is given by rotations in the space spanned by the 0, 1 and 2 axes. Thus, if $\theta^{\mu 3} = \theta^{3\mu} = 0$, then

$$e^{i\theta^{\mu\nu} L_{\mu\nu}} | \hat{p}_\mu , \alpha > = \sum_{\alpha'} M^{\alpha'}_{\alpha} | \hat{p}_\mu , \alpha' >$$

in analogy with (3.3). The important difference is that the group represented by this formula is not the rotation group, but the group SO(2, 1) of Lorentz transformations in a space with one time and two space dimensions. The states $| \hat{p}_\mu , \alpha >$ thus form a representation of SO(2, 1), and as before it has to be irreducible if we want the representations of the whole group to be irreducible.

In general, the stability group of p_μ is called the little group corresponding to p_μ. The little group is the ordinary compact rotation group if p_μ is timelike, but if p_μ is spacelike then it is isomorphic to the noncompact SO(2, 1). This is an essential complication, because the interesting representations (principally the unitary ones) are infinite dimensional. However, once we have mastered the infinite representations of SO(2, 1) there is no essential difference in the construction of the representations of the whole group.

Finally there is one more interesting case, when the spectrum of P_μ is given by

$$P_\mu | \alpha > = p_\mu | \alpha > \quad , \text{ with } p_\mu = 0 \tag{3.5}$$

The stability group of P_μ is in this case the entire homogeneous Lorentz group SO(3, 1). This is, of course, also noncompact, so once again we have to contend with infinite representations.

3.4. THE LOCAL REPRESENTATION. If we had worked out the detailed forms of the generators of the irreducible representations, then we should have discovered that $L_{\mu\nu}$ have the form

$$L_{\mu\nu} = i\left[p_\mu \frac{\partial}{\partial p^\nu} - p_\nu \frac{\partial}{\partial p^\mu}\right] + S_{\mu\nu} = L^x_{\mu\nu} + S_{\mu\nu}$$

with $\left[L^x_{\mu\nu}, S_{\lambda\rho}\right] \neq 0$. That is, the orbital and spin parts of $L_{\mu\nu}$ do not commute with each other. Although the irreducible representations are very useful in phenomenological work they are very inconvenient in other contexts, precisely for this reason. This is specially true in local field theory, where one likes to write down local invariance, e.g.

$$\int dx \sum_{\sigma\sigma'} C_{\sigma\sigma'} \psi_\sigma^*(x) \psi_{\sigma'}(x)$$

with constant $C_{\sigma\sigma'}$. Local invariants exist only if $L_{\mu\nu}$ commute with $S_{\mu\nu}$. We shall therefore say that a representation of the Poincaré group is local if

$$\left[L_{\mu\nu}, S_{\lambda\rho}\right] = 0 \tag{3.6}$$

In this case it follows from the commutation relations that the $S_{\mu\nu}$ satisfy the same commutation relations among themselves as the $L_{\mu\nu}$. That is, the operators $S_{\mu\nu}$ form a representation of the homogeneous Lorentz group SO(3, 1). Local field theory has always made use of local representations of the Poincaré group, and up to recently finite-dimensional representations have always been taken for the $S_{\mu\nu}$. Such representations are not unitary, but in some cases this does not conflict with the positiveness of physical probability. A notable example is the Dirac equation.

Recently there has been some interest in local field theories that take unitary (and hence infinite-dimensional) representations for the spin group. This was originally motivated by the search for relativistic SU(6). The point is the following. When (3.6) is satisfied it is possible to consider Lorentz transformations as made up of two independent parts, that generated by the $L_{\mu\nu}$ (orbital part) and that generated by the $S_{\mu\nu}$ (spin part). We have then in fact introduced a larger group, namely the direct product,

$$\mathcal{P}^x \otimes S$$

where $\mathcal{P}^x$ (the orbital Poincaré group) is generated by P_μ and $L^x_{\mu\nu}$, and S (the spin group) is generated by the $S_{\mu\nu}$. The actual physical Poincaré group is of course generated by P_μ and $L_{\mu\nu}$ =

$L^x_{\mu\nu} + S_{\mu\nu}$, so the larger group is not a direct product of the physical Poincaré group and an internal group. (This point is related to relativistic SU(6), because one can now simply replace the spin group S = SO(3, 1) with a larger group that contains both SU(6) and SO(3, 1). Further elaboration of this point will be given by Professor White later on).

Here we have once again run up against a noncompact group, and the need to study the unitary representations.

4. SOME REPRESENTATIONS OF SO(f, 1)

4.1. THE ANALYTIC METHOD. As we have seen, both SO(2, 1) and SO(3, 1) must be studied as preliminaries to understand the representations of the Poincaré group. Time does not allow us to discuss all the representations of these groups; we shall have to limit ourselves to those representations that are useful for the analysis of spinless scattering.

There are two approaches to the study of infinite-dimensional group representations, the analytic and the algebraic. Among mathematicians the analytic method is by far the most popular, Harish-Chandra being a very notable exception. Harish-Chandra's works are nearly incomprehensible, but they are worth studying because he lumps all the difficulties together in a few deep theorems. Once you know the theorems you can proceed with the most naive type of method, secure in the knowledge that you are not making any subtle mistakes. Here I shall use both methods, because being ambidextrous is to enjoy a tremendous advantage. I start with the analytic approach.

Let z_μ, $\mu = 0, 1, \ldots, f$ be a set of f + 1 real variables that satisfy $z_\mu^2 = 0$, and let $\mathcal{H}_N$ be the space of all functions f(z) that satisfy the following two conditions:

$$f(\lambda z) = \lambda^N f(z) \tag{4.1}$$

$$(f, f) < \infty \tag{4.2}$$

The first condition says that all f(z) are homogeneous of degree N in the variables, and the second condition says that the norm of the f(z) can be defined. For the definition of the norm let us take, for the time being,

$$(f, f') = \int f^*(z) f'(z) \delta(z^2) dz \tag{4.3}$$

A representation of SO(f, 1) is now given as follows. For every (f + 1)-dimensional square matrix g of the group SO(f. 1) we define a linear operator T_g acting in $\mathcal{H}_N$:

$$T_g f(z) = f(zg)$$

or, in the notation of the mathematical literature:

$$T_g : f(z) \rightarrow f(zg)$$

This defines a representation, because

$$T_{g'} T_g f(z) = T_{g'} f(zg) = f(zg'g) = T_{g'g} f(z)$$

This representation is obviously unitary, because (4.3) is invariant and positive definite, provided only that (4.3) exists. We may insert (4.1) into (4.3) and find out. Let

$$\xi_i = \frac{z_i}{z_o}, \quad i = 1, \ldots, f$$

and let $f(z) = z_o^N h(\xi)$. Then,

$$(f, f') = \int z_o^{N*} h^*(\xi) z_o^N h'(\xi) \delta(z^2) z_o^f dz_o d^f \xi$$

$$= \int z_o^{N* + N + f - 1} \frac{dz_o}{z_o} \int h^*(\xi) h'(\xi) \delta(\xi^2 - 1) d^f \xi \quad (4.4)$$

The second integral is over a finite domain of integration. The first integral diverges, but it can be made convergent by smearing over N, provided the exponent is imaginary. Thus, (4.3) exists if and only if

$$N = \frac{1 - f}{2} + i\lambda \ , \quad \lambda = \text{real} \qquad (4.5)$$

In the case of SO(2,1), $N = -1/2 + i\lambda$, which is the range of variation of j in the Regge representation "background" integral.

4.2. MULTIPLIER REPRESENTATIONS. We may mention, in passing, that a popular form of the representation is obtained if we write everything in terms of the functions $h(\xi)$. Thus

$$T_g : h(\xi) = \left[\frac{(zg)_o}{z_o}\right]^N h(\xi * g)$$

This follows directly from the definitions. The factor is homogeneous of degree zero in the z, hence it is a function $\mu(\xi)$; this is called a multiplier, and the representation is called a multiplier representation. The symbol $\xi * g$ means

$$(\xi * g)_i = \frac{(zg)_i}{(zg)_o}$$

In the special case when g leaves invariant the time-axis, $\xi * g$ reduces to ξg. The inner product is given by (4.4):

$$(h, h') = \int h^*(\xi)\, h'(\xi)\, \delta(\xi^2 - 1)\, d^f(\xi) \tag{4.6}$$

Here the domain of integration is finite and there is no question of convergence.

The representation D(N) with N in the range (4.5) is one of the principal series of irreducible unitary representations of SO(f, 1). We shall see that unitary representations exist for real N as well.

4.3. THE ALGEBRAIC METHOD. Now let us go over to an algebraic notation. The most important step is to introduce a basis in $\mathcal{H}_N$. Let

$$\tilde{\Psi}_{i_1 \ldots i_\ell} \overset{\text{Def.}}{\equiv} z_o^{N-\ell}\, T z_{i_1} \ldots z_{i_\ell} \qquad i_1, \ldots i_\ell = 1, \ldots f$$

where T is the projection operator that projects out the traceless part of the ℓ'th rank tensor. This tensor is the basis for a representation of the subgroup SO(f). If ℓ is a non-negative integer, then the tensor has a finite number of components, and provides a finite number of basis vectors in $\mathcal{H}_N$. Now SO(f) is compact, and all its representations are finite, therefore ℓ must be integer. Taking all non-negative integer values of ℓ, $\ell = 0, 1, 2, \ldots$ we obtain a complete system of basis vectors in $\mathcal{H}_N$. Next we calculate the effect of the group on one of these tensors. This is trivial for those group elements that belong to the compact subgroup; that is, those that leave the time axis invariant. In fact it is rather trivial for any group element:

$$T_g : \tilde{\psi}_{i_1 \dots i_\ell} \rightarrow \left[(zg)_o\right]^{N-\ell} (zg)_{i_1} \dots (zg)_{i_\ell}$$

Taking g infinitesimal we obtain the representation of a generator:

$$S_{\mu\nu} \tilde{\psi}_{i_1 \dots i_\ell} = i\left[z_\mu \frac{\partial}{\partial z^\nu} - z_\nu \frac{\partial}{\partial z^\mu}\right] z_o^{N-\ell} \, T z_{i_1} \dots z_{i_\ell}$$

The right-hand side must be expressed in terms of the tensors $\tilde{\psi}_{i_1 \dots i_\ell}$. Some trivial algebraic manipulations give

$$-iS_{oi} \cdot \tilde{\psi}_{i_1 \dots i_\ell} = (N-t)\, \tilde{\psi}_{i i_1 \dots i_\ell}$$

$$+ \frac{\ell(N+\ell+f-2)}{2+f-2} S\left[\delta_{i i_1} \tilde{\psi}_{i_2 \dots i_\ell}\right.$$

$$\left. - \frac{\ell-1}{2\ell+f-4} \delta_{i_1 i_2} \tilde{\psi}_{i i_3 \dots i_\ell}\right] \qquad (4.7)$$

Unitarity of the representation means hermiticity of the S_{oi}; that is

$$< \ell+1 \,|\, S_{oi} \,|\, \ell >^* = < \ell \,|\, S_{oi} \,|\, \ell+1 >$$

or

$$(N^* - \ell)(N+\ell+1-f) < 0$$

or

$$\left[\left(N+\frac{1-f}{2}\right)^* - \left(\ell+\frac{1-f}{2}\right)\right]\left[\left(N+\frac{1-f}{2}\right) + \left(\ell+\frac{1-f}{2}\right)\right] < 0$$

or

$$\left(N+\frac{1-f}{2}\right)^2 < \left(\ell+\frac{1-f}{2}\right)^2$$

The most severe condition is obtained by taking $\ell = 0$, hence the representation is unitary if and only if

$$\left(N + \frac{1-f}{2}\right)^2 < \left(\frac{1-f}{2}\right)^2 \tag{4.8}$$

Note the superiority of the algebraic method; we obtain necessary and sufficient conditions of unitarity; the analytic method gave only a sufficient condition.

There are two solutions of (4.8), the principal series defined by (4.5) and

$$0 > N > 1 - f$$

Representations D(N) with N in this new range are said to belong to the supplementary series of representations.

Inspection of (4.7) reveals that two representations D(N) and D(N') are equivalent if $N + N' = 1 - f$, and also that the representations are irreducible.

The biggest problem for the analysis is to determine the inner product for representations of the supplementary representations. This may be solved quite easily by first calculating the invariant inner product in the algebraic formulation. An even simpler method will be given by the method of generalized tensors.

4.4. GENERALIZED TENSORS. Suppose that we are interested in finite-dimensional representations of SU(f, 1). Then we should have introduced a single tensor $\psi_{\mu_1 \ldots \mu_N}$ whose components span the whole representation space of D(N). Irreducibility demands that the tensor be symmetric and traceless. To reduce this tensor according to the compact subgroup SO(f) we notice that this subgroup leaves invariant the index value o; hence a preliminary reduction can be made by dividing the components into classes according to the number of indices that equal zero. For example,

$$\psi_{\mu_1\mu_2} = \psi^T_{\mu_1\mu_2} + 2S\left[\delta_{\mu_1 o}\,\psi^T_{o\mu_2}\right] + \delta_{\mu_1 o}\,\delta_{\mu_2 o}\,\psi_{oo}$$

where the superscript T means that the tensor on which it hangs is to be replaced by 0 when one of the Greek indices left on it equals zero. The scalar ψ_{oo} and the vector $\psi^T_{o\mu_2}$ are irreducible under SO(f), but the tensor $\psi^T_{\mu_1\mu_2}$ is not, because it is not traceless. We therefore put

$$\psi^T_{\mu_1\mu_2} = \tilde{\psi}_{\mu_1\mu_2} + \frac{1}{3}\,g_{\mu_1\mu_2}\,\psi^T_{\lambda\lambda}$$

$$\psi^T_{o\mu_2} = \tilde{\psi}_{\mu_2}, \quad \psi_{oo} = \tilde{\psi}$$

where all tensors with $\sim$ are transverse and traceless. The tracelessness of $\psi_{\mu_1\mu_2}$ gives

$$\psi^T_{\lambda\lambda} + \psi_{oo} = 0\ ,$$

and hence finally

$$\psi_{\mu_1\mu_2} = \tilde{\psi}_{\mu_1\mu_2} + 2S\,\delta_{\mu_1 o}\,\tilde{\psi}_{\mu_2} + \frac{2}{3}\,\delta_{\mu_1 o}\,\delta_{\mu_2 o}\,\tilde{\psi}$$

Notice that, in general, only one term with any number of indices occur, due to the tracelessness of the tensor to be reduced. This allows us to write down the complete reduction formulae for the general case:

$$\psi_{\mu_1 \ldots \mu_n} = S \sum_{n=0}^{\infty} \tilde{\psi}_{\mu_1 \ldots \mu_n} \sum_{t=n, n+2, \ldots} \frac{N!}{(N-t)!\,(t-n)!!\,(t+n+f-2)!!}$$

$$\theta_{\mu_{n+1}\mu_{n+2}} \ldots\ldots \theta_{\mu_{t-1}\mu_t} \lambda_{\mu_{t+1}} \ldots\ldots \lambda_{\mu_N} \qquad (4.9)$$

Here λ_μ is a unit vector parallel to the "time" axis ($\lambda_\mu = \delta_{\mu o}$), or more generally any unit timelike vector, and θ_μ^ν is the projection to the plane transverse to λ: $\theta_\mu^\nu = -\delta_\mu^\nu + \lambda_\mu \lambda^\nu$. Multiplying both sides by $\lambda^{\mu_{n+1}} \ldots \lambda^{\mu_N}$ we find

$$\tilde{\psi}_{\mu_1 \ldots \mu_n} = \frac{(2n+f-2)!!}{n!} T(\psi_{\mu_1 \ldots \mu_N} \lambda^{\mu_{n+1}} \ldots \lambda^{\mu_N}) \qquad (4.10)$$

where T is the projection operator that picks out the transverse and traceless parts.

These formulae contains the essence of the method of generalized tensors. They are no less useful for infinite than for finite representations. They contain, for example, simple prescriptions for developing harmonic analysis in f + 1 dimensions. As a simple application let us calculate the kernel of the inner product in the case when N is real and negative. Define K(x, x') by

$$(f, f') = \int f^*(x) K(x, x') f'(x') \, dx \, dx'$$

$$dx = \delta(x^2) \prod_{\mu=0}^{f} dx_\mu$$

and F(x) by

$$F(x) = \int K(x, x') f^*(x') \, dx'$$

Then the unit operator is

$$I_{xx'} = \sum_f f(x)\,F(x') = \sum_f f(x) \int f^*(x'')\,K(x'', x')\,dx''$$

so that

$$K(x, x') = \left[\sum_f f(x)\,f^*(x')\right]^{-1} = \sum_F F(x)\,F^*(x')$$

Expand

$$F(x) = \varphi_{\mu_1 \ldots \mu_N}\, \chi^{\mu_1} \ldots \chi^{\mu_N}$$

so that, for real N

$$\sum_F F(x)\,F^*(x') = \sum_\varphi \chi^{\mu_1} \ldots \chi^{\mu_N}\, \varphi_{\mu_1 \ldots \mu_N}\, \varphi^{\nu_1 \ldots \nu_N}$$

$$\cdot\, \chi_{\nu_1} \ldots \chi_{\nu_N}$$

The sum is over traceless tensors, but can be expanded to all tensors since $x^2 = x'^2 = 0$. Thus, for real N

$$K(x, x') = (x\,x')^N$$

Of course, this result was known; there are many other ways of obtaining it. However, our method is so simple that it can even be extended to the case $x^2, x'^2 \neq 0$, for which, as far as I know, the answer was not known.

5. PARTIAL WAVES AND THE RELATIVISTIC S-MATRIX

5.1. INTRODUCTION. I shall talk here about partial wave analysis of scattering amplitudes describing two-particle spinless scattering. Spin causes a complication that is far from being inessential; the most general cases have been discussed at length by Toller and others. However, there are some interesting questions that are sufficiently hard in themselves, so the introduction of spin complications is a bit premature.

Consider the scattering process of Fig. 1. Two particles, with momenta p_1 and p_1', are coming in, and the two particles, with momenta p_2 and p_2' are going out.

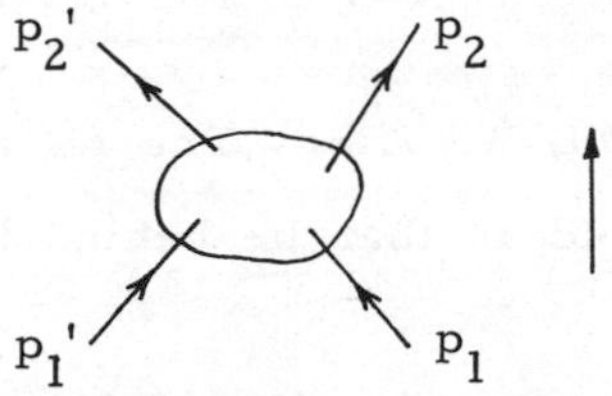

Fig. 1.

Throughout the discussion we shall remain in the physical scattering channel. The matrix elements of the S-matrix shall be denoted $S(p_1, p_2, p_3, p_4)$. Under Lorentz transformations

$$S \rightarrow S(p_1\Lambda, p_2\Lambda, p_3\Lambda, p_4\Lambda)$$

and by Lorentz invariance this must be equal to $S(p_1\, p_2\, p_3\, p_4)$. Translational invariance implies that $p_1 + p_2 = p_3 + p_4$.

Partial wave analysis is the art of diagonalizing the S-Matrix, and this may be done in two basically different ways. Actually

$S(p_1\ p_2\ p_3\ p_4)$ has four "indices" (namely the four momenta) rather than two, as would be more appropriate for a "matrix". Therefore, before $S(p_1\ p_2\ p_3\ p_4)$ becomes a matrix, the momenta must be grouped together in two sets, for example

$$\left.\begin{array}{l} S(p_1\ p_2\ p_1'p_2') = S(p_1\ p_1' \mid p_2\ p_2') \\ \text{or} \\ S(p_1\ p_2\ p_1'p_2') = S(p_1\ p_2 \mid p_1'p_2') \end{array}\right\} \qquad (5.1)$$

In the first case the S-matrix is an operator between the in-states and the out-states, in the second case S maps the "states on the left" on the "states on the right". In the first case S is a unitary operator; in the second case not.

5.2. DIRECT PARTIAL WAVES. The following serves as a remainder of the basic ideas that lie behind the familiar phase shift analysis.

We begin with the ordinary interpretation of the S-matrix as an operator that maps out-states on in-states. The S-matrix may be completely diagonalized by use of its property of being Lorentz invariant.

Any matrix may be diagonalized by introducing a basis on which a sufficiently large set of operators with which it commutes is diagonal. Since S commutes with Poincaré transformations we shall diagonalize as many operators of that group as we can, by a succession of changes of basis.

First we diagonalize P_μ. Noting that

$$P_\mu \mid p_1\ p_1' > \ = (p_1 + p_1')_\mu \mid p_1\ p_1' >$$

we introduce (take the masses to be equal)

$$|p_1 p_1'\rangle = |p, q_1\rangle$$

$$p_\mu = (p_1 + p_1')_\mu \quad , \quad q_{1\mu} = \frac{1}{2}(p_1 - p_1')_\mu$$

Next consider the Lorentz transformations. Not all of them commute with p_μ, but some of them can nevertheless be diagonalized. Consider the subgroup of Lorentz transformations that leave p_μ invariant — the little group. This is always isomorphic to SO(3) when p_μ is timelike, so it is sufficient to consider the case when $\mathbf{p} = 0$; that is, we shall go to the center of mass system. Then ordinary rotations leave p_μ invariant and the basis may be further changed so that some rotation operators become diagonal. Thus, let us diagonalize $\mathbf{L}^2$ and L_{12}:

$$|p, q_1\rangle = \sum_{\ell \ell_z} f_{\ell \ell_z}(q_1) \, |p, \ell, \ell_z\rangle$$

$$\mathbf{L}^2 f = \ell(\ell+1) f \quad , \quad \ell = 0, 1, 2, \ldots \tag{5.2}$$

$$L_{12} f = \ell_z f \quad , \quad \ell_z = -\ell, -\ell+1, \ldots$$

where

$$L_{ij} = i\left[q_{1i} \frac{\partial}{\partial q_{1j}} - q_{1j} \frac{\partial}{\partial q_{1i}}\right]$$

Clearly

$$f_{\ell \ell_z}(q_1) = Y_{\ell \ell_z}(\hat{q}_1) \quad , \quad \hat{q}_1 = \mathbf{q}_1 / |q_1| \tag{5.3}$$

(Note that the magnitude of $\mathbf{q}_1$ is already fixed by p). Since the two equations for f have only one normalizable solution for each value of ℓ and ℓ_z, there is only one single state characterized by $|p, \ell, \ell_z>$; therefore these states form a complete set.

On this basis, the S-matrix is diagonal and independent of ℓ_z

$$S\,|\,p, \ell, \ell_z > \; = e^{2i\delta_\ell(p)}\,|\,p, \ell, \ell_z >$$

Because S must be unitary, $\delta_\ell(p)$ must be real.

Every value of $p^2 = s$ and ℓ label one irreducible representation of the Poincaré group. To define ℓ for reference systems other than the center of mass frame we have to write it as the Poincaré invariant:

$$\ell(\ell + 1) = \frac{W^2}{P^2}$$

Lorentz invariance of the S-matrix means that S does not change ℓ or P^2, and that the matrix elements are independent of the labels that distinguish the states of one irreducible representation. Hence S is a function of ℓ and P^2:

$$S = e^{2i\delta_\ell(P^2)} = S(\ell, s)$$

If only one value of ℓ and one value of P^2 contributes to a scattering event then we usually say that the scattering took place in such and such a state, or that the scattering went through such and such an intermediate state.

Finally let us write the result as an expansion of $S(p_1\, p_1'\, p_2\, p_2')$:

$$S(p_1\, p_1'\, p_2\, p_2') = \; < p_1\, p_1' \,|\, S \,|\, p_2\, p_2' >$$

$$= \sum_{\ell \ell_z} \sum_{\ell' \ell_z'} < p, \ell, \ell_z | S | p, \ell', \ell_z' > Y^*_{\ell \ell_z}(\hat{q}_1) Y_{\ell' \ell_z'}(\hat{q}_2)$$

$$= \sum_{\ell \ell_z} < p, \ell, \ell_z | S | p, \ell, \ell_z > Y^*_{\ell \ell_z}(\hat{q}_1) Y_{\ell \ell_z}(\hat{q}_2)$$

$$= \sum_{\ell} (2\ell + 1) S(\ell, s) P_\ell (\hat{q}_1 \cdot \hat{q}_2) \qquad (5.4)$$

5.3. CROSSED PARTIAL WAVES AT NONZERO MOMENTUM TRANSFER. Let us define an operator $\tilde{S}$ by

$$< p_2 \, p_2' | S | p_1 \, p_1' > \; = \; (p_1 \, p_2 | \tilde{S} | p_1' \, p_2')$$

The quantity $| p_1 \, p_2)$ is not really a 2-particle states but rather a product

$$| p_1 \, p_2) = | p_2 > < p_1 |$$

of a bra (for the absorbed particle) and a ket (for the final particle). Therefore we have no assurance that $\tilde{S}$ must necessarily be a well-behaved operator. In fact it is not, as we shall see. Nevertheless, let us carry out the formal development.

The crossed partial wave expansion is constructed by treating $| p_1 \, p_2)$ just as we treated $| p_1 \, p_1' >$ in the ordinary partial wave expansion. This is certainly legitimate, for we know precisely the behavior of this object under Poincaré transformations. Thus

$$P_\mu \, | p_1 \, p_2) = (p_2 - p_1)_\mu \, | p_1 \, p_2)$$

The minus sign comes, of course, from the fact that the momentum p_1 is an attribute of a bra instead of a ket. As before, we assume equal masses and introduce

$$|p_1\, p_2) = |p, q)$$

$$p = p_2 - p_1 \quad , \quad q = \frac{1}{2}(p_1 + p_2)$$

The difference between this case and the usual one is that p is now a momentum transfer, instead of the total energy, and hence a spacelike vector. Its stability group is not SO(3), but SO(2,1). The most convenient frame in which to carry out the analysis is not the center of mass frame, but the system in which $p_\mu = (0, 0, 0, \sqrt{-p^2})$, the nonzero component being the z-component. Then, since $p_\mu q_\mu = 0$, q_μ has the form $(q_o, q_1, q_2, 0)$.

Next, we study the stability group of p_μ, which is the set of Lorentz transformations in the 3-dimensional space spanned by the 0, X, Y axes. We can diagonalize the Casimir operator $\mathbf{L}^2 = L_{12}^2 - L_{10}^2 - L_{20}^2$, and L_{12}, as before; writing

$$\left.\begin{aligned} |p, q> &= \sum_{\ell \ell_z} Y_{\ell \ell_z}(\hat{q})\, |p, \ell, \ell_z> \\ \mathbf{L}^2 Y_{\ell \ell_z} &= \ell(\ell + 1) Y_{\ell \ell_z} \\ L_{12} Y_{\ell \ell_z} &= \ell_z Y_{\ell \ell_z} \end{aligned}\right\} \qquad (5.5)$$

where now

$$\mathbf{L}^2 = L_{12}^2 - L_{10}^2 - L_{20}^2$$

From this we obtain the analogue of (5.4):

$$S(p_1\, p_1'\, p_2\, p_2') = \sum_{\ell}(2\ell + 1)\tilde{S}(\ell, t)\, P_{\ell}(\hat{q}\cdot\hat{q}') \tag{5.6}$$

The only difficult question is this: what is the range of ℓ? It is very tempting to restrict oneself immediately to those values of ℓ that correspond to unitary representations of SO(2, 1), but I don't know how to justify this; besides it is contradicted by experiments.

The first paper dealing with this type of phase shift analysis was published by H. Joos in 1961. Later several people repeated and extended the work, but most of the published papers are very naive. Their argument goes like this. Let us treat $|p,q)$ as an ordinary physical state, and let us try to form normalizable eigenstates $|p, \ell, \ell_z)$ of $\mathbf{L}^2$ and L_{12}:

$$|p, \ell, \ell_z) = \int d\Omega_q\, Y_{\ell\ell_z}(\hat{q})\, |p,q)$$

The normalization condition on the wave function $Y_{\ell\ell_z}(\hat{q}) = P_{\ell\ell_z}(\hat{q}_o)\, e^{i\ell_z\varphi}$ is

$$\int_1^{\infty} d(\cosh\theta)\, |P_{\ell\ell_z}(\cosh\theta)|^2 < \infty$$

and this cannot be satisfied. However if the range of ℓ is continuous, then the states should be normalized like plane waves:

$$\int_1^{\infty} d(\cosh\theta)\, P^*_{\ell\ell_z}(\cosh\theta)\, P_{\ell'\ell_z'}(\cosh\theta) = \delta_{\ell_z\ell_z'}\,\delta(\ell - \ell')$$

This is possible if $\ell = -\frac{1}{2} + i\lambda$. Another way of saying this is as follows. Consider an "arbitrary state"

$$\psi = \int d\Omega_q \, f(p,q) \, | \, p,q) \, ,$$

satisfying the normalization condition

$$\int d\Omega_q \, | \, f(p,q) \, |^2 < \infty$$

Then a well-known theorem assures us that f(p, q) has an expansion in terms of conical functions:

$$f(p,q) = \sum_{\ell_z = -\infty}^{+\infty} \int_{-\frac{1}{2} - i\infty}^{-\frac{1}{2} + i\infty} d\ell (2\ell + 1) f_{\ell\ell_z}(p) Y_{\ell\ell_z}(\hat{q})$$

Therefore, by this (questionable) argument, we obtain (5.6) in the sharpened form

$$S(s,t) = \int_{-\frac{1}{2} - i\infty}^{-\frac{1}{2} + i\infty} d\ell (2\ell + 1) \tilde{S}(\ell, t) P_\ell (\hat{q} \cdot \hat{q}') \qquad (5.7)$$

Unfortunately, this is in conflict with experiment.

The formula (5.7) is similar to the Regge representation, but without any pole terms, and as everybody knows, such an amplitude has the property that $\sqrt{s}\, S(s,t) \rightarrow 0$ as $s \rightarrow \infty$. There is an impressive body of evidence to show that some amplitudes actually increase like s as s tends to infinity, so that some extra terms are needed, with $\ell \sim 1$, in the representation (5.7).

A slight improvement is obtained by considering all values of ℓ that correspond to unitary representations of SO(2, 1). The number ℓ introduced here is the same as the number N introduced in our discussion of the representation D(N) of SO(f, 1), in the case f = 2, and the range of ℓ-values that occurs in (5.7) are those of the principal series of unitary representations. We could use the supplementary series too, and write

$$S(s,t) = \left[\int_{-\frac{1}{2}-i\infty}^{-\frac{1}{2}+i\infty} + \int_{-\frac{1}{2}}^{0}\right] d\ell(2\ell+1)\tilde{S}(\ell,t)P_{\ell}(\hat{q}\,\hat{q}') \qquad (5.8)$$

This amplitude can increase at $s \to \infty$, but not faster than a polynomial in log s. Experimentally we know that the second integral in (5.8) should extend to the neighbourhood of +1. Hence it is not sufficient to consider only unitary representations!

The individual terms of the crossed partial wave expansion have an interpretation similar to a term in the ordinary partial wave series. Each value of ℓ in (5.8) corresponds to the exchange of an object that forms a basis for an irreducible unitary representation of the Poincaré group. This suggests that the quantum number ℓ is measurable also in the case when it refers to the crossed expansion. A direct physical interpretation of ℓ would certainly be helpful in trying to understand the nature of the physical restriction that must be imposed on it. Later we shall give such an interpretation in the classical limit ($\hbar \to 0$) and in the nonrelativistic limit ($c \to \infty$).

5.4. CROSSED PARTIAL WAVES AT VANISHING MOMENTUM TRANSFER. Let us now repeat the same analysis when $p_\mu = 0$. In the case of equal mass scattering this is equivalent to $p^2 = 0$, because of Lorentz invariance, but if $p_1^2 \neq p_2^2$ then p_μ cannot vanish although p^2 can. Therefore the following analysis applies to the equal mass case only.

Playing the same game as before, we try to diagonalize some operators of homogeneous Lorentz transformations. In this case p_μ is invariant under all Lorentz transformations, so the little group is the entire homogeneous Lorentz group SO(3,1). The generators are, in the previous notation

$$L_{\mu\nu} \mid 0, q) = i \left[q_\mu \frac{\partial}{\partial q^\nu} - q_\nu \frac{\partial}{\partial q^\mu} \right] \mid 0, q)$$

A maximal set of commuting generators consists of the two Casimir operators

$$Q_1 = L_{\mu\nu} L^{\mu\nu}$$

$$Q_2 = L_{\mu\nu} L_{\lambda\rho} \varepsilon^{\mu\nu\lambda\rho}$$

and the two quantum numbers ℓ, ℓ_z associated with a three-dimensional subgroup. We may verify that Q_2 vanishes identically, so that a complete set of labels is given by

$$Q_1 \mid 0, N, \ell, \ell_z) = N(N+2) \mid 0, N, \ell, \ell_z)$$

$$\mathbf{L}^2 \mid 0, N, \ell, \ell_z) = \ell(\ell+1) \mid 0, N, \ell, \ell_z)$$

$$L_{12}|0, N, \ell, \ell_z) = \ell_z |0, N, \ell, \ell_z$$

The irreducible representation of SO(3, 1) defined by $Q_2 = 0$ and $Q_1 = N(N + 2)$ is precisely the representation D(N) that we have studied in an earlier lecture. The connection between the new and the old basis is

$$|0, q) = \sum_{N,\ell,\ell_z} Y_{N,\ell,\ell_z}(q)\,|0, N, \ell, \ell_z)$$

where the sum may be discrete or continuous, and Y_{N,ℓ,ℓ_z} are four dimensional spherical harmonics.

By exactly the same arguments as before,

$$S(p_1 p_1', p_2 p_2') = \sum_{N,\ell,\ell_z} Y^*_{N,\ell,\ell_z}(q) Y_{N,\ell,\ell_z}(q') S(N)$$

$$= \sum_N (2N + 2) P_{N,4}(q, q') S(N)$$

where Y_{N,ℓ,ℓ_z} and $P_{N,4}$ are four-dimensional spherical harmonics, and $q = \frac{1}{2}(p_1 + p_2) = p_1$, $q' = \frac{1}{2}(p_1' + p_2') = p_1'$, so that the argument of the four-dimensional Legendre function is simply related to the Mandelstam variable $s = (p_1 + p_1')^2$. The problem of identifying the range of N is exactly the same as before. For unitary representations we have found that $N = -1 + i\lambda$ (principal series) or $-2 < N < 0$ (supplementary series); whereas phenomenological analysis of high energy scattering shows that N may reach higher, close to +1.

Because this SO(3, 1) analysis applies only at $p_\mu = 0$, while the previous SO(2, 1) analysis has to be used for non-zero momentum transfer, it is convenient to label the vectors of the SO(3,1) representation by quantum numbers adapted to SO(2,1). Thus, in the above definition of ℓ, we shall take $\mathbf{L}^2$ to mean $L_{12}^2 - L_{10}^2 - L_{20}^2$, rather than $L_{12}^2 + L_{13}^2 + L_{23}^2$. In the above expression for $S(p_1 p_1' p_2 p_2')$ let us write down an intermediate step:

$$S(p_1\, p_1'\, p_2\, p_2') = \sum_{N,\ell} S(N) F_{N,\ell}(q, q')$$

where

$$F_{N,\ell}(q, q') = \sum_{\ell_z} Y^*_{N,\ell,\ell_z}(q) Y_{N,\ell,\ell_z}(q')$$

for fixed N, the sum over ℓ may be taken over the range

$$\ell = N,\ N-1,\ N-2,\ \ldots..$$

each term; that is, each value of ℓ, corresponds exactly to one term in the Regge expansion. Thus, if only one value of N occurs, then the amplitude is a sum of contributions of Regge-pole terms, with the Regge poles located at $\ell = N,\ N-1,\ \ldots..$

The Regge pole at $\ell = N$ is called the leading Regge pole; the others are called daughters. It is currently a popular idea to assume that the sum over N takes the form

$$S(p_1\, p_1'\, p_2\, p_2') = \int_{-1-i\infty}^{-1+i\infty} dN (2N+2) P_{N,4}(q\, q') S(N)$$

$$+ (2N_o + 2) P_{N_o,4}(q\, q') S(N_o) \quad ,$$

where N_o is near +1, and the last term dominates the scattering amplitude at high energies. This last term is called a "Lorentz pole term". In terms of Regge pole analysis a single Lorentz pole term corresponds to a series of Regge poles located at $\ell = N_o, N_o - 1, \ldots\ldots$

6. CROSSED PARTIAL WAVES IN NONRELATIVISTIC POTENTIAL SCATTERING, AND IN CLASSICAL RELATIVISTIC MECHANICS

6.1. THE CLASSICAL LIMIT. Consider a classical point particle that is deflected from a potential of finite range. For large negative times it travels on an orbit described by

$$\mathbf{x}_{in}(t) = \mathbf{v}_1(t - t_o) + \mathbf{x}_{in}(t_o) \quad , \qquad \mathbf{v}_1 = \frac{\mathbf{p}_1}{E_1}$$

$$\mathbf{x}_{out}(t) = \mathbf{v}_2(t - t_o) + \mathbf{x}_{out}(t_o) \quad , \qquad \mathbf{v}_2 = \frac{\mathbf{p}_2}{E_2}$$

Let us go to the reference system in which $E_1 = E_2$ and $(p_1 - p_2)_\mu = p_\mu = (0, 0, 0, \sqrt{-t})$. Consider the projections of the two above orbits into the x, y plane; from now on arrows will denote 2-vectors in this plane. Then the observables that correspond to the generators of SO(2, 1) are

$$L_{12} = (\vec{\mathbf{x}} \times \vec{\mathbf{p}})_{12} = E(\vec{\mathbf{x}} \times \vec{\mathbf{v}})_{12}$$

$$\vec{\mathbf{L}} = (L_{10}, L_{20}) = E\vec{\mathbf{x}} + t\vec{\mathbf{p}} = E(\vec{\mathbf{x}} + t\vec{\mathbf{v}})$$

The exchange quantum numbers are

$$L_{12} = E(\vec{\mathbf{x}} * \vec{\mathbf{v}})_{12}\Big|_{out-in} = E(\vec{\nabla} \times \vec{\mathbf{v}})_{12}$$

$$\vec{\mathbf{L}} = E(\vec{\mathbf{x}} + t\vec{\mathbf{v}})\Big|_{\text{out-in}} = E\vec{\nabla}$$

where

$$\nabla = \vec{\mathbf{x}}_{out}(t) - \vec{\mathbf{x}}_{in}(t) = X_{out}(t_o) - X_{in}(t_o)$$

The meaning of $\vec{\nabla}$ is illustrated in Fig. 2

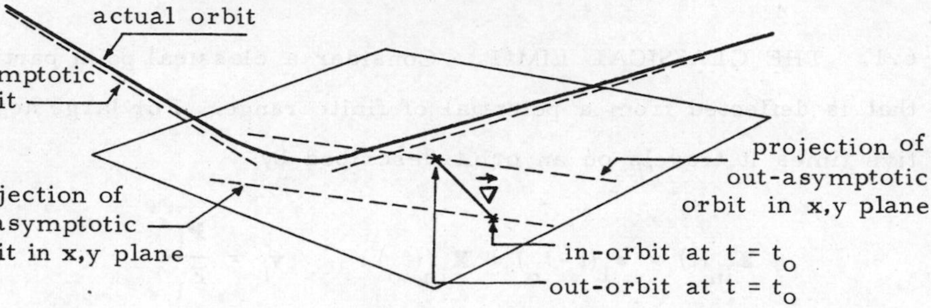

Fig. 2

Let t_o be a large positive time. Then $\vec{\nabla}$ is the difference between the actual position of the particle in the x, y plane, and the position at which the particle would have been found if the potential had been absent. The number L_{12}, of course, is the exchange of angular momentum between particle and scatterer; it vanishes if $\vec{\nabla}$ is parallel to $\vec{\mathbf{v}}$.

Next let us calculate

$$\ell(\ell + 1) = L_{12}^2 - \vec{\mathbf{L}}^2 = E^2\left[(\vec{\nabla} \times \vec{\mathbf{v}})^2 - \vec{\nabla}^2\right]$$

This is clearly negative, since $|\vec{\mathbf{v}}| < 1$. Thus $\ell(\ell + 1) < 0$

or

$$\text{either} \quad \ell = -\frac{1}{2} + i\lambda \quad \text{or} \quad -1 < \ell < 0$$

This is precisely the condition for unitary representations!

This discovery was made by I. T. Grodsky about five years ago. It is very tempting to jump to the conclusion that $\ell(\ell + 1)$ must be negative in quantum theory too, but this is, as we have seen, refuted by the high energy experiments. In fact experiment, as well as theory, indicates that $\ell(\ell + 1) < 1$, or in the proper units

$$\sqrt{\mathbf{L}^2} < \hbar$$

The bound found here is quite consistent with this, since the classical limit is defined by $\hbar = 0$. One should think it would be possible to find a simple physical interpretation of this inequality; perhaps the fact that, in quantum theory, the bound is lifted from zero to $\hbar$, is similar to a "barrier penetration effect".

6.2. THE NON-RELATIVISTIC LIMIT. In the following we shall use the notation of potential scattering, although everything can be generalized very easily to two-particle scattering.

The matrix elements of the T-matrix are defined by

$$T = \int d^3 p_1 d^3 p_2 T_{\vec{\mathbf{p}}_1 \vec{\mathbf{p}}_2} | \vec{\mathbf{p}}_2 > < \vec{\mathbf{p}}_1 |$$

where $\mathbf{p}_1$ and $\mathbf{p}_2$ are the initial and final momenta. This expression is an expansion of an operator in terms of a complete operator basis.

In general, the potential scattering T-matrix cannot be exactly diagonalized by means of the ordinary partial wave series, because the intermediate state of the potential, which may be very complicated. However, the crossed partial wave analysis diagonalizes the T-matrix.

Instead of Lorentz invariance we now have to use Galilei invariance. Please note that the behavior of the potential under Galilei transformations is irrelevant for the time being; we consider only the transformations of the "right hand states", i.e., the in and out-states of the particle.

The inhomogeneous Galilei group consists of the translations, ordinary rotations, and accelerations. Let

$$|p_1 p_2) \overset{\text{def}}{\equiv} |p_2 > < p_1| \ ;$$

then the translation generators are defined by

$$\vec{\mathbf{P}}\,|\,p_1 p_2) = (\vec{\mathbf{p}}_2 - \vec{\mathbf{p}}_1)\,|\,p_1 p_2)$$

Therefore we introduce, just as in the relativistic case

$$|p_1 p_2) \longrightarrow |p\,,\,q)$$

$$\vec{\mathbf{p}} = \vec{\mathbf{p}}_2 - \vec{\mathbf{p}}_1 \quad , \quad \vec{\mathbf{q}} = \frac{1}{2}(\vec{\mathbf{p}}_2 + \vec{\mathbf{p}}_1)$$

The generators of ordinary rotations are, of course

$$\vec{\mathbf{L}} = \vec{\mathbf{p}}_1 \times \vec{\mathbf{x}}_1 + \vec{\mathbf{p}}_2 \times \vec{\mathbf{x}}_2 = \vec{\mathbf{p}} \times \vec{\mathbf{x}} + \vec{\mathbf{q}} \times \vec{\boldsymbol{\xi}}$$

where

$$\vec{\mathbf{x}}_1 = -i\frac{\vec{\partial}}{\partial p_1} \quad , \quad \vec{\mathbf{x}}_2 = i\frac{\vec{\partial}}{\partial p_2}$$

$$\vec{x} = i\frac{\vec{\partial}}{\partial p} = \frac{1}{2}(\vec{x}_1 + \vec{x}_2)$$

$$\vec{\xi} = i\frac{\vec{\partial}}{\partial q} = \vec{x}_2 - \vec{x}_1$$

The generators of accelerations are

$$L_{io} = \left[i\frac{\partial}{\partial p_1} + i\frac{\partial}{\partial p_2} \right]_i = (x_2 - x_1)_i = \xi_i$$

Notice that, because we have now taken the non-relativistic limit, the three generators L_{io} commute with each other. The three components of ξ_i are therefore simultaneously diagonalizable. In the classical limit they have a very direct interpretation in terms of the orbit, as we have seen.

Now we must identify the subgroup of the "homogeneous Galilei group" that leaves $\vec{p}$ invariant. For this purpose let us take a coordinate system in which $\vec{p}$ points along the z axis. Then clearly L_{12}, ξ_1, ξ_2 leave $\vec{p}$ invariant (rotations about $\vec{p}$ and accelerations in the plane perpendicular to $\vec{p}$). These three generators form the algebra of the two-dimensional Euclidean group E(2), just as the homogeneous Galilei group is the three-dimensional Euclidean group E(3). We shall now introduce a basis adapted to E(2), this group playing a role that is closely analogous to that played by SO(2, 1). in the relativistic case.

The group E(2) has one Casimir operator

$$L_{10}^2 + L_{20}^2 = \xi_1^2 + \xi_2^2 = -\left[\frac{\partial}{\partial q_1}\right]^2 - \left[\frac{\partial}{\partial q_2}\right]^2 = -\nabla_q^2$$

Introduce spherical coordinates

$$q_1 = \rho \cos \varphi \qquad q_2 = \rho \sin \phi$$

$$-\nabla_q^2 = \frac{1}{\rho}\frac{\partial}{\partial \rho}\rho\frac{\partial}{\partial \rho} - \frac{1}{\rho^2}\frac{\partial^2}{\partial \phi^2}$$

In the algebra we diagonalize L_{12}

$$L_{12} = i\frac{\partial}{\partial \phi}$$

The analogues of the spherical harmonics are the simultaneous eigenfunctions of $L_{10}^2 + L_{20}^2$ and L_{12}

$$-\nabla_q^2 h_{\nu m} = \nu^2 h_{\nu m}$$

$$L_{12} h_{\nu m} = m h_{\nu m}$$

Note that $\nu^2 = \xi_1^2 + \xi_2^2$, from which we could conclude that ν^2 is a real number, but let us not jump to conclusions.

The solution of the two equations for $h_{\nu m}$ is well known to be:

$$h_{\nu m} \approx \sqrt{\nu\rho}\; J_m(\nu\rho)\, e^{im\rho}$$

These functions may be normalized so that

$$\int d\rho\, d\theta\, h^{*}_{\nu m}(q)\, h_{\nu m}(q) = \delta_{mm'}\, \delta(\nu - \nu')$$

$$\int_0^\infty d\nu \sum_m h_{\nu m}(q)\, h^{*}_{\nu m}(q') = \delta^{(2)}(q - q')$$

Now we decompose T as follows

$$T_{pq} = \int d\nu \sum_m h^{*}_{\nu m}(q_1\, q_2)\, T_{p,\, q_3,\, \nu,\, m}$$

If the potential is spherically symmetric, then

$$T_{p,\, q_3,\, \nu,\, m} = \delta_{m,0}\, T_{p,\, q_3,\, \nu}$$

On the mass shell we have $q_3 = 0$, and thus

$$T_{pq} = \int_0^\infty d\nu\, h^{*}_{\nu,o}\, h^{*}_{\nu,o}(\nu \rho)\, T_{p,\, o,\, \nu}$$

In this case one can be sure that the range of ν is indeed that of the unitary representations, because any contribution from imaginary ν gives a scattering amplitude that increases exponentially with energy. Instead, one has to worry about δ-functions and derivatives of δ-functions in $T_{p,o,\nu}$ near $\nu = 0$; this gives amplitudes with polynomial growth, and corresponds to relativistic Regge poles with $\alpha(t) > 0$. The reason for this is that in the nonrelativistic limit the near part of the j-plane is contracted to the origin $= 0$.

The subject of this last lecture is based on work carried out jointly with G. Cocho, I. T. Grodsky and V. G. Kadyshevsky.

8

EXACT RELATIVISTIC SU(6)

Roscoe White, University of California, Los Angeles, U.S.A.

1. INTRODUCTION

The defects of static SU(6) have already been pointed out in the lectures by Prof. Fronsdal. Its two main faults are, firstly the fact that in its static form vertices do not exist; one must introduce momentum spurious, and further many processes it has been used for are quite relativistic, and secondly the mass breaking within SU(6) multiplets is fairly large. The second difficulty is by far the most intractable, however one can ignore it and study the features of a theory in which the first difficulty is exacly solved. This immediately leads, as we shall see, to the additional complication of the static symmetry algebra containing an infinite number of particles. However the very presence of these states leads to many unexpected and extremely physical features in the theory.

We proceed then to examine the general features of such a theory, keeping in mind that results which one would expect to depend strongly on mass differences are to be taken with a grain of salt.

2. THE STRUCTURE OF THE SYMMETRY ALGEBRA

Consider the simplest possible relativistic extension of SU(6) which we can invent. How large must the algebra be and what can be its structure? Firstly it must contain the generators of the Poincaré group

$$P = \left\{L_{\mu\nu}, P_\lambda\right\} = \left\{L_{\mu\nu}\right\} \boxtimes \left\{P_\lambda\right\}$$

where the sign ⊡ means semi-direct sum, and simply means that commutators of elements in $\left\{L_{\mu\nu}\right\}$ with elements in $\left\{P_\lambda\right\}$ gives elements of $\left\{P_\lambda\right\}$. The Poincaré algebra has the commutation relations

$$\left[L_{\mu\nu}, P_\lambda\right] = -ig_{\mu\lambda}P_\nu + ig_{\nu\lambda}P_\mu$$

$$\left[P_\mu, P_\nu\right] = 0$$

$$\left[L_{\mu\nu}, L_{\lambda\rho}\right] = -i\left[g_{\mu\lambda}L_{\nu\rho} + g_{\nu\rho}L_{\mu\lambda} - g_{\mu\lambda}L_{\nu\rho} - g_{\nu\rho}L_{\mu\lambda}\right]$$

Let A be a relativistic extension of SU(6), which must contain P and in addition other generators such as isospin, hypercharge, etc. We first diagonalize the operator P_μ.

Then consider the set of all rest states $|m\alpha\rangle$, $\alpha = 1, 2, 3, \ldots$ The subalgebra leaving this subspace invariant we denote by A_o. By relativity all physical states may be obtained from the rest states by applying the generators L_{oi} of pure Lorentz transformations. Thus A has the form

$$A = \left\{A_o, L_{oi}\right\} \quad i = 1, 2, 3$$

Now choose $a \in A_o$, and consider

$$\left[a, L_{oi}\right] = C(a)_i^j L_{oj} + b \tag{2.1}$$

where $b \in A_o$.

Take the commutator with P_o

$$\left\{P_o, \left[a, L_{oi}\right]\right\} = C(a)_i^j P_j + 0$$

$$\left[P_o, aL_{oi} - L_{oi} a\right] = \left[a, P_i\right] = C(a)_i^j P_j$$

$$\therefore A_o = A' \boxtimes P_\mu$$

where A' consists of all elements in A_o except the P_μ.

Now take $a' \in A'$. Since $\left[a', P_o\right] = 0$ we have

$$\left[a', P_\mu\right] = \left[a', P_i\right] = C(a')_i^j P_j$$

$$0 = \left[a', P_\mu P^\mu\right] = P_\mu\left[a', P^\mu\right] + \left[a', P_\mu\right] P^\mu$$

$$0 = 2\, C(a')_i^j P_j P^i$$

Therefore the $C(a)_i^j$ are 3 x 3 skew symmetric matrices and form a faithful representation of $\left\{L_{ij}\right\}$, which is a subalgebra of A'.

Now by a well known theorem (Pontrjagin p. 11) A' must contain an invariant subalgebra S such that S commutes with $\left\{P_i\right\}$ and

$$A' = \left\{L_{ij}\right\} \boxtimes S$$

$$\left[S, P_i\right] = 0 \quad \text{i.e.} \quad C_i^j(S) = 0 \tag{2.2}$$

$$\therefore \quad A = \{\underbrace{\underbrace{L_{ij}, S}_{A'}, P_\mu}_{A_o}, L_{oi}\}$$

To see the structure of A, we find that

$$[S, L_{ij}] \subset S \quad \text{from} \quad (2.2)$$

$$[S, P_\mu] = 0 \quad \text{from (2.2) (and since } S \subset A_o)$$

$$[S, L_{oi}] \subset S \quad \text{from (2.1) since } C(S) = 0$$

These relations combined with the commutation relations for P give

$$A = \{L_{\mu\nu}\} \boxtimes [S \oplus \{P_\mu\}] = P \boxtimes S$$

for the structure of A. This fact was first realized by Michell and by Budini and Fronsdal.

However this is not the end of the story, as there is another very important restriction on possible choices for the algebra S.

Denote the elements in S by S_i, $i = 1, 2, 3, \ldots$ Then we have

$$[S_i, L_{\mu\nu}] = D^{ij}_{\mu\nu} S_j$$

where the $D^{ij}_{\mu\nu}$ form a real, finite dimensional representation of the Lorentz algebra $\{L_{\mu\nu}\}$. (We have restricted ourselves to finite dimensional algebras, so the number of elements in S is finite).

Such a representation is a direct sum of tensor representations and the commutation relations may be written in terms of tensors of various degree. Thus in general $S = \{s, s_\mu, s_{\mu\nu}, \ldots\}$

Now we must invoke a rather deep theorem concerning automorphisms of Lie algebras. One Lie algebra may form a non trivial representation space for another only provided that the first contains a subalgebra isomorphic to the smallest normal sub-algebra contained in the second. As the Lorentz algebra is semi-simple, its smaller subalgebra is itself.

The smallest non trivial possibility for S is then the covering group of O(3, 1), SL(2, c). $\left[\text{The trivial solution is } [S_i, L_{\mu\nu}] = 0\right.$ and S may for example be $\left.SU(3)\right]$.

This result is quite important since, because SL(2, c) is non-compact there must be an infinite number of states within the rest symmetry $\{L_{ij}\} \boxtimes S$. Thus an exact symmetry algebra containing the Poincaré algebra necessarily possesses an infinite number of rest states.

We therefore choose S to be the smallest possible algebra containing both SL(2, c) and the compact rest symmetry SU(6) in such a way that the rotation subgroup of SL(2, c) is the same as the spin subgroup of SU(6). This turns out to be SL(6, c). The method employed is much more general, however, and many different static theories may be made relativistic in the same manner.

Consider the generators $s_{\mu\nu}$ of S corresponding to the subgroup SL(2, c).

The commutation relations of the $s_{\mu\nu}$ and the $L_{\mu\nu}$ can only have the form

$$[L_{\mu\nu}, L_{\lambda\rho}] = -i[g_{\mu\lambda}L_{\nu\rho} + g_{\nu\rho}L_{\mu\lambda} - g_{\mu\lambda}L_{\nu\rho} - g_{\nu\rho}L_{\mu\lambda}] \quad (2.3)$$

$$[L_{\mu\nu}, s_{\lambda\rho}] = -i[g_{\mu\lambda}s_{\nu\rho} + g_{\nu\rho}s_{\mu\lambda} - g_{\mu\rho}s_{\nu\lambda} - g_{\nu\lambda}s_{\mu\rho}]$$

$$[s_{\mu\nu}, s_{\lambda\rho}] = -i[g_{\mu\lambda}s_{\nu\rho} + g_{\nu\rho}s_{\mu\lambda} - g_{\mu\rho}s_{\nu\lambda} - g_{\nu\lambda}s_{\mu\rho}]$$

by the fact that $\{s_\mu\}$ forms a representation of SL(2, c) and by covariance requirements. Thus we can define

$$L^x_{\mu\nu} = L_{\mu\nu} - s_{\mu\nu}$$

and these generators commute with $s_{\mu\nu}$. Using the commutation relations of SL(6, c) we can show that $L^x_{\mu\nu}$ commutes with the rest of S. Thus

$$A = L^x_{\mu\nu} \oplus S$$

(direct sum), and it is now quite easy to construct the representations of A. It must be remembered that

$$P^x = \{L^x_{\mu\nu}\} \boxtimes \{P_\lambda\}$$

is not the physical Poincaré algebra. Representations of A are fixed by choosing a representation of P^x and a representation of S. As P^x is isomorphic to the Poincaré group, its representations are fixed by choosing a fixed value for the $(\text{mass})^2$, $P_\mu P^\mu$, and for the "spin" $\omega^x_\mu \omega^{x\mu}$, where

$$\omega^x_\mu = \epsilon_{\mu\nu\lambda\rho} L^{x\,\nu\lambda} P^\rho$$

is the generator of elements belonging to the little group of P^x of momentum P. Thus

$$\omega^x_\mu \omega^{x\mu} = j^x(j^x + 1) \qquad j^x = 0,\ 1/2,\ 1,\ 3/2,\ \ldots$$

We must define generators for the little group of S also,

$$\tilde{\omega}_{\mu} = \epsilon_{\mu\nu\lambda\rho} s_{\nu\lambda} P^{\rho}$$

and as we wish S to contain ordinary SU(6), e.g. spin rotations, we wish to identify these with the generators of physical rotations. However, the generators of the physical little group are given by

$$\omega^{x}_{\mu} + \tilde{\omega}_{\mu}$$

We must therefore choose the representation of P^{x} given by $j^{x} = 0$. This provides the necessary coupling between the "spin" generators in S and those in P.

This determines the representation of P^{x}, and we need only discuss representations of S to complete the description of the representations of A. Note that the physical spin is not a Casimir operator of A, and in fact representations of A contain an infinite number of spin values.

3. SL(6, C) - SUBGROUPS AND REPRESENTATIONS.

3.1. SUBGROUPS. We will make use of the method of generalized tensors, first developed by Harish-Chandra, and used extensively by A. Barut and C. Fronsdal. The group SL(6, C) consists of all 6 x 6 complex matrices of determinant 1, the algebra consisting of all traceless 6 x 6 complex matrices.

Introduce primitive tensors (which may be thought of as quarks and anti-quarks if one wishes) with the transformation properties:

$$Z_A \rightarrow (SZ)_A \qquad Z^A \rightarrow (ZS^{-1})^A$$

$$Z_{\mathring{A}} \rightarrow \left[(S^{-1})^+ Z\right]_{\mathring{A}} \qquad Z^{\mathring{A}} \rightarrow (ZS^+)^{\mathring{A}}$$

SL(6, c) has 70 generators, which are given by

$$\lambda_A^B = \frac{1}{2}\left[M_A^B + N_A^B\right] \quad \text{(compact)}$$

$$\lambda'^B_A = \frac{1}{2}\left[M_A^B - N_A^B\right] \quad \text{(non-compact)}$$

with

$$M_A^B = Z_A \frac{\partial}{\partial Z_B} - Z^B \frac{\partial}{\partial Z^A} - \text{trace}$$

$$N_{\mathring{A}}^{\mathring{B}} = -Z^{\mathring{B}} \frac{\partial}{\partial Z^{\mathring{A}}} + Z_{\mathring{A}} \frac{\partial}{\partial Z_{\mathring{B}}} - \text{trace} \tag{3.1}$$

$$A, B = 1, 2, 3, \ldots 6$$

The group SL(6, c) has an infinite number of compact sub-groups, each one characterized by the four momentum left invariant by it. The dependence of the little group on the momentum is obtained through our choice $j^x = 0$, and Wigner's little group for momentum P_μ is easily seen to be generated by $(\sigma_\mu)^A_{\mathring{B}}\, \lambda_A^{\mathring{B}}(P)$;

$$\lambda_A^{\mathring{B}}(p) = \frac{1}{2m}\left[M_A^C P_C^{\mathring{B}} + P_A^{\mathring{C}} N_{\mathring{C}}^{\mathring{B}}\right]$$

where

$$P_C^{\mathring{B}} = P^\mu(\sigma_\mu)_C^{\mathring{B}} \qquad P_{\mathring{C}}^B = P^\mu(\sigma_u)_{\mathring{C}}^B$$

and $$(\sigma_\mu)_C^{\mathring{B}} = (1, -\vec{\sigma}) \times 1_3 (\sigma_\mu)_{\mathring{C}}^B = (1, \vec{\sigma}) \times 1_3$$

The operators $\lambda_A^B(p)$ generate a compact subgroup $SU(6)_p$ which is isomorphic to SU(6) and which reduces to static SU(6) in the limit $p_\mu \rightarrow (m, 0\ 0\ 0)$. This subgroup is the covariant generalization of SU(6).

The generators $s_{\mu\nu}$ of SL(6, c) which generate a subgroup isomorphic to the Lorentz group, are given by

$$s_{\mu\nu} = \frac{1}{2i}\left[(\sigma_{\mu\nu})_A^B M_B^A + (\sigma_{\mu\nu})_{\dot{A}}^{\dot{B}} N_{\dot{B}}^{\dot{A}}\right]$$

In particular, a pure Lorentz transformation L_{io} is the sum of L_{io}^x, which in momentum space transforms the momentum only (due to the choice $j^x = 0$), and s_{io}; thus

$$L_{io} = i\left[P_i \frac{\partial}{\partial P_o} - P_o \frac{\partial}{\partial P_i}\right] + (\sigma_i)_B^A \lambda'^B_A$$

The finite Lorentz transformation which connects the rest system to the system in which the momentum is P, without rotation, is

$$L(p) = \exp\left[i\theta^i L_{io}\right] \qquad \theta^i = \frac{P_i}{|P|}\tanh^{-1}\frac{|P|}{P_o}$$

Consider first the quark representation Z_A. In this case

$$2iL_{io} Z_A = 2iS_{io} Z_A = (\sigma_i)_B^C M_C^B Z_A = (\sigma_i)_A^C Z_C$$

and thus

$$L(p) = e^{i\theta\cdot\sigma} = \left[2m(P_o + m)\right]^{-1/2}\left[m + P_o + \mathbf{P}\cdot\boldsymbol{\sigma}\right]$$

Similar expressions are obtained for the action of L(p) on $Z_{\dot{A}}$, Z^A, $Z^{\dot{A}}$.

The result may be written

$$L(p)Z_A = \left[2m(P_o + m)\right]^{-1/2} \left[m\,\delta^B_A + P^B_{\mathring{A}}\right] Z_B$$

$$L(p)Z_{\mathring{A}} = \left[2m(P_o + m)\right]^{-1/2} \left[m\delta^B_A + P^{\mathring{B}}_A\right] Z_{\mathring{B}}$$

$$L(p)Z^A = \left[2m(P_o + m)\right]^{-1/2} \left[m\delta^B_A + P^{\mathring{A}}_B\right] Z^B \qquad (3.2)$$

$$L(p)Z^{\mathring{A}} = \left[2m(P_o + m)\right]^{-1/2} \left[m\delta^B_A + P^A_{\mathring{B}}\right] Z^{\mathring{B}}$$

From this we see that the "covariant trace" $\frac{1}{m} P^B_{\mathring{A}} Z_B Z^{\mathring{A}}$ is Lorentz invariant. Further by direct application of $\lambda(p)^B_A$ one verifies that it is also $SU(6)_p$ invariant.

3.2. REPRESENTATIONS. We first construct finite dimensional representations of SL(6, c) and then we will make use of the method of generalized tensors to construct from them unitary infinite dimensional ones. A finite dimensional irreducible representation is given by the tensor set

$$\psi^{A_1 \dots A_N \; \mathring{B}_1 \dots \mathring{B}_N}_{C_1 \dots C_L \; \mathring{D}_1 \dots \mathring{D}_K}$$

possessing definite symmetry properties with respect to each set of like indices. For a complete description of these representations see Fronsdal, Representations of SL(n, C), ICTP preprint 66/51, Trieste.

For simplicity, we limit ourselves to the most highly degenerate series of representations, given by

$$\psi^{\dot{B}_1 \ldots \dot{B}_N}_{A_1 \ldots A_{N+K}}$$

completely symmetric in upper and in lower indices.

3.3. REDUCTION WITH RESPECT TO $SU(6)_p$. The tensor

$$\psi^{\dot{B}_1 \ldots \dot{B}_N}_{A_1 \ldots A_{N+K}}$$

is irreducible with respect to SL(6, c), but not with respect to $SU(6)_p$, since as we have seen, the covariant trace

$$P^{A_1}_{B_1} \psi^{B_1}_{A_1}$$

is an $SU(6)_p$ invariant quantity. We define

$$\hat{\psi}^{\dot{B}_1 \ldots \dot{B}_t}_{A_1 \ldots A_{t+K}} = \begin{matrix}\text{(covariant}\\ \text{traceless}\\ \text{part)}\end{matrix} \left\{ P^{A_{t+K+1}}_{\dot{B}_{t+1}} \ldots\ldots P^{A_{N+K}}_{B_N} \psi^{\dot{B}_1 \ldots \dot{B}_N}_{A_1 \ldots A_{N+K}} \right\}$$

Using this definition, it is a straightforward exercise to derive the expansion

$$\psi^{\dot{B}_1 \ldots \dot{B}_N}_{A_1 \ldots A_{N+K}} = \sum_{t=0}^{\infty} S\, a^N_t\, \hat{\psi}^{\dot{B}_1 \ldots \dot{B}_t}_{A_1 \ldots A_{t+K}}\, P^{\dot{B}_{t+1}}_{A_{t+K+1}} \ldots P^{\dot{B}_N}_{A_{N+K}} \tag{3.3}$$

where S indicates a symmetrization over indices and

$$a_t^N = \frac{N!\,(N+K)!\,(2t+K+n-1)!}{t!\,(t+K)!\,(N-t)!\,(N+t+K+n-1)} \qquad (3.4)$$

[Here n = 6; results are just as easily derived for SL(n, C).]

Note that the sum over t may be taken to ∞ since for N integer a_t^N is zero for $t > N$.

Now the action of the generators λ_A^B, λ'^B_A on the states

$$\hat{\psi}^{B_1 \ldots B_t}_{A_1 \ldots A_{t+K}}$$

can be derived.

$$2\lambda^B_A \, \hat{\psi}^{B_1 \ldots B_t}_{A_1 \ldots A_{t+K}} = \sum_{r=1}^{t+K} \delta^B_{A_r} \, \hat{\psi}^{B_1 \ldots B_t}_{A_1 \ldots A \ldots A_{t+K}}$$

$$- \sum_{r=1}^{t} \delta^{B_r}_{A} \, \hat{\psi}^{B_1 \ldots B \ldots B_t}_{A_1 \ldots A_{t+K}}$$

$$- \frac{K}{n} \delta^B_A \, \hat{\psi}^{B_1 \ldots B_t}_{A_1 \ldots A_{t+K}}$$

$$2\lambda' \hat{\psi}^{B\,B_1\ldots B_t}_{A\,A_1\ldots A_{t+K}} = +2(N-t)\hat{\psi}^{B\,B_1\ldots B_t}_{A\,A_1\ldots A_{t+K}}$$

$$+\frac{2N+t+n}{2t+K+n}\,S\left\{\begin{array}{l} +\delta^{B_1}_{A}\hat{\psi}^{B\,B_2\ldots B_t}_{A_1\ldots\ldots A_{t+K}} + (t+K)\delta^{B}_{A_1}\hat{\psi}^{B_1\ldots\ldots B_t}_{A\,A_2\ldots A_{t+K}} \\ -\frac{2t+K}{n}\delta^{B}_{A}\hat{\psi}^{B_1\ldots B_t}_{A_1\ldots A_{t+K}} \\ -\frac{2t(t+K)}{2t+K+n-2}\delta^{B_1}_{A_1}\hat{\psi}^{B\,B_2\ldots B_t}_{A\,A_2\ldots A_{t+K}} \end{array}\right\}$$

$$-\frac{2(N+t+K+n-1)}{2t+K+n-2}\;\frac{t(t+K)}{(2t+K+n-1)(2t+K+n-2)}\;x$$

$$S\left\{\begin{array}{l} \delta^{B}_{A}\delta^{B_1}_{A_1}\hat{\psi}^{B_2\ldots B_t}_{A_2\ldots A_{t+K}} + (t-1)\,\delta^{B_1}_{A}\delta^{B_2}_{A_1}\hat{\psi}^{B\,B_3\ldots B_t}_{A_2\ldots\ldots A_{t+K}} \\ +(t+K-1)\,\delta^{B}_{A_1}\delta^{B_1}_{A_2}\hat{\psi}^{B_2\ldots\ldots B_t}_{A\,A_3\ldots A_{t+K}} \\ -\frac{(t-1)(t+K-1)}{2t+K+n-3}\,\delta^{B_1}_{A_1}\delta^{B_2}_{A_2}\hat{\psi}^{B\,B_3\ldots B_t}_{A\,A_3\ldots A_{t+K}} \\ -(2t+K+n-2)\,\delta^{B_1}_{A}\delta^{B}_{A_1}\hat{\psi}^{B_2\ldots B_t}_{A_2\ldots A_{t+K}} \end{array}\right\} \quad (3.5)$$

Once this have been done, the number N appears in the equations simply as an arbitrary parameter, and not as the number of indices on a tensor. If N is taken to be negative or complex, the equations (3.5) define a representation of the algebra of SL(n, C). One must still discuss unitarity, the existence of a parity operator, irreducibility, etc. Briefly, the results are the following. Unitarity is equivalent to the reality of the parameter ρ defined through $i\rho = 2N + K + n$. The existence of a parity operator for the representation requires that $\rho = 0$.

4. PHYSICAL PROPERTIES OF THE INVARIANTS: FORM FACTORS

Before examining invariants, we must first choose which representations we will use to represent physical particle states. The most obvious requirement is one of particle content, and the simplest choice for the baryons would seem to be the representation

$$\psi^{\mathring{B}_1 \ldots \mathring{B}_N}_{A_1 \ldots A_{N+K}}$$

Demanding that the smallest SU(6) representation occurring in the decomposition be $\underline{56}$, fixes $K = 3$, and that parity be well defined for all SU(6) levels fixes $N = -(K+n)/2 = -9/2$. There is a further requirement given us by nature, however, and that is the existence of anti-particles. To properly include charge conjugation in the theory it is necessary to introduce two non-unitary representations, those given by $N = -4$ and $N = -5$, coupled to one another by a "Dirac" equation which restores unitarity in the theory, exactly as in the ordinary finite dimensional Dirac theory.

For purposes of discussing invariant vertices, however, I will confine myself to the representation above. Firstly, the essential features of the theory will be illustrated fully in this manner, and secondly, vertices in the C-invariant case, while being no more complicated, have simply not yet been calculated.

If there is time I hope to return to discuss the C-invariant theory, as infinite component theories display some very unconventional properties, particularly concerning crossing.

4.1. THE ELECTRIC CHARGE FORM FACTOR. The proper exact form of the electromagnetic vertex is not yet known. However the charge part of the interaction is related to the local current

$$J_\mu = \overline{\psi}^{A_1 \ldots A_{N+K}}_{\dot{B}_1 \ldots \dot{B}_N}(x) \overleftrightarrow{\partial}_\mu Q \psi^{\dot{B}_1 \ldots \dot{B}_N}_{A_1 \ldots A_{N+K}}(x) \qquad (4.1)$$

which in momentum space is

$$\frac{1}{2m}(p+p')_\mu \overline{\psi}^{A_1 \ldots A_{N+K}}_{\dot{B}_1 \ldots \dot{B}_N}(p') Q \psi^{\dot{B}_1 \ldots \dot{B}_N}_{A_1 \ldots A_{N+K}}(p)$$

To compute the matrix elements of this current between two baryon states, we must replace $\overline{\psi}(p')$ by its projection onto the 56-dimensional representation of the little group $SU(6)_{p'}$ and $\psi(p)$ by its projection onto the 56-dimensional representation of $SU(6)_p$. To do this, one makes use of the expansion (3.3), and is left with a non trivial problem in combinatorics. It is in this connection that the method of generalized tensors is simpler than the analytic techniques. The equivalent calculation for the analyst consists of a 70-fold integration over the group space of SL(6, c).

Also, this projection onto $SU(6)_p$, for N negative, is a non local projection, and it is this fact which gives rise to the convergent form factors characteristic of the theory.

The result of the combinatorical calculation is, for proton states

$$J_\mu = \frac{1}{2m}(p+p')_\mu \left[1 - \frac{t}{4m^2}\right]^{-9/2} \left[\frac{(E+m)(E'+m)}{2E \cdot 2E'}\right]^{1/2} \chi^*$$

$$\cdot \left[1 + \frac{\boldsymbol{\sigma} \cdot \mathbf{p}\ \boldsymbol{\sigma} \cdot \mathbf{p}'}{(E+m)(E'+m)}\right] \chi \qquad (4.2)$$

The factor $\left[1 - \frac{t}{4m^2}\right]^{-9/2}$, or one similar to it, is characteristic of unitary theories involving an infinite number of spin values. The current appearing in the ordinary Dirac local limit also contains a factor of this form $\sim (1 - \frac{t}{4m^2})^{-1}$. If account is made for the vector meson poles, the SL(6, c) vertex gives an excellent fit to the experimental data.

4.2. THE BARYON-BARYON-MESON VERTEX. The choice of a meson representation is also determined by requirements of charge conjugation, parity, particle content, and the existence of a Yukawa vertex. It is more complicated than the baryon representation. There are two possibilities, given by the tensor

$$\Phi^{A_1 \ldots A_M \, \dot{B}_1 \ldots \dot{B}_L}_{\dot{C}_1 \ldots \dot{C}_M \, D_1 \ldots D_L}$$

with M = L or M = L+1. The SU(6) content in the two cases is only slightly different.

There is only one way to saturate indices between the three tensors $\bar{\psi}\psi\Phi$, and thus the invariant vertex is unique. We have, however, been unable to carry out the combinatorics involved in the projection onto the physical particle states. It is easy to show that the form factor will have a form similar to that obtained in the case of the electric charge form factor.

It is possible to carry out the calculation to the first order in the momentum, and this has been done for the case M = L and provides a non-relativistic (but not static!) limit of what one may expect from the theory. The results are quite promising. The D/F ratio is 1.8 which is consistent with the experimental data on strong interactions. All predictions regarding the BBM vertex are reasonably good. I do not wish to stress comparison with experiment or describe it in detail, as our primary interest still lies with the general features of the theory. The only descouraging feature regarding experimental predictions concerns meson decays. A calculation of the three meson vertex has been carried out, also only to first order in momentum, and has been shown to be identically zero as far the coupling (35 35 35) is concerned. (See K. Tripathy and R. White, Phys. Rev., in press).

4.3. CROSSING SYMMETRY IN INFINITE COMPONENT THEORIES.

As we have remarked earlier, the simple model for the baryons described earlier is not a theory which admits anti-particles. This may be seen very simply. Consider the coupling $\bar{B}$BM, describing a baryon decay into a baryon and a meson. This is a unique coupling which correctly describes the interaction with a pseudoscalar meson. It is an experimental fact, however, that the anti-baryons have opposite parity from the baryons. There is no way one can construct a vertex from the representation given which displays the correct parity dependence to describe anti-particles. Since the coupling is unique, it will necessarily be of the SU(2) form:

$$\chi_f \sigma \cdot \mathbf{p} \, \chi_i \, \phi$$

for spin 1/2 particles.

This fact makes it necessary to introduce a pair of conjugate irreducible representations, exactly as in the case of SL(2, c). An analogue of the Dirac equation restores unitarity to the physical theory, avoids the necessity of parity doubling, and ensures a correct physical interpretation. The most interesting result which we have found is that, although the scattering and annihilation form factors are closely related to each other, they are not connected by analytic continuation in the momentum transfer.

One introduces a pair of representations, ψ_N and $\psi_{N'}$, say, and considers the doubled space given by $(\psi_N , \psi_{N'})$. Then the requirements that there exist a vector operator Γ_μ coupling these representations and that there exist a hermitian invariant inner form in the doubled space fixes N = -5, N'= -4. The operators Γ_μ (acting on an infinite dimensional space) can then be explicitly calculated. (See C. Fronsdal and R. White UCLA preprint 35, March 1967).

For the purpose of displaying the unusual crossing results, consider the case where S is taken to be simply SL(2, c). Here the scattering and annihilation form factors may be calculated in closed form, giving

$$K(t) = \frac{\sinh\left[(N+1)\sinh^{-1}\left\{\frac{t(t-4m^2)}{4m^4}\right\}^{1/2}\right]}{(N+1)\left[\frac{t(t-4m^2)}{4m^4}\right]^{1/2}}$$

$$K^x(s) = \frac{\sinh\left[(N+1)\sinh^{-1}\left\{\frac{s(s-4m^2)}{4m^4}\right\}^{1/2}\right]}{(N+1)\left[\frac{s(s-4m^2)}{4m^4}\right]^{1/2}}$$

The correct branch of $\sinh^{-1}$ is in both cases that for which K is analytic in the neighborhood $p \cdot p' = m^2$ where

$$t = (p - p')^2 \quad , \quad s = (p + p')^2 .$$

Thus K(t) is regular at $t = 0$ and has a square root type singularity at $t = 4m^2$, while $K^x(s)$ is regular at $s = 4m^2$ and has a square root type singularity at $s = 0$. In the special case of non negative integer values of N the functions are entire, analytic in the whole complex plane of their respective variables.

REFERENCES

SU(6) and its extension:

1. F. Gürsey and L. A. Radicati, Phys. Rev. Letters 13, 173 (1964).
2. B. Sakita, Phys. Rev. 137 B1756 (1964).
3. P. Budini and C. Fronsdal, Phys. Rev. Letters 14, 968 (1965).

SL(6, c):

1. C. Fronsdal, Representations of SL(n, C), ICTP preprint 66/51 (1966).
2. R. White -Lecture notes, Summer School on Theoretical Physics, Odaipur, India (1966).
3. W. Rühl, CERN preprint TH 626, November 1965.
4. Harish Chandra, Trans. Amer. Math. Soc. 75, 185 (1953).
5. I. M. Gel'fand and M. A. Naimark, "Unitäre Darstellungen der Klassischen Gruppen", Akademie -Verlag, Berlin (1957).
6. R. Godement, Trans. Amer. Math. Soc. 73, 496 (1952).
7. C. Fronsdal, "Relativistic Symmetries", Proceedings of the Seminar on High Energy Physics and Elementary Particles, Trieste, 1965, published by IAEA, Vienna, 1965.

Invariants and vertices:

1. C. Fronsdal and R. White, Phys. Rev. 151, 1287 (1966).
2. G. Cocho, C. Fronsdal, Harun Ar-Rashid and R. White, Phys. Rev. Letters 17, H563 (1966).
3. K. Tripathy and R. White, Phys. Rev., in press.

Part II

Nuclear Physics

9
SOME PROBLEMS IN FAST NEUTRON PHYSICS[+]

Ivo Šlaus and Guy Paić
Institute "Ruđer Bošković", Zagreb, Yugoslavia

\+ Notes edited by Dr. Alex Trier.

1. INTRODUCTION

The experimental information on fast neutron induced reactions is qualitatively summarized in Fig. 1 and Fig. 2. Fig. 1 reflects the present status of available neutron facilities, i.e. fast neutron physics is mainly done in laboratories equipped with Cockcroft-Walton accelerators using D-D and D-T neutrons. Van de Graaff accelerators and particularly the advent of tandem Van de Graaff helped to accumulate some data up to about $E_n = 22$ MeV. Fig. 2 gives an insight into the state of art of various experimental techniques. In particular, total cross sections can be measured in a fairly straightforward manner, e.g. using activation techniques. However the measurements become prohibitively difficult if the total reaction cross section is small and this is the reason for meager data for the reactions (n, trion), (n, d) and (n, 2p). The angular correlation measurements of neutron induced reactions are at present at the border of feasibility.

The quality of the available experimental data is characterized by the accuracy achieved in the measurements.

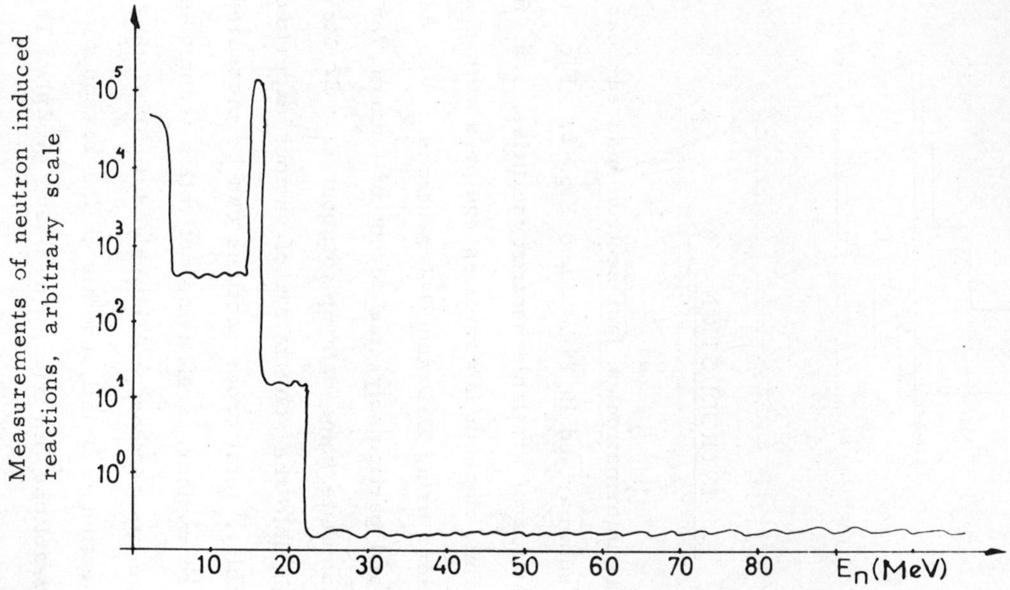

Fig. 1

The available experimental information as a function of incident neutron energy

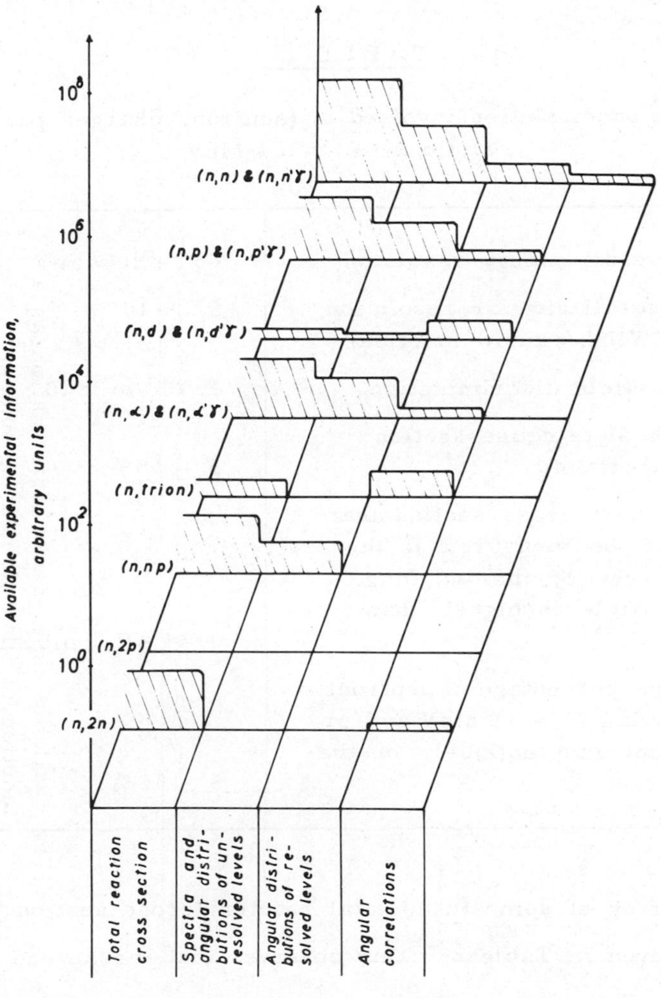

Fig. 2

The available experimental information for various neutron induced processes grouped according to the type of measurement.

Table 1 lists some typical uncertainties involved in the best presently available studies of (neutron, charged particle) reactions.

TABLE 1

Some uncertainties involved in (neutron, charged particle) reactions, $E_n = 14$ MeV

Overall energy resolution	450 - 800 keV
Overall angular resolution (FWHM window function)	5° - 10°
Particle discrimination	$1:10^3$ to $1:10^5$
Absolute cross section uncertainty	5 - 15%
Lowest cross section that can be measured if the energy of the outgoing particle is higher than 6 MeV	0.04 - 0.1 mb/sr
The percentage of neutrons having $E_n < 14$ MeV and/or impinging obliquely on the target	5 - 10%

A survey of some (n, p) total reaction cross section measurements is given in Table 2. One observes that the spread of quoted values for cross sections is in some cases several times larger than the error claimed. Principal errors sometimes underestimated by experimentalists are: 1) The uncertainty in the incident neutron energy particularly related to the kinematic spread due to the large source-sample solid angle and the presence of an unknown amount of neutrons with lower energy; and 2) nonuniform neutron flux.

TABLE 2

Survey of some (n, p) total reaction cross section measurements

Target nucleus	Incident neutron energy	Cross section (in mb)	Reference
0^{16}	14.5	39. ± 4	Ka 61
	14.7	38.2 ± 0.5	Ka 62
	14.76	33.29 ± 2.4	Di 62
	14.8	40.1 ± 2.7	Mi 66
	14.8	29.2 ± 2	Pr 66
		49 ± 25	Pa 53
F^{19}	14.7	14.3 ± 2.5	Ka 62
	14.8	23.3 ± 2.8	Mi 66
	14.8	51 ± 10	Pr 66
		135 ± 50	Pa 53
		16.4 ± 0.7	Pa 67
Al^{27}	14.0	115 ± 10	Kh 60
	14.0	79 ± 6	Fo 52
	14.1	80.0 ± 5	Po 61
	14.8	97 ± 10	Ni 66

For an extensive review of (n, p) total reaction cross sections see also Le 64, Ga 62 and Ch 65.

A comparison between accuracies achieved in fast neutron induced reactions and those characterizing charged particle induced reactions is given in Fig. 3.

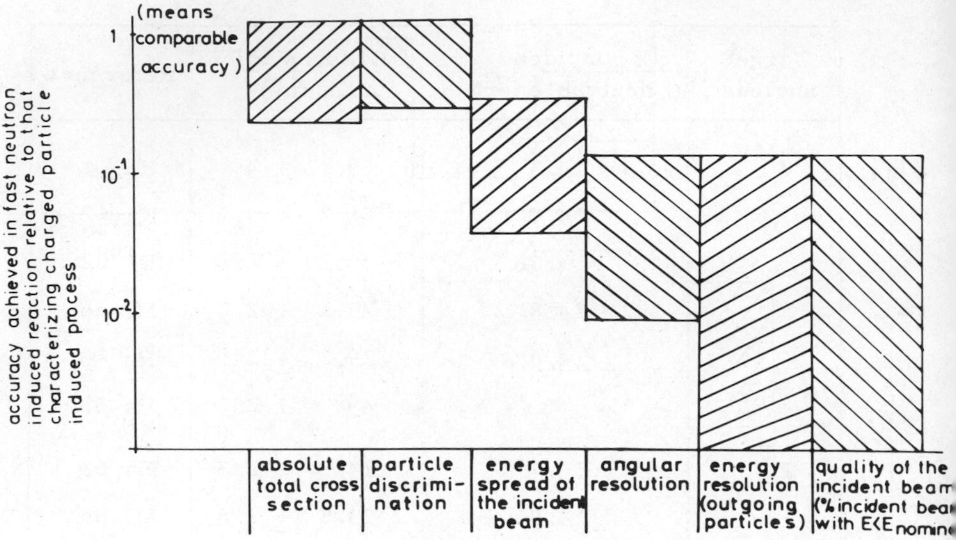

Fig. 3

Accuracy achieved in fast neutron induced reactions relative to that characterizing charged particle induced processes, grouped according to the type of the measurement.

Fig. 4 presents the time necessary to accumulate enough data in various measurements of neutron and charged particle induced reactions. The assumption is made that the statistical accuracies in both cases are comparable, while the quality of the experimental data with respect to energy and angular resolution as well as the features of the incident beam are as indicated in Fig. 3. If better energy and/or angular resolution in neutron physics were desired, the duration of the measurement would increase one to two orders of magnitude.

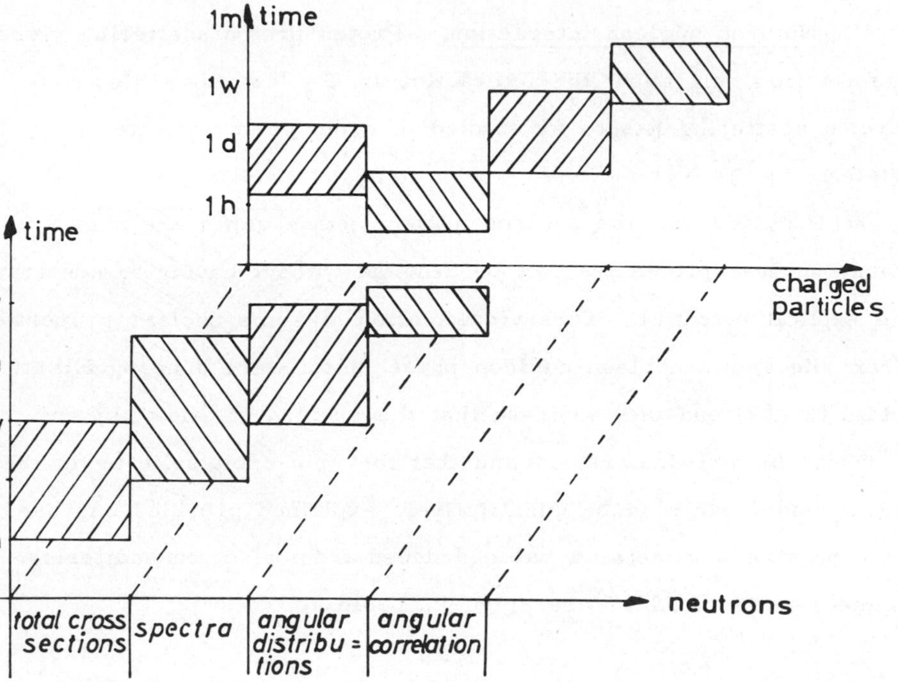

Fig. 4

Time necessary to accumulate enough data in various measurements of neutron and charged particle induced reactions

This presentation led to the question: Is the information to be obtained by studying fast neutron induced reactions with accuracy as indicated in Fig. 3 useful and does it add something fundamental to our understanding of nuclear physics so as to justify incomparably longer and often more difficult experiments than the ones where charged particle beams are employed?

The answer is affirmative and the following is a list of some important information which can be obtained only by investigating neutron induced processes.

1.1. Nucleon-nucleon interaction. Proton-proton scattering gives information only about the interaction in T = 1 states. Neutron-proton scattering has to be studied in order to investigate T = 0 states.

Provided that the nucleon-nucleon phase shifts are known many nuclear properties can be deduced without having to construct an explicit potential. Direct calculation of some nuclear properties from the known nucleon-nucleon phase shifts were done by Elliott et al (El 67) and they indicate that the spectra of ^{6}He, ^{6}Li and ^{18}O can be well understood and that the spin-orbit splitting in the shell model can also be quantitatively explained provided one uses for the size parameter a value deduced from electron scattering. Some results of El 67 are given in Table 3.

TABLE 3

Nucleus	Size parameter (in fm)	Spin-orbit splitting (in MeV)	
		Calculated	Experimental
^{5}He	1.6 ± 0.5	4.1 ± 0.6	4
^{17}F, ^{17}O	1.75 ± 0.5	5.6 ± 0.8	5.1

The comparison between n-p and p-p $^{1}S_{o}$ effective range parameters as well as the nuclear structure data indicate that the nuclear interaction is not completely charge independent. Most likely, the charge independence is violated by about 3 - 5 % (for a recent review on the subject see He 66). The breakdown of charge independence by about 3 percent is to be expected since the nuclear interaction is mediated by mesons and it is experimentally established that charged and neutral pions have different mass. Therefore neutron-proton scattering has to be investigated in order to understand the breakdown of charge independence.

It is possible that the nuclear interaction violates even charge symmetry, i. e. that the p-p and n-n interactions in equal space and spin states are different. (For a recent review on the neutron-neutron interaction see Sl 67. Arguments for and against possible charge symmetry breakdown are presented in Sy 67). Thus, the study of the neutron-neutron interaction becomes necessary, and it seems that the best way to investigate it is to perform neutron-neutron collision experiments (Sl 67, Mo 64, Di 67).

A complete understanding of the nuclear interaction requires the knowledge of the off-energy-shell interaction. The most suitable process to obtain such information is the nucleon-nucleon bremsstrahlung. Thus, the necessity to study neutron-proton bremstrahlung.

Particularly important specific questions which demand a prompt answer are:

(i) ^1S_o n-p effective range, r_{np}. The present value of r_{np}, obtained from an analysis which includes the measurement of the n-p total cross section by Engelke et al. (En 63), would require about 30 % departure from charge independence. The measurement of Engelke et al. should be repeated with a higher (or at least comparable) accuracy.

(ii) Neutron-proton scattering: differential cross section, polarization, triple scattering and spin-spin correlation measurements in the energy region E_{inc} = 40 - 300 MeV. Understanding of the nuclear interaction in T = 0 states imperatively demands the above measurements.

(iii) Neutron-proton bremsstrahlung cross section. The measurement of the proton-deuteron bremsstrahlung at 200 MeV was used to extract the neutron-proton bremsstrahlung cross section. There are indications that the experimental value is significantly different from the theoretical prediction. The use of pdγ to obtain the npγ cross section is subject to severe criticism. Therefore, the need to measure directly the neutron-proton bremsstrahlung (see Si 67).

(iv) It seems that the neutron-proton differential cross section in the energy region from 10 - 30 MeV is not very accurately known (see Ho 67). Although the improved measurements of np angular distribution presumably will not appreciably increase our understanding of nuclear interactions, accurate np differential cross sections are needed as a standard relative to which most of the (neutron, charged particle) angular distributions are normalized.

1.2. <u>Few nucleon systems.</u> Few nucleon systems which are predominantly composed of neutrons can easily be formed through the interaction of fast neutrons and light nuclei. Examples of such systems are:

a. 2n via D(n, p)2n, or ^{3}H(n, d)2n, or ^{9}Be(n, 2α)2n

b. 3n via ^{3}H(n, p)3n, or ^{7}Li(n, pα)3n

c. ^{7}He via ^{7}Li(n, p) ^{7}He

Such systems can often be formed by charged particle induced reactions, e.g. $^3H(d, ^3He)2n$ or $^3H(d, 2p)3n$ or $^7Li(t, ^3He)\ ^7He$, but due to the fact that these processes involve more complex particles their interpretation might be uncertain.

Significant progress in the understanding and theoretical treatment of the three body problem has been recently achieved due to the work of Fadeev (Fa 60), Amado and coworkers (Aa 65), Mitra and coworkers (Mi 67) and others. The Fadeev type formalism has been applied successfully to the neutron-deuteron elastic scattering and somewhat less successfully to the n-d inelastic scattering. The extension of this work to the proton-deuteron system is prevented by complications connected with the treatment of the Coulomb interaction, which at the present stage of computational art are prohibitively difficult. Systems like 2np, 3np or 3nα do not contain the Coulomb interaction (α is treated as a single particle) and thus seem a convenient starting point for the rigorous treatment of three and four body systems.

The study of few nucleon systems via neutron induced processes has been criticized arguing that kinematically completely determined measurements (e.g. for a process $1+2 \rightarrow 3+4+...+N$ there are $3N - 10$ independent kinematic variables) cannot at present be performed in neutron physics due to enormous experimental difficulties. This criticism is invalid since:

I) Measurements in which less than $3N-10$ variables are determined are not invalid, and on the contrary represent very valuable information; granted not as detailed and complete as that obtained in general in kinematically completely determined measurements (see e.g. Sl 67a).

II) Measurements in which all $3N-10$ variables are determined are becoming feasible in neutron physics.

If the nuclear interaction contains many-body forces, it is conceivable that these forces can also be charge dependent, i.e. nnn $\neq$ npp $\neq$ nnp. Systems formed by neutron irradiation of light nuclei can be suitable to study nnn and nnp three-body forces.

The problem of time reversal invariance has recently revived the interest to study $n+p \rightarrow d+\gamma$ together with $d+\gamma \rightarrow n+p$. Neutron capture by a proton has been studied at thermal energies and at 14 MeV. Measurements at higher energies are required.

The neutron capture by deuterons $n+d \rightarrow t+\gamma$ has also been studied at low energies. More measurements are needed.

Some of the most important few-nucleon problems to be studied:

i) D(n, p) 2n in the energy range 20 - 100 MeV. It has been argued (Oe 67) that proton spectra measured at several forward angles would allow to determine the n-n ^1S_o scattering length, since the charge symmetric process D(p, n) 2p in that energy range yields the correct pp scattering length.

Except at 14 MeV the reaction D(n, p) 2n is very poorly understood. Even at 14 MeV there is only one measurement performed at several forward angles.

Correlation measurements D(n, 2n)p have been performed at 14 MeV (Ni 66) (Bo 67). Much more extensive studies are required.

ii) The nucleon induced trion breakup processes could not be understood in terms of simple knock-out or pick-up mechanisms (Oe 67). The reactions ^{3}H(n, d) 2n and ^{3}He(n, d) np were studied at 14 MeV, (Aj 65) (An 66) and the former also at 20 MeV (Th 66) and 22 MeV (De 67). The measurements are restricted to deuteron spectra analyzed at one or a few forward angles.

iii) Differential cross section, polarization, triple scattering and spin-spin correlation measurements for neutron-deuteron, neutron-triton and neutron-^{3}He elastic scattering. This study is related to the problem of excited states in A = 3 systems and in A = 4 systems, particularly T = 1 levels (^{4}H levels). It should be mentioned that elastic nucleon-deuteron scattering can reveal only T = 1/2 levels in A = 3 systems.

The problem of excited states in A = 4 systems is to some extent understood, though much remains to be done (see e.g. Me 67). The system A = 3 and its excited levels are at present very poorly understood (see e.g. Sl 67a).

iv) The reaction ^{3}H(n, p) 3n has been investigated at 14 MeV (Aj 65a) and revealed an appreciable cross section at forward angles ($d\sigma/d\Omega \sim$ few mb/sr) and it also offered some indication for a possible bound state of three neutrons. Subsequent measurements did not corroborate the existence of a bound trineutron, but it is important to emphasize that none of these measurements was performed with an accuracy better than or even comparable to the original measurement (see discussion in Sy 67).

The value for the cross section of the reaction ^{3}H(n, p)3n presents an additional problem. The measurements at 14.4 MeV (Aj 65a) and at 15.2 MeV (Fu 67) both yield 15 mb/sr, and the results at 20 (Th 66) and 22 MeV (De 67) are not in direct contradiction with these data. However, the study of the charge symmetric process ^{3}He(p, n)3p at 14 MeV (An 65, Co 66) yields a cross section 10 - 1000 times smaller.

v) Neutron induced breakup processes have revealed the importance of the sequential mechanism, e.g.

$$^{7}Li\,(n,t)\,^{5}He\,,\quad ^{5}He \rightarrow n+\alpha$$
$$^{10}B\,(n,t)\,^{8}Be\,,\quad ^{8}Be \rightarrow \alpha+\alpha$$
and
$$^{6}Li\,(n,d)\,^{5}He\,,\quad ^{5}He \rightarrow n+\alpha$$

(Va 67, Va 64).

Charged particle induced reactions have revealed besides a sequential mechanism also direct knock-out processes, in which one system in the entrance channel has a small separation energy for breakup into two components, and thus represents a fairly large structure. The other system (or particle) in the entrance channel can interact with only one component, leaving the other one as a spectator:

$$a + \underbrace{b + B}_{\text{small binding energy}} \longrightarrow a' + b' + \underset{\text{(spectator)}}{B}$$

In order that particle B can be a spectator, it is necessary that the wavelength of relative motion be smaller than the average b-B separation. This in turn requires E_a typically about 20 MeV or larger (for b+ B = deuteron, ^{9}Be, ^{7}Li, etc.). A large number of processes in which one component is a spectator has been observed at 30 - 100 MeV and even at 10 - 20 MeV incident energy (see e.g. Sl 67a).

The direct knock-out mechanism demonstrating a spectator effect has not been clearly established in neutron induced reactions. It is necessary to perform kinematically completely determined measurements and to investigate particle-particle correlations at incident energies higher than 14 MeV.

1.3. Nuclear spectroscopy. Essentially any direct reaction induced by neutrons which involves a given target and a given residual nucleus can be related to a charged particle induced reaction which deals with the same target and same residual nucleus. For example

(n, p) - (t, ^{3}He)
(n, d) - (d, ^{3}He) or (t, α)
(n, t) - (p, ^{3}He)
(n, ^{3}He) - (p, 3p) or (t, αp) or (d, ^{3}He p)
(n, α) - (p, ^{3}He p) or (d, αp)
(n, np) - (p, 2p)
(n, 2n) - (p, pn)
(n, 2p) - (t, ^{3}He p)

It would seem as if it is unnecessary to study neutron induced reactions to obtain spectroscopic information. This is not so and the reasons are:

I) Though the reaction mechanism for (n, d) and (d, ^{3}He) is probably the same, e.g. pick-up of a proton, and the same holds for (n, t) vs (p, ^{3}He), (n, np) vs (p, 2p) and (n, 2n) vs (p, pn), the reaction mechanisms for (n, ^{3}He) and (p, 3p) are presumably quite different. The same holds for (n, α) vs (p, ^{3}He p) and many other processes.

A necessary prerequisite to employ a nuclear reaction to extract spectroscopic information is the understanding of the mechanism of that reaction.

II) In general neutron induced reactions are simpler than their charged particle counterparts. For example the cross section for the reaction (d, ^{3}He) involves in addition the overlap integral describing the formation of ^{3}He from p+d. The exact calculation of that overlap factor would require the solution of the wave function of ^{3}He. A phenomenological approach is to determine the factor from the cross section for those (d, ^{3}He) reactions where the spectroscopic factor involving the target and the residual nucleus is known. An additional requirement is that the uncertainties in the distorted waves describing d-target and ^{3}He-residual nucleus are negligible.

III) The agreement between spectroscopic information extracted from (d, ^{3}He) and (n, d) reactions on one side and their inverse (d, n) and (^{3}He, d) on the other side has been in general successful. However, disquieting differences were also observed.

IV) The reactions (n, p) and (n, α) at E_n 14 MeV, providing the target nuclei are light or medium heavy, predominantly proceed via a statistical compound nucleus mechanism. Therefore, all energetically possible final states are populated with comparable probability. As a consequence, these reactions are well suited to investigate energy levels.

V) Neutron induced reactions can form neutron rich isotopes and consequently can help to investigate and determine the stability curve on the $N > Z$ side.

1.4 <u>Reaction mechanisms and nucleon-nucleus interaction.</u> Neutron physics played a remarkable role in the formulation of both compound nucleus and direct interaction mechanisms. The birth of the optical model was also facilitated by the discoveries in neutron physics.

It is beyond the scope of this introduction to go into this subject in all details as it deserves. At the same time, it is not quite clear what information about reaction mechanisms and nucleon-nucleus interaction is easier and more accurate to obtain studying neutron induced reactions than investigating charged particle induced processes.

A few examples of useful neutron induced processes for reaction mechanism studies are enumerated:

I) (n, 2p) reaction. The charge symmetric counterpart (p, 2n) reaction has been investigated on few nuclei at several energies up to E_p = 700 MeV (see e.g. Le 66). It is likely that the (p, 2n) process proceeds in two steps: one, charge exchange reaction: (p, n); two, subsequent neutron evaporation (see Gr 64). This model is corroborated by the fact that the ratio of reaction cross sections σ(p, 2n): σ(p, n) is almost energy independent for various nuclei (Le 66). Namely, the mean excitation energy of the intermediate nuclei, i.e. after the stage (p, n), weakly depends upon incident proton energy. This causes a weak dependence of the neutron evaporation process on E_{inc}, and hence σ(p, 2n): σ(p, n) is energy independent.

The mechanism of the reaction (n, 2p) can be quite different, specially the dependence on incident neutron energy. At lower energies and for heavy targets the coulomb barrier will hinder proton evaporation and a direct interaction mechanism might become more important. In the direct interaction picture the reaction (n, 2p) is related to the multiple scattering process.

II) Reactions like (n, ^{6}He) and (n, ^{9}Be) are appropriate to study consecutive pickup processes; e.g. $n + \alpha \rightarrow {}^5He$, ${}^5He + n \rightarrow {}^6He$.

III) Investigation of the nucleon-nucleus spin-spin interaction. The total cross section for parallel and antiparallel orientations of neutron and ^{165}Ho spins were investigated by Wagner et al (Wa 64) and it was concluded that the spin-spin term to be added to a general optical potential describing neutron-nucleus interaction, assuming the Saxon radial dependence, is characterized by a potential depth V_{ss} bracketed by

$$-0.06 \text{ MeV} < V_{ss} < 0.13 \text{ MeV}$$

More data are needed to solve the problem of the importance of neutron-nucleus spin-spin interaction. The development of several polarized target nuclei and polarized neutron beams in a broad energy range should be able to stimulate this type of research.

1.5. Neutron physics and other fields. An intimate connection exists between neutron physics and radiation physics and health physics, nuclear engineering, shielding problems, astrophysics, notably stellar interior synthesis of heavier and medium heavy nuclei, solid state physics, and even elementary particle physics.

As an example of the last relationship we discuss the problem of neutron structure. It has been observed that the elastic scattering of neutron exhibits an increase as the scattering angle is decreased below 15°. Alexandrov et al (Al 56) suggested that this phenomenon can be caused by the interaction of the nuclear Coulomb field $\mathbf{E}$ and the induced dipole moment $\mathbf{p} = \alpha \mathbf{E}$ of the neutron. The magnitude of the increase at small angles is related to the neutron polarizability α.

Monahan et al (Mo 66) measured the elastic scattering and polarization of 0.83 MeV neutrons from uranium in the angular range from 1.65° to 23°. The data are compared with a calculation which uses a potential containing a standard nuclear optical model potential, a term which describes the interaction of the neutron magnetic moment $\boldsymbol{\mu}$ and the electric field $\mathbf{E}$:

$$\mu \frac{e\hbar}{2m^2c^2} \boldsymbol{\sigma} \cdot \mathbf{E} \times \mathbf{p}$$

and a term which represents the interaction of the induced dipole moment $\alpha\mathbf{E}$ of the neutron and the electric field:

$$\frac{1}{2}\alpha E^2$$

If one uses $\alpha = 10^{-41}$ the theory does not explain the observed increase in the angular distribution. A larger value for α is required or an additional long range force.

Other small angle scattering data (Wa 65, An 66) also do not solve the problem. It is not clear to what extent the increase at small angles is attributable to neutron polarizability.

Therefore, the progress in various fields of science also requires the study of neutron induced reactions.

Since the question of the justification for doing fast neutron physics has been affirmatively answered, the entire topic of these lectures is somewhat justified. Before turning to the actual content of these lectures, i.e. neutron sources, detection methods, nuclear spectroscopy and few body problems and finally the problem of the future of fast neutron physics, let me briefly deal with the question

Is neutron physics a poor man's physics?

As long as we stick to 2 and 14 MeV neutrons, which can be produced using a very inexpensive 200 keV accelerator, and in view of the rather low neutron intensity and consequently low counting rate, which do not demand fast data accumulation and data handling systems, neutron physics can indeed be done quite inexpensively.

However, if one extends the neutron energy range, as we have seen the accumulation of necessary information requires, and if complicated experiments are performed (which again is needed), the neutron physics research requires tandems, SF cyclotrons, meson factories, fast electronics, elaborate detection systems, on-line computers and it is as expensive as the study of charged particle induced reactions.

In these lectures some problems in fast neutron physics will be briefly outlined. The reader is referred to existing books, proceedings and review articles, such as Ma 63, Me 66, Ci 66 and Ph 63.

2. NEUTRON SOURCES

A neutron source is characterized by several important parameters:

i) process used for the generation of neutrons.

ii) maximum neutron energy available and energy spectrum of outgoing neutrons.

iii) intensity

iv) lifetime of the source

v) possibility of pulsing

vi) purpose

Sources can be classified in various ways and the following is one of these:

1. radioactive neutron sources
2. reactors
3. accelerator-based neutron sources:
   - 3a. electrostatic devices accelerating charged particles up to about 25 MeV; e.g. Cockcroft-Walton accelerators, isolated core transformers (ICT), tandems.
   - 3b. conventional cyclotrons
   - 3c. SF cyclotrons
   - 3d. synchrocyclotrons
   - 3e. linear accelerators
   - 3f. separated orbit cyclotrons

   Another possible classification under 3. is according to the type of accelerated particle:

   - 3.i. nucleons and atomic nuclei
   - 3.ii. electrons
4. nuclear explosions and
5. neutrons in the stars.

2.1. Radioactive neutron sources. The alpha radioactivity of natural radioisotopes made it possible in the early thirties to construct neutron sources using (α, n) reactions on light nuclei, e.g. Li, Be, B and F. The commonly employed alpha sources are radium (^{226}Ra) and actinium(^{227}Ac).

The yield of (α, n) sources is relatively low and it amounts to $\sim 10^7$ n/s Ci for an ^{227}Ac-α-Be source.

The energy of outgoing neutrons depends on the alpha energy and the target metarial used for neutron production. Fig. 5 shows the neutron energy spectrum of the Ra-α-Be source. Typical source size for 500 mg of radium producing 7×10^7 n/sec, is 2 cm dia x 2 cm height.

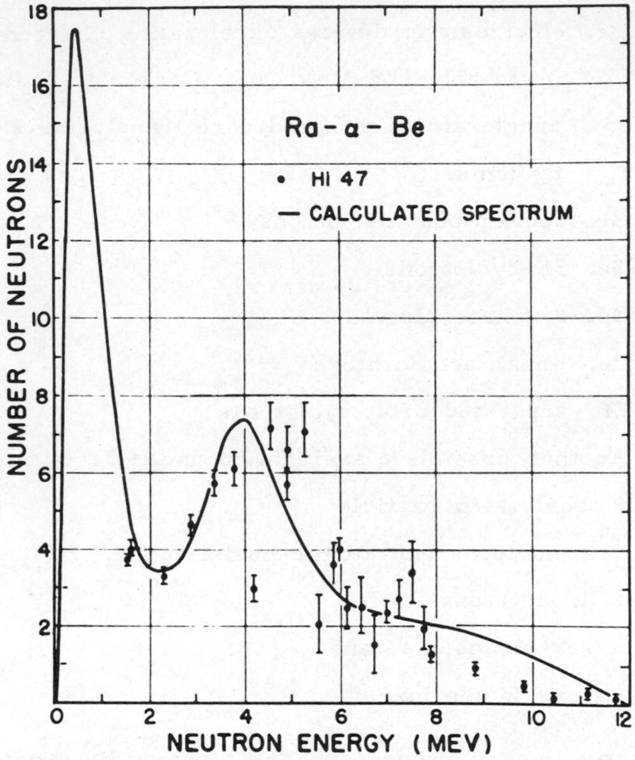

Fig. 5

The neutron energy spectrum from Ra- Be as measured by Hill (Hi 47). The soild line is the calculation of Hess (He 59) using the $^9Be(\alpha, n)^{12}C$ cross section.

Gamma radioactivity can be also used for neutron production via the (γ, n) reaction. Photoneutron sources have in general smaller neutron yield than (α, n) sources. However, photoneutron sources can have a less complex energy spectrum. Gamma radio-active isotopes with a useful lifetime and a conveniently large gamma yield are e.g. ^{124}Sb (E = 1.69 MeV), ^{88}Y (E = 1.85 MeV), ^{24}Na (E = 2.76 MeV). Radium can be also used as a gamma source in view of its long lifetime. However, the gamma spectrum of radium is complicated and produces a complex energy spectrum of neutrons (see Fig. 6). Since convenient gamma sources have gamma energy below 3 MeV, only deuterium and beryllium can be used as a material:

$$D + \gamma \rightarrow n + p - 2.226 \text{ MeV}$$

$$^{9}Be + \gamma \rightarrow n + {}^{8}Be - 1.666 \text{ MeV}$$

The common features of radioactive sources are: they are small and portable; have a constant output and do not require maintenance. Radioactive sources serve as standards in calibration of neutron fluxes.

2.2. Reactors will not be discussed in these lectures because they are of little interest for fast neutron physics.

2.3. <u>Production of neutrons using charged particle accelerators.</u>
The development of intense beams of charged particles of various energies: from several keV to several GeV, has opened the possibility of producing neutron beams at almost arbitrary energy up to several GeV. The problems to cope with are:

- the intensity of the neutron beam, which is mainly determined by the current the accelerator can give on the target, and by properties of the target: heat dissipation, the properties of the material at higher temperatures.

- the energy spectrum of the neutron beam.

The survey of the production of neutrons with accelerators will be divided in three groups:

i) accelerators up to 1 MeV

ii) accelerators up to 30 MeV

iii) accelerators producing higher energy particles.

2.3.1. <u>Accelerators up to 1 MeV</u>. Low energy accelerators are characterized by intense currents of charged particles, and they are reasonably inexpensive.

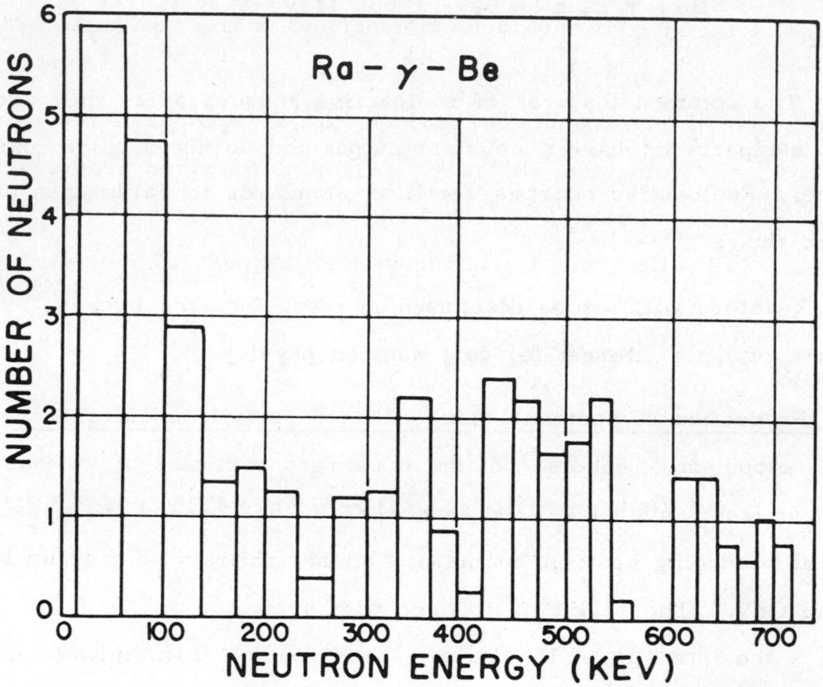

Fig. 6

Neutron spectrum from a Ra-γ-Be source (Eg 50)

Table 4a lists various reactions producing neutrons with the incident energy below 1 MeV. All the listed reactions, except the last one: $^{9}Be(\alpha, n)^{12}C$, produce a monoenergetic group of neutrons. At higher incident energy other neutron producing reactions become energetically possible on the same target. However, the thresholds for these competing reactions are considerably higher than 1 MeV.

The neutron beam in the experimental area even at these low bombarding energies is not monochromatic. The effects which cause the energy spread are:

1. the energy spread of the incident charged particle beam:
   i) as given by the accelerator,
   ii) dispersion in energy of the charged particles traversing the window (if any) of the neutron producing target,
   iii) Coulomb scattering of the charged particle beam in the target material.
2. the neutron producing target:
   i) energy loss in the target (finite thickness of the target material),
   ii) thermal motion of the target nucleus. This effect in most cases is negligible.
3. the geometrical conditions:
   i) angular divergence of the incident charged particle beam,
   ii) large solid angle subtended by the target on which a neutron induced reaction is studied
4. the environment
   i) neutrons generated in the source may be degraded in energy by passage through materials necessarily

placed between the source, the target and the detector,

ii) neutrons scattered from the surrounding material.

5. other reactions producing neutrons:

i) whenever the incident particle is a deuteron, the reaction $D(d,n)^3He$ is almost unavoidable.

ii) the reactions $^{12}C(d,n)^{13}N$ (Q = -0.28 MeV) and $^{13}C(d,n)^{14}N$ (Q = +5.32 MeV) can occur on the carbon contamination present in the system.

It is important to emphasize that in most of the existing neutron facilities of this category the quality of the energy spectrum of the neutrons has not been investigated carefully enough. Ordinarily one measured the proton spectrum emitted from the neutron bombardment of a polyethylene foil (containing C and H) and since the only energetically possible process producing protons is the n-p scattering the spectrum of protons reflects the components in the neutron beam having energy different from the nominal energy or impinging obliquely on the target. An additional test, which is aimed at separating the effect due to neutrons scattered from the environmental structure from other effects, consists in a coincidence measurement of a convenient reaction, e.g. Li(n,t) (see Fig. 7).

The intensity of neutrons of lower energy can be experimentally reduced in various ways:

i) careful design of the experimental facility so as to reduce the scattering from the surrounding material.

ii) shielding. However, an effective shielding has to be quite large and consequently leads to a large source-target separation.

iii) coincidence: neutron-associated particle can in principle be

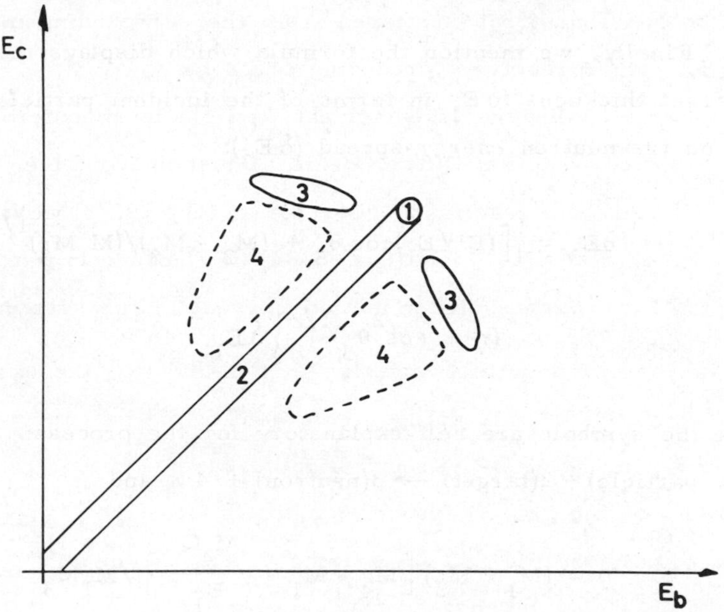

Fig. 7

Study of the quality of the incident neutron energy spectrum investigating the reaction A(n, b)c. Particles b and c emitted in directions θ_b and θ_c are detected in coincidence. The monoenergetic neutrons give group 1. Neutrons of lower energy, but still incident perpendicularly on the target give a group 2. Neutrons incident obliquely and having full energy yield groups 3, and those having lower energies groups 4.

very effective (see e.g. Mo 66a).

iv) time of flight of the incident neutron beam.

Finally, we mention the formula which displays the effect of the target thickness (δE_1 in terms of the incident particle energy loss) on the neutron energy spread (δE_3):

$$\delta E_3 = \left\{ \left[(E_3/E_1) \cos \theta_3 + (M_2 - M_3)/(M_1 M_3)^{1/2} (E_3/E_1)^{1/2} \right. \right.$$

$$\left. (\eta + \cos^2 \theta_3)^{1/2} \right\} \delta E_1$$

where the symbols are self explanatory for the process:
1(inc. particle) + 2(target) $\longrightarrow$ 3(neutron) + 4 and

$$\eta = (M_1 + M_2) \left[M_4 - M_1 + \frac{M_4 Q}{E_1} \right] / M_1 M_3$$

Of the reactions quoted in Table 4.a. the reaction $D(d,n)^3He$ and $T(d,n)^4He$ are the most frequently used. Table 5 gives the laboratory differential cross section at $\theta = 0°$ for the reaction $D(d,n)^3He$. Even at very low energy (0.1 - 0.2 MeV). this reaction is not isotropic in the c.m. system.

Due to the exceptionally large positive Q value the reaction $T(d,n)\alpha$ enjoys a privileged position among neutron producing reactions. The special feature of this reaction (see Table 4.a) is that it produces monoenergetic neutrons with energy as high as 20.7 MeV. Also, the neutron energy spread caused by the incident deuteron energy spread percentagewise decreases as the Q value increases. The high Q value makes the neutron energy relatively insensitive to the angle of emission. The additional feature of the $T(d,n)\alpha$ reaction which makes it particularly suitable for low energy accelerators is the J = 3/2+ resonance in ^{5}He which produces a peak cross reaction of 5 barns at 110 keV deuteron energy. The width of the resonance is about 140 keV.

TABLE 4

Neutron producing reactions

Reaction	Q(MeV)	Threshold	Competing reaction	Threshold of competing reaction (MeV)	Range of monoenergetic neutrons at 0°
a)					
$D(d,n)^{3}He$	+3.26		D(d,n)pd	4.45	2.45 - 7.70
$T(d,n)^{4}He$	+17.6		T(d,n)pT	3.71	14.0 - 20.7
			$T(d,n)n\,^{3}He$	4.99	
$^{12}C(d,n)^{13}N$	-0.28	0.33	$^{12}C(d,n)^{13x}N$	3.09	0.03 - 2.76
$^{13}C(\alpha,n)^{16}O$	+2.2		$^{13}C(\alpha,n)^{16x}O$	5.05	2.07 - 7.06
$^{9}Be(\alpha,n)^{12}C$	+5.71		$^{9}Be(\alpha,n)^{12x}C$	0	
b)					
$T(p,n)^{3}He$	-0.76	1.02	T(p,n)pd	8.4	0.3 - 7.58
$^{7}Li(p,n)^{7}Be$	-1.65	1.88	$^{7}Li(p,n)^{7x}Be$	2.4	0.1 - 0.65
$D(\gamma,n)p$	-2.22				
$^{9}Be(\gamma,,n)^{8}Be$	-1.66				

TABLE 5

Laboratory differential cross section at θ = 0° for the $D(d,n)^3He$ reaction (Ma 63)

E_D (in MeV)	Differential cross section (mb/sr)
0.156	4.30
0.206	6.33
0.466	16.24
1.96	44.80
3.02	57.53
5.80	81.78
8.15	89.43
10.4	94.88
12.2	99.38
13.8	100.94

Table 6 gives the laboratory differential cross section for the reaction $T(d,n)^4He$.

Below E_d = 0.4 MeV the c.m. differential cross section is isotropic.

The discussion about technology of targets is postponed to the end of 2.3.2.

Neutron generators based on low energy charged particle accelerators typically produce neutron yields of 10^9 - 10^{11} n/sec. One of the most intense 14 MeV neutron generators is the Berkeley generator (Fl 65) which yields up to 4×10^{13} n/sec using a 250 ma 250 keV deuteron beam on a water cooled 18 inch dia TiT target.

TABLE 6

Laboratory differential cross section at $\theta = 0^\circ$ for the $T(d,n)^4He$ reaction (Ma 63)

E_D (in MeV)	Differential cross section (mb/sr)
0.2	218 ± 22
0.5	57.9 ± 2.9
1.0	23.8 ± 1.2
2.0	15.0 ± 0.6
3.0	16.1 ± 0.6
4.0	20.7 ± 0.8
5.0	24.5 ± 1.0
6.0	25.8 ± 1.3
7.0	25.7 ± 1.3

2.3.2. Accelerators up to 30 MeV. The increase of the energy of the bombarding particle allows other neutron producing reactions (see Table 4b). However, monoenergetic neutron sources turn into non-monoenergetic sources, since many competing reactions become energetically possible (see Table 4, fourth and fifth columns). The range where the given reactions produce monochromatic neutrons is given in a sixth column in Table 4. Since a 4 MeV deuteron beam produces via the T-D process a 20.8 MeV neutron, one can see that conventional Van de Graaff accelerators represent a 14 - 21 MeV neutron facility. The conventional Van de Graaff would also produce neutrons from $E_n = 0$ to 7.7 MeV.

The competing reactions have been studied in the energy region of tandem accelerators and the results are shown in Figs. 8, 9, 10 and 11. The importance of various competing reactions is clearly demonstrated. To summarize: 1) already at $E_d = 10$ MeV the reaction D(d,n)pd gives as many neutrons as the reaction $D(d,n)^3He$; 2) already at $E_d = 5.5$ MeV the reactions $^3H(d,n)n^3He$ and $^3H(d,n)pT$ give more neutrons than the reaction $^3H(d,n)\alpha$; 3) at $E_p = 9$ MeV the $^7Li(p,n)^7Be^*$ yield becomes comparable to the $^7Li(p,n)^7Be$ yield.

The situation is more favorable only for the reaction $T(p,n)^3He$ where at $E_p = 13$ MeV the yield of "monoenergetic" neutrons is still six times larger than the neutron yield from breakup processes.

When planning a neutron facility, its purpose should be clearly defined, i.e. whether one is interested only in a total neutron yield, or one is concerned with the energy spectrum of the neutrons.

TABLE 7

The yield of 14 MeV neutrons and the yield of lower energy

Reaction	Yield Neutrons/sr-mA-s		Bombarding energy	Q (MeV)
	14 MeV neutrons	Lower energy neutrons		
$T(d,n)^4He$	1.25×10^{10}	none	0.2	+ 17.6
$D(d,n)^3He$	100×10^{10}	150×10^{10}	11.0	+ 3.26
$^7Li(p,n)^7Be$	17×10^{10}	40×10^{10}	16.0	- 1.65
$^7Li(d,n)^8Be$	0.7×10^{10}	4×10^{10}	1	+ 15
$^{12}C(d,n)^{13}N$	5.3×10^{10}	40×10^{10}	15	- 0.28

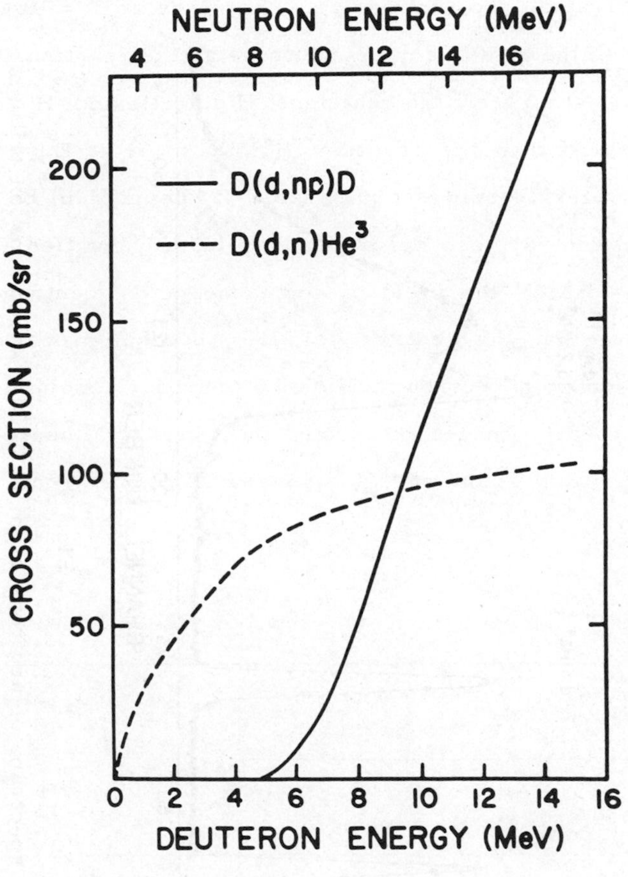

Fig. 8

Zero degree differential cross section for the production of neutrons from the D-D reaction (Ba 64)

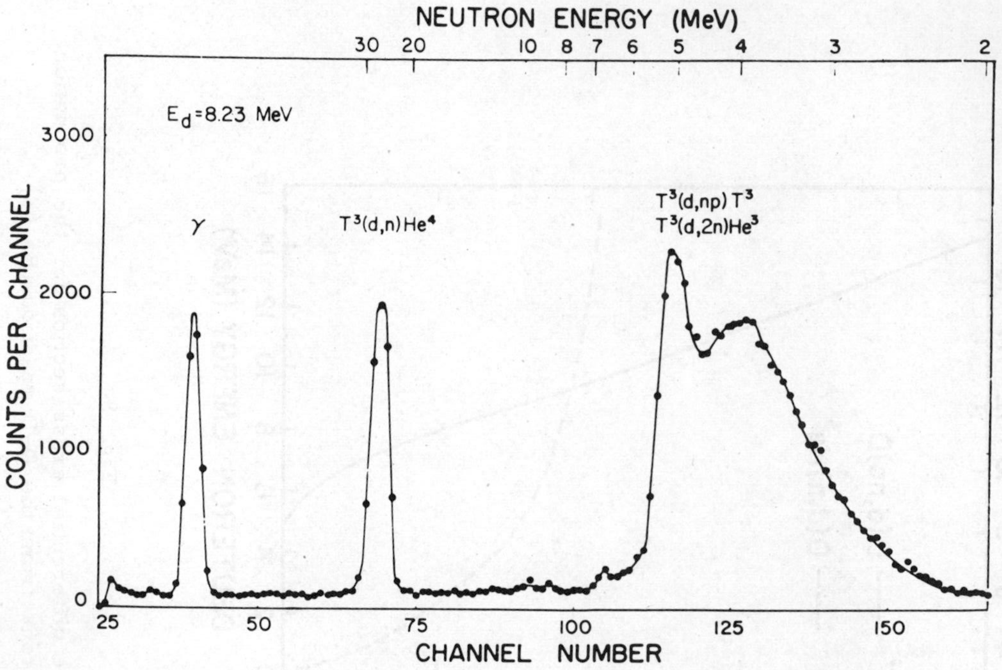

Fig. 9

Time spectrum of neutrons from 8.23 MeV deuterons on tritium (Wi 61)

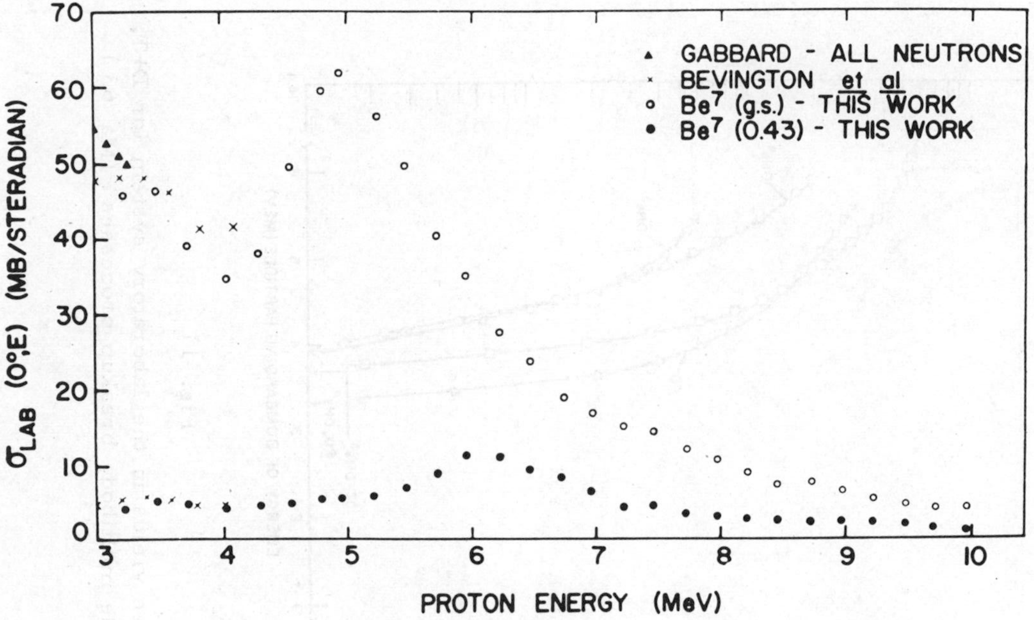

Fig. 10

Zero degree differential cross section for neutrons from ^7Li+p. The upper points refer to neutrons leaving ^7Be in the ground state, the lower to the formation of $^7Be^*$ (1st. excited state at 0.43 MeV) (Ba 64)

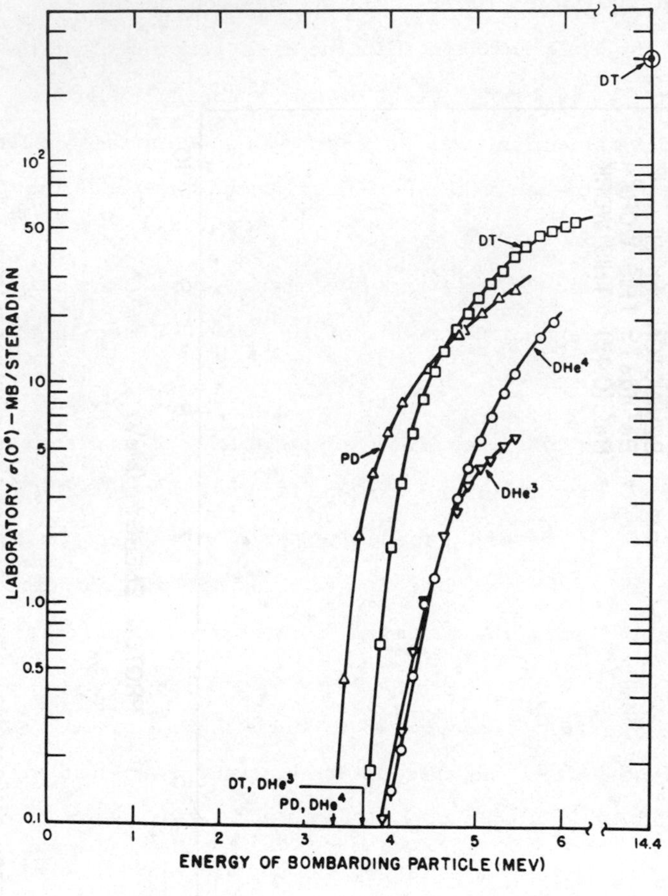

Fig. 11

Zero degree yields in the laboratory system for D+T, P+D, D+^{3}He multibody breakup processes (Ma 63).

Table 7 gives the yield of neutrons of a given energy (in this case 14 MeV) and the yield of lower energy neutrons. One sees that about 100 times more intense neutron beams can be obtained using the D-D reaction than the D-T reaction, but the price one has to pay is a large yield of lower energy neutrons.

The most convenient way to cope with non-monoenergetic neutron sources is to use a time-of-flight technique to define the energy of the neutron beam.

Tandem Van de Graaffs and low energy cyclotrons offer a possibility to produce neutron yields of $10^8 - 10^{11}$ n/sec in the neutron energy range from 2 to 25 MeV.

2.3.2a. Targets for the production of neutrons. The discussion will be limited to deuterium and tritium targets. Targets can be divided into solid, liquid and gaseous. For a given neutron producing reaction the greatest yield of neutrons per unit incident beam current is obtained when the target is composed of a pure target element rather than a chemical compound or a mixture. The yield of neutrons is inversely proportional to the stopping cross section associated with the atom and this determines the rang-list for example for deuterium targets: D_2, D_2O, TiD, ZrD, AuD.

In the construction of a target one should also consider: a) the heat dissipation problem and b) the amount of beam current which can be transmitted through a thin foil without causing a rupture of that foil. These factors seriously limit the usefulness of gaseous or liquid D_2 (and T_2) and heavy ice (D_2O) targets, and often make solid targets (hydrogen isotopes absorbed in metals) more appropriate.

A list of several types of deuterium and tritium targets follows:

i) D_2O ice: D_2O ice is formed by condensing D_2O vapor on a metal plate refrigerated with liquid nitrogen. When the temperature of the ice rises above -100°C, the target vaporizes relatively fast. Local heating of the ice target caused by the incident beam should be avoided. This can be done by defocussing the incident beam and by moving the spot where the beam impinges on the target. A high-yield D_2O ice target was reported (Do 55) which could stand 500 μa of 1 MeV deuterons and gave a continuous neutron yield of 10^{10} n/sec. The target thickness was approximately 20 microns. D_2O ice targets often contain massive materials near the neutron source and therefore produce many low energy neutrons.

It should be pointed out that D_2O ice targets though rather inconvenient for continuous neutron production could be very useful for a pulsed beam operation, where currents up to 10 ma could be employed.

T_2O ice targets were also considered, but the beta activity of tritium caused a rather rapid chemical descomposition.

ii) hydrogen isotopes absorbed in metals. Tritium and deuterium targets in operation are mostly T or D in zirconium or titanium deposited on copper, tungsten or gold. Recently (La 65, Re 64a) some rare earths, especially erbium, were used for the absorption of tritium.

These targets have an atomic ratio of about two hydrogen atoms to one zirconium (or Ti, or Er) atom. The impregnation of zirconium or titanium with hydrogen is usually carried out by heating the metal to about 400°C in an atmosphere of a hydrogen isotope. When allowed to cool, the metal absorbs hydrogen.

Evaporated films of rare earths metals can be maintained at

400 °C whilst still retaining the occluded gas in the ratio 1.8 : 1. The TiT and ZrT targets should be kept below 250 °C. Particular care has to be taken in order to assure adequate cooling. The standard design typically permits about 200 - 400 W dissipation.

iii) liquid targets. Liquid deuterium targets are commonly used in high energy neutron production. The density of liquid deuterium at 20.3°K is 0.169 g/cm^3.

A detailed description of liquid targets can be found in the original literature (e.g. Me 66a, Se 67). Fig. 12 shows the liquid deuterium target employed by Measday (Me 66a).

iv) gas targets. The main problem in gas targets is associated with the thin windows which have to withstand high temperatures. Frequently, the windows are cooled by a jet air and in some cases it was found desirable to cool the air to below 0 °C. The material of the window has to be chosen according to the specification of the target, e.g. high pressure, high heat dissipation, concern over multiple Coulomb scattering in the window.

Since all targets contain some material besides D or T, one should consider possible (d, n) reactions on this material. These reactions cause the production of neutrons of undesired energy. The use of a thin TiT target on a copper backing, for example, on an accelerator producing 10 MeV deuterons will obviously yield a large number of neutrons with an energy different from that of T-D neutrons.

The yields of neutrons and gamma rays produced by proton bombardment of various materials which can serve as target backings are shown in Fig. 13.

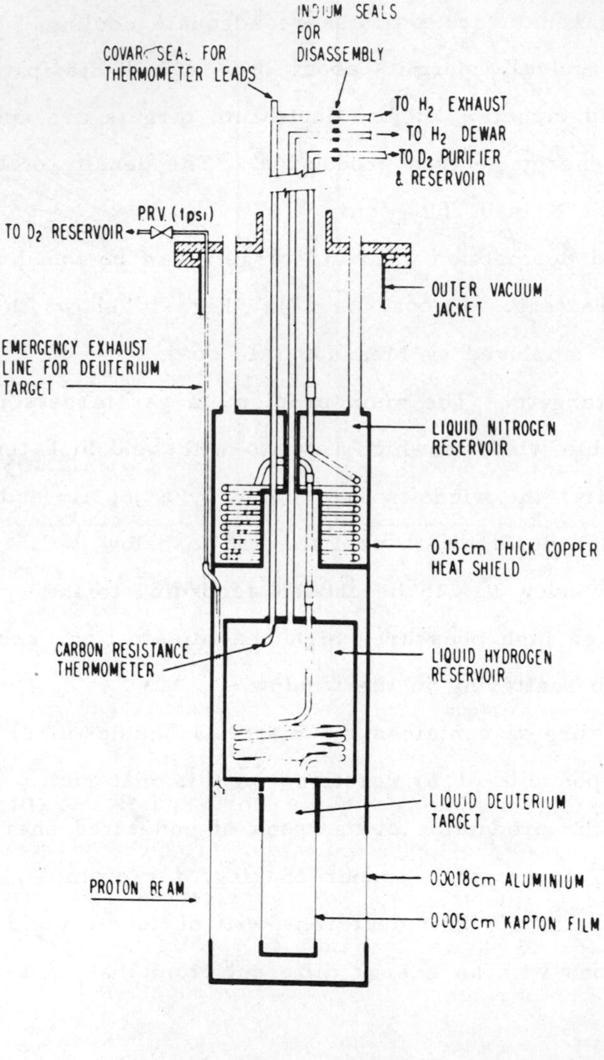

Fig. 12

Cryostat for liquid deuterium target. (Me`66 a)

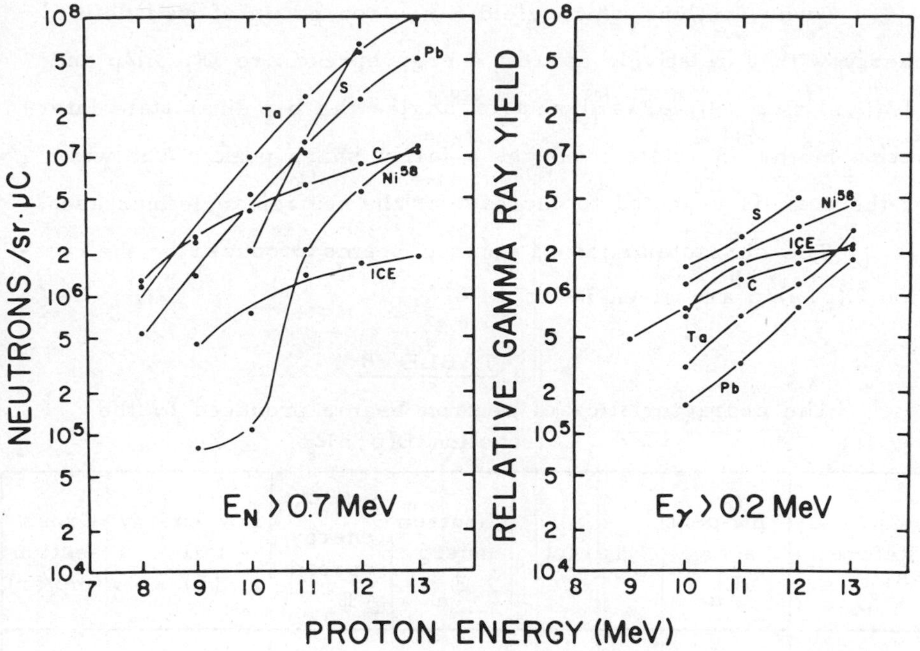

Fig. 13

Neutron and gamma ray yields from thick targets of various materials bombarded by protons (Ba 64)

2.3.3. Accelerators producing higher energy particles. At energies of 300 MeV and higher the neutron beams, produced via essentially any of the reactions discussed in the two previous subsections, have a large energy spread (typically about 20 - 30 %) and a low energy tail of intensity comparable to the main component.

The use of the time-of-flight technique to specify the incident neutron energy is unfortunately convenient only for neutron energies below about 150 - 200 MeV. For example, a 150 MeV neutron is travelling with a speed equal to one half the speed of light and the precision of the energy determination via time-of-flight is reduced.

At higher energies the method becomes inapplicable.

Two reactions which yield a neutron group of well defined energy with a relatively narrow energy spread are D(p, n)2p and ^{7}Li(p, n)^{7}Be. At forward neutron angles the p-p final state interaction in the ^1S_o state produces a fairly sharp peak. The width of the peak is expected to increase as the neutron angle increases.

The characteristics of neutron beams produced by the reaction D(p, n)2p are given in Table 8.

TABLE 8

The characteristics of neutron beams produced by the reaction D(p, n)2p

Reference	Incident energy E_p	Target	Neutron energy E_n	Neutron energy spread ΔE_n	Low energy tail (%)	Cross section (mb/sr)
La 60	740	liquid deuterium	710	14		
Pa 55	340	LiD (internal cyc. target	307	54		
Me 66a	158.5	liquid deuterium	152.5	6	(16 ± 3) %	
Ba 62	143				(13 ± 3) %	40
Me 66a	140	liquid deuterium		6	(32 ± 3) %	
Es 65	135					34 ± 9
Me 66a	115	liquid deuterium		11	(28 ± 3) %	
Me 66a	80	"		10	(19 ± 3) %	
Ba 65	50					
Ba 65	30				65 %	

The layout of the monoenergetic neutron beam facility developed at Harvard is shown in Fig. 14. The external beam of the 160 MeV synchrocyclotron, after passing through a degrader box (where if desired its energy can be reduced) and a 20° bending magnet, impinges on a liquid deuterium target. The beam of neutrons emitted at 0° goes through a collimator in the experimental area, while the proton beam which losses about 5 - 7 MeV in the liquid deuterium target (4.9 MeV for 160 MeV protons and 6.6 for 100 MeV protons) is deflected and stopped in a beam stop.

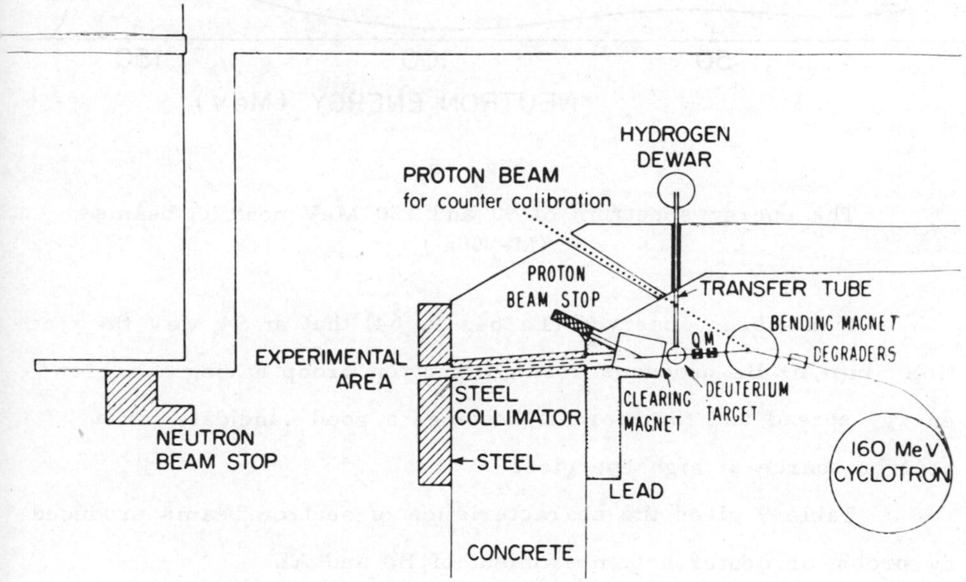

Fig. 14

Layout of the monoenergetic neutron beam facility at Harvard (Me 66a)

The neutron yield is determined by the proton current from the accelerator; for 3×10^{10} p/sec striking the target a flux of 4×10^4 n/sec is obtained. Fig. 15 shows the energy spectra of 90 and 150 MeV neutron beams.

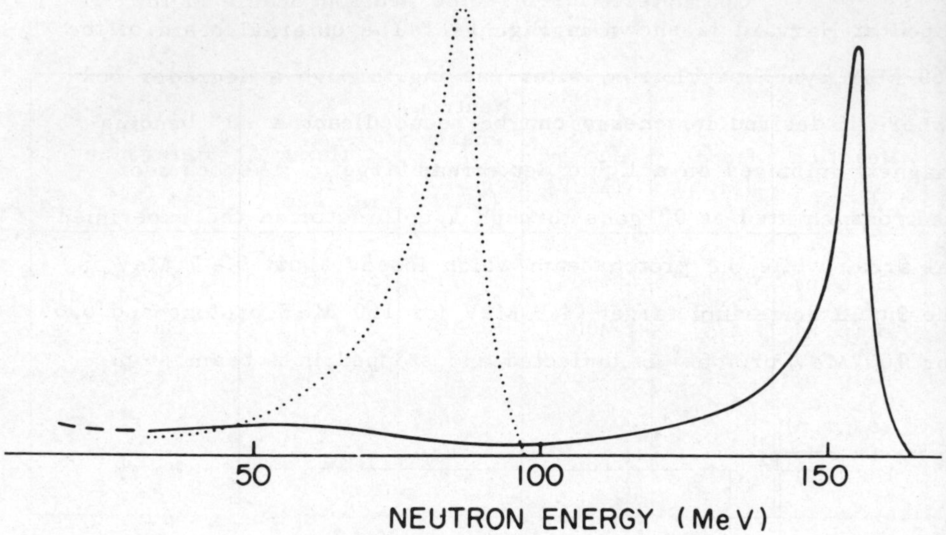

Fig. 15

The energy spectrum of 90 and 150 MeV neutron beams
(Me 66a)

It has been observed (La 64, Ri 64) that at 94 MeV the reaction $^{7}Li(p,n)^{7}Be$ produces a single neutron group having a narrow energy spread and therefore it becomes a good candidate for a neutron source at high energies.

Table 9 gives the characteristics of neutron beams produced by proton or deuteron bombardment of Be and Al.

TABLE 9

Characteristics of some neutron beams in the energy range 100 - 700 MeV

Reaction	Incident energy (MeV)	Neutron energy (MeV)	Neutron energy spread (MeV)	Neutron flux cm^{-2} sec^{-1}	Reference
$^{9}Be(p,n)$	680	600	90	2×10^{4}	Ki 59
$^{9}Be(p,n)$	427	400	35	2×10^{5}	Ha 54
$^{9}Be(p,n)$	350	260	120	$10^{4} - 10^{5}$	Pa 55
$^{27}Al(p,n)$	140	135	90	3×10^{4}	
$^{9}Be(d,n)$	180	90	30	-	Ha 49

The possibility of using high energy and high current charged particle beams makes it possible to conceive extremely intense neutron sources e.g. intensities higher than 10^{16} n/sec. Such sources can favourably compete in intensity and in cost with reactors of similar performance, as far as the irradiation and activation purpose is concerned, and give the additional facility of high energy neutrons. An example of this type of facility is the intense neutron generator (ING) under consideration at Chalk River (Ba 66). It is proposed to use a three-stage separated orbit cyclotron producing a 65 ma beam of 1 GeV protons. In planning a neutron facility an important factor is the heat penalty or the heat output per neutron. On that basis the spallation process of a heavy element by a high energy proton is the most convenient reaction. The ING project intends to use the Bi(p, xn) spallation process, the proton impinging on molten lead-bismuth eutectic. The expected polyenergetic neutron yield is 9×10^{18} n/s. With the target assembly set in a D_2O moderator, the thermal neutron flux is expected to be $10^{16}/cm^2$ sec at 12 cm from the target. The expected energy spectrum of neutrons from ING is given in Fig. 16. The authors claim that it is possible to build the same type of facility with the intensity of neutron flux increased by a factor 100.

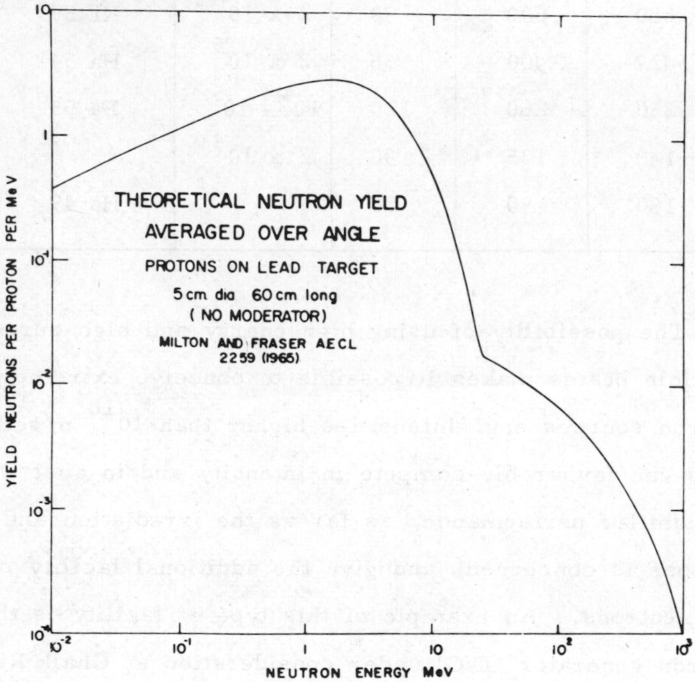

Fig. 16

Theoretical neutron spectrum from ING (Ba 66).

2.4. Nuclear explosion. Nuclear explosion produces neutrons the energy spectrum of which depends upon the type of nuclear bomb and the material used.

Small nuclear explosion devices of the fission type have a

degraded fission spectrum with peak intensity around 1 MeV.

Thermonuclear devices produce 14 MeV neutrons in addition to fission neutrons.

The moderator can be designed to enhance the neutron flux in some particular energy region. The velocity of the moderator can be controlled by the lead shielding. The thermalized neutrons are emitted from the moving moderator, and thus the lowest neutron energy is determined by the moderator velocity (e.g. in the Petrel experiment 18 eV corresponding to the moderator velocity of 5.5 cm/μsec.)

The nuclear explosion produces $\sim 10^{24}$ neutrons per burst. Pulse duration is about 0.1 μsec. In many ways the nuclear explosion as a neutron generator is similar to the pulsed beam time-of-flight work performed with accelerators. The total amount of neutrons produced per year from nuclear explosions (assuming 1 or 2 explosions per year) is larger than the one produced by the accelerators in operation.

Due to the high neutron flux in an explosion, the detection of nuclear particles differs from the methods used with other neutron sources, e.g. individual events cannot be recorded, and thus, particle identification and coincidence techniques are not applicable.

The layout of a typical experiment using a nuclear explosion neutron source is given in Fig. 17. The neutron flight path extends from the moderator to the surface of the ground. It consists of an evacuated pipe with suitable baffles. Below the surface, one or more beams are formed by collimators.

The beam of neutrons can be scattered from a target, but also, since the intensity of neutrons produced in an explosion is 10^{24} neutrons/burst, which is comparable to the number of nuclei in a typical target, one can perform colliding beam experiments.

The setup for various experiments is mounted in a tower. When the explosion occurs, neutrons travel their flight path in a few msec and about 100 msec later a mild shock reaches the surface of the earth. A few minutes afterwards a crater forms and the tower collapses. All equipment that must be saved is pulled away automatically.

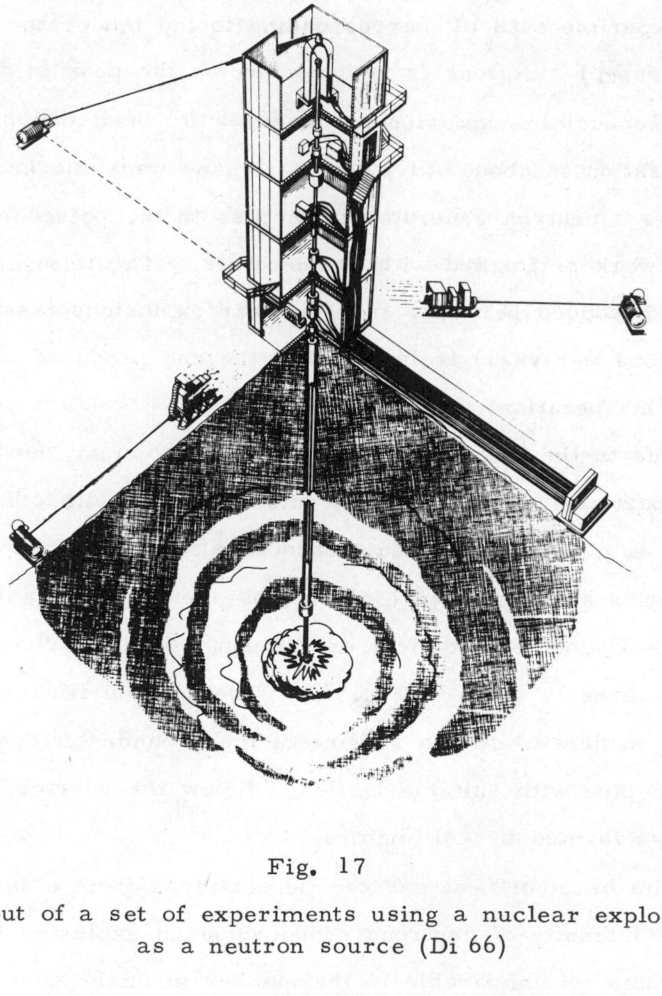

Fig. 17

Layout of a set of experiments using a nuclear explosion as a neutron source (Di 66)

2.5. Neutron in the stars. The cosmic abundance of chemical elements is given in Fig. 18. The theory that elements are made from hydrogen by successive numerous capture of neutrons had to be given up because of the absence of stable A = 5 and A = 8 nuclei. The present day theory of nucleosynthesis attributes the production of elements up to A = 65 to charged particle reactions in the stars. These reactions can be divided into two groups:

1. Capture reactions when the rate of capture is much larger than the rate of photodisintegration of the compound nucleus. This group of reactions is responsible for the peak in abundance at small A. The high negative slope of the peak reflects the fact that capture reactions are governed by Coulomb effects.

2. Equilibrium reactions in which the rate of capture and the rate of disintegration are equal. As predicted by statistical thermodynamics, the abundance distribution is dominated by stability effects and this explains the peak at iron.

Heavier elements are made by neutron capture processes. Heavy elements can be divided into three groups: 1) elements at the bottom of the valley of nuclear stability ("s group"); 2) on the neutron rich side ("r group"); 3) on the proton rich side ("p group").

Successive neutron capture leads to a beta radioactive isotope. If the neutron capture lifetime is much longer than the lifetime for beta decay, one will stick to the bottom of the stability valley ("s element"). If, on the contrary, $t(\beta) \gg t(n, \gamma)$, one forms "r elements". If one plots the product of the "s" abundances with neutron capture cross sections at 25 keV as a function of A, one finds that although each individual curve has a highly marked structure, the resulting curve is smooth. This is the best argument in favor of the natural occurrence of neutron capture reactions, which indicates that there are neutrons in the stars.

The formation of "s elements" where the neutron capture time is longer than beta decay, implies that neutron densities not much in excess of 10^{10} n/cm^3 are involved.

Processes responsible for "r elements" buildup and elements with Z > 82 require neutron densities of 10^{20} n/cm^3.

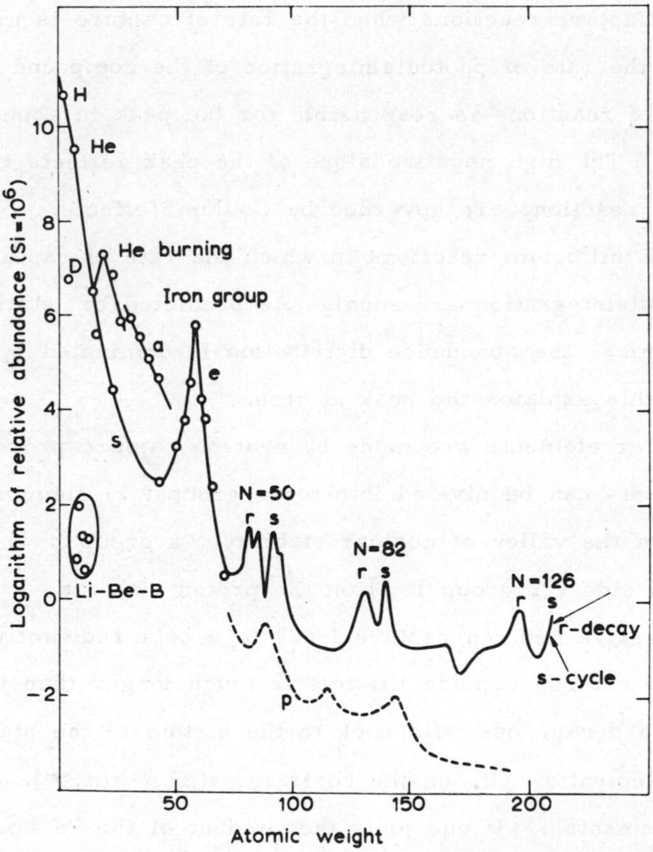

Fig. 18

Schematic curve of the atomic abundances as a function of the atomic weight

An additional argument in favor of the existence of neutrons in the stars is the existence of nuclear reactions in the normal course of stellar evolution that produce neutrons.

No important sources of neutrons seem to occur during the hydrogen burning stage.

In helium burning stars, the sequence

$$^{14}N(\alpha,\gamma)^{18}F(\beta\nu)^{18}O(\alpha,\gamma)^{22}Ne(\alpha,n)^{25}Mg \quad Q = 482\ keV$$

$$\hookrightarrow (\alpha,\gamma)^{26}Mg \quad Q = 0$$

becomes important. Another source is $^{12}C(p,\gamma)^{13}N(\beta\nu)^{13}C(\alpha,n)^{16}O$. Also, $^{12}C(^{12}C,n)^{23}Mg$ $Q = -2.602$ MeV, and $^{16}O(^{16}O,n)^{31}S$ (exothermic).

3. PHILOSOPHY OF THE APPROACH TO THE DETECTION OF REACTION PRODUCTS IN NEUTRON INDUCED PROCESSES

The measurement of the neutron induced reaction differs from that of the charged particle induced reaction in two important aspects:

1. The intensity of the incident beam is typically a few orders of magnitude in favor of the charged particles.

2. One can easily and effectively shield the detecting devices from the incident charged particle beam. The same does not hold for neutron induced processes. Often, any detector is itself a target for the neutron beam, and one has to discriminate these events from those coming from the actual target under investigation.

These are the main reasons for which the measurements of neutron induced reactions represent a difficult task.

The low neutron intensity results in performing experiments with poor geometry: the sizes of the target and the detectors are comparable to their relative distances.

The problem of counter irradiation has been coped with in various ways:

1. Using detectors which are composed of elements characterized by negative Q values for neutron induced processes and by a small cross section for those neutron induced reactions which are energetically possible.

2. Thin counters. The thickness of the counter is just enough to stop the particle under investigation.

3. Counter telescopes: a set of counters in coincidence.

4. Detecting devices which have the property that the reaction events occurring in them can be reliably discriminated against by some special criterium (e.g. in ionographic emulsions one can specify that only tracks which begin at the surface should be counted thus eliminating almost all reaction products induced by neutrons in the plate material).

5. Coincidence measurement with the associated particle in the neutron generating reaction provides a reasonably well defined cone of neutrons.

6. Pulse shape discrimination, and

7. Time-of-flight techniques.

The philosophy of the approach to the detection of reaction products in neutron induced processes should incorporate successful solutions to the low incident beam intensity and detector irradiation and besides should satisfy all general conditions imposed on any nuclear detector.

Various types of detectors have been used in neutron physics. The list of detection devices that are used in many laboratories and in many experiments includes:

1. Counter telescopes composed of proportional counters and/or solid state counters and/or scintillation counters.

2. Time-of-flight spectrometers with the timing signal either taken from the accelerator, or from the associated particle in the neutron generating reaction, or from the associated particle produced in the reaction under consideration.

4. Measurements of radioactive decays.

Several other techniques were successfully applied to various specific problems. Some of these techniques are:

1. Cloud chambers
2. Thin detectors
3. Magnetic spectrometers
4. Bubble chambers.

In these lectures we will discuss only i) counter telescopes for the study of (n, charged particle) reactions; ii) detection in correlation measurements.

3.1. Counter telescopes. A telescope consisting of two counters in coincidence, a thin one used to determine the energy loss of a particle which passes through it (this counter will be called ΔE counter) and a thick one in which the same particle is finally stopped (this counter is called E counter), represents a well-known general method for the identification of charged particles. While in the work with charged particle beams the use of such a telescope is sufficient, an additional counter is required if the study of neutron induced reactions is intended. This is due to the neutron irradiation of detectors causing a high counting rate in both counters even in the absence of a target. This results in a high random coincidence rate which disturbs the measurements. Also a large number of real coincidences is produced, each detector acting as target for the other one.

A way of reducing the random coincidence rate is to insert a third counter in the telescope. This third counter should be thinner than the ΔE counter and then it is placed between the target and the ΔE counter. This counter in coincidence with the two others considerably reduces the rate of random coincidences. Furthermore this counter must be constructed so as to give a small yield of the charged particles of interest, since at least a part of it acts as a target.

The material that is in between the neutron source and the target under investigation is also exposed to neutron irradiation and thus represent an additional target. Two approaches are used to solve this difficulty:

a. Introducing a counter between the target and the neutron source, which is in anticoincidence with the other counters of the telescope. Naturally, a part of that counter would unavoidably act itself as a target.

b. Using between the source and the target a material in which neutron irradiation produces a low yield of charged particles (e.g. lead, graphite, gold).

Sometimes, both remedies have been used in a telescope.

A schematic drawing of a counter telescope is given in Fig. 19. If the experiment is performed without any shielding, so that each counter in the telescope is exposed to neutron irradiation, then counter ΔE_1 and counter E can act as potential targets. Provided that the particle identification information is given by detector ΔE_2

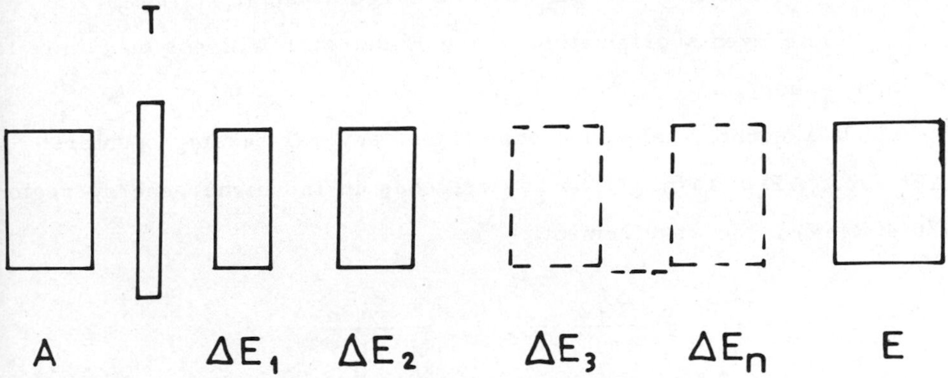

Fig. 19

Counter telescope, schematic diagram. A is the counter in front of the target (T), which is in anticoincidence with the ΔE_1, ΔE_2 ..... E. ΔE_1, ΔE_2 and ΔE_3 .....ΔE_n (if they are included) are transmission counters. E is the counter where the particle finally stops.

alone (or ΔE_2, ΔE_3 .....ΔE_n) these events cannot be distinguished from normal events occurring in the target. (The assumption is made that the energy of the particle produced in the E counter and going backward is not high enough to penetrate into the A counter and trigger the anticoincidence). In principle this problem is handled by requiring an identification pulse from both ΔE_1 and ΔE_2 counters. The relationship between ΔE_1 and ΔE_2 signals is $\Delta E_1 = (t_1/t_2)\Delta E_2$ where t_1 and t_2 are respective counter thicknesses, and ΔE_1 and ΔE_2 are corresponding energy losses, and therefore, corresponding pulse heights. Only those events which satisfy the above relationship within the limits imposed by the Landau spread are real events that occurred in the target. The ΔE_1 - ΔE_2 pairs which fall outside the specified region should be rejected. They belong to either random coincidences, or to events originating in the ΔE_1 counter (in this case $\Delta E_1 < (t_1/t_2)\Delta E_2$ or in the E counter (then ΔE_1 can be larger than $(t_1/t_2)\Delta E_2$).

Some events originating in the E detector will not be eliminate by this technique.

If a counter telescope consists of several passing counters: $\Delta E_1 \ldots\ldots \Delta E_n$, as might be advantageous in the higher energy region (20-40 MeV), the requirement

$$\frac{\Delta E_1}{t_1} = \frac{\Delta E_2}{t_2} = \ldots\ldots = \frac{\Delta E_n}{t_n}$$

can be imposed.

This technique is successful as long as the ΔE_1 counter is such that it provides a fairly narrow Landau distribution for a group of particles of a given energy. The implication of this is that the counter ΔE_1 is reasonably thick (i.e. comparable to ΔE_2). An opposite approach consists in making ΔE_1 as thin as possible. The function of ΔE_1 is then only to trigger the multiple coincidence and the requirements on its Landau distribution are not too stringent. (One should be sure that the trigger is caused by the actual event and not by the noise).

The total amount of material of the counters $\Delta E_1 + \ldots + \Delta E_n$ imposes a limit on the lowest energy particle from the target that one can detect. The detection of low energy particles is obviously accomplished with a minimum set of counters. One approach is to design a telescope specialized for low energy work, where all counters are very thin. An arrangement that has been used consists of four counters:

$\bar{A} - \Delta E_1 - \Delta E_2 - \bar{E}$, where bars indicate the anticoincidence operation, and the actual event, therefore, passes only through ΔE_1 and is stopped in ΔE_2.

The counter telescope should be designed so that the amount of material, which is not a target, seen by the detectors is minimum, and preferably covered with lead, graphite or gold.

It has been suggested that the width of the Landau distribution can be reduced by choosing the smallest of Δ_i (i = 1, 2, ...) signals. The other alternative would be to add the signals $\sum_1 \Delta E_i$. These possibilities have been considered, but it was found that they do not help in improving the design of a telescope.

Counter telescopes that have been successfully used in many experiments are listed in Table 10. Various telescopes can be grouped in two ways:

i) according to the type of the E detector

ii) according to the type of the ΔE detectors.

i) Two types of E detectors have been used: solid state detectors which are distinguished by excellent energy resolution, and CsI(Tl) detectors which have a considerably poorer energy resolution. The overall energy resolution is composed of three main effects: E-detector energy resolution, target thickness and incident neutron beam energy resolution. For solid state detectors the E-detector resolution is negligible, and the overall energy resolution is typically $\sim$450 keV, but a better resolution ($\sim$300 keV) could be obtained without having to use unreasonably thin targets. For CsI(Tl) detectors, the energy resolution of which is typically $\sim$3% for 12 MeV particles (i.e. 360 keV), the overall energy resolution becomes about 600 - 700 keV.

TABLE 10

Counter telescopes used in neutron physics

Anticoincidence counter	ΔE_1 counter	ΔE_2 counter	ΔE_3 counter	E counter	Ref.
CO_2 proportional	CO_2 proportional		CO_2 proportional	CsI(Tl)	Ku61
	surface barrier		surface barrier	surface barrier	La63
	scintillation		scintillation	scintillation	Va64
CO_2 proportional	CO_2 proportional		CO_2 proportional	surface barrier	Co64
	CO_2 proportional		surface barrier	surface barrier	An66a
H_2 proportional	H_2 proportional		H_2 proportional	CsI(Tl)	Re67
	proportional	proportional	proportional	surface barrier	Ba67
	gas scintillator		gas scintillator	CsI(Tl)	De67

ii) Two types of ΔE detectors have been used: gas and non-gas. The features of the gas detectors are;

a) the uniformity of the absorbers in front of the E detector.

b) detectors are equally thin in all directions.

Two types of telescopes will be compared:

1. A telescope consisting of three CO_2 proportional counters and a CSI(Tl) counter (Ku 61). (Hencefo th it will be called gas telescope).

2. A telescope consisting of surface barrier detectors (La 63). (Henceforth: semiconductor telescope).

Both telescopes were used for several years at the Institute "R. Bošković" by the same group of physicists in numerous measurements of energy spectra and angular distributions.

The ΔE_1 and ΔE_2 counters in the gas telescope are not of equal size. ΔE_2 is constructed to give an optimum resolution necessary for a discrimination of particles. In order to present the smallest possible target to incident neutrons, the ΔE_1 counter is quite small (its active length is 3 cm compared to 12.5 cm for the ΔE_2 counter). For a pressure of 6 - 10 cm Hg of CO_2 the resolution of the ΔE_1 counter is $\sim 40\%$ for 12.8 MeV deuterons. Of course, the resolution becomes better for lower energy particles.

The qualities of the gas telescope are:

1. Good particle discrimination. The spectrum of energy losses in the ΔE_2 counter with a resolution of $\sim 25\%$ for 12.8 MeV deuterons, allows a discrimination between protons and deuterons, as well as between deuterons and tritons of the order of 1:1000.

2. A relatively wide range of energies of detected particles is covered: e.g. from 16 MeV to 3 MeV for protons.

3. The possibility of changing the thickness of the ΔE_1 and ΔE_2 counters in a limited range by changing the pressure of the gas. Successful operation was achieved in the range from 4 to 16 cm Hg of CO_2.

4. The low noise of proportional counters which is 5 - 10 keV after the preamplifier stage. This is a very important quality which enables one to obtain very good ΔE spectra even when energy losses are quite small. The energy lost by a proton of 14 MeV in our ΔE_2 counter is only ~ 60 keV. In fact the broadening of the spectra of energy loss for a particle of a given energy stems mostly from the statistical fluctuations in the number of created ion pairs, so that the influence of electric noise is negligible.

5. The practically unlimited life of proportional and scintillation counters in the neutron flux.

6. The size and thicknesses of either counter are not limited by technological considerations.

7. The low background of the arrangement when irradiated by neutrons. The inherent background of the telescope is due to those materials in the telescope which, in spite of the coincidence system, act as secondary targets. The main secondary target is the gas with which the ΔE_1 counter is filled. The use of the gas CO_2 is very convenient owing to large negative Q values for neutron induced reactions in ^{12}C and ^{16}O and to the reasonably small $^{16}O(n,d)$ and $^{16}O(n,p)$ cross sections (Pa 64).

As seen from Table 11 only the low energy parts of the spectra are hampered by greater background.

The gas telescope in connection with a two-dimensional multichannel analyzer has proved to be suitable for measuring cross sections of the order of 0.1 mb/sr when the energy of detected particles is higher than 6 MeV. At lower energies the lowest detectable cross section both for protons and deuterons begins gradually to increase and reaches a value of 0.8 mb/sr at the energy of 4 MeV. If one intends to study the energy region below 5 MeV it is essential that the ΔE_1 counter be thin.

8. The low cost.

Besides the good properties listed above the work with a gas telescope is limited by some disadvantages we would like to stress:

1. The variable pulse delay from the proportional counters due to the finite transit time necessary for electrons to reach the central wire. In telescope (Ku 61) this delay is of the order of 1 μs, which limits the time resolution of the coincidence unit to the microsecond region. The slow coincidence limits the maximum neutron flux one can use in measurements. The measurements are made with a yield of $\sim 2 \times 10^9$ neutrons/sec with a neutron source-target distance of 10 cm.

2. The relatively poor resolution of the scintillation crystal.

3. The relative position of the target and the counters is closely related to the desired performances. This makes it difficult to change the geometry.

4. The dependence of the light output of the scintillation crystal on the kind of charged particles detected.

5. The sensitivity of the response of the proportional counters to slight variations of the applied high voltage and to small admixtures of impurities in the counter gas. This necessitates frequent checking of the positions of the characteristic peaks in the ΔE_1, ΔE_2 and E-counters. These checks are made in 2-3 hour intervals replacing the target under investigation by a target convenient for normalization, e.g. a target containing deuterium or hydrogen and taking spectra of recoil particles (e.g. deuterons or protons) in each of the three coincident counters.

In the last few years semiconductor detectors have found a wide field of application in particle spectrometry owing to their good energy resolution and compactness.

In our semiconductor telescope, the ΔE_1 counter had a thickness of 25 μ while the ΔE_2 counter was usually $\sim 50\ \mu$ thick. The E detector was made of a silicon wafer ~ 1 mm thick, depleted to $\sim 800\ \mu$. All the detectors had a 1 cm^2 active area and were of the surface barrier type.

The qualities of a semiconductor telescope are:

1. The resolution: the energy resolution obtainable with thick large area semiconductor detectors ranges to ~ 20 keV, which practically means that the E-counter resolution becomes an almost negligible factor in the overall energy resolution of the experimental arrangement.

2. Compactness of these detectors. Easy changes in the geometrical setup are possible.

3. Pulse height stability. Connecting the detectors to appropriate charge sensitive preamplifiers the pulse height does not depend upon small bias variations -provided the depletion layer is thick enough to stop the detected particles.

4. Linear response as a function of energy (certainly in the energy region of interest) which is equal for all kinds of particles.

5. Fixed relations between the energy loss and the collected charge. This makes it easy to sum the pulses of two or more detectors, contrary to the situation in proportional counters where the charge multiplication depends on several factors sometimes difficult to control.

6. The possibility to vary the depletion region within certain

limits. The range is limited by two factors:

i) the smallest bias necessary to have a good charge collection. The necessary field is ~ 2000 V/cm.

ii) The highest applicable bias.

7. Fast charge collection. This makes the use of a fast coincidence circuit possible.

8. The low noise level of the E detector.

Inconvenient properties of silicon counters in such arrangements can be summed up as follows:

1. The noise level of these semiconductor detectors is much higher than that of gas proportional counters. The typical noise figure was 70 keV for the 25 μ detector which was depleted to ~ 20 μ. This noise is due partially to the thermal noise component which is proportional to the square root of the absolute temperature and the detector capacitance. The thermal noise energy equivalent for a 20 μ detector at room temperature is about 35 keV. Other computable sources of noise give much lower values, so that one can attribute a considerable fraction of the measured noise to the "excess noise" which can be assigned to the nature of electrodes or to the surface treatment which the detector has undergone. One must bear in mind that not only the resolution is affected by the noise r.m.s. value but that the maximum noise amplitude conditions the triggering of the coincidence. For this reason one must allow the particles to lose more energy in the semiconductor ΔE counters than in the proportional ones. In the case of the semiconductor telescope we used minimum energy losses which were 4 times greater than those in the gas telescope. The resolution of the ΔE_2 counter coming from noise sources was measured to be ~ 50 keV.

2. Inconvenient Q values for (n, charged particle) reactions in silicon. Q values for (n, p) and (n, d) reactions in silicon are such that a larger energy region is obstructed by protons and deuterons from the ΔE_1 counter than is the case when a CO_2 counter is used as the ΔE_1 counter. The cross sections and the Q values for (n, p), (n, d), (n, ^{3}He) and (n, alpha) reactions on ^{16}O, ^{12}C and ^{28}Si are listed in Table 11. In view of the very high cross section for the (n, p) reaction and the forward peaked angular distribution it is obvious that silicon is not a suitable material for the ΔE_1 counter.

TABLE 11

Element	Reaction	Q-value (MeV)	σ_{total} (mb)	Ref.
^{28}Si	(n, p)	- 3.857	250	Ga 62
^{28}Si	(n, d)	- 9.372		
^{28}Si	(n, α)	- 2.656		
^{12}C	(n, p)	- 12.586		
^{12}C	(n, d)	- 13.731		
^{12}C	(n, α)	- 5.704		
^{16}O	(n, p)	- 9.625	35	Jo 63
^{16}O	(n, d)	- 9.886	15	Li 52
^{16}O	(n, α)	- 2.215		
^{12}C	(n, ^{3}He)	- 19.5		
^{16}O	(n, ^{3}He)	- 14.6		

The use of a silicon ΔE_1 counter increases the minimum detectable (n, p) cross section to a value of ~0.5 mb/sr in the region where cross section of 0.1 mb/sr can be measured with a gas telescope. The minimum detectable (n, d) cross section is ~ 0.2 mb/sr.

3. The limited life of the detectors in the neutron flux. After a dose of $\sim 10^{13}$ neutrons the detectors rapidly lose their primary electrical characteristics, which requires the relatively frequent replacement of the detectors, specially of the E-detector. That is easy but expensive.

4. The overall quantity of the material of both the ΔE counters is greater than that of their counterparts in the gas telescope, which makes the ΔE counters have a greater counting rate, thus increasing the random coincidence rate.

5. The high cost.

The comparison between the two types of telescopes leads to the following conclusions:

1. Particle discrimination is about the same in both telescopes.

2. If the energy resolution is a primary concern and particularly if resolution better than 600 keV is needed, one should use a semiconductor telescope.

3. The semiconductor telescope has a higher background, at least unless one operates with a considerable faster coincidence. The use of nanosecond coincidence is certainly a possibility, but it has not been investigated in practice in neutron physics. As an example of background problems let us quote the results obtained for the gas-gas-CsI(Tl) telescope (Ku 61) and for the gas-gas surface barrier telescope (Ba 67). The ratio of the background (measured with a graphite or gold target, which is equivalent to a

"no target" measurement) in (Ku 61) relative to (Ba 67) is $\sim 1/6$ to 1/10.

4. The geometry of the telescope is essentially well specified when one decides on the angular resolution coupled with the time one is able to spend to do the measurement. The easy changes in the geometrical setup for a semiconductor telescope become of secondary importance.

5. The counter telescope consisting of a thin proportional counter (ΔE_1) and two semiconductor counters (ΔE_2 and E) combines some essential qualities of both types of telescopes. Such combined telescopes have been used, but in a regime of slow triple coincidence. A modification which uses a fast coincidence between the solid state detectors and a slow one for the gas counter might bring an additional improvement. Another alternative is the telescope: gas scintillator, two solid state detectors.

The telescopes discussed above were used up to about E_n = 22 MeV. The use at higher neutron energies e.g. 30 - 100 MeV will be faced with a number of problems:

1. There are no materials which have convenient Q values and cross sections for (neutron, charged particle) reactions. This fact affects both counters and the construction of the "wall" (housing) of the telescope. Hydrogen can be used to fill proportional counters in cases when one is primarily interested in observing ^{3}He and α, and may be t.

2. For high energy particles (50 MeV and up) the reactions in the E counter cause a tail associated with each group of particles. The tail extends into a region of lower E, but has the same ΔE as the main group has. This phenomenon could spoil the particle

discrimination. The quality of the particle discrimination could still be kept as good as at lower energies, if instead of an E counter a series of E_1', E_2' ... E_n' is introduced.

In concluding this subsection on counter telescopes it is important to emphasize that the typical angular resolution used so far (essentially determined by the counting rate requirement) is $\Delta\theta \approx$ 5° - 10°. Fig. 20 shows an arrangement under investigation aimed at improving $\Delta\theta$. The arrangement employs position sensitive detectors, and the angular resolution depends only on the size of the neutron source (Ja 67).

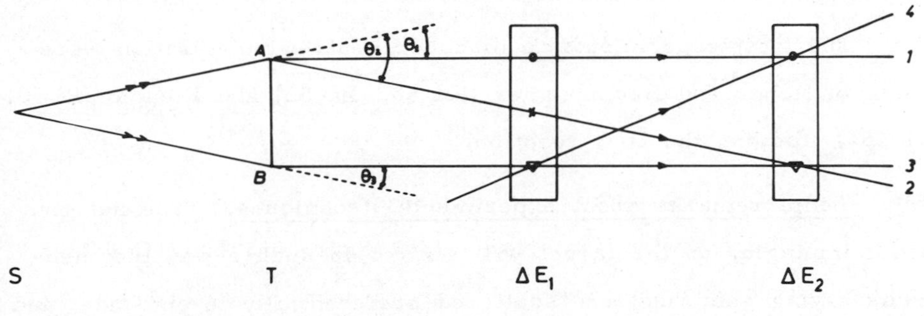

Fig. 20

Schematic drawing of a counter telescope using position sensitive detectors. The neutron source is assumed to be a point source. Neutrons impinging on any point of a target T can cause a reaction, and the trajectory of the emitted particle is determined by two numbers in counters ΔE_1 and ΔE_2. E.g. trajectory 1 has to originate at A and it is the emission of a given particle at angle θ_1. Trajectory 4 corresponds to reactions in the counters.

4. POLARIZATION OF NEUTRONS*

Neutrons produced in reactions listed in Table 4 are in general polarized even when neither the incident beam nor the target are polarized. The polarization of neutrons is a result of spin-orbit coupling in nuclear reactions.

The fact that the neutrons from the D-D reactions are polarized was pointed out already in 1948 by Wolfenstein (Wo 49).

The polarization of fast neutrons is commonly detected employing elastic scattering as an analyzer. Schwinger showed in 1946 (Sc 46) that the scattering of neutrons by ^{4}He demonstrates a large spin-orbit splitting in the p-state. ^{4}He can be used as a polarization analyzer. Similarly, the scattering from ^{12}C and ^{16}C can be used.

The first experiments to discover neutron polarization were those of Huber and Baumgartner (Hu 53, Ba 53) and Ricamo (Ri 53, Ri 53a) studying the D-D reaction.

4.1. Some remarks about experimental techniques: The neutron beam impinging on the target will scatter in such a way that neutrons having spin "up" are scattered preferentially to one side, and those with spin "down" to the other. This behavior is a consequence of spin-orbit coupling.

If the incident neutron beam is polarized, the yield of neutrons scattered to one side will be different from the yield of neutrons scattered to the other. This asymmetry essentially measures the product of the polarization of the incident beam and the analyzing

---

* For a more extensive review the reader is referred to Ha 63.

power of the scatterer or analyzer.

The first problem is to know the analyzing power of the analizer.

The second is to measure the left-right asymmetry. One can measure either the neutron scattered from ^{4}He, ^{12}C, ^{16}O, etc. or the recoil particles. Another possibility is to measure the scattered neutrons in coincidence with the recoil particle.

In the coincident arrangement the scatterer serves also as a scintillator. Dubbeldam and Walters (Du 61) used a gas scintillator: 95% He, 5% Xe at 160 atmospheres. Perkins and Simmons (Pe 61) used a liquid helium detector, since it was demonstrated that liquid helium also scintillates.

The main problem of polarization measurements are false asymmetries. A method to eliminate false asymmetries used by Hillman et al (Hi 56) consists in reversing the polarization of the incident neutron beam by means of a magnetic field placed between the target-analizer and the target that generates the polarized neutrons. The magnetic field is along the direction of motion of the neutrons and it is produced by a solenoid through which the neutrons pass. The solenoid is capable of rotating the neutron spin through $\pm$ 90°. The solenoid was first applied to small angle scattering of 95 MeV neutrons from uranium (Hi 56).

An example of a neutron polarization tarjet-analyzer is shown in Fig. 21.

The measurement of the polarization of neutrons compares with that of charged particle polarization (as far as the accuracy and the time involved is concerned) approximately as the measurements of angular distributions in neutron and charged particle reactions, respectivelv. The preceding statement is based on the assumption that $(\text{polarization})^2$ x (intensity) for the incident neutron beam and incident charged particle beam is the same.

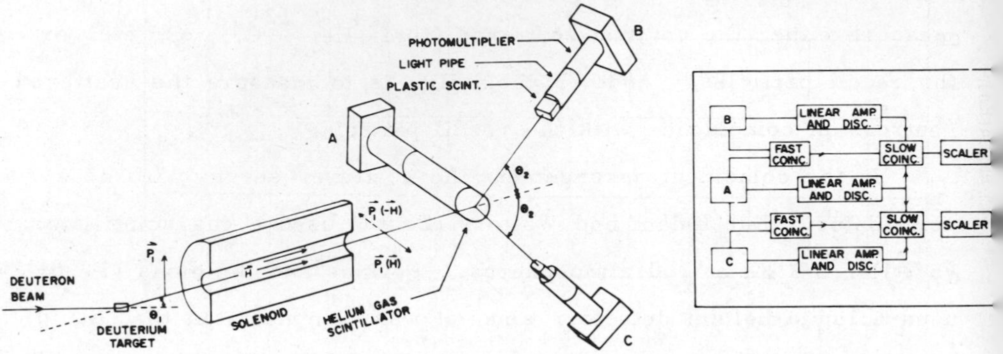

Fig. 21

Neutron polarization analyzer (Du 61, Ba 64). Polarization vector P_1 can be turned through 90° in either direction by a solenoid. Recoiling α-particles are detected in gas scintillator A. Neutrons scattered at θ_2 are detected in B and C scintillators. The ratio of the coincidences between A and B to that between A and C is used to obtain P_1.

4.2. Neutron polarization in various reactions. The reaction $D(d,n)^3He$.

Already at $E_d \approx 90$ keV this reaction produces polarized neutrons. At $E_d = 93$ keV, $\theta_1 = 46°$ a polarization $P = -0.106 \pm 0.023$ was found (Ka 59). At $E_d = 350$ keV, $\theta_1 = 46.5°$, $P = -0.138 \pm 0.014$ (Mu 66). The polarization seems to reach its largest value at $E_d = 2$ MeV ($P \approx -0.2$). At $E_d > 2$ MeV, around $\theta = 45°$ there is a large discrepancy between existing data. The more recent data favor the upper dashed curve of Fig. 22.

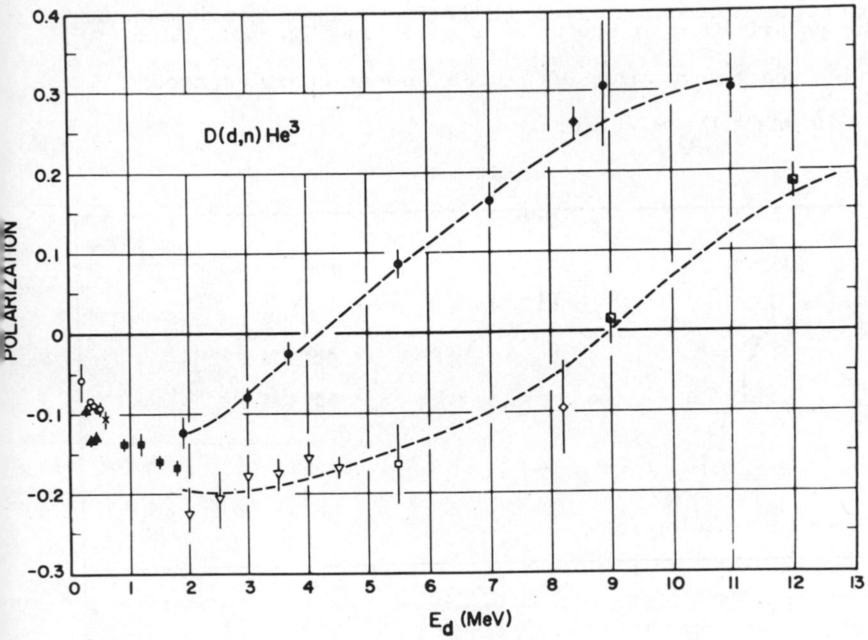

Fig. 22

Polarization of neutrons from the $D(d,n)^3He$ reaction (Ha 63). The upper dashed curve connects the Wisconsin data and the lower dashed curve data from Columbia, Orsay, Washington University and Institute for Theor. and Exper. Physics in Moscow.

The angular dependence $P(\theta)$ is given by

$$P(\theta) = \left[\sigma(\theta)\right]^{-1} \left[A \sin 2\theta + B \sin 4\theta + \ldots \right] \tag{4.1}$$

At $E_d \lesssim 300$ keV only $A \sin 2\theta$ should be considered. Formula (4.1) with only A and B terms should be sufficient up to 2 MeV.

The reaction $T(p,n)^3He$.

The polarization of neutrons is given in Fig. 23. At $E_p \approx$ 3 MeV, P_n reaches a value of ~ 0.25 and at energies around $E_p \sim 7 - 10$ MeV $P_n \sim -0.20$.

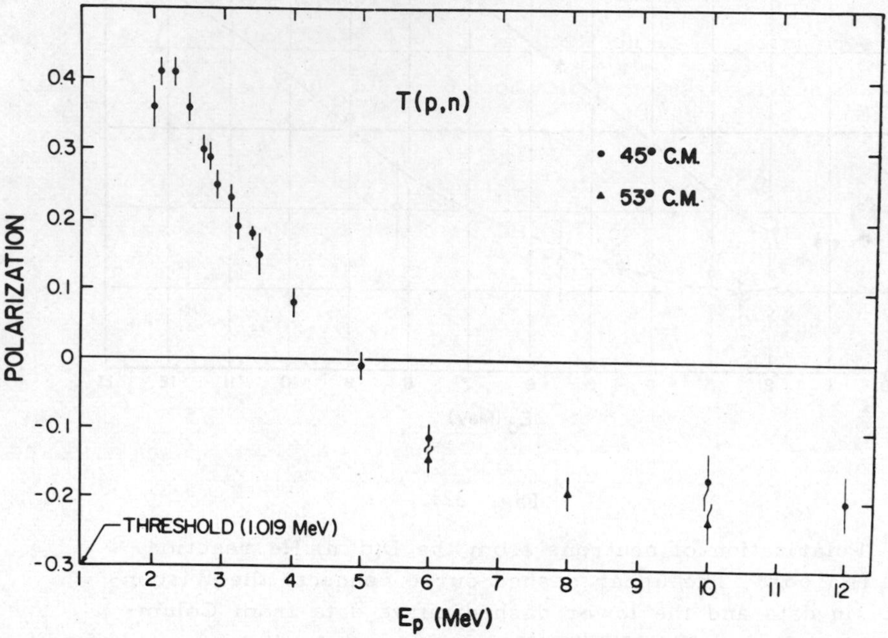

Fig. 23.

Polarization of neutrons from the T(p, n) reaction (Wa62, (Ke 64).

The reaction $T(d,n)\alpha$

At $E_d \sim 0.1 - 0.3$ MeV no polarization was found ($P \lesssim 0.05$, neutron angles = 45° and 90°). At $E_d = 1.8$ MeV the largest observed polarization was found at an angle of 67.5° and it amounted to $P = 0.12 \pm 0.03$. At $E_d = 5$ MeV the polarization has two extremes: at an angle of 30°, $P = 0.26$, and at an angle of 90°

$P = -0.43$. The large neutron polarization observed at these energies is corroborated by large proton polarizations in the charge symmetric process $^{3}He(d,p)\alpha$.

Two additional remarks will be made:

i. Neutrons from the reaction $D(\gamma,n)p$ are also polarized. The polarization of neutrons at $E_\gamma = 2.754$ MeV (Na^{24}) is about -0.25 and it is symmetric about $\theta_{c.m.} = 90°$ (Je 65).

ii. R. J. N. Phillips (Ph 59) suggested that neutrons from the reaction $D(p,n)2p$ are polarized (of course $\theta_n \neq 0$). Polarized neutron beams at $\theta_n = 0$ could be obtained using a polarized incident proton beam.

5. THE STUDY OF MULTIPARTICLE BREAKUP REACTIONS AND THE NEUTRON-NEUTRON INTERACTION

5.1. Multiparticle reactions.

The multiparticle breakup reactions

$$1 + 2 \longrightarrow 3 + 4 + \ldots\ldots N \qquad (5.1)$$

have been and are the subject of much interest both in low energy and high energy nuclear physics. The reasons for such interest are manifold: e.g.

- interactions between unstable particles,
- resonances,
- reaction mechanisms,
- measurements of lifetimes of nuclear processes in the domain of 10^{-21} sec.

The process depends upon 3N-10 independent kinematic variables. In fact there are N-2 particles in the final state, each one of them characterized by its momentum, giving 3N-6 variables. Energy and momentum conservation impose 4 additional conditions, but of course the incident energy has to be known. Finally, for unpolarized particles in the entrance channel, the observables (e.g. cross-section) are invariant under rotations about the direction of the incident beam. The total number of independent kinematic variables is $n = 3N - 10$. For $N = 4$ there are $n = 2$ independent kinematic variables. For $N = 5$ it follows $n = 5$, etc.

A convenient choice for these kinematic variables are the Galilean invariants

$$(\mathbf{v}_i - \mathbf{v}_j)^2 \qquad i, j = 1, 2, 3, \ldots\ldots N$$

if i and j are from the subset $3, 4, \ldots\ldots N$, the quantity $(\mathbf{v}_i - \mathbf{v}_j)^2$ measures the relative energy in the final state.

The reaction (5.1) proceeds as a sequential decay if its cross section has maxima at certain specific values of $(\mathbf{v}_i - \mathbf{v}_j)^2$, $i, j \in 3 \ldots N$. The values of $(\mathbf{v}_i - \mathbf{v}_j)^2$ where these maxima appear should be independent of the incident energy and of the angles of the outgoing particles. For $N = 5$, a sequential process is e.g.

$$\left.\begin{array}{l} 1 + 2 \longrightarrow k + (ij)_{E_{ij}} \\ \\ (ij) \longrightarrow i + j \end{array}\right\} \qquad (5.2)$$

Process (5.2) has to be distinguished from the simultaneous break-up process:

$$1 + 2 \longrightarrow k + i + j$$

The cross section for (5.2) can be written as a product of two terms. The first term describes the primary interaction:

$$| < (ij) + k \mid H' \mid 1 + 2 > |^2 .$$

The second term describes the system (ij) decomposing into i and j. If the interaction between i and j is represented in terms of the phase shifts δ_{ij}, the second term can be written as

$$\frac{d\,\delta_{ij}}{d\,E_{ij}}$$

The sequential process model makes the assumption that the dependence of the cross section for (5.2) on E_{ij} is essentially given by $d\delta_{ij}/dE_{ij}$, and that the first term $| < (ij) + k \mid H' \mid 1 + 2 > |^2$ is E_{ij}-independent.

In order that the sequential mechanism model be valid, it is necessary that the lifetime of the $(ij)E_{ij}$ system be long compared with the time it takes particle k to leave the domain of interaction with the other participants of the nuclear reaction.

A measure of the lifetime T_{ij} of the system of two interacting particles i and j is given by

$$T = \frac{2}{v}(R + \frac{1}{k} + \frac{d\delta}{dk}) \qquad (5.3)$$

The relative velocity of both particles is v, and k is the relative wave number. δ are i, j phase shifts, and R measures the interaction radius.

The scattering through a resonance in the (ij) subsystem, with

$$\delta = \delta_o + \tan^{-1} \frac{\Gamma}{E_o - E_{ij}}$$

where Γ is the width and E_o the position of a resonance, yields the lifetime:

$$T = \frac{2h}{\Gamma} \frac{\Gamma^2}{(E - E_o)^2 + \Gamma^2/4} + \frac{2}{v}(R + \frac{1}{k})$$

and the condition for a sequential process is

$$\frac{h}{\Gamma} \gg \frac{1}{v}(R + \frac{1}{k}) \qquad (5.4)$$

which implies a narrow resonance (i.e. a longlived resonance; typically $\Gamma \ll$ 4 MeV).

The cross section for a sequential process via a resonance $(ij)E_o$ in the spirit of a sequential mechanism model is given by

$$d\sigma = \text{const.} \times \frac{\Gamma^2}{(E - E_o)^2 + \Gamma^2/4} \times \text{(phase space)} \qquad (5.5)$$

If the i-j scattering demonstrates the effect of a virtual state, the phase shifts being given by

$$k \cot \delta = -\frac{1}{a} + \frac{1}{2} r_o k^2 + \ldots.. \qquad (5.6)$$

where a is the scattering length and r_o is the effective range parameter, then the lifetime T is

$$T = \frac{2}{v}(R + \frac{1}{k} + \frac{|a|}{1 + (k|a|)^2})$$

The condition for the sequential decay being

$$|a|\, k \ll 1 \qquad \text{and} \qquad |a| \gg R$$

The effective range term in (5.6) has been neglected.

The cross section for a sequential process via a virtual state is

$$d\sigma = \text{const.} \times \frac{1}{1 + k^2 a^2 (1 - \frac{r_o}{a})} \times \text{(phase space)} \qquad (5.7)$$

Formula (5.7) includes the effect of r_o up to order k^2.

Formulae (5.5) and (5.7) were derived first by Watson and Migdal. The subsequent work on the sequential mechanism model, notably that of G. C. Phillips and collaborators (Ph 60) is essentially equivalent to expressions (5.5) and (5.7) with the exception that it predicts effects related to a spatial localization.

Formulae (5.5) and (5.7) as well as those in (Ph 60) do not predict the absolute cross section.

The process under investigation normally does not proceed only via a sequential mechanism $\longrightarrow k + (ij)E_{ij}$. The contribution of a nonresonant, simultaneous process is possible, and also the contribution of a sequential process involving more than one resonance. In the case of a nonresonant process admixed with the decay via a virtual state the scattering amplitude can be written as a sum of the scattering amplitudes for the two processes:

$$f = f_o + \text{const.} \frac{1}{1 + iak}$$

where f_o describes the nonresonant process. The cross section is composed of three terms: a pure sequential term, an interference term and a simultaneous breakup term (Ph 62, Re 64). The interferences involving two sequential decays via resonances have also been considered (Il 63, Ph 65).

The cross section for a sequential process can be calculated in a Born approximation type of calculation. The matrix element for a process

$$a + A \longrightarrow k + (ij) \quad ; \quad (ij) \longrightarrow i + j$$

is

$$M = < \chi_{k-ij} \, \psi_k \, \phi(ij) \sum_n V_{an} \mid \chi_{aA} \, \psi_a \, \psi(A) > \qquad (5.8)$$

where χ describes the relative motions of the a-A and k-ij systems. $\psi(A)$ is the wave function of the target nucleus, ψ_a and ψ_k describe particles a and k, respectively, and $\phi(ij)$ is the wave function of particles i-j in the resonant state. $\sum_n V_{an}$ takes into account the interaction between the incident particle a and any member of the target nucleus. The strength of the potential V_{an} can be determined from the free a-n scattering. In such a model, the absolute cross section <u>is</u> determined. The cross section is

$$d\sigma = |M|^2 \times \text{(phase space)} \qquad (5.9)$$

Formula (5.8) reduces to (5.5) or (5.7) if the wave function $\phi(ij)$ can be factored out of (5.8) and the remaining part can be assumed to be independent of E_{ij}. It is obvious how (5.8) can be generalized to include interference effects.

The results of calculations based on formula (5.8) and on the

Watson-Migdal formula (5.5 or (5.7) are in general different. The models could be tested versus the experimental data for those reactions where the sequential mechanism involves an intermediate system of well known properties, e.g. p-p, α-nucleon, α-α, etc. It has been found that in processes $p + d \longrightarrow n + (pp)$ the Watson-Migdal approach does not explain the data. The Born approximation type calculation, even with fairly crude nucleon-nucleon potentials V_{an}, provided that the wave function $\phi(ij) = \phi(pp)$ was an ^1S_o wave function, gave a good fit to the data in the region from $E_p = 30 - 100$ MeV. This model gives the shape of the spectrum, but fails to give the absolute cross-section at all except highest energies. The analysis of the process nucleon + trion $\longrightarrow$ deuteron + (2 nucleon) indicates that neither Watson-Migdal nor Born approximation type calculations fit the data in the energy range from 6 to 50 MeV.

The processes

deuteron + trion $\longrightarrow$ trion + (2 nucleon)

nucleon + ^{6}Li $\longrightarrow$ deuteron + (α-nucleon)

nucleon + ^{7}Li $\longrightarrow$ trion + (α-nucleon)

nucleon + ^{10}B $\longrightarrow$ trion + (α - α)

etc.

have been well explained using the Watson-Migdal model. The Born approximation type calculation has not been done for these processes.

The exact treatment of the three body problem based on the Fadeev approach (Fa 60) should at least in principle provide a possibility to analyze the multiparticle reaction $1 + 2 \longrightarrow 3 + 4 + 5$. In order to carry out such a task, one should use the nucleon-nucleon interaction in its full complexity, possess an adequate knowledge of the nuclear interaction off the energy shell, and estimate the effect of a possible 3-body force. Such a program is impossible to perform at present. A more modest analysis has been undertaken by Aaron and Amado (Aa 65) using a non-local separable S-wave spin-dependent nuclear force. This model gives a good fit to the elastic neutron-deuteron scattering and to the total neutron-deuteron inelastic cross section. Since the theory does not include the Coulomb interaction it can be applied only to the neutron-deuteron system. A comparison with the experimental data on the reaction D(n, p)2n (Ce 64, Il 63) at E_n = 14 MeV and θ_p = 5°, 10°, 20°, 30° and 45° shows that:

1. The absolute cross section predicted by the model disagrees with the absolute cross section determined experimentally;
2. the model gives a wrong angular distribution;
3. if normalized to the data, the model can explain the shape of the 5° and 10° spectra with a reasonable value for the n-n ^1S_o scattering length.

The inability of the model to produce a correct absolute cross section and the fact that it yields an angular dependence less peaked at forward angles than found experimentally presumably arises from the crude nucleon-nucleon interaction used in the calculation.

It is instructive to compare the prediction of Amado's calculation with those using Born approximation and the Watson-Migdal model. In Fig. 24 the results of all three calculations for the process D(n, p)2n at E_n = 14 MeV and θ_p = 5° are given, normalizing all of them to the same peak cross section value. The Watson-Migdal model gives a considerably broader curve than either Amado or the Born approximation model. The predictions of Amado and the BA model are in reasonable agreement.

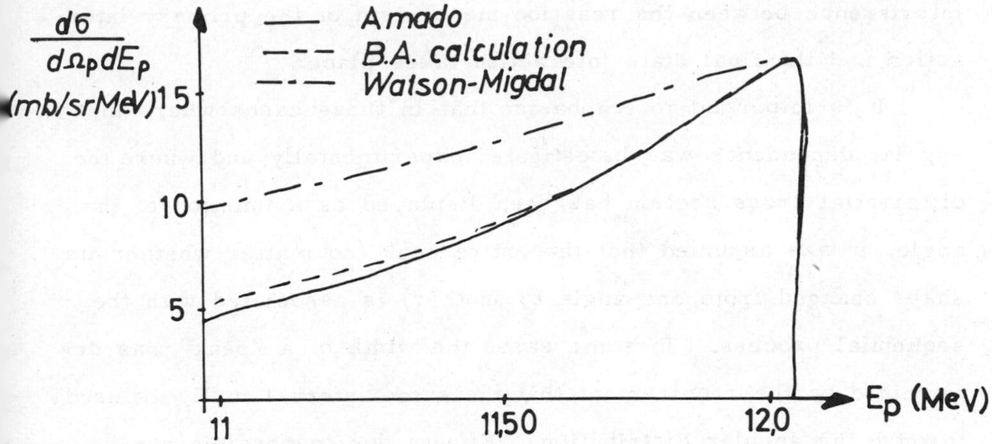

Fig. 24

Calculations for the reaction D(n, p)2n at E_n = 14 MeV, θ_p = 5°, normalized to the same peak cross section. a_{nn} = -19 F.

Essentially all analyses of sequential processes, investigated through the measurements of the spectrum of only one particle, are restricted to the spectrum at the smallest measured angle. Before one could dare to infer anything from such analyses it is imperative to understand the angular dependence. The reaction mechanism, particularly the characteristics of the primary interaction, are contained in the angular distribution. For those cases where the angular distribution has been measured with good angular resolution, it was found to display a characteristic diffraction pattern. The angular dependence can be introduced in formulae (5.5) and (5.7) by assuming that the term $< (ij) + k \,|H'|\, 1 + 2 >$ depends upon θ. In such a model the width of a peak associated with the sequential decay remains determined by the term $d\delta/dE_{ij}$. The actual angular dependence is presumably more complex than this and an involved interference between the reaction mechanism of the primary interaction and the final state interaction takes place.

It is important to emphasize that in those cases where the angular dependence was investigated experimentally and where the differential cross section has been displayed as a function of the angle, it was assumed that the entire peak (no matter whether its shape changed from one angle to another) is associated with the sequential process. In some cases the width of a "peak" was determined by the requirement that the same interval in E_{ij} is used through the angular distribution. Effects due to possible non-sequential processes or interference effects were usually neglected in the determination of an angular distribution.

The understanding of the sequential processes, and particularly those involving the ${}^1S_o$ dinucleon final state, is closely connected with the understanding of the angular distributions.*

The discussion in this chapter, concerning the comparison of models with the experimental data, has dealt only with those measurements where less than a complete set of independent kinematic variables has been specified. It has been argued that the analysis of

---

* For the spectra $d\sigma/d\Omega\, dE$ taken at 0° the transformation between the cm and lab angles involves only the ratio of the velocities in the cm and lab system, which multiplies the cross section. This is related to the fact that $V d\Omega\, dE$, where V is the velocity, is a Galilean invariant. It turns out that the same transformation holds at relativistic energies. The spectrum measured at $\theta_{lab} \neq 0$ <u>does not</u> correspond to a spectrum at one cm angle, but rather to pieces of spectra at many cm angles. This is a reflection of the well known dependence of the cm $\longleftrightarrow$ lab transformation on the Q value of the reaction.

such measurements is subject to strong criticism because various processes like sequential mechanism, spatial localization, phase space maxima and spectator maxima cannot be distinguished and could actually fall on top of each other. Therefore, the parameters extracted from the analysis of such processes would be meaningless.

We will enumerate the counter arguments:

1. Reactions like $\alpha + d \rightarrow \alpha + (p + n)$ and $d + d \rightarrow d + (p + n)$ where the isospin selection rule forbids a sequential process via the ^1S_o dinucleon system, have been studied and no peaks in the cross section have been observed. If the peaks attributed to the sequential reaction in processes like $^3He(d,t)2p$ or $^7Li(n,t)^5He$ were actually due to spectator, phase space or spatial localization effects, one would expect such peaks to show up in the reaction $^4He(d,\alpha)np$ as well.

2. Effects related to spatial localization have not been uniquely demonstrated. There are many cases, like $^6Li(n,d)^5He$ and all reactions involving ^5He or ^5Li intermediate systems where spatial localization could be observed if they occur at α-n relative energy equal zero.

3. The one particle spectra could not have phase space factors that would produce relatively sharp peaks.

4. The spectator enhancement occurs when two particles scatter in such a way that their angles satisfy the condition for the free scattering of the same two particles. The enhancement will still persist even if this condition is not exactly satisfied, because of the momentum distribution of constituents in either of the particles in the entrance channel. The final state interaction (sequential

process) occurs when two particles are emitted in such a way that they strongly interact. In general, the spectator enhancement and final state interaction enhancement do not fall on the same energy of the outgoing particles. There are special conditions when the two enhancements coincide. For example, in the reaction D(p,n)2p, the neutron emitted by a knock-out process at practically 0° will be associated with a proton that essentially is at rest. This is a spectator type direct knock-out process. The third particle stays unperturbed. However, a proton that in a collision process was placed in a state of almost zero energy will be in strong final ^1S_o state interaction with the proton that was a spectator of the entire process. Such processes have been studied (Šl 67b). In single particle spectra such FSI-spectator enhancements are treated in the analysis by assuming from the beginning a direct spectator type process.

Nevertheless, the unpleasant truth is that at present there is no theory which is capable of analyzing the multiparticle breakup processes. The calculations based on the Fadeev approach should in principle be able to offer a sound treatment of such processes, but due to computational difficulties the models that are constructed within Fadeev theory use unrealistic nuclear interactions and consequently fail to explain the data. It should be mentioned that not only data where less than a complete set of variables was measured, but also the data where all independent variables are specified, could not be successfully analized in terms of any existing theory.

Some of the difficulties encountered in the understanding of kinematically completely determined measurements are (see e.g. Šl 67a):

1. Spectator model fails to predict the absolute cross sections

correctly;

2. Modifications of the spectator model which include the FSI fail to predict the absolute cross section correctly;
3. Sequential process models of Watson-Migdal type using known spectroscopic information do not explain the data;
4. Interference phenomena are only qualitatively described;
5. The angular dependence, and particularly the azimuthal angle dependence, is not understood.

Problems that remain to be solved are also:

1. Rescattering effect: proximity scattering (see e.g. Ai 67)
2. The relative importance of sequential vs simultaneous processes. The importance of quasifree (spectator) processes.

Since in the kinematically completely determined measurements the amount of data to be accumulated, in order to have a complete picture of the angular dependence, is about $10^4 - 10^5$ times the amount needed in an experiment where only the spectrum of a single particle is measured, it is obvious that many "complete" measurements end "uncompleted".

We will conclude this subsection by reviewing what has been learned from the study of neutron induced multiparticle reactions and by enumerating processes which should be investigated in the future.

Neutron induced multiparticle reactions gave the following information:

i. Evidence for the neutron-neutron and neutron-alpha final state interaction, as well as evidence for many sequential processes.

In spite of the difficulties of subjecting the data to a quantitative analysis, it seems fair to say that a statement that the FSI has been observed is quite correct.

ii) The spectra, the angular distribution (or at least a fraction of it) the total reaction cross section and particularly its absolute value for many multiparticle reactions have been determined. These data are of utmost importance for fundamental research as well as for various applications.

However the data on spectra, angular distributions and total reaction cross sections are still insufficient. Many more measurements are needed and such data are useful even if the mechanism of the multiparticle reaction is not completely understood.

Some quantitative aspects of the three-body final state interactions could be obtained by studying processes:

$$p + {}^{3}He \rightarrow n + (3p) \quad ; \quad p + {}^{3}He \rightarrow p + (npp) \quad ;$$

$$p + {}^{3}H \rightarrow n + (ppn) \quad ; \quad n + {}^{3}He \rightarrow p + (nnp) \quad ;$$

$$n + {}^{3}H \rightarrow p + (nnn)$$

The shape of the spectra and the relative cross sections could by themselves and without any detailed knowledge of the multiparticle processes, indicate a departure from the statistical breakup and the presence of a final state interaction. The ratio of the cross sections can yield important information on three-nucleon systems.

5.2. Neutron-neutron interaction. (See e.g. Šl 67). The equality of the proton-proton and neutron-neutron interaction, or the equivalence of a system of nucleons and pions with its charge-symmetric counterpart, is referred to as charge symmetry. If charge symmetry holds, essentially all the information about the neutron-neutron interaction would be contained in the proton-proton system. In spite of the fact that there is an overwhelming evidence indicating that charge symmetry is valid to an accuracy of ~ 1 in 10^2, there are reasons why the neutron-neutron interaction should be studied. These are:

1. Small violations of charge symmetry are expected. Radiative corrections to pion-nucleon vertices and $\pi - \eta$ and $\rho - \omega$ mixing could produce about 1% departure from charge symmetry. Finally, there is also the $M_n - M_p$ mass difference.

2. The parameter describing the nucleon-nucleon interaction contains besides a nuclear effect also the influence of other interactions: Coulomb interaction between point charges, magnetic interaction, effects due to finite charge and magnetic moment distributions of nucleons, and vacuum polarization. The magnitude of these effects depends on the nuclear potential used in the calculation. For example, the value of the ^1S_o scattering length has a spread of about 3 fm depending on whether one uses a hard core or a velocity-dependent potential to correct for non-nuclear effects.

Any system containing neutrons can in principle be a source of information about the neutron-neutron force. However, the study of complex systems is subject to many uncertainties. To mention some:

i. Treatment of the many-body system.

ii. Adequate knowledge of the off-energy-shell interaction.

iii. Possibility of many-body forces.

Therefore one has to study rather simple systems.

5.2.1. Two-neutron system. Many attempts to find a bound di-neutron were unsuccessful and led to the conclusion that the bound two-neutron system very likely does not exist. The words "very likely" are included to point out that evidence is somewhat indirect, but a large amount of data leaves little doubt.

Three proposals to investigate the n-n force by means of two colliding beams have been made:

i. Underground nuclear explosions. It seems that the total n-n cross section can be measured to an accuracy of $\pm$ 10%, implying an accuracy of effective range parameters: scattering length and effective range of $\pm$ 7% and $\sim$ 50%, respectively (Di 66, Di 67).

ii. The use of a high-flux reactor.

iii. A colliding-beam experiment at an altitude of 400 - 500 km with a pulsed reactor placed there by a rocket. It is estimated that the background is below 15% and that the n-n scattering cross section can be measured with an accuracy of 20% (Bo 66).

None of these proposals has been realized so far.

5.2.2. Three-nucleon systems. The comparison between the difference Δ in the binding energies of ^{3}He and ^{3}H and the Coulomb energy E_c of ^{3}He indicates, according to Okamoto (Ok 64, Ok 65), the breakdown of charge symmetry by about 1%. The experimental value for Δ is 0.76384 $\pm$ 0.00026 MeV while Okamoto obtains E_c about 0.500 - 0.600 MeV; a net discrepancy of about 0.150 to 0.200 keV. This analysis requires a knowledge of the trion wave function and the uncertainties in the wave functions could invalidate Okamoto's argument.

5.2.3. Final state interaction in multiparticle reactions. Reactions such as D(n, p)2n, ^{3}H(n, d)2n, ^{3}H(d, ^{3}He)2n, ^{3}He(π^-, p)2n, D(π^-, γ)2n and $D(\mu^-,\nu)2n$ could yield n-n interaction parameters. The discussion in 5.1. indicated the difficulties in understanding the neutron induced multiparticle processes leading invariably to final states where more than one strong interaction was present. It is an interesting curiosity that the various analyses of the reaction D(n,p)2n at E_n = 14 MeV in both kinematically incomplete and kinematically complete experiments (two neutrons at $\theta_{n1} = \theta_{n2} = 30°$ have been detected in coincidence and their energies have been measured) yield for the neutron-neutron scattering length a value around -23 fm, which is in disagreement with the charge symmetry postulate, which predicts a_{nn} = -17 fm.

The reaction $D(\pi^-,\gamma)2n$ is particularly suitable to study the neutron-neutron interaction since all three particles in the final state can be detected, and yet there is only one strong interaction in the final state. It has been emphasized that the analysis of the reaction can be performed with an accuracy of the order of $\pm$ 1 fm. The study of this reaction (Ha 65, Sa 65a) gives the only presently available parameter describing the n-n interaction:

$$a_{nn} = -(16.47 \pm 1.27) \text{ fm}$$

5.2.4. <u>Direct, peripheral processes.</u> Such processes could yield n-n cross sections, but the interpretation of these processes is still uncertain.

In conclusion, the present knowledge of the n-n interaction is not adequate, and precise neutron-neutron scattering data are required.

6. REACTION MECHANISMS AND NUCLEAR SPECTROSCOPY

A nuclear process which occurs within a time comparable to the transit time of the interacting particle through the region of interaction is called a direct process. For these processes only a small number of degrees of freedom of the nuclear system are excited. On the contrary, nuclear processes where many degrees of freedom are excited involve long times, often several orders of magnitude longer than the transit time. This class of processes involves the formation of a long lived compound state.

Any nuclear reaction, whether it is direct or via a compound nucleus, or whether it belongs to a vast rather poorly understood domain in between these extremes, could in principle be used to obtain important spectroscopic information. However, the extraction procedure requires the understanding of at least the basic features of the particular reaction mechanism.

6.1. Direct reactions. A large number of experimental data shows that direct reactions occur in nature. The evidences are:

1. Energy spectra which indicate a departure from the Maxwellian type predicted by the statistical model. Data show that there are more high energy particles produced than the compound nucleus picture can explain.

2. The yield of various emitted particles indicates that the process has a better "memory" than allowed by the compound nucleus model.

3. Angular distributions of particles which leave the residual nucleus in a group of unresolved levels are peaked forward. A compound nucleus model would yield angular distributions symmetric

around 90°.

4. Angular distributions for specific sharply resolved groups show a diffraction-like pattern. The statistical model predicts a distribution symmetric around 90°.

5. Particle-gamma angular correlations give clear evidence for direct processes.

The data show that the gamma rays emitted in reactions e.g. $(d, p\gamma)$, $(\alpha, p\gamma)$, $(p, p'\gamma)$ etc., are correlated with the recoil vector:

$$\mathbf{q} = \mathbf{k}_i - \mathbf{k}_f$$

k_i and k_f are incident and outgoing particle wave vectors. The direct mechanism model first predicted this type of correlation.

The criterium used most frequently to establish whether a certain reaction proceeds via a direct or compound nucleus mechanism is the shape of the angular distribution. Sometimes it was even tried to "subtract" the isotropic component and thus quantitatively estimate direct vs compound nucleus mechanisms. The shape of the angular distribution can rarely be taken as a final conclusive evidence in favor of one or another mechanism. The reasons are:

1. There are direct mechanisms which produce a forward peaking, but there are direct mechanisms, like heavy particle stripping, which produce backward peaking. The importance of heavy particle stripping has been demonstrated in many cases in both charged particle and neutron induced reactions.

It is obvious that a combination of two direct mechanisms, e.g. knock-out (or pick-up) and heavy particle stripping can produce an angular distribution symmetric around 90°.

2. The angular distribution can reveal a pronounced peaking at some specific incident energy. When studied at different energies, the shape of the angular distribution can change. In such a case the mechanism of the process certainly involves contributions of both direct and compound nucleus mechanisms.

Examples that prove the above statements:

a. The reaction $^{9}Be(n,\alpha)^{6}He$ has been studied (Pa 67a) at E_n = 14 MeV, and since both particles in the final state, α and ^{6}He, could be detected, the entire angular distribution was obtained (see Fig. 25). The shape of the angular distribution immediately reveals the importance of the heavy particle stripping mechanism, which is confirmed by the comparison of the theoretical calculation with the data. It is instructive to compare the angular distribution $^{9}Be(n,\alpha)^{6}He$ with that of $^{9}Be(p,\alpha)^{6}Li$ at the closest energy available, i.e. E_p = 15.6 MeV. The angular distributions are similar, but the backward cross section is two times larger for the reaction $^{9}Be(n,\alpha)^{6}He$. This can be related to a difference in the structure of the final nucleus, i.e. the neutron reduced width in ^{6}He is larger than the proton reduced width in ^{6}Li, which is actually known to be quite well represented by $^{6}Li = \alpha + d$.

b. Angular distributions of alpha particles from the 14 MeV neutron bombardment of nuclear emulsions (C-N-O) show a pronounced forward and backward peak (see Fig. 26, from Se 63; Pa 67a).

c. The angular distributions of alpha particles from the reaction $^{40}Ca(n,\alpha)^{37}A$ for E_n = 3.6 MeV, E_n = 4.0 MeV and E_n = 4.5 MeV, are shown in Fig. 27. This example can be an excellent memento to those who do not see the value of extending the energy of neutron generators.

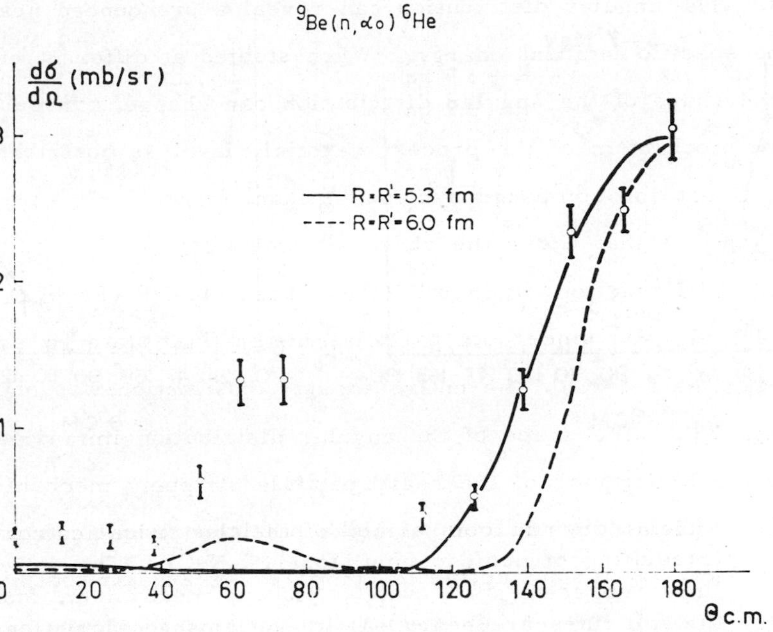

Fig. 25

The angular distribution of the $^9Be(n,\alpha)^6He$ reaction. The curves represent heavy particle stripping theory predictions. R is the core-alpha interaction radius, and R' is the core-neutron interaction radius.

In many cases the angular distribution of charged particle reactions and almost invariably of neutron induced reactions are measured in a limited domain of angles, and sometimes only angles $\leq 90°$ are investigated. Conclusions about reaction mechanisms drawn from such experimental data could be completely wrong.

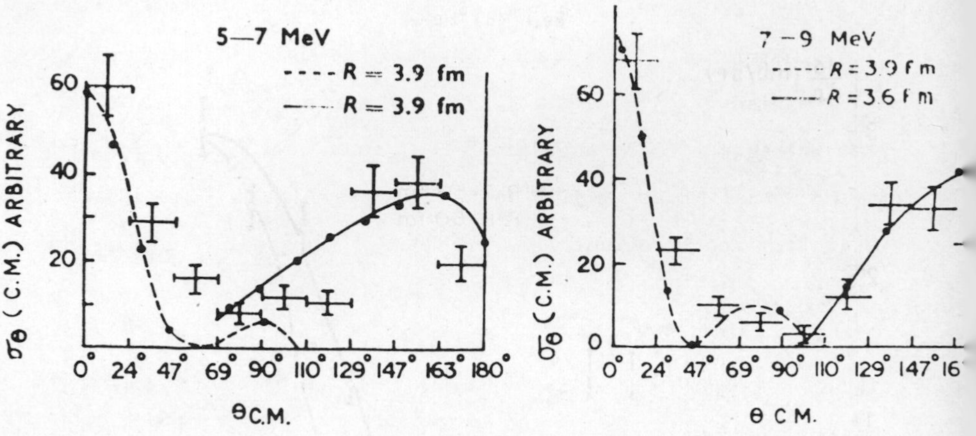

Fig. 26

Angular distributions of alpha particles from neutron irradiation of nuclear emulsions (C-N-O). The dotted lines represent a fit with a pick-up mechanism, and the full lines are heavy particle stripping calculations. The radius used and the alpha particle energies are indicated in the figure (Ci 66).

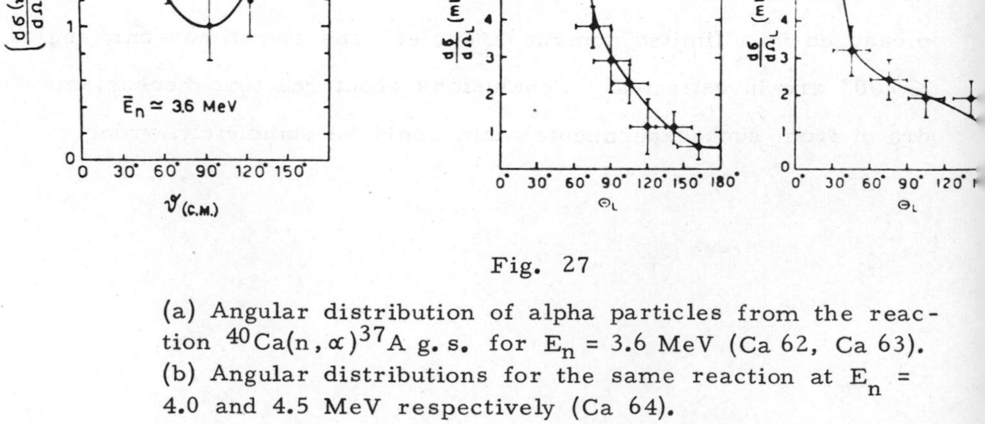

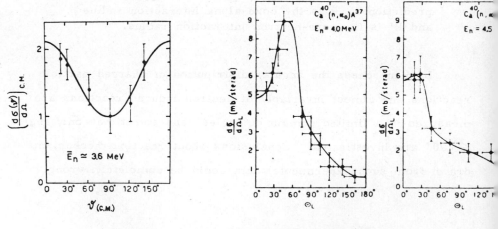

Fig. 27

(a) Angular distribution of alpha particles from the reaction $^{40}Ca(n,\alpha)^{37}A$ g. s. for E_n = 3.6 MeV (Ca 62, Ca 63).
(b) Angular distributions for the same reaction at E_n = 4.0 and 4.5 MeV respectively (Ca 64).

From the above discussion it follows that the shape of the angular distribution alone cannot be used to uniquely determine the mechanism of a process. A much better insight is offered by particle-gamma ray angular correlations. For example, if the differential cross section for a process A(a, bγ)B is isotropic in a certain region of energy, it does not necessarily follow that the process goes via a compound nucleus. The mechanism can be tested by investigating the b-γ correlation as a function of energy, particularly for those energies where the angular distribution of b is isotropic.

Additional information about the reaction is given by polarization measurements. Both the statistical model and the crude direct reaction models predict zero polarization. Polarization can be produced by absorptive distortion, whereby the incident and/or outgoing particles do not penetrate the entire nucleus.

When the mechanism of a reaction is determined, one can employ the reaction to study nuclear spectroscopy. If the reaction A(a, b)B leading to well resolved states of B proceeds via direct interaction, then the angular distribution measurements can yield information on angular momentum, parity and the details of the wave functions of states: A(g. s.) and of states B that are investigated.

One example of a direct reaction will be discussed:

6.1.1. <u>One-nucleon transfer reactions.</u> One-nucleon transfer reactions connect nuclei A and A$\pm$1. The reaction can be a stripping or a pick-up process.

Examples of one-nucleon transfer reactions are:

(p, d)	(d, p)	(d, n)	(n, d)
(d, t)	(t, d)	(^{3}He, d)	(d, ^{3}He)
(^{3}He, α)	(α, ^{3}He)	(α, t)	(t, α)
pick-up	stripping	stripping	pick-up
probing neutron configuration		probing proton configuration	

The exact transition amplitude T_{fi} describing a direct process is given by

$$T_{fi} = \langle \phi_f^-(\mathbf{k}_f) \mid V_f \mid \psi^+(\mathbf{k}_i) \rangle \tag{6.1}$$

where the wave function $\psi^+(\mathbf{k}_i)$ is a solution of the Schrödinger equation for a complete Hamiltonian H:

$$H\psi^+ = E\psi^+$$

The Hamiltonian can be decomposed as:

$$H = H_o^i + V_i = H_o^f + V_f \tag{6.2}$$

where H_o^i gives the unperturbed motion of particles in the entrance channel and similarly H_o^f gives the unperturbed motion in the outgoing channel.

ϕ_f^- is an eigenvector of H_o^f. Thus, ϕ_f^- is the product of wave functions describing the particles b and B in the final state of reaction A(a, b)B, times a function describing the elastic b-B scattering in channel f to the extent that this is required by H_o^f.

The plane wave Born approximation (PWBA) is introduced by describing the relative b-B motion in ϕ_f^- by a plane wave and also by replacing the exact wave function ψ^+ by a product of internal wave functions for particles a and A, times a plane wave describing the a-A relative motion.

The distorted wave Born approximation (DWBA) consists in replacing plane waves in PWBA by wave functions describing the elastic scattering in channels i and f. In principle these elastic wave functions are determined by doing the elastic a-A and b-B scatterings, and DWBA does not have any free parameters.

The wave function of the (A+1) nucleus, ψ_{A+1}, can be expanded in terms of wave functions constructed by vector coupling the extra nucleon in the $| l, j \rangle$ state to the wave function of the nucleus A.

The cross section for a one-nucleon-transfer is

$$d\sigma_{fi} = \frac{M_i M_f}{(2\pi\hbar^2)^2} \frac{k_f}{k_i} \sum_{Av} | T_{fi} |^2 \qquad (6.3)$$

where M's are reduces masses, and $\sum_{Av}$ represents the summation over final spins and the average over initial spins. Introducing for T_{fi} expression (6.1) and using the expansion of wave function ψ_{A+1} one finds the cross section:

$$d\sigma_{fi} = \sum_{\ell, j} G_{\ell j} \sigma_{\ell j} \qquad (6.4)$$

The quantity $G_{\ell j}$ is a product of the square of the isospin Clebsch-Gordan coefficient and of the spectroscopic factor $S_{\ell j}$:

$$G_{\ell j} = (C)^2 S_{\ell j} \qquad (6.5)$$

$S_{\ell j}$ is a measure of the overlap of the wave functions ψ_{A+1} and the wave function constructed by vector coupling the extra nucleon in the $|\ell, j\rangle$ state to the wave function of the nucleus A.*

$\sigma_{\ell j}$ is the "reduced" cross section and it contains the integral over the elastic wave functions of both entrance and outgoing channels. This factor depends sensitively on the value of the orbital angular momentum ℓ of the transferred nucleon.

6.1.2. <u>(n, d) reactions.</u> The study of these reactions can:

i. Determine the orbital angular momentum of the transferred nucleon and sometimes even the total angular momentum and consequently yield information about spins and parities of nuclear states involved.

ii. Test the wave functions of states involved. In particular, it is simple to establish the admixture of low ℓ components in a predominantly large ℓ state. The details of the wave function could be established and compared with various model predictions.

The determination of ℓ is reasonably straightforward and it can be performed with a large degree of confidence. Actually, the determination of ℓ depends on the position of the first diffraction-maximum in the angular distribution and it does not require the knowledge of the absolute cross section. The position of the maximum in the angular distribution of (n, d) reactions can be easily established within $\sim 3°$.

The determination of the spectroscopic factor requires an absolute cross section measurement. It is also necessary that

---

* For one-nucleon transfer reactions involving more complex particles like (α, t) or $(^3He, d)$ another spectroscopic factor appears in the cross section which describes the overlap of e.g. the alpha wave function with the (t + p) wave function.

the theory yields a reliable absolute value. A detailed discussion of the uncertainties in the DWBA calculation is given in Le 64a. The overall uncertainty in the theoretical calculation is approximately 10-20 % and should be coupled to the experimental uncertainty in the absolute cross section, which for neutron induced reactions is typically 10%.

The (n, d) reactions were studied almost exclusively at E_n = 14 MeV. The data are concentrated toward low A nuclei. The general trend of the cross section is to decrease as A(target) increases. The forward maximum being of the order of 10 mb/sr for A ≈ 10, decreases to about 0.5 - 2.0 mb/sr for A ≈ 50, and only an upper limit of 0.08 mb/sr can be placed for A ≈ 200.

A survey of existing (n, d) data is given in Table 12 (Mi 67a). The characteristics of the data are:

1. Data actually extend to A = 75. Only ^{103}Rh and ^{197}Au were studied beyond this region.

2. The systematics of $\ell = 0$, $\ell = 1$, $\ell = 2$ and $\ell = 3$ transitions as a functions of A shows a smooth behavior. The $\ell = 0$ transitions being more intense than $\ell = 1$, $\ell = 1$ more than $\ell = 2$, etc.

3. Angular distributions in general extend to about θ ≈ 90-100°. There is a lack of data in the backward direction.

4. All the data are at 14 MeV.

5. The analyses have been done using PWBA and DWBA.

The agreement between the extracted spectroscopic information and that predicted on the basis of nuclear structure models is in general quite good, and comparable to the agreement found for charged particle induced reactions.

Only in a few cases (e.g. ^{48}Ti(n, d)) the extracted spectroscopic factor and the one predicted from the shell model significantly disagree. The cross section found for this particular reaction is considerably higher than the systematics of (n, d) $\ell = 3$ transitions would allow. Since the measurement was done simultaneously with the $^{16}O(n, d)$ using a TiO_2 target it is hard to see what could go wrong in the measurement.

6. The agreement between several measurements involving the same nuclei is in general good. There are only few examples where large discrepancies were observed (e. g. $^{16}O(n,d)$ and $^{14}N(n,d)$) and in these cases it was always possible to find the source of error in one experiment (e.g. deuteron-triton discrimination or inadequate knowledge of the number of nuclei in the target).

Since the cross section for (n, d) reactions involving light nuclei is in general somewhat larger than for those on heavier nuclei and since the level spacing in light nuclei is often ~ 1 MeV or higher, while it tends to be smaller for heavier nuclei, the concentration of data toward lower A is natural. However, the study of very light nuclei is open to some criticism as far as the application of the DWBA goes. Namely, the optical model parameters are generally chosen in such a way that they give a good fit to n-target and d-residual nucleus scattering. Often it turns out that there are no data for particular nuclei, and sometimes it is not possible to acquire such data because the residual nucleus is unstable. Naturally, the problem always exists when one is concerned with excited levels. Rather than trying to obtain a perfect fit to a particular nucleus, one tries to obtain an overall fit to a number of nuclei and in a range of energies. In this way some experimental idiosyncrasies are also washed out. For very light nuclei the meaning of the optical model is questionable and particularly when nuclei like

^{5}He, ^{8}Be, ^{6}He, etc. are involved, it is not clear how large an error one makes by substituting the "actual" elastic scattering involving these nuclei with the elastic scattering from some stable neighbouring nucleus; e.g. $^{5}He \rightarrow {}^{4}He$, $^{8}Be \rightarrow {}^{9}Be$, $^{6}He \rightarrow {}^{6}Li$.

The data and the analysis of four (n, d) reactions are discussed to give a more detailed picture of the field (the data and the analysis are taken from Va 65).

The spectra of deuterons from the reaction ^{10}B(n, d) and ^{16}O(n, d) are shown in Figs. 28 and 29, respectively.

The angular distribution for the reaction ^{48}Ti(n, d)^{47}Sc is shown in Fig. 30. The DWBA calculation is done using an optical potential determined by fitting the 14 MeV neutron scattering from Ti and 4.07 MeV deuteron scattering from Ti (natural) (Fig. 31). The fact that Ti is used to determine the deuteron potential instead of ^{47}Sc is not expected to introduce significant changes.

The data would require G = 9, while the proton $(f_{7/2})^2$ configuration would give only G = 2.

The ^{16}O(n, d)^{15}N data are shown in Fig. 32. The DWBA calculation gives an excellent fit to the expected G = 2 for pick-up from the filled $p_{1/2}$ shell. These calculations include finite range effects exactly. A Gaussian-range function of range 1.25 fm reduces the cross section from a zero-range approximation value by a factor 0.76, without changing the shape by more than a few percent. No radial cut-off was used. Introducing a cut-off reduces the cross section appreciably and spoils the agreement in shape.

The calculation has been done using both surface and volume absorption potentials for deuterons (S and V). It should be pointed out that the agreement in magnitude found here could at least partly be fortuitous. The calculation with another surface deuteron potential would lead to G = 3.

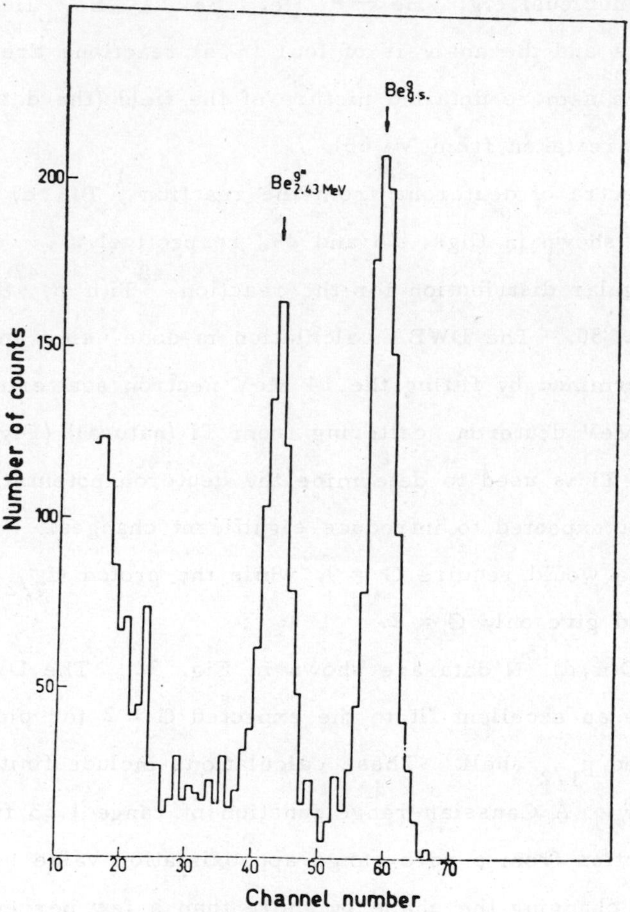

Fig. 28

The energy spectrum of deuterons from the reaction $^{10}B(n,d)^{9}Be$ at zero degrees, after the background has been subtracted (Va 65).

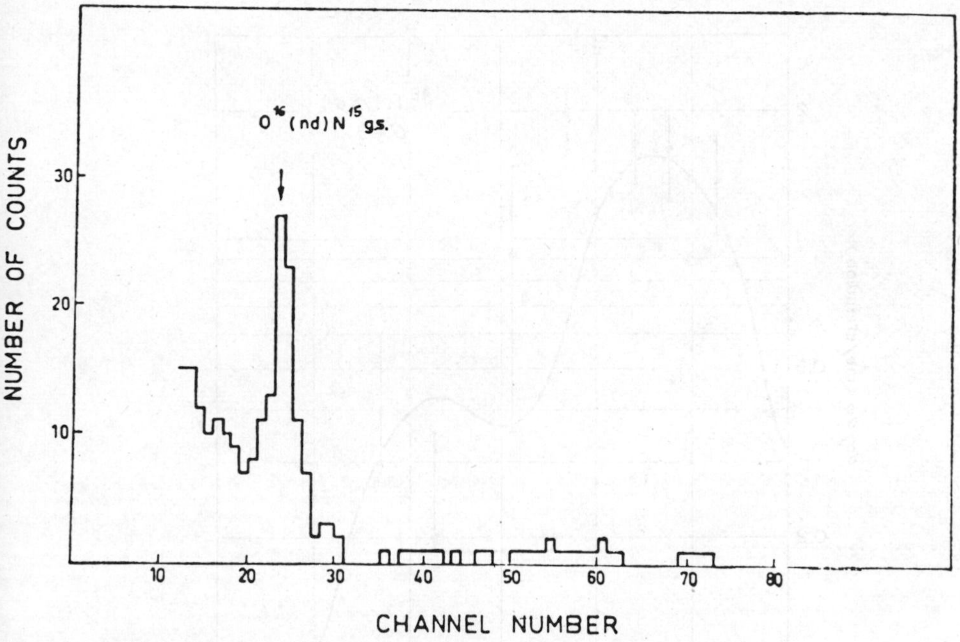

Fig. 29

The background spectrum at zero degrees. Since the counter telescope contained CO_2, the reaction $^{16}O(n,d)^{15}N$ yields a peak (Va 65).

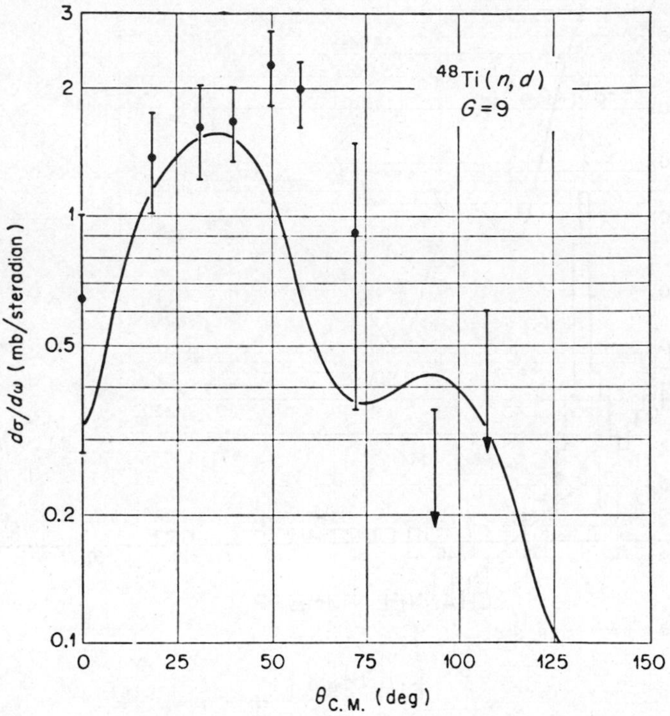

Fig. 30

Differential cross section for $^{48}Ti(n,d)^{47}Sc$ compared with a zero-range DWBA calculation. The theoretical curve has been smeared out to take into account the experimental angular resolution (Va 65).

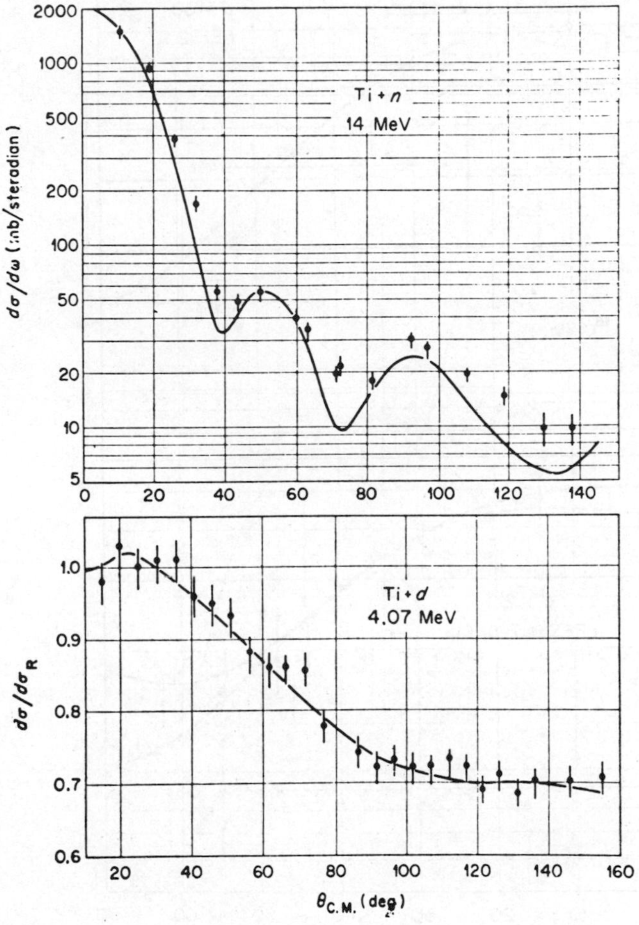

Fig. 31

Elastic scattering of neutrons from Ti (Pi 59) and elastic scattering of deuterons from Ti (Sl 59).

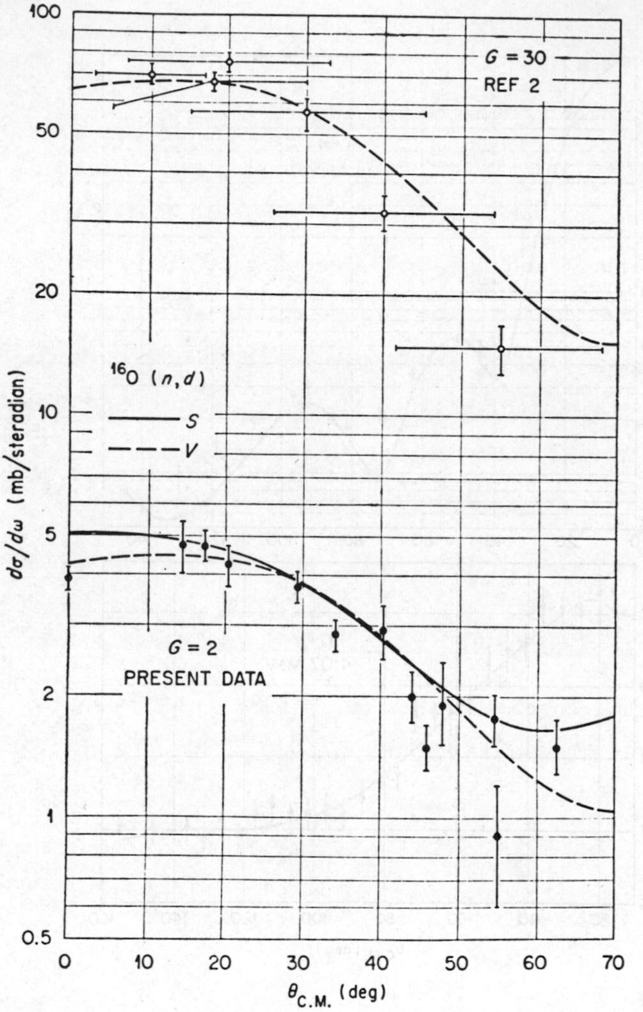

Fig. 32

The reaction $^{16}O(n,d)^{15}N$ g.s. Ref. 2 in Ga 64, and "present data" from Va 65. The curves are DWBA calculation with surface (S) and volume (V) deuteron absorption. The effects of finite angular resolution are negligible in this case (Va 65).

The differential cross sections in the reaction $^{10}B(n,d)^{9}Be$ leaving ^{9}Be in its ground state (Q = -4.36 MeV) and in the first excited state (Q = -6.78 MeV) are shown in Fig. 33 together with the DWBA predictions for zero range and for finite range.

The DWBA calculation was done using two different deuteron potentials, one that gives a good fit to the 10.2 MeV deuteron-^{9}Be elastic scattering, and one that gives a good fit to 8.0 MeV d-^{9}Be scattering. Fortunately, the two potentials give very similar (n,d) predictions, and Fig. 33 shows the result of a calculation using the potential that fitted the 10.2 MeV data.

The extracted spectroscopic factors are in good agreement with the values suggested by shell model calculations.

The data $^{6}Li(n,d)^{5}He$ and the DWBA fit obtained using a neutron potential which fits n-^{6}Li elastic scattering and a deuteron potential which fits d-^{9}Be are shown in Fig. 34. The complete lack of agreement between the theory and the data can be due to the fact that the pickup model is inappropriate to describe the reaction $^{6}Li(n,d)^{5}He$, which maybe proceeds predominantly via the knock-out of a deuteron.

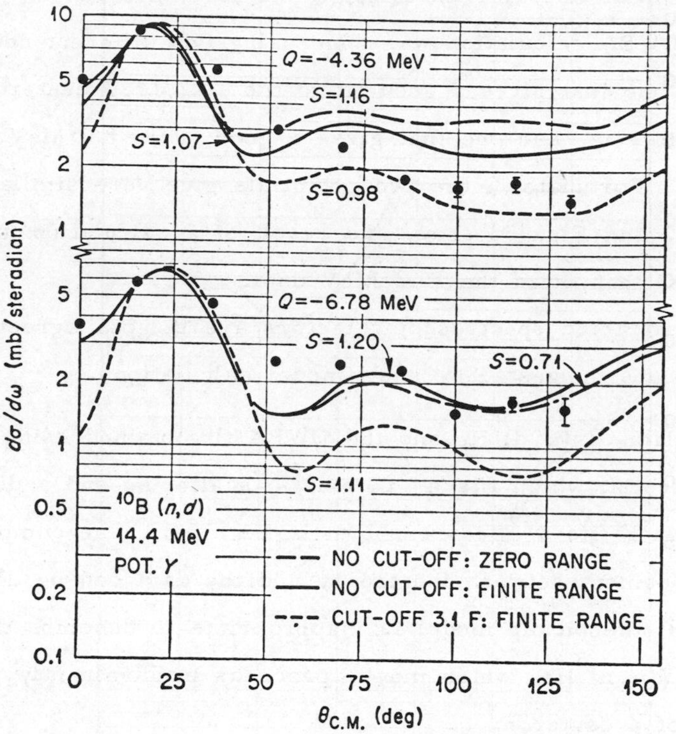

Fig. 33

The data: $^{10}B(n, d)^9Be$ (g.s.) and $^{10}B(n, d)^9Be^*$ (2.43) together with the DWBA calculation. Spectroscopic factors extracted are quoted in the figure (Va 65).

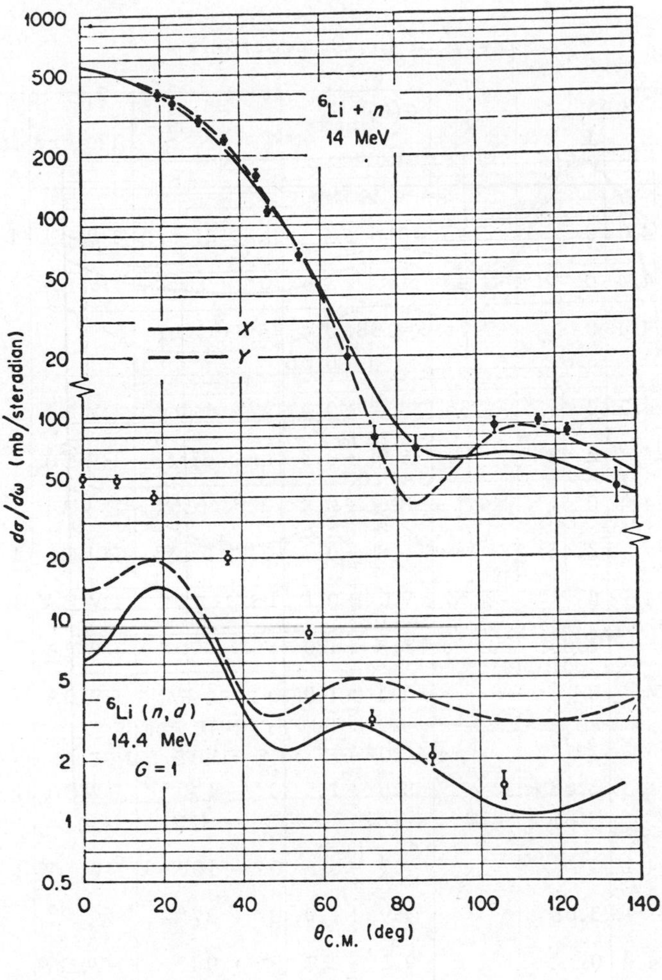

Fig. 34

Cross section for the elastic scattering of neutrons from ^{6}Li (Lu 63) and the ^{6}Li(n, d) reaction (Va 65). Two neutron potentials -X and Y- have been used, and the DWBA calculation used both of these. DWBA used a zero-range approximation. Corrections for the experimental angular resolution were not folded in.

TABLE 12

Survey of (n, d) reactions

Reaction	E_n	E_{exc}	Q (MeV)	$\sigma(\theta)_{max}$ mb/sr	Measurement	Theory	ℓ	Ref.
$^6Li \rightarrow {}^5He$	14.0	0	-2.43	45 ± 4	ang distr.	PWBA	1	Fr 54
	14.4	0	-2.43	50 ± 4	0° - 105°	DWBA	1	Va 65
$^7Li \rightarrow {}^6He$	14.4	0	-7.76	$1.38^{+0.4}_{-0.06}$	spectrum			Va 67
$^{10}B \rightarrow {}^9Be$	14.0	0	-4.36	8.4 ± 0.4	any distr.	PWBA	1	Ri 54
		2.43		5.0 ± 0.3	any distr.	PWBA	1	Ri 54
	14.4	0		8.6 ± 0.4	0° - 130°	DWBA	1	Va 65
		2.43		5.8 ± 0.3	0° - 130°	DWBA	1	Va 65
$^{14}N \rightarrow {}^{13}C$	14.1	0	-5.32	9.0 ± 0.1	15° - 70°	PWBA	1	Ca 57
		3.68		12.5 ± 1.0	15° - 70°	PWBA	1	Ca 57
	14.1	0		10.4 ± 1.9	0° - 140°	PWBA	1	Za 63
		3.09		< 0.5				Za 63
		3.68+ 3.85		8.5 ± 1.5	0° - 140°	PWBA	1	Za 63
	14.1	0		7.3 ± 0.5	0° - 100°	PW,DW	1	Fe 67
		3.68		4.9 ± 1.9	0° - 37°			Fe 67
	14.4	0		9.2 ± 0.7	0° - 94°	PW,DW		Mi 67b
$^{15}N \rightarrow {}^{14}C$	14.1	0	-7.98	4.35 ± 0.65	0° - 60°	PW,DW		Fe 67
	14.8	0		3.3 ± 0.45	0° - 60°			Fe 67
$^{16}O \rightarrow {}^{15}N$	14.0	0	-9.9	77 ± 4	10° - 50°	PWBA	1	Ga 63
	14.4	0		4.7 ± 0.7	0° - 60°	DWBA	1	Va 65
$^{19}F \rightarrow {}^{18}O$	14.1	0	-5.77	18 ± 2	10° - 30°	PWBA	0	Ve 60
	14	0		17 ± 1.5	8° - 160°	PWBA	0	Sa 65

Table 12 (continued)

Reaction	E_n	E_{exc}	Q (MeV)	$\sigma(\theta)_{max}$ mb/sr	Measure-ment	Theory	ℓ	Ref.
	14.1	0		24 $\pm$ 1.5	ang. distr.	PWBA	0	Ri 57
		1.99		1.6 $\pm$ 0.6	ang. distr.			Ri 57
	14.4	0		23 $\pm$ 1	0° - 120°	PW, DW	0	Pa 67b
		1.98		1.5 $\pm$ 0.1	0° - 120°	DW	2	Pa 67b
$^{23}Na \rightarrow ^{22}Ne$	14	0	-6.57	1.0 $\pm$ 0.2	8° - 70°			Sa 65
		1.3		3.5 $\pm$ 0.4	8° - 70°			Sa 65
		3.3		3.0 $\pm$ 0.3	8° - 70°			Sa 65
$^{27}Al \rightarrow ^{26}Mg$	14		-6.05		spectrum (14°)			Co 59
	14.8	0		0.75 $\pm$ 0.01	10° - 140°	PWBA	2	Gl 61
		1.9		1.25 $\pm$ 0.09	10° - 140°	PWBA	2	Gl 61
		3.6		0.33 $\pm$ 0.06	10° - 140°	PWBA	0,2	Gl 61
		4.9		1.15 $\pm$ 0.1	10° - 140°	PWBA	0,2	Gl 61
$^{31}P \rightarrow ^{30}Si$	14		-5.06		spectrum (140°)			Co 59
	14	0		15 $\pm$ 1.5	7° - 135°	PWBA	0	Co 60
	14.1	0		19.2 $\pm$ 2.7	10° - 30°	PWBA	0	Ve 60
	14	0		20 $\pm$ 2	10° - 160°	PWBA	0	Sa 65
	14.1	0		19.3 $\pm$ 2.0	0° - 63°	PWBA	0	Za 63
		2.24		1.2 $\pm$ 0.5	0° - 48°	PWBA	2	Za 63
$^{32}S \rightarrow ^{31}P$	14	0	-6.64		spectrum (14°)			Co 59
	14	0		15 $\pm$ 1	7° - 160°	PWBA	0	Co 60
	14.1	0		18.2 $\pm$ 2.6	10° - 30°	PWBA	0	Ve 60

Table 12 (continued)

Reaction	E_n	E_{exc}	Q (MeV)	$\sigma(\theta)_{max}$ mb/sr	Measure-ment	Theory	ℓ	Ref.
	14.0	0		21.5 ± 2.3	0° - 63°	PWBA	0	Za 63
		1.27		≈ 0.75				Za 63
	14.0	0		7.0 ± 0.7	10° - 30°	PWBA	0	Co 64
		0.45		4.5 ± 0.7	10° - 30°	PWBA	0	Co 64
	14.1	0		25	0° - 40°			Wa 66
		0.45		not found				Wa 66
		1.27		1.4	0° - 40°	PWBA		Wa 66
		2.23		1.6	0° - 40°	PWBA		Wa 66
$^{34}S \rightarrow {}^{33}P$	14.1	0	-8.66	3.9	0° - 40°	PW, DW		Wa 66
$^{35}Cl \rightarrow {}^{34}S$	14.4	0	-4.15	2.7 ± 0.4	0° - 83°	PW, DW	2	Mi 67b
		2.13		5.3 ± 0.5	0° - 83°	PW, BA	0	Mi 67b
		3.31		7.0 ± 0.5	0° - 83°	PW, BA	0	Mi 67b
	14.1	0		1.65 ± 0.15	10° - 63°	DW	0,2	Fa 67
		2.13		4.1 ± 0.35	10° - 63°	DW	0,2	Fa 67
		3.31		5.4 ± 0.5	10° - 63°	DW	0,2	Fa 67
$^{39}K \rightarrow {}^{38}A$	14.4	0	-4.15	1.2 ± 0.2	0° - 93°	PW, BA	2	Mi 67b
		2.17		2.1 ± 0.3	0° - 93°	PW, BA	2	Mi 67b
$^{40}Ca \rightarrow {}^{39}K$	14	0	-6.11		spectrum (14°)			Co 59
	14.4	0		2.9 ± 0.3	0° - 93°	PW	0	An 67
		2.53		1.43 ± 0.1	0° - 93°	PW	2	An 67
$^{45}Sc \rightarrow {}^{44}Ca$	14	0	-4.67	≤ 0.3	spectrum (14°)			Co 61
$^{48}Ti \rightarrow {}^{47}Sc$	14.4	0	-9.22	2.3 ± 0.5	0° - 110°	DW	3	Va 65

Table 12 (continued)

Reaction	E_n	E_{exc}	Q (MeV)	$\sigma(\theta)_{max}$ mb/sr	Measure-ment	Theory	ℓ	Ref.
$^{51}V \rightarrow {}^{50}Ti$	14.4	0	-5.83	1.8 ± 0.4	10° - 120°	PW	3	Sl 61
	14.0	0		0.48 ± 0.05	spectrum (14°)			Co 61
	14.4	0		0.39 ± 0.03	0° - 120°	DW	1,3	Il 62
		1.59		0.18 ± 0.02	0° - 120°	DW	1,3	Il 62
		2.76		0.22 ± 0.02	0° - 120°	DW	1,3	Il 62
		3.27		0.20 ± 0.02	0° - 120°	DW	1,3	Il 62
$^{52}Cr \rightarrow {}^{51}V$	14	0	-8.28	1.11 ± 0.11	spectrum (14°)			Co 61
$^{55}Mn \rightarrow {}^{54}Cr$	14	0	-5.83	0.35 ± 0.07	spectrum (14°)			Co61
$^{54}Fe \rightarrow {}^{53}Mn$	14	0	-6.63	2.44 ± 0.24	spectrum (14°)			Co 61
	14	0+0 38		2.85 ± 0.2	8° - 115°	DW	1,3	Ba 62
$^{56}Fe \rightarrow {}^{55}Mn$	14	0	-7.97	1.15 ± 0.1	spectrum (14°)			Co 61
	14	0+0.126		1.4 ± 0.1	8° - 90°	DW	3	Ba 62
$^{58}Ni \rightarrow {}^{57}Co$	14	0	-5.95	2.84 ± 0.3	spectrum (14°)			Co 61
	14.8	0		2.4 ± 0.2	10° - 130°	PW	1,3	Gl 61a
	14.1	0		2.7 ± 0.4	10° - 70°	DW	3	Wa 65a
		1.37		1.5 ± 0.15	10° - 70°	DW	1	Wa65a
		1.88		1.3 ± 0.15	10° - 70°	DW	3	Wa65a
		2.51		1.2 ± 0.25	10° - 70°			Wa65a
		3.24		1.9 ± 0.3	10° - 70°			Wa65a

Table 12 (continued)

Reaction	E_c	E_{exc}	Q (MeV)	$\sigma(\theta)_{max}$ mb/sr	Measurement	Theory	ℓ	Ref.
		3.74		1.9 ± 0.3	10° - 70°			Wa65a
$^{60}Ni \rightarrow ^{59}Co$	14	0	-7.3	1.9 ± 0.2	spectrum (14°)			Co 59
$^{63}Cu \rightarrow ^{62}Ni$	14.1	0	-3.9	3.2 ± 0.4	10° - 90°	DW	1	Wa65a
		1.13		1.65 ± 0.03	10° - 90°	DW	1	Wa65a
		3.86		0.85 ± 0.25	10° - 90°	DW	3	Wa65a
		4.1		1.0 ± 0.2	10° - 90°			
	14.1	0		3.4 ± 0.3	10° - 56°	DW	1	Fa 65
		1.17		1.0 ± 0.15	10° - 56°	DW	1	Fa 65
$^{65}Cu \rightarrow ^{64}Ni$	14.1	0	-5.22	2.3 ± 0.2	10° - 73°	DW	1	Ch 67
		1.34		0.55 ± 0.1	10° - 73°	DW	1	Ch 67
$^{64}Zn \rightarrow ^{63}Cu$	14.1	0	-5.48	2.7 ± 0.35	10° - 70°	DW	1	Wa65a
		0.67		1.6 ± 0.3	10° - 70°	DW	1	Wa65a
		1.31		1.4 ± 0.3	10° - 70°	DW	3	Wa65a
		1.95		2.5 ± 0.4	10° - 70°			
		2.55		1.2 ± 0.3	10° - 70°			
		3.01		2.5 ± 0.4	10° - 70°			
$^{66}Zn \rightarrow ^{65}Cu$	14.1	0	-6.68	1.28 ± 0.1	10° - 73°	DW	1	Ch 67
		0.77		0.50 ± 0.06	10° - 73°	DW	1	Ch 67
		1.62		0.20 ± 0.06	10° - 73°	DW	1	Ch 67
$^{68}Zn \rightarrow ^{67}Cu$	14.1	0	-7.76	0.73 ± 0.1	10° - 73°	DW	1	Ch 67
$^{75}As \rightarrow ^{74}Ge$	14.4	0	-4.68	1.0 ± 0.2	0° - 75°	DW	1	Mi 67b
		0.596		0.54 ± 0.16	0° - 75°			Mi 67b
		1.2+1.5 +2.2		1.0 ± 0.4	0° - 75°			Mi 67b
$^{103}Rh \rightarrow ^{102}Ru$	14	0	-3.98	spectrum (14°)				Co 59

7. FUTURE OF FAST NEUTRON PHYSICS

As has been pointed out in the introduction there is a number of problems in nuclear physics the solution of which has to be searched for in neutron induced reactions. We want to emphasize now what the basic trends are that experimental neutron physics should take in order to secure the solution of these and other problems.

First, the development of neutron facilities in the neutron energy range from 15 to 100 MeV. This region is particularly suitable because the time-of-flight technique is still applicable and can ensure monoenergetic neutron beams.

If intense monoenergetic beams in the region 1 - 100 MeV were available, the following studies could be made:

i. Many processes that cannot be studied having only 14 MeV neutrons, because of rather high negative Q values, could be investigated with neutrons of $E_n = 20$ MeV. Tables 13, 14 and 15 give Q values for (n,t); (n, ^{3}He) and (n,2p) reactions induced on A < 70 nuclei, respectively. At higher neutron energies transitions leading to many excited states of the same nucleus can be studied. This is very important for nuclear spectroscopy.

ii. Dependence upon incident energy can be investigated and thus many ambiguous interpretations could be avoided. This is crucial for the understanding of the reaction mechanism.

One should also mention that some approximations, like the impulse approximation, become better at higher incident energies.

Second, the accuracy achieved in fast neutron experiments should become comparable with that achieved in charged particle induced reactions (see again Fig. 3). It is particularly important to improve the energy and angular resolution. Any significant progress in nuclear spectroscopy and reaction mechanism studies can hardly be made without resolutions of $\Delta\theta \sim 2 - 3$ and $\Delta E \approx 0.2$ MeV.

At the same time, the measurements in neutron physics should not become longer. The time required to study some neutron induced processes is already prohibitively long (see again Fig. 4). Therefore, one should try to improve experimental techniques so as to shorten data accumulation time.

When neutron physics achieves these goals: high accuracy coupled with not too lengthy measurements, and neutron facilities over a wide energy range, it will be possible to accumulate such vital data as:

1. np, T = 0 phase shifts;
2. nn phase shifts, and possible departure from charge symmetry;
3. Characteristics of few nucleon systems mainly composed of neutrons;
4. Study of proton configurations in nuclei via (n, d) and (n, ^{3}He) reactions, and
5. Investigation of mechanisms of neutron induced reactions, e.g. (n, 2p).

TABLE 13

Q value for some (n, t) reactions

Reaction	Q values (MeV)
$^{6}Li(n,t)\alpha$	+ 4.79
$^{7}Li(n,t)^{5}He$	- 3.42
$^{9}Be(n,t)^{7}Li$	-10.44
$^{10}B(n,t)^{8}Be$	+ 0.23
$^{11}B(n,t)^{9}Be$	- 9.56
$^{12}C(n,t)^{10}B$	-18.9
$^{14}N(n,t)^{12}C$	- 4.01
$^{16}O(n,t)^{14}N$	-14.5
$^{17}O(n,t)^{15}N$	- 7.8
$^{19}F(n,t)^{17}O$	- 7.6
$^{23}Na(n,t)^{21}Ne$	-10.7
$^{24}Mg(n,t)^{22}Na$	-15.6
$^{27}Al(n,t)^{25}Mg$	-10.9
$^{31}P(n,t)^{29}Si$	- 9.4
$^{35}Cl(n,t)^{33}S$	- 9.5
$^{39}K(n,t)^{37}A$	- 9.7
$^{45}Sc(n,t)^{43}Ca$	- 9.5
$^{51}V(n,t)^{49}Ti$	-10.5
$^{55}Mn(n,t)^{53}Cr$	- 9.3
$^{63}Cu(n,t)^{61}Ni$	- 8.2

TABLE 14

Q values for some (n, ^{3}He) reactions

Reaction	Q (MeV)
$^{10}B(n, {}^3He)^8Li$	-15.8
$^{12}C(n, {}^3He)^{10}Be$	-19.5
$^{16}O(n, {}^3He)^{14}C$	-14.6
$^{24}Mg(n, {}^3He)^{22}Ne$	-12.8
$^{27}Al(n, {}^3He)^{25}Na$	-14.7
$^{28}Si(n, {}^3He)^{26}Mg$	-12.1
$^{35}Cl(n, {}^3He)^{33}P$	- 9.54
$^{39}K(n, {}^3He)^{37}Cl$	- 8.89
$^{40}Ca(n, {}^3He)^{38}A$	- 7.0
$^{51}V(n, {}^3He)^{49}Sc$	-12.6
$^{54}Fe(n, {}^3He)^{52}Li$	- 7.7
$^{58}Ni(n, {}^3He)^{56}Fe$	- 6.5
$^{66}Zn(n, {}^3He)^{64}Ni$	- 8.7

TABLE 15

Q values for some (n, 2p) reactions

Reaction	Q (MeV)	Residual nucleus (lifetime)
$^{22}Na(n,2p)^{21}F$	-11.66	2.58 y, 4.6 sec.
$^{24}Mg(n,2p)^{23}Ne$	-15.29	stable
$^{25}Mg(n,2p)^{24}Ne$	-13.7	3.38 min.
$^{28}Si(n,2p)^{27}Mg$	-13.4	9.5 min.
$^{32}S(n,2p)^{31}Si$	- 9.6	2.62 h.
$^{40}Ca(n,2p)^{39}A$	- 8.2	260 y
$^{45}Si(n,2p)^{44}K$	-12.2	22 min.
$^{48}Ti(n,2p)^{47}Ca$	-12.6	4.7 d.
$^{51}V(n,2p)^{50}Sc$	-13.6	1.8 min.
$^{52}Cr(n,2p)^{51}Ti$	-12.2	5.8 min
$^{54}Fe(n,2p)^{53}Cr$	- 7.5	stable
$^{56}Fe(n,2p)^{55}Cr$	-12.2	3.5 min.
$^{58}Ni(n,2p)^{57}Fe$	- 6.55	stable
$^{60}Ni(n,2p)^{59}Fe$	-10.3	45 d.
$^{63}Cu(n,2p)^{62}Co$	-10.6	14 min.
$^{66}Zn(n,2p)^{65}Ni$	-10.2	2.6 h.

REFERENCES

Aa 65: Aaron et al., Phys. Rev. 140, B 1291 (1965).

Ai 67: I. J. R. Aitchinson, Proc. Symp. few body problems, light nuclei, nuclear forces, Brela 1967, to be published, Gordon and Breach.

Aj 65: Ajdačić et al., Phys. Rev. Lett. 14, 442 (1965).

Aj 65a: Ajdačić et al., Phys. Rev. Lett. 14, 444 (1965).

Al 56: Y. A. Aleksandrov and I. I. Bondarenko, JETP 31, 726 (1956).

An 65: Anderson et al., Phys. Rev. Lett. 15, 66 (1965).

An 66: Anikin et al., in Nuclear Structure Study with Neutrons, North Holland Publ. Comp.; Editors M. Neve de Mévergnies et al., 1966, p. 574.

An66a: Antolković et al., Phys. Letters 23, 477 (1966).

An 67: B. Antolković and D. Miljanić, Izv. Akad. Nauk SSSR (Ser, Fiz.) 31, 105 (1967).

Ba 53: E. Baumgartner and P. Huber, Helv. Phys. Acta 26, 545 (1953).

Ba 62: Bassani et al., Nucl. Phys. 36, 471 (1962).

Ba 64: H. H. Barshall, Nucl. Instr. Methods 28, 44 (1964).

Ba 65: Batty et al., Phys. Letters 16, 137 (1965).

Ba 66: G. A. Bartholomew in Me 66, page 458.

Ba 67: Bar Avraham et al., Nucl. Phys. B1, 49 (1967).

Bo 66: I. I. Bondarenko et al., Soviet Journal of Nuclear Physics 2, 598 (1966).

Bo 67: R. Bouchez, Proc. Symp. few body problems, light nuclei, nuclear forces, Brela 1967, to be published: Gordon and Breach.

Ca 57: R. R. Carlson, Phys. Rev. 107, 1094 (1957).

Ca 62: G. Calvi et al., Nucl. Phys. 39, 621 (1962).

Ca 63: G. Calvi et al., Nucl. Phys. 48, 408 (1963).

Ca 64: G. Calvi et al., Proc. Conf. on Nucl. Phys. Paris (Dunod et Cie) Paris 1964.

Ce 64: M. Cerineo, Phys. Rev. 133, B 948 (1964).

Ch 65: A. Chatterjee, Nucleonics 23, 112 (1965).

Ch 67: Chursin et al., Nuclear Phys. A93, 209 (1967).

Ci 66: N. Cindro, Rev. Mod. Phys. 38, 391 (1966).

Co 59: Colli et al., Nuovo Cimento 13, 868 (1959).

Co 60: Colli et al., Nuovo Cimento 16, 991 (1960).

Co 61: Colli et al., Nuovo Cimento 20, 94 (1961).

Co 64: Colli et al., Nucl. Phys. 54, 253 (1964).

Co 66: A. Cookson, Phys. Lett. 22, 612 (1966).

De 67: Dbertin et al., in Proc. Symp. few body problems, light nuclei, nuclear forces, 1967, Gordon and Breach, to be published.

Di 66: B. C. Diven, in Nuclear Structure Study with Neutrons, North Holland Publ. Comp., edited by M. Neve de Mévergnies et al., 1966, p. 441.

Di 67: W. C. Dickinson, Rev. Mod. Phys. 1967, to be published.

DJ 62: De Juren et al., Phys. Rev. 127, 1229 (1962).

Do 55: A. C. Van Dorsten, Phillips Tech. Rev. 17, 109 (1955).

Du 61: P. S. Dubbeldam and R. L. Walters, Nucl. Phys. 28, 414 (1961).

Eg 50: C. Eggler and D. J. Hughes, USAEC ANL 4476 (1950).

El 67: Elliott et al., Phys. Lett. 24B, 358 (1967).

En 63: Engelke et al., Phys. Rev. 129, 324 (1963).

Es 65: Esten et al., Rev. Mod. Phys. 37, 533 (1965).

Fa 60: L. D. Fadeev, JETP 39, 1459 (1960).

Fa 65: Fazio et al., Nuovo Cim. 38, 1938 (1965).

Fa 67: Fazio et al., in print.

Fe 67: P. Fessenden and D. R. Maxson, Phys. Rev. (in print).

Fl 65: A. Fleischer et al., IEE Trans. NS 12, 262 (1965).

Fo 52: S. G. Forbes, Phys. Rev. 88, 1309 (1952).

Fr 54: G. M. Frye, Phys. Rev. 93, 1086 (1954).

Fu 67: Fuschini et al., preprint.

Ga 62: D. Gardner, Nucl. Phys. 29, 373 (1962).

Ga 63: E. Gadioli and S. Micheletti, Phys. Letters 6, 229 (1963).

Gl 61: R. U. Glover and E. Weingold, Nucl. Phys. 24, 630 (1961).

Gl61a: R. U. Glover and N. H. Purser, Nucl. Phys. 24, 431 (1961).

Gr 64: J. R. Grover and A. A. Caretto, Ann. Rev. Nucl. Sci. 14, 51 (1964).

Ha 49: Hadley et al., Phys. Rev. 75, 351 (1949).

Ha 54: Hartzler et al., Phys. Rev. 95, 185, 591 (1954).

Ha 63: W. Haeberli, in Progress in Fast Neutron Physics, (Univ. of Chicago Press, 1963).

Ha 65: Haddoch et al., Phys. Rev. Letters 14, 9 (1965).

He 59: W. N. Hess, Ann. Phys. 6, 115 (1959)

He 66: E. M. Henley, in Isobaric Spin in Nuclear Physics, (J. D. Fox and D. Robson, Academic Press, New York 1966, page 3).

Hi 46: Hillman et al., Nuovo Cim. 4, 67 (1956).

Hi 47: D. L. Hill, Studies with the Ranger, USAEC (1947).

Ho 67: J. Hopkins, in Proc. Symposium in few body problems, light nuclei, nuclear forces, 1967, Gordon and Breach, to be published.

Hu 53: P. Huber and E. Baumgartner, Helv. Phys. Acta 26, 420 (1953).

Il 62: Ilakovac et al., Phys. Rev. 128, 2739 (1962).

Il 63: Ilakovac et al., Nucl. Phys. 43, 254 (1963).

Je 65: Jewell et al., Phys. Rev. 139, B71 (1965).

Jo 63: Joanon et al., Reactor Sci. Techn. 17, 425 (1963).

Ka 59: P. P. Kane, Nucl. Phys. 10, 429 (1959).

Ka 61: J. Kantele, Bull. Am. Phys. Soc. 6, 252 (1961).

Ka 62: J. Kantele and D. G. Gardner, Nucl. Phys. 35, 354 (1962).

Ke 64: Kelsey et al., Nucl. Phys. 51, 395 (1964).

Kh 60: Khurana et al., Proc. 4th Symp. NP Bombay 297 (1960).

Ki 59: Kiselev et al., JETP 8, 564 (1959).

Ku 61: Kuo et al., Nucl. Instr. Methods 13, 29 (1961).

La 63: B. I. Lalović and V. S. Ajdačić, Proc. Symp. Nucl. Electronics Paris (1963).

La 64: (^{7}Li(p,n)) Langsford et al., AERE Progress report PR/NP 7, 28 (1964).

La 65: L. N. Large and M. Hill, Nucl. Instr. Methods 34, 100 (1965).

Le 64: V. Levkovski, JETP 18, 213 (1964).

Le64a: Lee et al., Phys. Rev. 136, B 971 (1964).

Le 66: Levenberg et al., Nucl. Phys. 81, 81 (1966).

Li 52: A. B. Lillie, Phys. Rev. 87, 716 (1952).

Lu 63: Lutz et al., Nucl. Phys. 47, 521 (1963).

Ma 63: J. B. Marion and J. L. Fowler, Fast Neutron Physics, Interscience Publishers, 1960 (part I), 1963 (part II).

Me 66: M. Neve de Mévergnies et al., Nuclear Structure Study with Neutrons, North Holland Publ. Comp. 1966.

Me66a: D. F. Measday, Nucl. Instr. Methods 40, 213 (1966).

Mi 66: B. Mitra and A. M. Ghose, Nucl. Phys. 83, 157 (1966).

Mi 67: A. Mitra, in Proc. Symp. few body problems, light nuclei and nuclear forces, 1967, Gordon and Breach, to be published.

Mi67a: from D. Miljanić, M.Sc. Thesis, Zagreb, 1967.

Mi67b: Miljanić et al., to be published.

Mo 64: M. J. Moravcsik, Phys. Rev. 136, B624 (1964).

Mo 66: Monahan et al., in Nuclear Structure Study with Neutrons, North Holland Publ. Comp. Editors: M. Neve de Mévergnies et al., 1966 p. 558.

Mo66a: Monier et al., Nucl. Instr. Methods 45, 282 (1966).

Mu 66: J. P. F. Mulder, Phys. Letters 23, 589 (1966).

Ni 66: A. Niiler et al., Bull Am. Phys. Soc. 11, 303 (1966).

Oe 67: WTH van Oers and I. Šlaus, Phys. Rev. 160, 853 (1967).

Ok 64: K. Okamoto, Phys. Letters 11, 150 (1964).

Ok 65: K. Okamoto, Progr. Theor. Phys. 34, 326 (1965) Phys. Letters 19, 676 (1965).

Pa 53: E. B. Paul and R. L. Clarke, Can. J. Phys. 31, 267 (1953).

Pa 55: J. de Pangher, Phys. Rev. 99, 1447 (1955).

Pa 67: A. Pasquarelli, Nucl. Phys. A93, 218 (1967).

Pa67a: Paić et al., Nucl. Phys. A96, 476 (1967).

Pa67b: G. Paić and D. Rendić, priv. com.

Pe 61: R. B. Perkins and J. E. Simmons, Phys. Rev. 124, 1153 (1961).

Ph 59: R. J. N. Phillips, Proc. Phys. Soc. 74, 652 (1959).

Ph 60: G. C. Phillips et al., Nucl. Phys. 21, 327 (1960)

Ph 62: R. J. N. Phillips, Nucl. Phys. 31, 643 (1962).

Ph 63: G. C. Phillips et al., Proc. Fast Neutron Physics Conference, Rice 1963 (Univ. of Chicago Press).

Ph 65: G. C. Phillips, Rev. Mod. Physics 37, 400 (1965).

Pi 59: C. St. Pierre et al., Phys. Rev. 115, 999 (1959).

Po 61: Pollehn et al., Z. Naturf. 16a, 227 (1961).

Pr 66: R. Prasad et al., Nucl. Phys. 85, 476 (1966).

Re 64: D. Rendić et al., Glasnik mat. fiz. i astr. 19, 276 (1964).

Re64a: R. Redstone and M. C. Rowland, Nature 201, 1115 (1964).

Re 67: D. Rendić, Ph. D. Thesis, Zagreb, 1967.

Ri 53: R. Ricamo, Helv. Phys. Acta 26, 423 (1953).

Ri53a: R. Ricamo, Nuovo Cimento. 10, 1607 (1953).

Ri 54: F. L. Ribe and J. D. Seagrave, Phys. Rev. 94, 934 (1954).

Ri 57: F. L. Ribe, Phys. Rev. 106, 767 (1957).

Ri 64: R. A. J. Riddle, priv. com. and Ph. D. Thesis.

Sa 65: B. Saeki, Nucl. Phys. 73, 631 (1965).

Sa65a: R. M. Salter, Jr. Ph. D. Thesis, Univ. of California, Los Angeles, (1965).

Sc 46: J. Schwinger, Phys. Rev. 69, 681 (1946).

Se 63: B. Sen, Nucl. Phys. 41, 435 (1963).

Se 67: J. Seagrave, Proc. Symp. few body problems, light nuclei, nuclear forces, Brela 1967, to be published, Gordon and Breach.

Si 67: P. Signell, in Proc. Symp. few body problems, light nuclei and nuclear forces, 1967, Gordon and Breach, to be published.

Sl 59: I. Šlaus and W. P. Alford, Phys. Rev. 114, 1054 (1959)

Sl 61: Šlaus et al., Nucl. Phys. 22, 692 (1961).

Sl 67: I. Šlaus, Rev. Mod. Phys. 1967, to be published.

Sl 67a: I. Šlaus, in Proc. Symp. few body problems, light nuclei, nuclear forces, 1967, Gordon and Breach, to be published.

Sl 67b: I. Slaus et al., to be published.

Sy 67: Symposium on few body problems, light nuclei, nuclear forces, 1967, Gordon and Breach, to be published.

Th 66: Thornton et al., Phys. Rev. Letters 17, 701 (1966).

Va 64: V. Valković, thesis, Zagreb 1964.

Va 65: Valković et al., Phys. Rev. 139, B331 (1965).

Va 67: Valković et al., Nucl. Phys. to be published 1967.

Ve 60: G. E. Veljukov et al., JETP 39, 563 (1960).

Wa 62: Walter et al., Nucl. Phys. 30, 292 (1962).

Wa 64: R. Wagner et al., Phys. Letters 10, 316 (1964).

Wa 65: M. Walt and D. B. Fossan, Phys. Rev. 137, B629 (1965).

Wa 65a: W. N. Wang and E. J. Winhold, Phys. Rev. 140, B882 (1965).

Wa 66: R. R. Wagner and R. A. Peck, BAPS 11, 349 (1966).

Wo 49: L. Wolfenstein, Phys. Rev. 75, 342 (1949).

Za 63: M. R. Zatzick and D. R. Maxson, Phys. Rev. 129, 1728 (1963).

Part III

Solid State Physics

10
ELECTRODYNAMICS OF SOLIDS+

Sergio Rodríguez++
Department of Physics, Purdue University, Lafayette, Indiana

++ John Simon Guggenheim Memorial Fellow, 1967-68.

+ Preliminary notes of these lectures were taken by Dr. Carlos Abeledo and Mr. Mario Weber.

These notes represent a summary of a set of 10 lectures given at the IX Latin American School of Physics in Santiago, Chile, during July of 1967. The lectures were informal and considerably more detailed than the written material that follows. No attempt has been made to give a thorough study of any of the subjects presented and we have made no literature survey. The discussion centered mainly on the description of the physical phenomena which are useful for the determination of the electronic structure of conducting solids with emphasis on the case of metals. Since the detailed theories are rather complicated we have preferred at all times to give simple discussions of models that reveal the features we wished to exhibit. During the preparation of these notes I have had the assistance of Dr. P. R. Antoniewicz, Dr. C. Abeledo, and Mr. Mario Weber.

1. MOTION OF AN ELECTRON IN A PERIODIC POTENTIAL

In a metal we regard the electrons as classified into two categories: the core electrons that are rather tightly bound to the atoms of the solid and the conduction electrons which are more or less free to move through the crystal. Usually one imagines each electron as moving under the influence of a potential field produced by the ion cores plus an average potential arising from the presence of the other conduction electrons. This picture is called the independent particle model of solids. The eigenstates of the system of conduction electrons are described by antisymmetrized products of one-electron wave functions which are to be found, in a self-consistent manner, by solving a set of appropriate Hartree-Fock equations[1]. This model is quite adequate for the description of a variety of observable properties of solids, but we shall not discuss the reasons for its success. Furthermore, we do not study how one obtains the Hartree-Fock potential in which each electron moves. It is sufficient for our purposes to consider each conduction electron as moving in a potential $V(\mathbf{r})$ having a periodicity characterized by the three primitive translations $\mathbf{a}_1$, $\mathbf{a}_2$ and $\mathbf{a}_3$ of the crystal lattice, i.e. if

$$\mathbf{n} = n_1\mathbf{a}_1 + n_2\mathbf{a}_2 + n_3\mathbf{a}_3$$

where $n_1, n_2, n_3 = 0, \pm 1, \pm 2, \ldots\ldots$ is a lattice vector, then

$$V(\mathbf{r} + \mathbf{n}) = V(\mathbf{r})$$

In order to simplify the future development we shall consider a finite crystal composed of $N_o^3 = N$ primitive cells in a lattice arrangement with n_1, n_2, n_3 having the values $0, 1, \ldots (N_o - 1)$. To simplify the mathematical treatment we assume periodic boundary conditions with our crystal as the basic period. This means that we take all quantities (including the wave functions describing the physical states of electrons in the crystal) to be periodic with periods $N_o\mathbf{a}_1$, $N_o\mathbf{a}_2$ and $N_o\mathbf{a}_3$. This assumption is, admittedly an artificial one. In fact, it neglects all possibility of consideration of surface effects. However, if we concentrate on bulk properties of matter it should lead to correct conclusions because the ratio of the number of bulk atoms, to the number of surface atoms is of the order of $N_o^2 = N^{2/3}$.

The dynamical behavior of each electron is thus characterized by the Hamiltonian

$$H_o = \frac{p^2}{2m} + V(\mathbf{r}) \qquad (1.1)$$

where $\mathbf{p}$ is the momentum operator and m the free electron mass.

Let $T(\mathbf{n})$ be an operator representing a translation of the reference frame by the lattice vector $\mathbf{n}$, i.e. the point P with radius vector $\mathbf{r}$ is represented, in the new reference frame after the operation $T(\mathbf{n})$, by $\mathbf{r}' = \mathbf{r} - \mathbf{n}$. Then, if $f(\mathbf{r})$ is a function of position $T(\mathbf{n}) f(\mathbf{r}) = f\left[T^{-1}(\mathbf{n})\mathbf{r}\right] = f(\mathbf{r} + \mathbf{n})$. We notice immediately that

$$\left[H_o, T(\mathbf{n})\right] = 0 \tag{1.2}$$

Furthermore any two translation operators commute. It is possible to find a complete set of orthonormal functions which simultaneously diagonalize H_o and $T(\mathbf{n})$ for all lattice vectors $\mathbf{n}$. Let ψ be an eigenfunction of this set so that $H_o \psi = \varepsilon \psi$ and $T(\mathbf{n})\psi = t(\mathbf{n})\psi$ where $t(\mathbf{n})$ is a number. Now, from $T(\mathbf{n})T(\mathbf{n}') = T(\mathbf{n} + \mathbf{n}')$ it follows that $t(\mathbf{n})t(\mathbf{n}') = t(\mathbf{n} + \mathbf{n}')$. If we consider further that $T(\mathbf{n})\psi(\mathbf{r}) = \psi(\mathbf{r} + \mathbf{n}) = t(\mathbf{n})\psi(\mathbf{r})$ and that the function $\psi(\mathbf{r})$ is normalizable over the volume of the crystal it follows that

$$|t(\mathbf{n})|^2 = 1 \tag{1.3}$$

It is a simple matter now to demostrate that

$$t(\mathbf{n}) = \exp(i\mathbf{k} \cdot \mathbf{n}) \tag{1.4}$$

where $\mathbf{k}$ is a real vector. The particular value of $\mathbf{k}$ depends, of course, on the particular wave function. Not all possible values of $\mathbf{k}$ need to be considered. In fact, two vectors $\mathbf{k}$ and $\mathbf{k}'$ for which $(\mathbf{k}' - \mathbf{k}) \cdot \mathbf{n}$ is 2π times an integer for all $\mathbf{n}$ cannot be regarded as distinct since they lead to the same value of $t(\mathbf{n})$. Now, this occurs if $(\mathbf{k}' - \mathbf{k}) \cdot \mathbf{a} = 2\pi k_i$ where $k_i = 0, \pm 1, \pm 2, \ldots$ These three vector equations can be solved if one introduces the reciprocal lattice whose primitive translations are $\mathbf{b}_1, \mathbf{b}_2, \mathbf{b}_3$ satisfying the nine equations $\mathbf{a}_i \cdot \mathbf{b}_j = 2\pi\delta_{ij}$. The solutions of these equations are

$$\mathbf{b}_1 = \left(\frac{2\pi}{\Omega_o}\right)\mathbf{a}_2 \wedge \mathbf{a}_3 \tag{1.6}$$

and two similar ones. The quantity $\Omega_o = (\mathbf{a}_1 \times \mathbf{a}_2) \cdot \mathbf{a}_3$ is the volume of the primitive cell. This implies that $\mathbf{k}' - \mathbf{k} = k_1\mathbf{b}_1 + k_2\mathbf{b}_2 + k_3\mathbf{b}_3$, i.e., $\mathbf{k}$ and $\mathbf{k}'$ differ by a vector of the reciprocal lattice. We conclude, therefore, that two $\mathbf{k}$-vectors which differ by a vector $\mathbf{K}$ of the reciprocal lattice are equivalent. It is useful to consider a region of distinct values of $\mathbf{k}$. We define this by the inequalities

$$-\pi < \mathbf{k} \cdot \mathbf{a}_i \leq \pi \tag{1.5}$$

A vector $\mathbf{k}$ outside this range is equivalent to one inside. The proof is obvious and hinges on the remark that $\mathbf{K} \cdot \mathbf{a}_i$ is a multiple of 2π. Of course, the requirement of periodic boundary conditions imposes further restrictions on the allowed values of $\mathbf{k}$. In fact, we must have $t(N_o\mathbf{n}) = 1$ for all $\mathbf{n}$. In particular, this must be true if $\mathbf{n}$ is chosen succesively to be $\mathbf{a}_1, \mathbf{a}_2, \mathbf{a}_3$ so that

$$\mathbf{k} = \frac{1}{N_o}(k_1\mathbf{b}_1 + k_2\mathbf{b}_2 + k_3\mathbf{b}_3) \tag{1.7}$$

The allowed values of $\mathbf{k}$ form a finely divided lattice of points with fundamental translations (b_i/N_o). The number of distinct points in this lattice is $N_o^3 = N$ equal to the number of primitive cells in the crystal. Associated with each value of $\mathbf{k}$ there are, in general, an infinite number of stationary states. We associate the numbers $\nu = 0, 1, 2, \ldots$ etc. to these states.

We denote the energy eigenfunctions by $\psi_{\nu k}(\mathbf{r})$ and the corresponding eigenvalues by $\mathcal{E}_\nu(\mathbf{k})$. We write then

$$H_o \psi_{\nu k}(\mathbf{r}) = \mathcal{E}_\nu(\mathbf{k})\psi_{\nu k}(\mathbf{r})$$

Now, since

$$T(\mathbf{n})\psi_{\nu k}(\mathbf{r}) = t(\mathbf{n})\psi_{\nu k}(\mathbf{r})$$

we have

$$\psi_{\nu k}(\mathbf{r}+\mathbf{n}) = e^{i\mathbf{k}\cdot\mathbf{n}}\psi_{\nu k}(\mathbf{r}) \tag{1.8}$$

This result is known as Bloch's theorem[2] but it had been known to mathematicians as Floquet's theorem since the XIXth century. Bloch's theorem can be rewritten in a slightly different form if we define

$$u_{\nu k}(\mathbf{r}) = \exp(-i\mathbf{k}\cdot\mathbf{r})\psi_{\nu k}(\mathbf{r}) \tag{1.9}$$

From here it follows that $u_{\nu k}(\mathbf{r}+\mathbf{n}) = \exp(-i\mathbf{k}\cdot\mathbf{r})\exp(-i\mathbf{k}\cdot\mathbf{n})\psi_{\nu k}(\mathbf{r}+\mathbf{n}) = u_{\nu k}(\mathbf{r})$, i.e. $u_{\nu k}(\mathbf{r})$ is a periodic function having the period of the lattice. Hence

$$\psi_{\nu k}(\mathbf{r}) = \exp(i\mathbf{k}\cdot\mathbf{r})u_{\nu k}(\mathbf{r}) \tag{1.10}$$

We shall call states of this form Bloch states or Bloch functions.

Before proceeding further into the study of the dynamics of electrons in crystals it is useful to study some possible forms that the energy eigenvalues $\varepsilon_\nu(\mathbf{k})$ can take. We shall do this by considering two simple examples.

2. THE TIGHT-BINDING APPROXIMATION

In this approximation we take the potential as seen by the electrons to be

$$V(\mathbf{r}) = \sum_n v(\mathbf{r} - \mathbf{n}) \tag{2.1}$$

where $v(\mathbf{r} - \mathbf{n})$ is the atomic potential. We assume that the electron wave functions of the free atom are known, i.e. that we have solved the equation

$$\left[\frac{p^2}{2m} + v(\mathbf{r} - \mathbf{n})\right] \phi_\nu(\mathbf{r} - \mathbf{n}) = \varepsilon_\nu^o \phi_\nu(\mathbf{r} - \mathbf{n}) \tag{2.2}$$

for its eigenvalues and eigenfunctions. Further we assume $\phi_\nu(\mathbf{r})$ to be normalized to unity.

We must interpret $v(\mathbf{r} - \mathbf{n})$ to be the Hartree potential or a local approximation to the Hartree-Fock potential for the free atom. If $v(\mathbf{r})$ approaches zero when $\mathbf{r}$ approaches the smallest of $\mathbf{a}_1$, $\mathbf{a}_2$, $\mathbf{a}_3$, then the electrons can be regarded as tightly bound and there are 2N states (the factor of 2 arising from the spin degeneracy) which are degenerate with $\phi_\nu(\mathbf{r} - \mathbf{n})$ all having energy ε_ν^o. However, if $\phi_\nu(\mathbf{r} - \mathbf{n})$ and $\phi_\nu(\mathbf{r} - \mathbf{n}')$ overlap to some extent (for $\mathbf{n} \neq \mathbf{n}'$) this degeneracy is lifted. As a better approximation we take linear combinations of the $\phi_\nu(\mathbf{r} - \mathbf{n})$. We write

$$\psi_{\nu k}(\mathbf{r}) = N^{-1/2} \sum_n \alpha(\mathbf{n}, \mathbf{k}) \phi_\nu(\mathbf{r} - \mathbf{n}) \qquad (2.3)$$

Since $\psi_{\nu k}(\mathbf{r})$ must satisfy the Bloch condition, we choose

$$\alpha(\mathbf{n}, \mathbf{k}) = \exp(i\mathbf{k} \cdot \mathbf{n}) \qquad (2.4)$$

and write

$$\psi_{\nu k}(\mathbf{r}) = N^{-1/2} \sum_n \exp(i\mathbf{k} \cdot \mathbf{n}) \phi_\nu(\mathbf{r} - \mathbf{n}) \qquad (2.5)$$

Now, the energy $\varepsilon_\nu(\mathbf{k})$ is given by

$$\varepsilon_\nu(\mathbf{k}) = \frac{< \psi_{\nu k}(\mathbf{r}) \,|\, (p^2/2m) + V(\mathbf{r}) \,|\, \psi_{\nu k}(\mathbf{r}) >}{< \psi_{\nu k}(\mathbf{r}) \,|\, \psi_{\nu k}(\mathbf{r}) >} \qquad (2.6)$$

or

$$\varepsilon_\nu(\mathbf{k}) = \varepsilon_\nu^o - \frac{\sum_{nn'} \exp\left[i\mathbf{k} \cdot (\mathbf{n} - \mathbf{n}')\right] J_{nn'}}{\sum_{nn'} \exp\left[i\mathbf{k} \cdot (\mathbf{n} - \mathbf{n}')\right] I_{nn'}} \qquad (2.7)$$

In this equation

$$I_{nn'} = \int d\mathbf{r}\, \phi_\nu^*(\mathbf{r} - \mathbf{n}')\phi_\nu(\mathbf{r} - \mathbf{n}) = I_\nu(\mathbf{n} - \mathbf{n}') \tag{2.8}$$

and

$$J_{nn'} = -\int d\mathbf{r}\, \phi_\nu^*(\mathbf{r} - \mathbf{n}')\left[V(\mathbf{r}) - v(\mathbf{r} - \mathbf{n})\right]\phi_\nu(\mathbf{r} - \mathbf{n})$$

$$= J_\nu(\mathbf{n}' - \mathbf{n}) \tag{2.9}$$

We notice that I and J depend only on the difference $\mathbf{n}' - \mathbf{n}$. Thus the writing of the final result is simplified to

$$\varepsilon_\nu(\mathbf{k}) = \varepsilon_\nu^o - \frac{\sum_n \exp\left[-i\mathbf{k}\cdot\mathbf{n}\right] J_\nu(\mathbf{n})}{\sum_n \exp\left[-i\mathbf{k}\cdot\mathbf{n}\right] I_\nu(\mathbf{n})} \tag{2.10}$$

This approximation is accurate and practical for calculations if the overlap integrals $I(\mathbf{n}' - \mathbf{n})$ are small for $\mathbf{n} \neq \mathbf{n}'$ and the $J(\mathbf{n}' - \mathbf{n})$ decrease to zero rapidly as $|\mathbf{n}' - \mathbf{n}|$ increases. We consider only the case in which it is necessary to retain contributions arising from the nearest neighbors only. Thus we write, for simplicity

$$\sum_n e^{-i\mathbf{k}\cdot\mathbf{n}} I_\nu(\mathbf{n}) \approx 1$$

and

$$\sum_n e^{-i\mathbf{k}\cdot\mathbf{n}} J_\nu(\mathbf{n}) \approx J_\nu(0) + \sum e^{-i\mathbf{k}\cdot\boldsymbol{\delta}} J_\nu(\delta)$$

In these sums $\boldsymbol{\delta}$ ranges over all the vectors directed to atoms which are nearest neighbors of the atom at the origin. The simplest result follows for s-states, i.e. for states in which $\phi_\nu(\mathbf{r})$ is spherically symmetric. When this is the case, all the $J_\nu(\delta)$ are the same and we designate them by the symbol $J_\nu(1)$. Then, to first order in small quantities,

$$\varepsilon_\nu(\mathbf{k}) = \varepsilon_\nu^o - J_\nu(0) - J_\nu(1)\sum_\delta e^{-i\mathbf{k}\cdot\boldsymbol{\delta}} \qquad (2.11)$$

We now give a few examples of the form of $\varepsilon_\nu(\mathbf{k})$.

(i) For the simple cubic structure (s.c.) we have $\boldsymbol{\delta} = a(\pm 1, 0, 0)$, $a(0, \pm 1, 0)$ and $a(0, 0, \pm 1)$, a being the lattice parameter. Then

$$\varepsilon_\nu(\mathbf{k}) = \varepsilon_\nu(0) - J_\nu(0) - 2J_\nu(1)\left\{ \cos k_x a + \cos k_y a + \cos k_z a \right\} \qquad (2.12)$$

(ii) For the body centered cubic structure (bcc):

$$\boldsymbol{\delta} = \frac{a}{2}(\pm 1, \pm 1, \pm 1)$$

and

$$\varepsilon_\nu(\mathbf{k}) = \varepsilon_\nu(0) - J_\nu(0) - 8J_\nu(1)\cos\left(\frac{k_x a}{2}\right)\cos\left(\frac{k_y a}{2}\right)\cos\left(\frac{k_z a}{2}\right) \qquad (2.13)$$

(iii) For the face centered cubic structure

$$\boldsymbol{\delta} = \frac{a}{2}(\pm 1, \pm 1, 0) \quad , \quad \frac{a}{2}(\pm 1, 0, \pm 1) \text{ and } \frac{a}{2}(0, \pm 1, \pm 1)$$

and we obtain

$$\varepsilon_\nu(\mathbf{k}) = \varepsilon_\nu(0) - J_\nu(0) - 4J_\nu(1)\left[\cos\left(\frac{k_x a}{2}\right)\cos\left(\frac{k_y a}{2}\right) + \right.$$

$$+ \cos\left(\frac{k_y a}{2}\right)\cos\left(\frac{k_z a}{2}\right) + \cos\left(\frac{k_z a}{2}\right)\cos\left(\frac{k_x a}{2}\right)\Bigg]\Bigg\} \qquad (2.14)$$

The approximate eigenfunctions that we have found are linear combinations of atomic functions centered on different lattice sites, i.e.,

$$\psi_{\nu\mathbf{k}}(\mathbf{r}) \approx N^{-1/2} \sum_{\mathbf{n}} \exp\left[i\mathbf{k}\cdot\mathbf{n}\right] \phi_\nu(\mathbf{r}-\mathbf{n})$$

where N is the number of primitive cells in the crystal. The band indeces can be regarded as labels of the atomic states (1s, 2s, 2p, etc.). The wave vector $\mathbf{k}$ has already been discussed. Let us consider a simple, one-dimensional crystal. Here $\mathbf{n} = n\mathbf{a}$. The fundamental Brillouin Zone here is $-\pi/a < k \leq \pi/a$ and $\psi_{\nu, k+\pi/a} \equiv \psi_{\nu,k}$. In order to avoid redundancy in the enumeration of values of k we restrict them to the fundamental Brillouin Zone. Now using the tight binding approximation we have (for s-states)

$$\varepsilon_\nu(\mathbf{k}) = \varepsilon_\nu^{(0)} - J_\nu(0) - 2J_\nu(1)\cos ka \qquad (2.15)$$

$\varepsilon_\nu(\mathbf{k})$ differs from ε_ν^{o} in two ways. Firstly there is a shift of $J_\nu(0)$ caused by the potential of the other nuclei and electrons (notice $J_\nu(0) > 0$). Secondly, since for $-\pi/a < k \leq \pi/a$ the second correction shows that the levels have broadened into a band of energy levels. The width of this band is $2J_\nu(1)$, which, in turn depends on the amount of overlap between atomic wave functions in nearest neighbor sites. We expect this overlap to increase as the principal quantum number of the atomic states increases (K, L, M shells). Let us consider J(1). We write

$$J(1) \approx - \int \phi^{*}(\mathbf{r} - \mathbf{a})\, v(\mathbf{r} - \mathbf{a})\, \phi(\mathbf{r})\, d\mathbf{r}$$

where v(r - a) is the potential arising from the ion at a. For the K-shell $\phi(\mathbf{r}) \propto \exp(-Zr/a_o)$ (a_o is the Bohr radius) for an atom of atomic number Z. Thus

$$\phi(\mathbf{r}) = \exp\left[Za/a_o\right] \phi(\mathbf{r} - \mathbf{a})$$

Hence the magnitude of J(1) is of the order of e^{-Za/a_o} times the potential energy of an electron in the K-shell in the free atom. Therefore

$$J(1) \approx \exp\left[-Za/a_o\right] \frac{Z^2 e^2}{a_o} \approx 10^{-19} \text{ eV}$$

for the K-shell of Na. This quantity is indeed very small, however, as we consider higher shells, the overlap becomes larger and in fact can become so great that for the valence electrons of Na it is necessary to adopt a different approach.

3. FREE ELECTRON APPROXIMATION

Another elementary approach to band theory which is applicable to a considerable extent to many metals and to metals such as sodium in particular is the almost free electron approximation which we now discuss briefly. This approximation consists in regarding the fluctuations of the crystal potential from its average value as a small perturbation. Since the potential is periodic with the period of the lattice it can be expanded in a Fourier series as follows

$$V(\mathbf{r}) = \sum_{K} V_{K} \exp\left[i\mathbf{K} \cdot \mathbf{r} \right] \tag{3.1}$$

where the sum over $\mathbf{K}$ extends over all the vectors in the reciprocal lattice. This perturbation gives matrix elements connecting plane wave states $\mathbf{k}$ with states $\mathbf{k}+\mathbf{K}$. The most important departures from the free electron energy eigenvalues occur when the states $\mathbf{k}$ and $\mathbf{k}+\mathbf{K}$ are degenerate. These degeneracies are split whenever $V_K \neq 0$. For a one-dimensional crystal the energy eigenvalues behave as shown schematically in Fig. 1. Since two

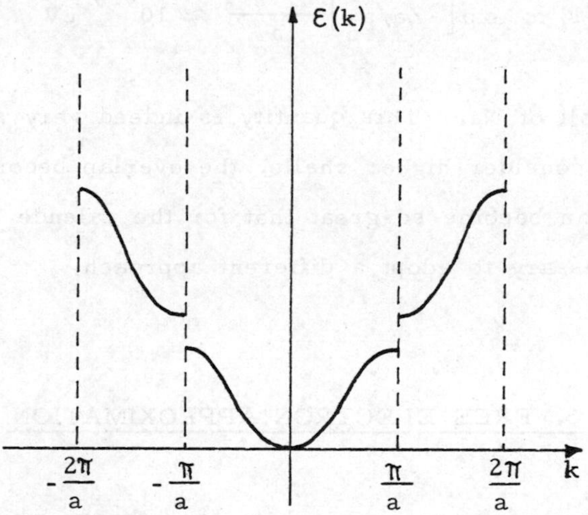

Fig. 1

states having $\mathbf{k}$ vectors differing by a vector $\mathbf{K}$ can be described by the same wave vector in the fundamental Brillouin Zone we can draw all these energy eigenvalues as belonging to values of $\mathbf{k}$ within the fundamental Brillouin Zone. This is shown schematically in Fig. 2. A description of the electron states in this manner is

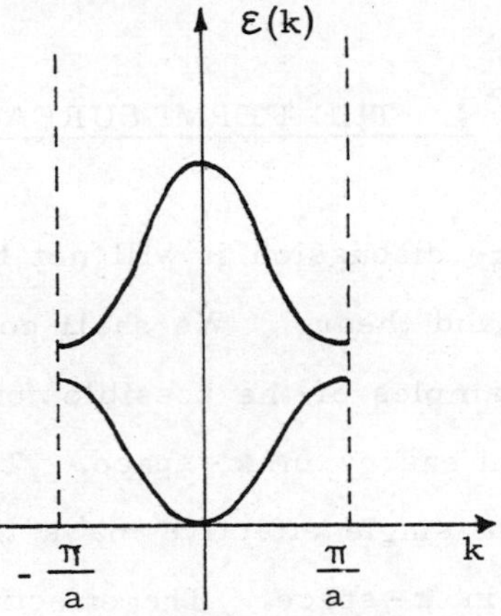

Fig. 2

called the reduced zone scheme. We can equally well regard the functions $\varepsilon_\nu(\mathbf{k})$ as periodic functions in $\mathbf{k}$ space with periods $\mathbf{b}_1$, $\mathbf{b}_2$, $\mathbf{b}_3$ and construct the contours of energy vs. $\mathbf{k}$ as periodic functions in the manner done for one-dimensional crystal in Fig. 3.

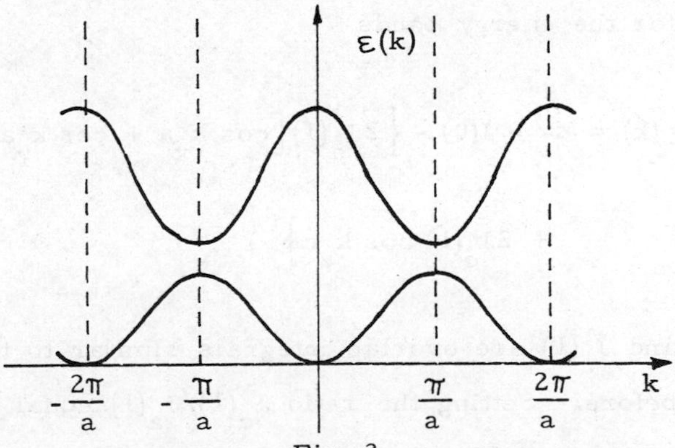

Fig. 3

This description of the states is called the extended zone scheme. We shall find it useful in our studies of the possible form of motion of electrons in crystals in the presence of external fields.

4. THE FERMI SURFACE

For our future discussion it will not be necessary to enter more deeply into band theory. We shall content ourselves with exhibiting some examples of the possible forms of behavior of the surfaces of constant energy in **k**-space. To begin with, it is not possible to assign a single effective mass to the electron states at different points in **k**-space. The effective mass is, in general, anisotropic as can be seen by considering expansion of the energy vs. **k** functions given above in our discussion of the tightly bound model in the vicinity of various values of **k** within the fundamental Brillouin Zone. Let us consider a simple example in some detail. Let us take a tetragonal crystal with lattice parameters a and c. For s-bands, the tightly bound approximation gives the following expression for the energy bands

$$\varepsilon(\mathbf{k}) = \mathcal{E}^0 - J(0) - \left\{ 2J_a(1)\left[\cos k_x a + \cos k_y a\right] + 2J_c(1)\cos k_z c \right\} \tag{4.1}$$

Here $J_a(1)$ and $J_c(1)$ are overlap integrals similar to those we considered before. Setting the ratio $J_c(1)/J_a(1)$ equal to R, we have, in the vicinity of k = 0

$$\varepsilon(k) = \varepsilon^{o} - J(0) - 2J_a(1)\Big\{2 + R - \frac{1}{2}k_x^2a^2$$

$$- \frac{1}{2}k_y^2a^2 - \frac{R}{2}k_z^2c^2\Big\} \qquad (4.2)$$

so that the constant energy surfaces are ellipsoids of revolution of the form

$$\frac{\hbar^2}{2m_\perp^*}(k_x^2 + k_y^2) + \frac{h^2k_z^2}{2m_\parallel^*} = \text{const.} \qquad (4.3)$$

Here

$$m_\perp^* = \frac{\hbar^2}{2J_a(1)a^2} \qquad (4.4)$$

and

$$m_\parallel^* = \frac{\hbar^2}{2J_a(1)Rc^2} \qquad (4.5)$$

Let us look at the cross section of the Brillouin Zone by the plane $k_x = 0$ and assume quite arbitrarily $(c/a) < 1$ and $R < 1$. Several constant energy surfaces are shown in Fig. 4.

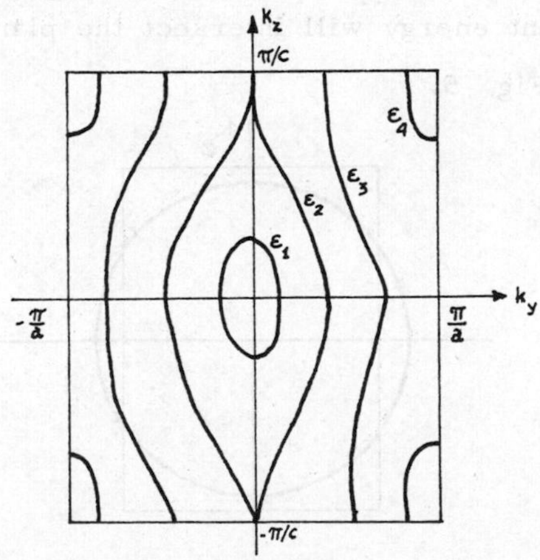

Fig. 4

The constant energy surfaces corresponding to the energy ε_3 are open in the extended zone scheme. By this we mean that the surface $\varepsilon(\mathbf{k}) = \varepsilon_3$ is not closed. The surface $\varepsilon(\mathbf{k}) = \varepsilon_1$ is a simply connected surface around $\mathbf{k} = 0$. In the extended zone scheme it consists of several separated and identical surfaces. The surface $\varepsilon(\mathbf{k}) = \varepsilon_4$ is also closed as can be seen by suitable translations of the different pieces by reciprocal lattice vectors. The particular significance of open surfaces (or orbits) will be studied again later on in connection with the motion of Bloch electrons in the presence of a uniform magnetic field. Another way in which the appearance of this type of surfaces can be illustrated is considering the almost free electron approximation. Let us consider again a tetragonal crystal and let us look at electron states having energy

$$\varepsilon > \frac{h^2 \pi^2}{2m\,a^2} \quad \text{but less than} \quad \frac{h^2 \pi^2}{2m\,c^2}$$

(again we take $c < a$). In the free electron approximation the surface of constant energy will intersect the plane $k_x = 0$ along the circle shown in Fig. 5.

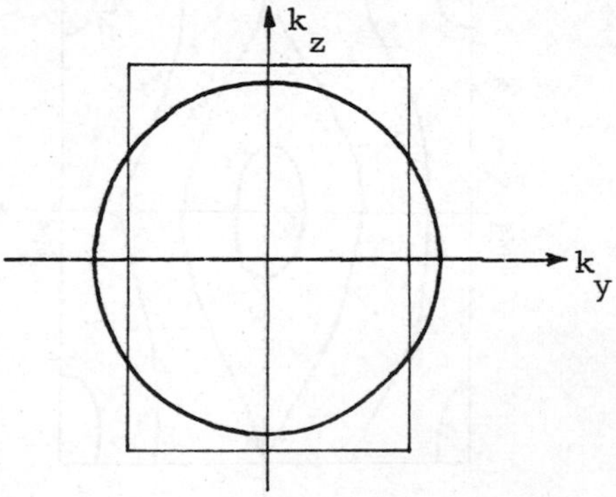

Fig. 5

Within the reduced scheme these states can be drawn as in the figure 6.

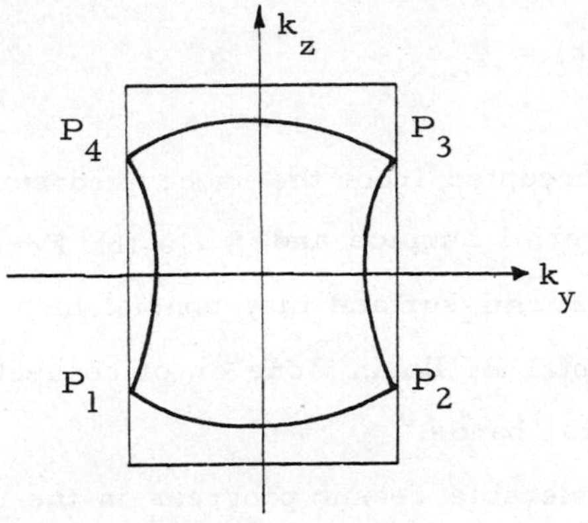

Fig. 6

Now, the crystal potential will, in general, split the states at the cusps P_i $(i = 1, 2, 3, 4)$ and we obtain states (in one band) as shown in Fig. 7 within the framework of the extended zone scheme.

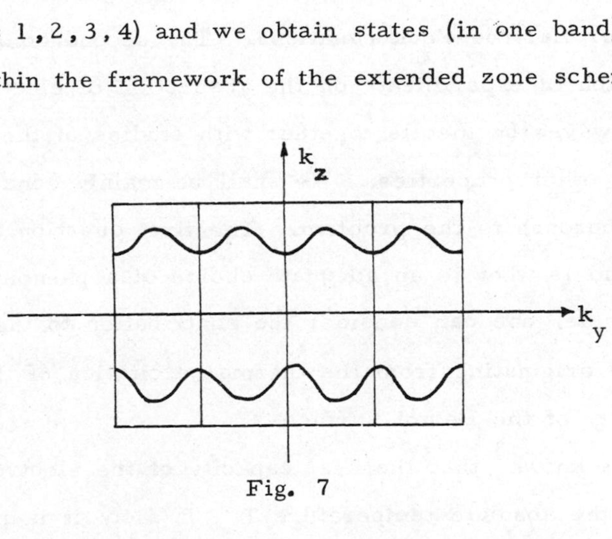

Fig. 7

At absolute zero of temperature all the one-electron states having energy less than a certain energy ζ_o are occupied by electrons while all states having energy larger than ζ_o are empty. The surface (or surfaces) in k-space defined by

$$\varepsilon_\nu(\mathbf{k}) = \xi_o \qquad (4.6)$$

separates the occupied from the unoccupied states. This surface is called the Fermi surface and ξ_o is the Fermi energy. It is clear that the Fermi surface may consist of a closed surface within the fundamental Brillouin Zone or of connected or disconnected pieces in several bands.

The considerable recent progress in the understanding of the electronic structure of metals has come mainly from two lines of research. The first consists in the calculation of the energy band structure by means of a self-consistent solution of the appropriate Hartree or Hartree-Fock equations. The second consists in the interpretation of experiments on the absorption of electromagnetic or acoustic waves by metals together with studies of their galvanomagnetic and other properties. We shall be mainly concerned with this second approach to the problem. The first question that arises in one's mind is what is an adequate choice of a phenomenon to study. For example, one can consider the contribution to the heat capacity of metals originating from the thermal excitation of the electrons in the vicinity of the Fermi surface.

It is known[3] that the heat capacity of the electrons is proportional to the absolute temperature T. In fact, it is possible to show that it is γT where the constant γ is defined by the relation

$$\gamma = \frac{1}{2}\pi^2 k_B^2 g(\xi_o)\Omega \qquad (4.7)$$

In this expression k_B is the Boltzmann constant, Ω the volume of the material, and $g(\xi_o)$ is the value of the density of states at energy $\varepsilon = \xi_o$. The density of states $g(\xi_o)$ is defined as the number of one-particle states per unit volume and per unit energy range at energy ε. One can readily establish that

$$g(\varepsilon) = \frac{1}{4\pi^3} \int \frac{dS}{|\nabla_k \varepsilon_n|} \qquad (4.8)$$

where the integral is taken over that surface in $\mathbf{k}$ - space for which the energy possesses the value ε and dS is an element of area on this surface. We shall soon prove that the expectation value of the velocity of an electron in the Bloch state νk is

$$\mathbf{v} = \hbar^{-1} \boldsymbol{\nabla}_k \varepsilon_\nu(\mathbf{k}) \qquad (4.9)$$

Therefore,

$$g(\xi_o) = \frac{1}{4\pi^2 \hbar} \int_{FS} \frac{dS}{|\mathbf{v}|} = \frac{S}{4\pi^3 \hbar} < \mathbf{v}^{-1} > \qquad (4.10)$$

where the integral is to be evaluated over the Fermi surface, S is the total area of the Fermi surface and $< \mathbf{v}^{-1} >$ is the average over the Fermi surface of the reciprocal of the velocity $|\mathbf{v}|$ at different points on this surface. Thus, a measurement of the electronic heat capacity of metals yields the product of S and $< \mathbf{v}^{-1} >$. We shall be concerned later with experiments that yield more specific information; this discussion of the electronic heat capacity has been given as an example only. Before we discuss this subject it is necessary to investigate how the k-vector of a Bloch electron varies in time when we place it in the presence of an electromagnetic field. We shall show that, within certain conditions, the

k-vector of a Bloch electron in an electromagnetic field of electric field **E** and magnetic induction **B** varies according to the differential equation

$$\hbar \dot{\mathbf{k}} = -e\mathbf{E} - \frac{e}{c}\mathbf{v} \wedge \mathbf{B} \tag{4.11}$$

Here $-e$ is the charge on the electron and **v** is given by Eq. (4.9).

5. MOTION OF BLOCH ELECTRONS IN AN EXTERNAL ELECTRIC FIELD

The problem to which we address ourselves in the present section is the investigation of the evolution of the state of an electron in the presence of an electric field E if at a certain time which we choose as $t = 0$, the electron was known to be in state $\psi_{\nu k}(\mathbf{r})$. We must then solve the equation

$$i\hbar \frac{\partial \phi(\mathbf{r}, t)}{\partial t} = (H_o + e\mathbf{E} \cdot \mathbf{r})\phi(\mathbf{r}, t) \tag{5.1}$$

with the condition

$$\phi(\mathbf{r}, 0) = \psi_{\nu, k_o}(\mathbf{r}) \tag{5.2}$$

Before attempting to do this however we shall give a proof of Eq. (4.9). The periodic part of the Bloch function (1.9) satisfies the equation

$$(H_o + \frac{\hbar}{m}\mathbf{k} \cdot \mathbf{p})u_{\nu k}(\mathbf{r}) = \left(\varepsilon_\nu(\mathbf{k}) - \frac{\hbar^2 k^2}{2m}\right)u_{\nu k}(\mathbf{r}) \tag{5.3}$$

For each value of $\mathbf{k}$, the set $u_{\nu k}(\mathbf{r})$ forms a complete set of periodic functions having the periodicity of the lattice. Now, the expectation value of the velocity for an electron in the state

$$\mathbf{v} = \frac{1}{m}\int \psi^*_{\nu k}(\mathbf{r})\mathbf{p}\,\psi_{\nu k}(\mathbf{r})\,d\mathbf{r}$$

$$= \frac{\hbar\mathbf{k}}{m} + \frac{1}{m}\int u^*_{\nu k}(\mathbf{r})\mathbf{p}\,u_{\nu k}(\mathbf{r})\,d\mathbf{r}$$

If we rewrite the last integral we obtain

$$\mathbf{v} = \frac{\hbar\mathbf{k}}{m} + \frac{1}{\hbar}\int u^*_{\nu k}\left[\frac{\partial}{\partial t}(H_o + \frac{\hbar}{m}\mathbf{k}\cdot\mathbf{p}\right] u_{\nu k}\,d\mathbf{r} \qquad (5.4)$$

$$= \frac{1}{\hbar}\partial\varepsilon_\nu(\mathbf{k})/\partial\mathbf{k}$$

The last equality has been obtained making use of Feynman's theorem. The operation $\partial/\partial\mathbf{k}$ is defined as the gradient in $\mathbf{k}$-space.

Let us now return to the object of this section, namely the study of the effect of an electric field on a Bloch electron. The solution of Eq. (5.1) with the boundary condition (5.2) is

$$\phi(\mathbf{r},t) = e^{-\frac{iHt}{\hbar}}\psi_{\nu k_o}(\mathbf{r}) \qquad (5.5)$$

From the form of the Hamiltonian operator H and using Bloch's theorem in the form (1.8) we find

$$\phi(\mathbf{r}+\mathbf{n},t) = e^{i\mathbf{k}(t)\cdot\mathbf{n}}\phi(\mathbf{r},t) \qquad (5.6)$$

where $\mathbf{k}(t) = \mathbf{k}_o - (\frac{e\mathbf{E}t}{\hbar})$

Thus

$$\hbar \frac{d\mathbf{k}}{dt} = -e\mathbf{E} \tag{5.7}$$

This means that the $\mathbf{k}$-vector of an electron in a uniform electric field increases uniformly in time. At time t the state of the electron is in general, a linear combination of Bloch states with identical wave vectors $\mathbf{k}(t)$.

6. MOTION OF ELECTRONS IN A MAGNETIC FIELD

The purpose of this section is to present a description of the motion of the conduction electrons in a metal when the material is in the presence of a magnetic field $\mathbf{B}_o$. The path of a free electron from the classical point of view, is a circular helix whose axis is parallel to the direction of the magnetic field. However, for an electron in a crystal lattice such a description is insufficient. In the following we shall discuss the motion of a Bloch electron in a magnetic field following the work of Onsager[4].

We assume that the motion of an electron of wave vector $\mathbf{k}$ in the presence of the electromagnetic field $\mathbf{E}$, $\mathbf{B}$ is described by the equation

$$\hbar \frac{d\mathbf{k}}{dt} = -e\mathbf{E} - \frac{e}{c}\mathbf{v} \times \mathbf{B} \tag{6.1}$$

We shall not concern ourselves with the limits of validity of this result. It is possible to construct a classical Hamiltonian which will lead to this equation as follows. First we introduce electromagnetic potentials $\mathbf{A}$ and ϕ in the usual manner, i. e. we require them to satisfy the condition

$$\mathbf{B} = \nabla \times \mathbf{A} \quad \text{and} \quad \mathbf{E} = -\nabla \phi - \frac{1}{c}\frac{\partial \mathbf{A}}{\partial t}$$

If we now write

$$\mathcal{H} = \varepsilon_\nu \left[\left(\frac{\mathbf{p}}{\hbar} + e\frac{\mathbf{A}}{\hbar c} \right) \right] - e\phi \qquad (6.2)$$

where we have defined $\mathbf{p}$ by means of

$$\hbar \mathbf{k} = \mathbf{p} + \frac{e}{c}\mathbf{A} \qquad (6.3)$$

in the energy vs. $\mathbf{k}$ relation $\varepsilon_\nu(\mathbf{k})$. From $\dot{\mathbf{p}} = -\partial \mathcal{H}/\partial \mathbf{r}$ and $\dot{\mathbf{r}} = \partial \mathcal{H}/\partial \mathbf{p}$ we find Eq. (6.1) after we make use of $\hbar \mathbf{v} = \partial \varepsilon_\nu / \partial \mathbf{k}$. Thus p and r are canonically conjugate variables. In a quantum description of the motion of the Bloch electron in the fields $\mathbf{E}$ and $\mathbf{B}$, we replace $\mathbf{r}$ and $\mathbf{p}$ by operators satisfying the commutation relations $[x, p_x] = i\hbar$, etc. In the coordinate representation we write $\mathbf{p} = i\hbar \nabla$ so that the stationary states of the electrons in the crystal (when $\mathbf{A}$ and ϕ are time independent) are obtained by solving the equation

$$\varepsilon_\nu(-i\nabla + \frac{e}{hc}\mathbf{A})\psi = \varepsilon \psi \qquad (6.4)$$

Clearly a solution of this differential equation is in general impossible. We can, however, give a geometrical representation of the energy eigenvalues of a Bloch electron in a uniform magnetic field as follows. We consider the two complementary descriptions of the motion of the electron in terms of **k** - space and real space as being described by the differential equation (6.1) when $\mathbf{E} = 0$ and $\mathbf{B} = \mathbf{B}_o$, a uniform magnetic field and take further the magnetic field to be directed along the z axis of a cartesian coordinate system. Then, the equation of motion reduces to

$$\hbar \frac{d\mathbf{k}_\perp}{dt} = -\frac{e}{c}\mathbf{v}_\perp \times \mathbf{B}_o \tag{6.5}$$

and

$$\frac{d\mathbf{k}_z}{dt} = 0 \tag{6.6}$$

where the vectors $\mathbf{k}_\perp$ and $\mathbf{v}_\perp$ are the components of **k** and **v** on a plane perpendicular to the z axis. We also notice that, because $(d\varepsilon/dt) = \hbar\mathbf{v} \cdot (d\mathbf{k}/dt) = 0$, the vector **k** remains on the surface $\varepsilon(\mathbf{k}) = \varepsilon$ throughout its motion. Integration of Eq. (6.5) with respect to time leads to

$$\mathbf{k}_\perp = -\frac{e}{\hbar c}\mathbf{r}_\perp \times \mathbf{B}_o \tag{6.7}$$

where the projection $\mathbf{r}_\perp$ of the position vector on the (x-y) plane has been measured from a suitably chosen origin. This equation shows that the path of an electron in real space has the same shape as its path in **k** - space. However, it is rotated about the z-axis by an angle of -90° and its linear dimensions are amplified by the factor $\hbar c/eB_o$.

The Onsager theory is based on the observation that the variables **p** and **r**, are canonically conjugated in the Hamiltonian sense.

This result permits us to quantize the motion on a plane perpendicular to the constant magnetic field $\mathbf{B}_o$, provided it is periodic.* The energy spectrum of a Bloch electron is obtained using the Sommerfeld quantization rule.

$$\oint \mathbf{p}_\perp \cdot d\mathbf{r}_\perp = 2\pi\hbar(n+\delta) \tag{6.8}$$

Here n is a non-negative integer and δ a phase factor between zero and unity. The integral in (6.8) is to be taken around the path of the electron. Some simple transformations show that (6.8) implies that the area $S(\varepsilon, k_z)$ of the path in **k**-space for an electron of energy ε and having component of **k** parallel to $\mathbf{B}_o$ equal to $\mathbf{k}_z$ must satisfy the relation

$$S(\varepsilon, k_z) = \frac{2\pi e B_o}{\hbar c}(n+\delta) \tag{6.9}$$

This result permits us to label the different energy levels of a Bloch electron by the quantum numbers n and k_z. However n and k_z are not a complete set of observables and such levels are highly degenerate, the degeneracy being proportional to the area in **k**-space enclosed by two orbits for a given value of k_z. We shall refer to these energy states as the Landau levels. The energy difference between two adjacent Landau levels for the same values of k_z is

$$\Delta\varepsilon = \hbar\omega_c = \frac{2\pi e B_o}{\hbar c}\left(\frac{\partial S}{\partial \varepsilon}\right)^{-1} \tag{6.10}$$

---

* Thus this treatment is not applicable to situations where one has open orbits.

The quantity ω_c is called the cyclotron frequency because it is the frequency of electromagnetic radiation which causes transitions between two adjacent Landau levels. It is interesting to notice that ω_c is the reciprocal of the period of the motion described by Eq. (6.5). Of course this must be the case in virtue of the correspondence principle. A cyclotron effective mass m^* is defined by the condition $\omega_c = eB_o/m^*c$. Using Eq. (6.10) we obtain

$$m^+ = \frac{\hbar^2}{2\pi} \cdot \frac{\partial S}{\partial \varepsilon} \qquad (6.11)$$

The Onsager theory has been very useful in the interpretation of experimental measurements of the de Haas-van Alphen effect. This effect consists of an oscillatory dependence of the magnetic susceptibility of metals and semimetals as a function of B_o. The oscillations are periodic in B_o^{-1} with period

$$\Delta\left(\frac{1}{B_o}\right) = \frac{2\pi e}{\hbar c S}$$

where S is an extremal cross section of the Fermi surface, i.e. one for which $\mathbf{v}_z = 0$.

7. CYCLOTRON RESONANCE

We shall investigate the theory of several phenomena which can be used as experimental tools in the study of the Fermi surface of metals. The first will be cyclotron resonance. In cyclotron resonance we measure the spacing in energy of two Landau levels by using electromagnetic radiation of the appropriate frequency. Usually one keeps the frequency of the radiation fixed and varies the magnetic field. There are several forms of cyclotron resonance that will concern us. Firstly we investigate that which is most useful in semiconductors and semimetals in which the electromagnetic field can penetrate uniformly into the sample. We call this form of cyclotron resonance diamagnetic resonance.

(i) Diamagnetic resonance. Let us consider a material shaped as a plane slab and assume that it is placed in a magnetic field of induction $\mathbf{B}_o$ perpendicular to the plane of its surface. We assume further that a circularly polarized plane electromagnetic wave of angular frequency ω propagating parallel to $\mathbf{B}_o$ propagates incident to the surface. Taking $\mathbf{B}_o$ parallel to the z-axis of Cartesian coordinate system, the electric field of the wave at a given point (for left-handed circular polarization) is given by

$$E_x = E_o \cos \omega t$$
$$E_y = E_o \sin \omega t \qquad (7.1)$$
and
$$E_z = 0$$

We shall consider the case in which the wavelength and the skin depth are large compared with the dimensions of the specimen along z-axis, i.e. that $\mathbf{E}_o$ can be regarded as uniform. It is possible to describe the dynamics of the conduction electron by means of the simple equation

$$m^* \dot{\mathbf{v}} = -\frac{1}{\tau} m^* \mathbf{v} - e(\mathbf{E} + \frac{1}{c} \mathbf{v} \times \mathbf{B}_o) \qquad (7.2)$$

In this equation $\mathbf{v}$ is the velocity of the center of mass of the electrons and we have assumed that all band effects can be incorporated in the effective m^* so that $m^*\dot{\mathbf{v}}$ is equal to the average external force applied to the electrons; the collision time is introduced phenomenologically and it is such that if at time t_o the external fields are removed, then for $t > t_o$, $v(t) = v(t_o)\exp\left[-(t-t_o)/\tau\right]$ Finally we have neglected the magnetic field B of the wave as compared to $\mathbf{B}_o$. Since we are interested in the linear response of the system terms in $\mathbf{v} \times \mathbf{B}$ are of second order and therefore neglected. It is convenient to introduce instead of $\mathbf{E}$ the complex field $\boldsymbol{\mathcal{E}} = \mathbf{E}_o(e^{i\omega t}, -ie^{i\omega t}, 0)$ whose real part is $\mathbf{E}$. From this equation we obtain, in the steady state condition

$$J_{x,y} = \sigma_{eff}\,\mathcal{E}_{x,y} \tag{7.3}$$

where σ_{eff} is the effective conductivity

$$\sigma_{eff} = \frac{\sigma_o}{1 + i(\omega - \omega_c)\tau} \tag{7.4}$$

Now the effective dielectric constant of the medium is

$$\varepsilon_{eff} = \varepsilon_o - \frac{4\pi i\,\sigma_{eff}}{\omega} \tag{7.5}$$

where ε_o is the dielectric constant arising from the polarization of the ion cores. We shall for convenience drop the subscript "eff" from ε_{eff} in the subsequent development. It is enough to remember that this is the dielectric constant for the circular polarization we are considering now.

$$\epsilon = \epsilon_o - \frac{4\pi ne^2}{m^* \omega} \cdot \frac{(\omega - \omega_c)\tau^2}{1 + (\omega - \omega_c)^2 \tau^2} - i \frac{4\pi ne^2}{m^* \omega} \cdot \frac{\tau}{1 + (\omega - \omega_c)^2 \tau^2} \qquad (7.6)$$

If we suppose τ very large one can neglect the imaginary part of ϵ and if further we neglect ϵ_o as compared with $4\pi ne^2/m^*\omega(\omega - \omega_c)$ then we see that if $\omega_c < \omega$, $\epsilon < 0$ and the reflectivity

$$R = \left| \frac{1 - \sqrt{\epsilon}}{1 + \sqrt{\epsilon}} \right|^2$$

is equal to unity. If $\omega_c > \omega$, $\epsilon > 0$ and $R < 1$. A plot of the reflectivity as a function of B_o is given in Fig. 8.

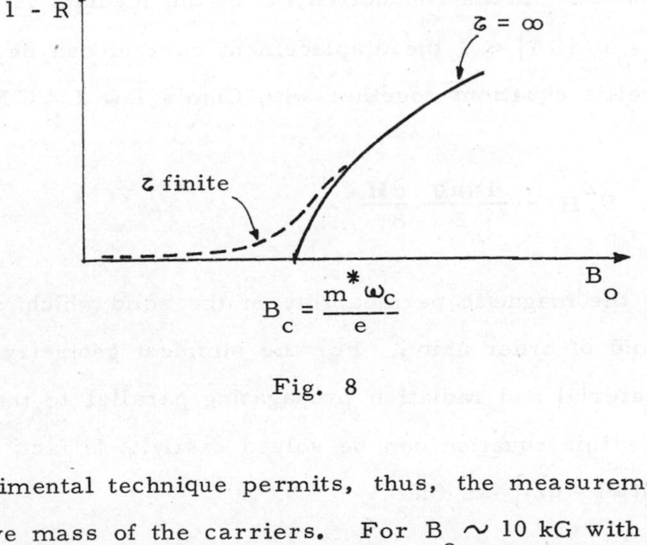

Fig. 8

This experimental technique permits, thus, the measurement of the effective mass of the carriers. For $B_o \sim 10$ kG with $m^* \sim m$ the edge in R occurs at a frequency of 20 kMHz. Of course, the position of the edge is clearly determined only if τ is sufficiently large so that we must have pure samples at low temperatures.

An advantage of this technique is that it permits to distinguish between electrons and holes. The edge in R for the latter will require the circularly polarization opposite to the one considered above, or alternatively, the inversion of the magnetic field. It is left as an excercise for the student to plot Re ϵ, Imϵ and R for a system containing both electrons and holes.

We now turn to some of the questions that we have omitted from our considerations above. An overriding assumption was the one that permitted us to write the dynamical equation (7.2) in which the field $\mathbf{E}_o$ was assumed uniform within the specimen. In a conducting medium the field will vary in space and give rise to the well-known decrease in the intensity of the a.c. electromagnetic field referred to as the skin effect. We give now a brief review of this subject. If the conductivity σ of the medium is large enough so that $[\varepsilon_o \omega / 4\pi\sigma] \ll 1$ the displacement current can be neglected and Maxwell's equations together with Ohm's law $\mathbf{J} = \sigma \mathbf{E}$ lead to the equation

$$\nabla^2 \mathbf{H} = \frac{4\pi\mu\sigma}{c^2} \frac{\partial \mathbf{H}}{\partial t} \tag{7.7}$$

Here μ is the magnetic permeability of the solid which we will take constant and of order unity. For the simplest geometry of a plane slab of material and radiation propagating parallel to the normal to the surface this equation can be solved easily. In fact, if we take $\mathbf{H} \propto \exp[i(\omega t - qz)]$ we find

$$q = \frac{1 - i}{\delta_c} \tag{7.8}$$

where

$$\delta_c = \left(\frac{c^2}{2\pi\mu\sigma\omega}\right)^{1/2} \tag{7.9}$$

In the derivation we assume $\omega\tau \ll 1$ so that σ can be taken as real. The length δ_c is called the skin depth. For a metal having carrier concentration $n \sim 10^{22}$ cm^{-3} and $\tau \sim 10^{-12}$ sec, $\sigma \sim 10^{18} - 10^{19}$ sec^{-1} and $\delta_c \sim 3 \times 10^{-5}$ cm for $(\omega/2\pi) \sim 10$ kMHz. We call δ_c the "classical" skin depth.

The electromagnetic fields vary as $\exp\left[i(\omega t - z/\delta_c) - z/\delta_c\right]$. However, the quantity that is accesible to measurement is the surface impedance:

$$Z = \frac{4\pi}{c} \frac{E_t(0)}{H_t(0)} \tag{7.10}$$

where $E_t(0)$ and $H_t(0)$ are the tangential components of the electric and magnetic fields at the boundary $z = 0$ of the specimen. It is understood that $\mathbf{E}$ and $\mathbf{H}$ are expressed in complex notation so as to take into account their phase differences. Now it is easy to demostrate that the real part of $Z = R + iX$, i.e. the surface resistence is proportional to the average power absorbed by the sample. In fact the average power absorbed by the sample is the Poynting vector $\mathbf{S} = \frac{1}{2}\,\mathrm{Re}\left[(c/4\pi)\mathbf{E}_t(0) \times \mathbf{H}_t^*(0)\right]$ and this is immediately shown to be proportional to R. While R is then related to the change in the Q of cavity in which one wall is replaced by the sample, X is related to the shift in the resonance frequency in the microwave cavity from its value in the absence of the sample. From Maxwell's equation

$$Z = -\frac{4\pi}{c^2}\, i\mu\omega \left[\frac{E_t(z)}{\partial E_t/\partial z}\right]_{z=0^+} \tag{7.11}$$

If $\mathbf{E}(z)$ varies as $\exp\left[i(\omega t - z/\delta_c) - z/\delta_c\right]$ then

$$Z = \frac{4\pi\mu\omega\delta_c}{c^2}(1 + i) \tag{7.12}$$

Then $R \propto \omega^{1/2} \sigma^{-1/2}$. The development given above is valid if $\delta_c \gg \ell$, the mean free path of the electrons. If this requirement is not satisfied, Ohm's law $\mathbf{J} = \sigma\mathbf{E}$ is invalid. In fact, one can easily convince oneself that if $\delta_c \lesssim \ell$ then the current density at a point $\mathbf{r}$ does not depend on the field $\mathbf{E}$ at that point but on the values of the electric field within a sphere of radius of order ℓ around r. The most general linear form between $\mathbf{J}$ and $\mathbf{E}$ that one can write is of the form

$$\mathbf{J}(\mathbf{r}, t) = \int d\mathbf{r}' dt' \sigma(\mathbf{r} - \mathbf{r}'; t - t') \cdot \mathbf{E}(\mathbf{r}', t') \tag{7.13}$$

Here we have disregarded all effects of the crystal potential except as they enter into the form of the energy as a function of $\mathbf{k}$. The tensor $\sigma(\mathbf{r} - \mathbf{r}', t - t')$ can be obtained from dynamical consideration which we shall not discuss in this course. The problem is complicated further when the effects of the boundary are taken into account.

A simple manner of dealing with the case $\ell \gg \delta_c$ was developed by Pippard[5]. It consists in the observation that only the electrons whose velocities form an angle less than δ/ℓ with the surface of the specimen can contribute to the current. Here δ is not the classical skin depth but an actual skin penetration to be determined self-consistently. We take, instead of σ, in the expression for δ_c and effective conductivity $\sigma_{eff} = n_{eff} e^2 \tau / m^*$ where $n_{eff} = \beta n \delta/\ell$. The number β is of the order of unity and is to be determined by the more accurate theory.

We now write

$$\delta = (c^2/2\pi\mu\sigma_{eff}\omega)^{1/2}$$

and obtain

$$\delta = (c^2 m^* V_F / 2\pi \mu n e^2 \beta \omega)^{1/3} \tag{7.14}$$

We notice that now δ is proportional to $\omega^{-1/3}$ instead of $\omega^{-1/2}$ and that it is independent of the collision time. We do not discuss this matter but go directly to the analysis of cyclotron resonance in metals. The first question that we study is the Azbel-Kaner effect[6].

(ii) Cyclotron resonance. In the Azbel-Kaner (AK) effect the cyclotron resonance takes place taking advantage of the skin depth. We consider the case, which is the most usual in practice, of a metal in which $\ell \gg \delta_c$ and

$$\delta \ll r_c = \frac{m^* c V_F}{e B_o}$$

where r_c is the radius of the cyclotron orbit. For example, for $B_o \approx 10$ kG, $r_c \approx 10^{-3}$ cm while $\delta \approx 10^{-5}$ at microwave frequencies. The magnetic field B_o is taken parallel to the surface of the specimen as shown in Fig. 9 and the microwave radiation is incident along the normal to the surface. Resonant absorption of energy by the electrons occur whenever $\omega_c = \omega/n$, $n = 1, 2, 3, \ldots$ because then the electromagnetic field has the same phase each time the

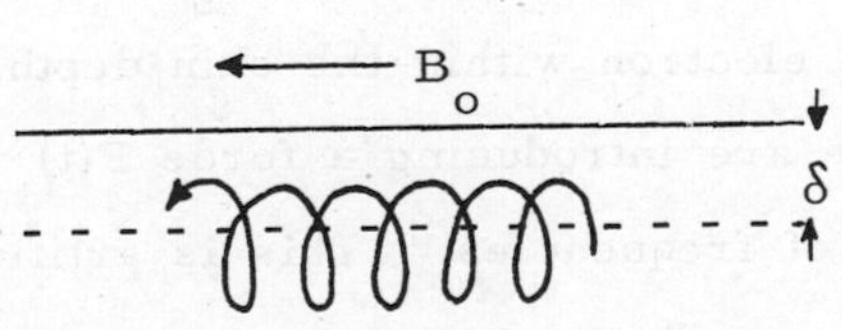

Fig. 9

carriers enter within the region of the skin depth. The absorption then shows a series of maxima and minima. The detailed theory is rather complicated and we prefer to give a simplified version of it using Pippard's concept of the ineffectiveness already discussed in connection with the anomalous skin effect. The simple argument given here was communicated to the author by Dr. A. D. Brailsford. We consider that the effective number of electrons is, as before, $n_{eff} = (n\delta\beta/\ell)$. Now if we take the microwave electric field parallel to $\mathbf{B}_o$ (i.e. along the z-axis of a Cartesian coordinate system) we can write for a typical electron

$$m^* \frac{dv_z}{dt} = -\frac{m^* v_z}{\tau} + F(t) \qquad (7.15)$$

F(t) is a force that varies with time according to the trajectory of the electron in the material. For example, when the electron is within the skin depth the force is $-eE_o \exp(i\omega t)$, the electric field times the charge on the electron while during the part of the trajectory in the bulk it is essentially zero. We write approximately

$$F(t) = -eE_o e^{i\omega t} \tau_s \sum_{n=0}^{\infty} \delta(t - nT_c - t_o) \qquad (7.16)$$

where t_o is the time at which the electron first enters the skin depth and T_c is the cyclotron period, $\tau_s (\ll \tau, T_c)$ is roughly the time spent by the electron within the skin depth. It appears at first sight that we are introducing a force F(t) which has a uniform distribution of frequencies. This is artificial and does not correspond to the actual physical situation. The solution for v_z is

$$v_z = \frac{1}{m^*} \int_0^t e^{-\frac{t-t'}{\tau}} \, dt' \, F(t')$$

$$= (eE_o \tau_s / m^*) e^{i\omega t} \gamma(B_o, \omega) \qquad (7.17)$$

where

$$\gamma(B_o, \omega) = \left[1 - \exp\left\{ -\frac{2\pi}{\omega_c}(i\omega + \frac{1}{\tau}) \right\} \right]^{-1}$$

This result is obtained assuming $t - t_o \gg \tau$. Now

$$\sigma_{eff} = n_{eff} e V_z = (\tau_s/\tau)\gamma(B_o, \omega)\, \sigma_{eff}(0) \qquad (7.18)$$

where $\sigma_{eff}(0)$ signifies the effective conductivity at zero applied magnetic field. Using the arguments developed above for the anomalous skin effect we find

$$\delta = \left[\frac{c^2 m^* V_F}{2\pi \mu n e^2 \beta \omega} \right]^{1/3} \left[\frac{\tau}{\tau_s} \right]^{1/3} \gamma^{-1/3}(B_o, \omega) \qquad (7.19)$$

which has the property of giving rise to absorption peaks whenever $\omega_c = \omega/n$. A more exact theory yields

$$Z = \frac{8}{9} \left[\frac{\sqrt{3}\, \pi \omega^2 \ell}{c^4 \sigma} \right]^{1/3} (1 + i\sqrt{3}) \tanh^{1/3} \left[\frac{\pi}{\omega_c \tau}(1 + i\omega\tau) \right]$$

$$(7.20)$$

It is interesting to give a quantum mechanical description of the difference between diamagnetic resonance and the Azbel-Kaner effect. We shall do this by considering the Hamiltonian of a free electron in the presence of a d.c. magnetic field parallel to the z-axis and of a microwave field. The vector potentials which gives rise to the fields are designated by $\mathbf{A}_o$ and $\mathbf{A}$ respectively. We can take $\mathbf{A}_o = (0, B_o x, 0)$. For diamagnetic resonance

$$\mathbf{A} = \mathbf{a}\, e^{i(\omega t - qz)} + \mathbf{a}^{*} e^{-i(\omega t - qz)} \tag{7.21}$$

$$\mathbf{a} = (a_x, a_y, 0)$$

while for the Azbel-Kaner effect it can be written in the form

$$\mathbf{A} = \mathbf{a}(x)\, e^{i\omega t} + c\,c \tag{7.22}$$

with

$$\mathbf{a} = (0, a_y(x), a_z(x)) \quad \text{(See Fig. 10)}$$

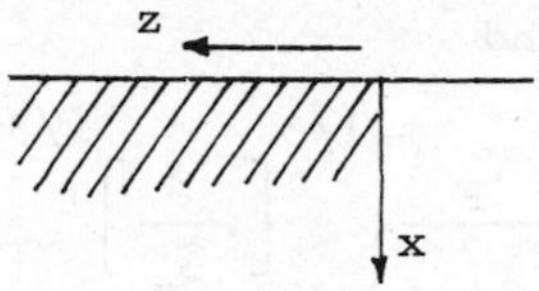

Fig. 10

if $$\mathbf{v} = \frac{1}{m}\left(\mathbf{p} + \frac{e}{c}\mathbf{A}_o\right) \tag{7.23}$$

then

$$H = H_o + H_1 \tag{7.24}$$

where

$$H_o = \frac{1}{2} m v^2 \tag{7.25}$$

and $$H_1 = \frac{e}{2c}(\mathbf{v} \cdot \mathbf{A} + \mathbf{A} \cdot \mathbf{v}) \tag{7.26}$$

In either case we can write

$$H_1 = \frac{e}{c}\mathbf{A}\cdot\mathbf{v} \tag{7.27}$$

Now it is possible to show that the operators p_z, p_y and $(a^+ a)$ form a complete set of commuting operators where

$$a = \sqrt{\frac{m\omega_c}{2\hbar}}\left(x + \frac{c}{eB_o}p_y\right) + \frac{i}{\sqrt{2m\hbar\omega_c}}p_x \tag{7.28}$$

We can easily prove that

$$\left[a, a^+\right] = 1 \tag{7.29}$$

and that

$$H_o = \hbar\omega_c\left(a^+ a + \frac{1}{2}\right) + \frac{p_z^2}{2m} \tag{7.30}$$

It is well known that the eigenvalues of an operator such as $a^+ a$ are non-negative integers. This immediately give us the energy eigenvalues of H_o.

$$\varepsilon_n(k_z) = \hbar\omega_c\left(n + \frac{1}{2}\right) + \frac{\hbar^2 k_z^2}{2m} \tag{7.31}$$

The eigenvectors of H_o are characterized by $|nk_y k_z>$:

$$H_o\,|nk_y k_z> = \varepsilon_n(k_z)\,|nk_y k_z> \tag{7.32}$$

We also have

$$a^+\,|nk_y k_z> = \sqrt{n+1}\,|n+1, k_y, k_z> \tag{7.33}$$

and $$a \mid n k_y k_z > = \sqrt{n} \mid n-1, k_y, k_z > \qquad (7.34)$$

To establish the selection rules for absorption of a quantum we must calculate the matrix elements

$$< n' k'_y k'_z \mid \frac{e}{c} \mathbf{v} \cdot \mathbf{A} \mid n k_y k_z >$$

For diamagnetic resonance we see immediately that this matrix element is non-vanishing if $n' = n \pm 1$, $k'_y = k_y$ and $k'_z = k_z \pm q$. For the AK effect we find in a similar way, expanding $\mathbf{a}(x)$ in powers of x that the conditions

$$\Delta n = n' - n = \pm 1, \pm 2, \ldots.. \; k'_y = k_y \text{ and } k'_z = k_z$$

are required for the non-vanishing of the above matrix elements. One cannot keep linear terms in x in $\mathbf{v} \cdot \mathbf{A}$ because $\delta_c \gg \delta$ and the dipole approximation breaks down. Another way to say this is that one cannot neglect the higher order terms in $\mathbf{a}(x)$ because $\mathbf{a}(x)$ varies radically in a length δ which is much less than the extension r_c of the electron wave functions.

(iii) We now study a third form of resonance phenomenon. Before we discuss it, however, we will study a form of electromagnetic wave propagation in conducting solids in a magnetic field known as helicons or whistlers. This type of wave propagation was first detected during the first world war and interpreted as an ionospheric phenomenon by Barkhausen[7]. The correct description of this form of electromagnetic wave propagation was given first by Eckersley[8]. The suggestion that they can also be observed in metals and semiconductors was made simultaneously and independent by Konstantinov and Perel[9] and Aigrain[10]. The discussion is rather simple and will be given first for the case of long wave length. Consider, for example, a conducting material containing n electrons per unit volume in the presence of a magnetic field $\mathbf{B}_o$ which we take parallel to the z-axis of a Cartesian coordinate system. In the absence of the magnetic field the system is opaque to electromagnetic waves of frequency $\omega < \omega_p$ whose ω_p is the plasma frequency

$$\omega_p = (4\pi ne^2/m^* \epsilon_o)^{1/2}$$

Here m^* is the effective mass of the electrons and ϵ_o the dielectric constant of the ion cores. This arises from the fact that the dielectric constant of the system at frequency ω is

$$\epsilon(\omega) = \epsilon_o\left[1 - (\omega_p/\omega)^2\right]$$

and it is negative for $\omega < \omega_p$. In the above expression it has been assumed that the electron collision time τ is long compared to the period ω^{-1} of the waves. In general

$$\epsilon(\omega) = \epsilon_o\left[1 - \frac{\omega_p^2}{\omega(\omega - i/\tau)}\right]$$

The situation is altered considerably when the material is in the presence of a strong magnetic field. The dielectric constant associated with waves propagating parallel to the applied magnetic field depends as one expects on the sense of circular polarization of the waves. For the left- and right-circularly polarized waves they are respectively

$$\epsilon_{\pm}(\omega) = \epsilon_o \left[1 - \frac{\omega_p^2}{\omega(\omega \mp \omega_c - i/\tau)} \right] \tag{7.35}$$

We consider only low frequency waves by which we mean $\omega \ll \omega_c$ and $\omega \ll \omega_p$. If further the magnetic field is strong enough that $\omega_c \tau \gg 1$ and $\omega_p \gg \omega_c$ which is the usual case in metals we have

$$\epsilon_{\pm}(\omega) \simeq \pm \frac{\epsilon_o \omega_p^2}{\omega \omega_c} \tag{7.36}$$

The frequency ω and the wave number q of plane waves propagating in such a medium are related by $\omega = cq/\sqrt{\epsilon_{\pm}}$. We see immediately that the right circularly polarized wave has an imaginary wave number so that this sense of polarization is completely reflected. The other sense, corresponding to the positive sign gives a travelling wave which can propagate through the medium. We find

$$\omega = \frac{c^2 q^2 \omega_c}{\epsilon_o \omega_p^2} = \frac{c q^2 B_o}{4 \pi n e} \tag{7.37}$$

It is seen immediately that the dispersion relation of these waves called helicons by Aigrain, does not depend on ϵ_o in this limit. Furthermore it does not depend on the electron effective mass. This latter result is much more general than is indicated here and is always valid in the limit $\omega_c \tau \gg 1$. We consider to give an example a standing wave of wavelength of the order of 1 cm, then $q = 2\pi/\lambda \approx 6 \text{ cm}^{-1}$. For $n \approx 10^{22}$, $\omega \approx 150 \text{ sec}^{-1}$ and $\omega/q \approx 25$ cm/sec. Thus these waves travel very slowly indeed.

If we keep the term in τ we find

$$\omega = \pm \frac{c^2 q^2 \omega_c}{\epsilon_o \omega_p^2} \left(1 \mp \frac{i}{\omega_c \tau}\right) \qquad (7.38)$$

so that we can calculate the absorption coefficient. The details will be left to the reader.

We shall now come to the type of resonance phenomenon that we wished to discuss. We consider a metal in a magnetic field and in which there is a helicon propagating. Since the velocity of the electrons is of the order of the Fermi velocity which is much larger than the usual velocity of a helicon we can, to a first approximation regard the latter as stationary. As an electron with component of velocity v_z along the z-axis moves in the field of the helicon wave it experiences, in the frame of reference moving with velocity v_z an oscillatory field of frequency

$$\omega_{eff} = q v_z - \omega \approx q v_z \qquad (7.39)$$

Thus, there is a contribution to the electrical conductivity proportional to

$$\left[1 + i(\omega\tau \mp \omega_c \tau - q v_z \tau)\right]^{-1}$$

and for all the electrons we have

$$\sigma_{\pm} = \frac{e^2}{4\pi^2 \hbar^2} \int dk_z \frac{m^* \tau V_{\perp}^2}{1 + i(\omega\tau \mp \omega_c \tau - q v_z \tau)} \qquad (7.40)$$

where $V_\perp$ is the magnitude of the component of velocity perpendicular to the z-axis. Clearly, this gives rise to absorption whenever electron states having $v_z = \omega_c/q$ are occupied. Thus, as one lowers the magnetic field from above $B_c = (cq/e)m^* V_F$ to values below B_o then there is an absorption edge. This absorption edge is due to a resonant absorption called the Doppler-shifted absorption edge (DSAE). Clearly this condition occurs when the local theory is no longer valid so that the simple helicon dispersion formula given above no longer holds. The dispersion relation is

$$q^2 = (4\pi \omega n e/B_o c) f_\pm \tag{7.41}$$

where

$$f_\pm = \frac{3}{4}\int_0^\pi d\theta \sin^3\theta \left[q V_F/\omega_c)\cos\theta \pm 1 + (i/\omega_c \tau)\right]^{-1} \tag{7.42}$$

Under typical experimental conditions $\nu = (\omega/2\pi) = 10$ MHz, $B_o = 10$ kG, $n \approx 10^{22}$ cm^{-3} so that $|q| \approx 4 \times 10^3$ cm^{-1} and $(\omega/|q|) \sim 10^4$ cm/sec. The theoretical absorption edge B_e is defined as that field for which $\omega_c = (\mathrm{Re}\, q)(v_z)_{max}$. Experimentally one measures the surface impedance $Z = R + iX$ of the material as a function of the applied magnetic field. The experimental edge can be defined in an arbitrary way and we define it as that value B_x of B_o for which (dX/dB_o) has a maximum. If $\tau \rightarrow \infty$ then $B_e = B_x$, however as τ is decreased B_e decreases while B_x increases. The latter behavior is fairly easy to understand. In fact, as τ decreases the wave is attenuated and no longer a simple sinusoidal wave but possesses a distribution of values of q. Thus, the condition $q(v_z)_{max} = \omega_c$ is reached at higher magnetic fields for shorter collision times.

8. PROPAGATION OF ACOUSTIC WAVES IN METALS

a. First observations. The coefficient of absorption of sound waves in metals is a decreasing function of the temperature down to a few degrees absolute. This behavior can be explained in terms of the energy losses that arise because of the motion of the dislocation within the metal. However, as the temperature is lowered further, the attenuation of high frequency sound waves in very pure samples experiences an increase and exhibits a flat maximum as the temperature approaches 0°K. This pehnomenon was first observed by Bömmel[11] and by Mackinnon[12]. One can attribute the low temperature attenuation of ultrasonic waves in metals to the scattering of the sound by the conduction electrons. The acoustic phonons scatter the conduction electrons inelastically into states having energy larger than that corresponding to thermal equilibrium. Subsequently, the electrons transfer their excess energy irreversibly to the thermal lattice vibrations. The attenuation results from the net transfer of energy from the acoustic wave to the thermal phonons.

It is convenient to give the order of magnitude of the effect under study before discussing the experimental results and their interpretation. The usual procedure consists in producing acoustic pulses during about one microsecond each (extending over a distance of 0.3 cm if the velocity of sound is taken to be $s = 3 \times 10^5$ cm/sec which is typical of many metals). The dimensions of the sample are usually of the order of 3 cm. Let us designate by P(y) the energy per unit time and area of the acoustic wave transmitted across a plane perpendicular to the direction of propagation of the wave. Here y is a coordinate along this direction measured starting at the input end of the sample. The coefficient of attenuation γ is defined by the equation

$$P(y) = P(0) \exp\left[-\gamma y\right] \tag{8.1}$$

where P(0) is the acoustic power input per unit cross-sectional area. If W is the power dissipated per unit volume of the sample we obtain the expression

$$\gamma = W/P(0) \tag{8.2}$$

Bömmel found that for an acoustic frequency of 10 Mc/sec that part of the attenuation of sound in lead that did not arise from the motion of dislocations was 0.22 cm^{-1}. (A constant magnetic field of sufficient intensity was applied in order to insure that the sample is in its normal rather than in its superconducting phase). In a typical experiment 100 pulses per second each having a duration of one microsecond may be used. The power input during a pulse may vary from 0.01 watt/cm^2 to 0.1 watt/cm^2 so that the average power input is of the order of 10^{-6} to 10^{-5} watt/cm^2. Let

$$\boldsymbol{\xi}(\mathbf{r}, t) = \mathrm{Re}\, \boldsymbol{\xi}_0 \exp\left\{i(\omega t - \mathbf{q} \cdot \mathbf{r})\right\} \tag{8.3}$$

be the displacement of an atom in the position $\mathbf{r}$ at time t.

We shall consider longitudinal waves in which $\boldsymbol{\xi}_0$ is parallel to $\mathbf{q}$ with velocity s_ℓ and transverse waves in which ξ_o is perpendicular to $\mathbf{q}$ having velocity s_t. The velocity field associated with the displacements given by (8.3) is

$$\mathbf{u}(\mathbf{r}, t) = \mathrm{Re}\, \mathbf{u}_o \exp\left\{ i(\omega t - \mathbf{q} \cdot \mathbf{r})\right\} \tag{8.4}$$

with

$$\mathbf{u}_o = i\omega \xi_o \tag{8.5}$$

The power input per unit area is

$$P(0) = \frac{1}{2} \delta |\mathbf{u}_o|^2 s \tag{8.6}$$

where δ is the density of the material. For $P(0) = 0.1$ watt/cm^2, $s = 4.7 \times 10^5$ cm/sec and $\delta = 8.9$ gm/cm^3 (these values correspond to a copper sample) we obtain $u_o = 0.48$ cm/sec. The strain associated with the acoustic wave is

$$\mathcal{E} = \frac{\partial \xi}{\partial y} = \frac{u}{s} \approx 10^{-6}$$

It is found experimentally that the parameter of interest is $q\ell$ where ℓ is the electron mean free path as obtained from measurements of electrical resistivity. If $q\ell \ll 1$ then γ is proportional to the square of the acoustic frequency ω while if $q\ell \gg 1$ γ is proportional to ω. Experiments have been carried out in which the sample under investigation is placed in a transverse magnetic field B_o. It is observed that when $q\ell \ll 1$ the attenuation decreases monotonically with magnetic field while in the region in which $q\ell \gg 1$ there is a series of maxima and minima of γ as a function of B_o. The period of the oscillations is inversely proportional to the applied magnetic field.

In the remainder of this section we shall give the simplest theoretical interpretations of some of these results.

b. Simple theoretical interpretations.

(i) Viscosity approximation. Mason[13] suggested that the acoustic attenuation occurs because of the viscosity of the electron gas. Let us consider the case in which $q\ell \ll 1$, and, to fix the ideas, limit ourselves to a transverse wave travelling in the y-direction and polarized along the x-axis. Because of their high mobility, the electrons follow the motion of the positive ions of the crystal. However, those electrons that have appreciable component of velocity along the y-direction find themselves, upon travelling, in regions of varying drift velocity parallel to the direction of polarization. They are, therefore, capable of transferring momentum to the atoms of the crystal in the same way as molecules of a gas transfer momentum to others when they cross the interface between two gas layers moving relative to each other. Since the velocity field has a gradient $\partial u/\partial y$ along the direction of propagation there is a viscous drag exerted upon the fast moving layers by the slower ones given by the stress field

$$X(y,t) = \eta \frac{\partial u}{\partial y} \tag{8.7}$$

The coefficient η is the viscosity given from elementary kinetic theory by

$$\eta = \frac{1}{3} n m < v^2 \tau > \tag{8.8}$$

In Eq. (8.8) n is the number of free electrons per unit volume, m is the mass of the electron, v the velocity of a typical electron and τ the collision time for the electrons. The brackets designate the average over the thermal distribution. For a Fermi gas

$$\eta = \frac{1}{5} n V_F^2 \tau m \qquad (8.9)$$

where V_F is the velocity of an electron at the top of the Fermi distribution. The coefficient of attenuation is obtained from (8.2) and (8.6) once we note that

$$W = \frac{1}{2} \mathrm{Re}\left(\eta \frac{\partial u}{\partial y} \frac{\partial u^*}{\partial y}\right) = \frac{1}{2} \eta \, |\mathbf{u}|^2 q^2 \qquad (8.10)$$

so that

$$\gamma = \frac{nm V_F^2 \tau \omega^2}{s \delta s_t^3} \qquad (8.11)$$

We see that the attenuation increases quadratically with ω as if found experimentally. An argument of this nature can, in principle, be extended to the case $q\ell \gg 1$ but the analysis becomes rather complicated and it is more difficult to visualize the transfer of momentum between different regions because now the electrons have such long mean free paths that they can converge to a certain region of space with quite different drift velocities. We now consider the attenuation of acoustic waves in the high frequency range ($q\ell \gg 1$). The argument we shall give is due to Kittel[14] and Morse[15].

(ii) <u>Phonon-electron scattering.</u> Let us consider now a longitudinal sound wave propagating along q whose displacement field can be expressed in the form

$$\boldsymbol{\xi}(\mathbf{r}) = \left(\frac{\hbar}{2\delta\omega\Omega}\right)^{1/2} \mathbf{e}\left\{a^{+}\exp(-i\mathbf{q}\cdot\mathbf{r}) + a\exp(i\mathbf{q}\cdot\mathbf{r})\right\} \qquad (8.12)$$

where $\mathbf{e}$ is a unit vector in the direction of $\mathbf{q}$ and a^{+} and a are operators that create and destroy a phonon in the acoustic wave. We shall assume that the interaction energy between an electron and the acoustic phonons is proportional to the dilation of the lattice associated with the acoustic wave, i.e. the energy of interaction is

$$H' = E_1 \operatorname{div} \boldsymbol{\xi}(\mathbf{r}) \qquad (8.13)$$

where E_1 is a quantity of the order of magnitude of the Fermi energy.

The interaction H' has non-vanishing matrix elements for processes in which an electron absorbs a phonon or emits one. If n_a is the number of acoustic phonons the non-zero matrix elements of (8.13) are

$$\langle \mathbf{k}+\mathbf{q}, n_a - 1 \,|\, H' \,|\, \mathbf{k}, n_a \rangle = -iE_1\left[\frac{\hbar\omega n_a}{2\delta\Omega s_\ell^2}\right]^{1/2} \qquad (8.14a)$$

and

$$\langle \mathbf{k}, n_a + 1 \,|\, H' \,|\, \mathbf{k}+\mathbf{q}, n_a \rangle = -iE_1\left[\frac{\hbar\omega(n_a+1)}{2\delta\Omega s_\ell^2}\right]^{1/2} \qquad (8.14b)$$

The wave function $|\mathbf{k}, n_a\rangle$ designates a state in which an electron with wave vector $\mathbf{k}$ is present together with n_a acoustic phonons.

The matrix elements (8.14a) and (8.14b) permit us to calculate the transition probabilities for the emission and absorption of phonons. A simple kinetic calculation gives the decrease in the number of phonons in the wave as it progresses within the metal. We find

$$\gamma = -\frac{1}{n_a}\frac{\partial n_a}{\partial y} = \frac{2}{n_a s_\ell}\sum_{\mathbf{k}}\Big\{w(\mathbf{k}+\mathbf{q},\ n_a - 1;\ \mathbf{k}, n_a) f_o(\mathbf{k})\left[1 - f_o(\mathbf{k}+\mathbf{q})\right]$$

$$- w(\mathbf{k},\ n_a + 1;\ \mathbf{k}+\mathbf{q},\ n_a) f_o(\mathbf{k}+\mathbf{q})\left[1 - f_o(\mathbf{k})\right]\Big\} \tag{8.15}$$

The sum extends over all electron states and $f_o(\mathbf{k})$ is the probability for the state $\mathbf{k}$ to be occupied by an electron as given by Fermi-Dirac statistics. The factor 2 arises from the spin degeneracy of the electrons. The transition probabilities w are obtained using a Born approximation. Some simple transformations of (8.15) yield

$$\alpha = \frac{3\pi n E_1^2}{2m\delta v_F^3 s_\ell^3} \tag{8.16}$$

This treatment is correct only when the uncertainty in the momentum of the electrons is negligible as compared to the momentum of the phonon $\hbar\mathbf{q}$, i.e. when $\Delta p \ll \hbar q$. If the mean free path is ℓ, then the uncertainty in the momentum of an electron is given by $\Delta p \sim \hbar/\ell$ so that the present approach is only valid when $q\ell \gg 1$.

We now outline a theory which is valid for all values of $q\ell$.

c. Outline of the general theory. The problem at hand is that of finding the normal modes of vibration of the atoms within the metal. We are not only interested in finding the angular frequency ω of a disturbance with wave vector **q** but also the damping coefficient γ. It is our purpose to solve this problem in the same fashion in which one discusses the theory of the normal modes of vibration of the atoms of a crystal. For simplicity we consider a monatomic crystal. The displacement at time t of the atom whose position of stable equilibrium is n will be designated by $\xi_n(t)$. We shall assume that we can classify the interactions within the solid into short-range repulsive forces among the ions which arise because of the core exchange interactions and the Coulomb forces among the positive ions, among the electrons and between ions and electrons.*

The equations of motion of the ion at the lattice site n is

$$M \frac{d^2 \xi_n}{dt^2} = - \sum_{n'} \mathbf{C}(\mathbf{n} - \mathbf{n}') \cdot \xi_{n'} + ze\mathbf{E}_n + \frac{ze}{c} \frac{d^2 \xi_n}{dt} \times \mathbf{B}_o + \mathbf{F}_c \tag{8.17}$$

Here $\mathbf{C}(\mathbf{n} - \mathbf{n}')$ is a tensor of the second order that describes the core repulsions between the ions. We notice that the force on the atom whose lattice position is **n** arising from a displacement of the atom at **n**' depends only on **n** - **n**'. This result is, of course, a consequence of the translational symmetry of the structure. The vector $\mathbf{E}_n$ is the electric field at position n. This field originates because of the displacement of the other ions and one must properly take into account the dynamical readjustment of the charge density

---

* This model differs from the one used by Bohm and Staver and by Bardeen and Pines. In these papers the interactions between the ions included their Coulomb repulsions in the presence of a uniform background of negative charge, as well as the short-range forces between the positive ions.

of the conduction electrons (screening effect). The contribution

$$\frac{ze}{c}\frac{d\xi_n}{dt} \times \mathbf{B}_o$$

is the Lorentz force on the ion because of the presence of an external magnetic field of induction $\mathbf{B}_o$. Finally the force $\mathbf{F}_c$ is an average force on the ions arising because of the collisions of the conduction electrons with lattice imperfections such as thermal phonons, impurity atoms, etc. In the third term on the right hand side of Eq. (8.17) we have neglected a contribution involving the microscopic magnetic field $\mathbf{B}$. Such a contribution would, naturally, contain ξ_n to the second power so that we can neglect it in the present linear theory.

The collision force $\mathbf{F}_c$ is an indirect manifestation of the coherence of the applied acoustic wave. In fact, because of the ultrasonic wave and of the coupling between electrons and phonons, the conduction electrons acquire a momentum density P_e given by

$$\mathbf{P}_e = (4\pi^3)^{-1} \int d\mathbf{k}\, m\mathbf{v}_k\, f(\varepsilon_k) \tag{8.18}$$

where $\mathbf{v}_k$ is the group velocity of the electron in a state characterized by $\mathbf{k}$ and $f(\varepsilon_k)$ the distribution function appropriate to an electron with energy ε_k. The rate at which the conduction electron lose momentum per unit volume is

$$\left(\frac{\partial}{\partial t}\mathbf{P}_e\right)_{coll} = (4\pi^3)^{-1} \int d\mathbf{k}\, m\mathbf{v}_k \left(\frac{\partial f}{\partial t}\right)_{coll} \tag{8.19}$$

The total momentum density $\mathbf{P}_i + \mathbf{P}_e$ where $\mathbf{P}_i$ is the ionic contribution is, of course, not altered by the collisions. This implies that on the average the electrons excert a force upon the ions equal to

$$\mathbf{F}_c = \frac{z}{n_o}\left(\frac{\partial \mathbf{P}_i}{\partial t}\right)_{coll} = -\frac{z}{n_o}\frac{1}{4\pi^3}\int d\mathbf{k}\, m\mathbf{v}_k \left(\frac{\partial f(\varepsilon_k)}{\partial t}\right)_{coll} \qquad (8.20)$$

We assume as it is customary that

$$\boldsymbol{\xi}_n(t) = \boldsymbol{\xi}_o \exp(i\omega t - i\mathbf{q}\cdot\mathbf{n}) \qquad (8.21)$$

and substitute into Eq. (8.17). This substitution after the assumption is made that both $\mathbf{E}_n$ and $\mathbf{F}_c$ vary in the same manner as $\boldsymbol{\xi}_n(t)$ yields

$$\omega^2\boldsymbol{\xi} = \mathbf{A}_c(\mathbf{q})\cdot\boldsymbol{\xi} - \frac{ze\mathbf{E}}{M} - \frac{zei\omega}{Mc}\boldsymbol{\xi}\times\mathbf{B}_o - \frac{1}{M}\mathbf{F}_c \qquad (8.22)$$

The tensor $\mathbf{A}_c(\mathbf{q})$ is given by the expression

$$\mathbf{A}_c(\mathbf{q}) = \frac{1}{M}\sum_n \mathbf{C}(\mathbf{n})e^{i\mathbf{q}\cdot\mathbf{n}} = \frac{1}{M}\sum_n \mathbf{C}(\mathbf{n})\cos(\mathbf{q}-\mathbf{n}) \qquad (8.23)$$

To proceed further we must make some simplifying assumptions. The first is that we are concerned with acoustic wavelengths λ which are much larger than the lattice spacing of the crystal. With this approximation we can regard the crystal as a continuum. We shall first find an expression for the collision force and then relate the electric field E to the displacement field.

To find an expression for the collision force we make the simplifying assumption that the collision time τ for the conduction electrons is the same for all the electrons. This assumption will be implicit in all of our developments. For the time being we shall make the further assumption that the electrons behave as if they were free. It is true however that some of the results which we shall give are more general than what will be implied below but this added generality will not be emphasized in these lectures. We find $\mathbf{F}_c$ obtaining an expression for $(\partial f/\partial t)_{coll}$ and substituting into Eq. (8.20). It would be wrong, however, to take $(\partial f/\partial t)_{coll} = -(f - f_o)/\tau$ where f_o is the equilibrium distribution function. The reason for this is that the electrons will follow the motion of the ions in their motion during the passage of the acoustic wave. The situation becomes clear if we visualize what happens when $\omega \ll \tau^{-1}$. The electron will not relax to the time equilibrium distribution f_o but rather to a local distribution function $\bar{f}_o(\mathbf{r}, \mathbf{k}, t)$; $\bar{f}_o$ differs from f_o because of two causes. Firstly, in the presence of the acoustic wave the material suffers compressions and dilations that alter locally the position of the Fermi energy. The local value of this quantity at position $\mathbf{r}$ and time t will be designated by $\eta(\mathbf{r}, t)$ and it must be such that

$$\int_0^\infty g(\varepsilon, B_o) f(\varepsilon, \eta) d\varepsilon = n_o + n_1(\mathbf{r}, t) \tag{8.24}$$

where $g(\varepsilon, B_o)$ is the density of electron states per unit energy range and per unit volume of the material in the presence of the field $\mathbf{B}_o$; $n_1(\mathbf{r}, t)$ is the local deviation of the electron density from its equilibrium value and $f(\varepsilon, \eta)$ is defined by

$$f(\varepsilon, \eta) = \left[\exp\left(\frac{\varepsilon - \eta}{k_B T}\right) + 1\right]^{-1} \tag{8.25}$$

If $n_1 \ll n_o$ we obtain the approximate expression

$$\eta(\mathbf{r}, t) = \xi + \delta\xi(\mathbf{r}, t)$$

where

$$n_1(\mathbf{r}, t) = \left[\int_0^{\infty} g(\varepsilon, B_o)\left(-\frac{\partial f}{\partial \varepsilon}\right) d\varepsilon\right]^{-1}$$

and ξ is the equilibrium value of the Fermi energy.

Secondly, after the collisions the electrons retain on the average a drift velocity equal to the local velocity of the ions. Therefore

$$\bar{f}_o(\mathbf{k}, \mathbf{r}, t) = \left[\exp\left(\frac{\varepsilon_k' - \eta}{k_B T}\right) + 1\right]^{-1} \tag{8.26}$$

where ε_k' is the energy of the electron characterized by the wave vector $\mathbf{k}$ but relative to a reference frame moving with respect to the laboratory system with velocity $\mathbf{u} = \partial\xi/\partial t$. We find

$$\bar{f}_o(\mathbf{k}, \mathbf{r}, t) = f_o(\varepsilon_k) - \left[m\mathbf{v}_k \cdot \mathbf{u} + \delta\xi\right] \frac{\partial f_o(\varepsilon_k)}{\partial \varepsilon} \tag{8.27}$$

We take the rate of change of the distribution because of the collision to be

$$\left(\frac{\partial f}{\partial t}\right)_{coll} = -\tau^{-1}(f - \bar{f}_o) \tag{8.28}$$

Substitution of Eq. (8.26) into Eq. (8.20) yields

$$\mathbf{F}_c = -(zm/n_o e\tau)\mathbf{J}^{(1)} - (zm/\tau)\mathbf{u} \tag{8.29}$$

where $\mathbf{J}^{(1)}$ is the electron current density. The task that remains before us is that of relating $\mathbf{J}^{(1)}$ and $\mathbf{E}$ to the displacement field $\boldsymbol{\xi}$.

Obviously we need two vector equations relating $\mathbf{J}^{(1)}$, $\mathbf{E}$ and $\boldsymbol{\xi}$. The first of these relations is the so-called constitutive equation

$$\mathbf{J}^{(1)} = \boldsymbol{\sigma} \cdot \boldsymbol{\mathcal{E}} + e\mathbf{D} \cdot \nabla n \tag{8.30}$$

where

$$\boldsymbol{\mathcal{E}} = \mathbf{E} - (m/e\tau)\mathbf{u} \tag{8.31}$$

and

$$\mathbf{D} = \boldsymbol{\sigma}/e^2 g(\xi_o)(1 + i\omega\tau) \tag{8.32}$$

is a generalized diffusion tensor. These equations are obtained from the dynamics of the electrons solving the Boltzmann equation for the distribution function. These results are obtained by solving the Boltzmann equation

$$\frac{\partial f}{\partial t} + \mathbf{v} \cdot \frac{\partial f}{\partial \mathbf{r}} - \frac{e}{\hbar}\mathbf{E} \cdot \frac{\partial f}{\partial \mathbf{k}} - \frac{e}{\hbar}(\mathbf{v} \times \mathbf{B}_o) \cdot \frac{\partial f}{\partial \mathbf{k}} = \left(\frac{\partial f}{\partial t}\right)_{coll} \tag{8.33}$$

for the electron distribution function. The results (8.30) and (8.31) are obtained as solutions of (8.33) after some involved mathematical manipulations which we do not have time to discuss. The other equation that we need is just the requirement that the field $\mathbf{E}$ be self-consistent, i.e. that it be related to the total current $\mathbf{J}^{(1)} + n_o e(\partial \boldsymbol{\xi}/\partial t)$ by Maxwell's equations. We obtain

$$\mathbf{J}^{(1)} + n_o e \frac{d}{dt} \boldsymbol{\xi} = \boldsymbol{\Gamma} \cdot \mathbf{E} \tag{8.34}$$

where

$$\boldsymbol{\Gamma} = \frac{ic^2q^2}{4\pi\omega}\left(1 - \frac{\omega^2}{c^2q^2}\right)\mathbf{I} - \frac{ic^2}{4\pi\omega}\mathbf{q}\mathbf{q} \tag{8.35}$$

Here $\mathbb{I}$ is the unit tensor. With these equations combined with Eq. (8.22) we obtain the dispersion relation ω vs. $\mathbf{q}$ of the acoustic waves. The real part q_1 of q, gives the velocity of the wave and the imaginary part q_2, the coefficient of attenuation. It is simpler to regard q as real and ω as complex. Then, if $\omega = \omega_1 + i\omega_2$ the velocity of the acoustic wave is ω_1/q and the coefficient of attenuation is $\gamma = (2\omega_2/s)$. These results hold only if $q_2 << q_1$.

Instead of carrying out the detailed mathematical theory outlined above we shall restrict ourselves to the discussion of a few phenomena of interest in fairly qualitative terms.

d. <u>The magnetoacoustic effect</u>. The attenuation of an acoustic wave by the conduction electrons depends on the intensity of an applied magnetic field. This was first observed by Bömmel and a simple explanation was given by Pippard[5]. The power transferred from the acoustic wave to the electron gas is proportional to $\mathbf{J}^{(1)} \cdot \mathbf{E}$ in a crude first approximation (this is exact in the absence of collisions). Now since $\mathbf{E} = \boldsymbol{\rho} \cdot \mathbf{J}^{(1)}$ where $\boldsymbol{\rho}$ is the resistivity tensor. Then, the power absorbed is proportional to $\mathbf{J}^{(1)} \cdot \boldsymbol{\rho} \cdot \mathbf{J}^{(1)}$. Now, since the electrons are able to screen the motion of the ions very rapidly $\mathbf{J}^{(1)}$ is largely determined by the ionic motion and is thus fixed by the external driving system. Therefore, the acoustic attenuation is proportional to the magnitude of the diagonal terms in $\boldsymbol{\rho}$. Consider now that we have an acoustic wave propagating in a metal. To fix the ideas we take it to be a shear wave propagating at right angles to the applied magnetic field and with the direction of the particle motion also perpendicular to $\mathbf{B}_o$. Suppose that we vary the magnetic field. If the magnetic field is such that the diameter of the cyclotron orbit is equal to half the acoustic wave length we expect the conductivity to be a maximum as a function of $\mathbf{B}_o$, or the resistivity to be a minimum. Thus this situation corresponds to a minimum in the ultrasonic attenuation. In a similar way minima are obtained in γ if we lower the magnetic field so that the diameter of the cyclotron orbit is $\frac{3}{2}\lambda$, $\frac{5}{2}\lambda$, $\frac{7}{2}\lambda$,... etc. Maxima in the attenuation are then expected when the diameter of the cyclotron orbit is λ, 2λ, ... The question that one immediately asks is what do we mean by the cyclotron diameter. The cyclotron diameter is the diameter parallel to q of the projections of the orbit of the electron orbit on a plane perpendicular to $\mathbf{B}_o$. This is given by $(c\hbar/eB_o)\Delta k$, where Δk is the diameter of cross section of the Fermi surface by a plane perpendicular to the magnetic field and at right angles to q. There are several such diameters but clearly those which determine the positions of the maxima or minima are the extremal diameters, i.e. those for which $\mathbf{v}_z$ on the orbit is equal to zero. The condition for a maximum in the attenuation is thus

$$\left(\frac{c\hbar}{eB_o}\right)\Delta k_\perp = n\lambda$$

If one plots γ vs. $1/B_o$ one obtains, therefore, a periodic variation whose period is

$$\Delta\left(\frac{1}{B_o}\right) = \frac{\lambda e}{\hbar c \Delta k} = \frac{2\pi s e}{\hbar c \omega \Delta k_\perp} \qquad (8.36)$$

This result holds for longitudinal waves as well as for shear waves. It is useful to consider the order of magnitude of $\Delta(1/B_o) \approx 3 \times 10^{-3}$ G for $\nu = \omega/2\pi = 10^7$ sec^{-1}. This compares with the period for de Hass-van Alphen oscillations $\Delta(1/B_o) = (2\pi e/\hbar cS) \approx 3 \times 10^{-9}$ G^{-1}. The period of the oscillations for cyclotron resonance is $\Delta(1/B_o) = (e/m^* c\omega) \approx 0.3 \times 10^{-3}$ G^{-1} for $\nu = (\omega/2\pi) = 10^{10}$ sec^{-1}. In the estimates above we have assumed $m^* \approx m$ and $k_F \approx 10^8$ cm^{-1}. Thus we see that the period of the magnetoacoustic oscillations is much larger than that for de Haas-van Alphen oscillations. It is comparable to that of cyclotron resonance but for vastly different frequencies.

e. Open-orbit resonance. Consider an open orbit as shown in Fig. 11 and acoustic propagation as indicated. The actual motion of the electrons in real space is as shown in Fig. 12. If the distance R is equal to λ (or to a multiple of λ) we expect a resonance.

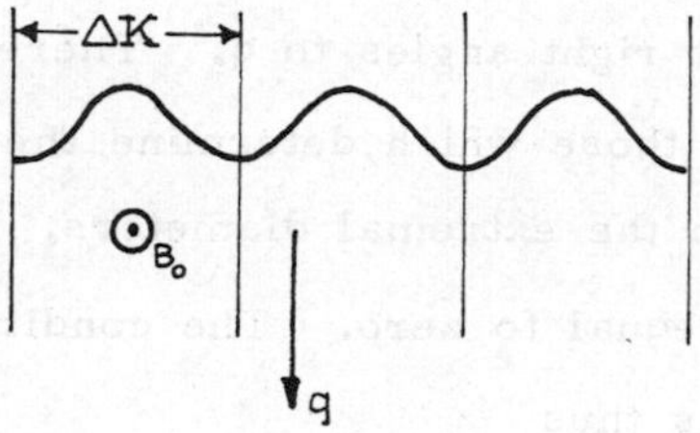

Fig. 11

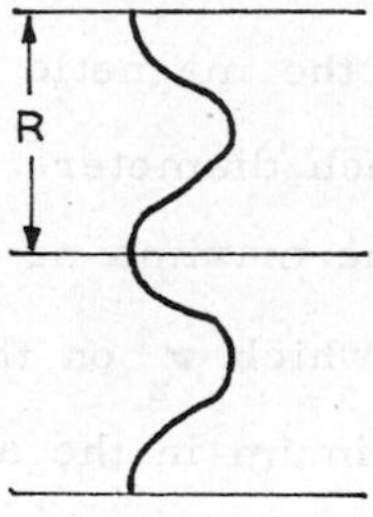

Fig. 12

Now, $R = (c\hbar/eB_o)\Delta K$. Thus, we have a resonance if

$$\frac{c\hbar}{eB_o} \Delta K = \lambda = \frac{2\pi s}{\omega} \tag{8.37}$$

Now ΔK is a dimension of the Brillouin Zone of the crystal and depends only on the lattice parameter. For $s \approx 3 \times 10^5$ cm/sec

$\omega/2\pi \simeq 10^8$ sec^{-1} and $\Delta K = (2\pi/a)$ with $a = 5 \times 10^{-8}$ cm, we find $B_o \approx 2500$ G. We have $(\nu/B_o) = (es/c\hbar\Delta K) \approx 0.04$ MHz/G. The most important characteristic of this type of resonance is that it is extrenely sharp.

f. Quantum effects.[16] There are several interesting quantum effects associated with the propagation of acoustic waves in metals. We shall limit ourselves to illustrate these phenomena. Let us consider a longitudinal acoustic wave propagating parallel to the direction of an applied magnetic field. The electric field of the wave behaves as $\exp(i\omega t - iqz)$, so that the selection rules for transitions caused by this field are $\Delta n = 0$, $\Delta k_y = 0$, $\Delta k_z = \pm q$. Now, from the law of conservation of energy we obtain

$$(\omega/q) = (\hbar k_z/m^*)\left[1 + (q/2k_z)\right]$$

This means that only those electrons whose velocity parallel to the z-axis is equal to the sound velocity contribute to the attenuation. The term

$$(q/2k_z) \approx (\hbar\omega/2m^* s^2) \sim 10^{-3}$$

for $\omega \sim 6 \times 10^8$ sec^{-1} and can therefore be neglected as compared to unity. However because of the Pauli principle, in order for absorption of a phonon of energy $\hbar\omega$ to occur we must have the initial state occupied by an electron while the final state is empty. Thus at zero degrees absolute there is absorption from the state $|n, k_y, k_z\rangle$ to $|n, k_y, k_z + q\rangle$ only if the Fermi level lies between the two energies $\varepsilon_n(k_z)$ and $\varepsilon_n(k_z + q)$. This gives rise to an oscillatory behavior of the attenuation γ as a function of magnetic field. The oscillations are periodic in B_o^{-1} with a period equal to that of the de Haas-van Alphen effect. Strictly speaking the period corresponds to a cross section for electrons having an average velocity along the z-axis (i.e. the direction of $\mathbf{B}_o$) equal to the velocity of the acoustic wave. At finite temperature the effect is considerably reduced in amplitude by the broadening $\hbar/\tau$ of the Landau levels and by the smearing of the tail of the Fermi distribution.

A second and more interesting quantum effect occurs when we consider the propagation of a transverse acoustic wave along the direction of an applied magnetic field. In this case the selection rules are $\Delta n = \pm 1$, $\Delta k_y = 0$, $\Delta k_z = q$. Conservation of energy requires that

$$k_z = (m^*/\hbar q)(\pm \omega_c + \omega) - \frac{1}{2} q$$

In a manner similar to that discussed above we again obtain oscillations in the ultrasonic attenuation as we vary the magnetic field. They differ from those discussed above in that now the period of the oscillation is related to a non-extremal cross section of the Fermi surface namely one determined roughly by $k_z \approx (m^* \omega_c/\hbar q)$. The oscillations are, however, only approximately periodic in B_o^{-1} the period changing as the magnetic field changes sufficiently to alter the cross sectional area for $k_z = (m^* \omega_c/\hbar q)$.

g. Helicon-phonon interaction. In the previous sections we discussed the properties of helicon waves propagating in a degenerate electron gas. We saw that these modes are self-sustained in a sufficiently strong magnetic field. In a metal, the positive ions are capable of propagating transverse acoustic modes whose velocity we shall designate by s. It is clear that when the frequencies and wave lengths of a helicon and an acoustic wave coincide we do not expect the normal modes of the system to be purely acoustic or purely electromagnetic. Under these conditions there is a strong coupling between these two forms of motion. The model used to describe the interaction has already been described in the introduction and is identical to that of section c above.

To discuss transverse waves we introduce parameters which describe circularly polarized disturbances. Thus, using

$$\xi_{\pm} = \xi_x \pm i\xi_y \tag{8.38}$$

and similarly defined quantities we find

$$(\omega^2 - s^2 q \pm \Omega_c \omega)\xi_{\pm} = -(ze/M)E_{\pm} - F_{c\pm}/M \tag{8.39}$$

We can eliminate $E_{\pm}$ and $F_{c\pm}$ using the constitutive equation (8.30) together with Maxwell's equations and the value of $\mathbf{F}_c$. Maxwell's equations relate the total electric current density

$$\mathbf{J} = \mathbf{J}^{(1)} + n_o e\mathbf{u} \tag{8.40}$$

to the self-consistent electric field $\mathbf{E}$. For transverse waves we are led to the result

$$J_{\pm}^{(1)} + n_o ei\omega\xi_{\pm} = i\beta\sigma_o E_{\pm} = (ic^2q^2/4\pi\omega)E_{\pm} \tag{8.41}$$

where we have made the assumption $\omega \ll cq$ and the second equality defines β. This approximation is equivalent to neglecting the displacement current. We are thus investigating the propagation of waves whose phase velocity is much smaller than the velocity of light. After some transformations we obtain

$$\left[\omega^2 - s^2 q^2 \pm \Omega_c \omega - \frac{zmi\omega}{M\tau} \frac{(1 - i\beta)(\sigma_o R_\pm - 1)}{1 - i\beta\sigma_o R_\pm}\right] \xi_\pm = 0 \qquad (8.42)$$

In this equation $R_\pm = 1/\sigma_\pm$. The frequencies of the normal modes sre to be found by setting the coefficients of $\xi_\pm$ equal to zero. We shall assume that $\beta \ll 1$ which is usually satisfied for pure materials at low temperature. Making use of the equations for the components of the conductivity tensor developed in Sec. 7 (iii) and using the approximations $\omega_c \tau \gg 1$ and $\omega \ll \omega_c$ we find the following results

$$\sigma_o R_\pm = \mp \left[i \omega_c \tau / g(w) \right] (1 \pm ia) \qquad (8.43)$$

Here $w = (qv_F/\omega_c)$, $a(w) = 0$ if $w \leq 1$ and $a(w)$ given by

$$g(w) = \frac{3}{w^2} \left[\frac{1}{2} - \frac{1 - w^2}{4w} \ln \left| \frac{1 + w}{1 - w} \right| \right] (1 + a^2) \qquad (8.44)$$

In the region in which $a \ll 1$ we obtain the relations

$$K_\pm(\omega) = \omega^3 \mp (\omega^2/g)\left\{\omega_H + \Omega_c(1 - g)\right\}$$

$$- \omega \left\{ s^2 q^2 + (\Omega_c \omega_H/g) \right\} \pm (s^2 q^2 \omega_H/g) = 0 \qquad (8.45)$$

Inspection of Eq. (8.45) reveals that

$$K_+(-\omega) = -K_-(\omega) \tag{8.46}$$

This result implies that it is sufficient to solve Eq. (8.45) for one polarization only. We consider the left-hand polarization to fix the ideas. This corresponds to the upper sign in Eq. (8.45) and to a helicon wave propagating along the direction of the magnetic field $\mathbf{B}_o$. The first question we study is the long-wavelength limit of the frequency spectrum of phonons and helicons. This result is obtained most simply as follows. If ω_1, ω_2 and ω_3 are the roots of $K_+(\omega) = 0$ we must have

$$\omega_1 + \omega_2 + \omega_3 = (\omega_H/g) + (\Omega_c/g)(1 - g) \tag{8.47}$$

$$\omega_1\omega_2 + \omega_2\omega_3 + \omega_3\omega_1 = -s^2q^2 - (\Omega_c\omega_H/g) \tag{8.48}$$

and $$\omega_1\omega_2\omega_3 = -s^2q^2\omega_H/g \tag{8.49}$$

We obtain solutions of these equations in the limit in which $qv_F/\omega_c \ll 1$. This allows us to expand $g(w) = f(w)$ in a power series and we find

$$\omega_1 = c_s q + \mu q^2 \tag{8.50}$$

$$\omega_2 = -c_s q + \mu q^2 \tag{8.51}$$

and $$\omega_3 = \mu' q^2 \tag{8.52}$$

The quantities involved in these relations are

$$c_s = s\left[1 + \frac{zm}{M}\left(\frac{c\,\omega_c}{s\,\omega_p}\right)^2\right]^{-1} \tag{8.53}$$

$$\mu = -\frac{zmv_o^2}{10M\omega_c} - \frac{c^2\,\omega_c}{2\,\omega_p^2}\left[1 + \frac{zm}{M}\left(\frac{c\,\omega_c}{s\,\omega_p}\right)^2\right]^{-1} \tag{8.54}$$

and

$$\mu' = \frac{c^2\,\omega_c}{\omega_p^2}\left[1 + \frac{zm}{M}\left(\frac{c\,\omega_c}{s\,\omega_p}\right)^2\right]^{-1} \tag{8.55}$$

The three waves obtained are, of course, left-hand circularly polarized. The branches (8.50) and (8.51) correspond to acoustic waves propagating in opposite direction and (8.52) is a helicon. We notice that the electron-phonon interaction gives rise to small corrections to both the speed of sound c_s and to the frequency ω_H of a helicon on long wavelength. These corrections are small; in particular, for sodium in a magnetic field of 5×10^4 G the quantity in the square bracket of Eq. (8.55) differs from unity by about 4×10^{-3}.

A second region of interest is that in which, in the absence of the electron-phonon interaction the frequencies and wave vectors of a helicon and a transverse phonon coincide. This occurs at the wave vector q_d defined by the trascendental equation

$$sq_d = c^2 q_d^2\,\omega_c/\omega_p^2\, g(w_d) \tag{8.56}$$

where

$$w_d = q_d v_F/\omega_c \tag{8.57}$$

This equation can be transformed into

$$g(w_d) = (c^2\omega_c^2/sv_F\omega_p^2)w_d \tag{8.58}$$

Given the applied magnetic field B_o we are in a position to obtain w_d at the cross over by solving Eq. (8.58) graphically. For example, if we take the constants for sodium ($s = 2.25 \times 10^5$ cm/sec, $v_F = 1.07 \times 10^8$ cm/sec, $\omega_p = 8.92 \times 10^{15}$ sec^{-1}) we find that the crossover for a magnetic field of abóut 10^5 G occurs at $w_d = 0.9$. The crossover frequency turns out to be $\omega_d = 3.29 \times 10^9$. A plot of the solutions of the cubic equation (8.45) is given in Fig. 13 taking this value of w_d. The solution for the splitting of the two branches that cross at w_d and ω_d can be carried out analytically as well if we assume that the third branch is not appreciably altered by the interaction. In fact, let us designate ω/ω_d by r, $g_d/g = \gamma$, $w/w_d = q/q_d = x$. Then we obtain

$$r = \frac{1}{2}(x + x^2\gamma) \pm \frac{1}{2}\left[(x - x^2\gamma)^2 + 4(\Omega_c/\omega_d)P(r)\right]^{1/2} \tag{8.59}$$

where

$$P(r) = \left[(r^2/g)(1 - g) + rx^2\gamma\right](r + x)^{-1} \tag{8.60}$$

These equations allow us to obtain the frequency as a function of q for the two branches in the vicinity of the degeneracy frequency ω_d. Clearly the result is to be obtained by iteration regarding the term $(4\Omega_c/\omega_d)P(r)$ as a small perturbation. When $q = q_d$ the frequencies of the two branches are

$$\omega = \omega_d\left[1 \pm (\Omega_c/2g_d\omega_d)^{1/2}\right] \tag{8.61}$$

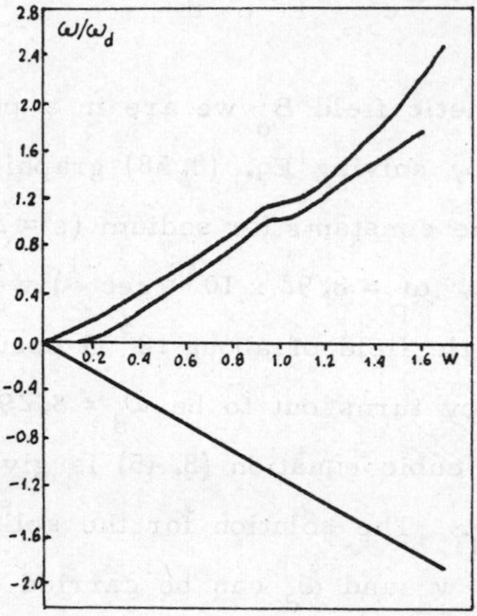

Fig. 13. Frequencies of the three roots of the equation $K_+(\omega) = 0$ for $w_d = 0.9$ using the parameters appropriate to sodium.

The relation between the amplitudes of the electric field and of the acoustic displacement is found using the result

$$E_{\pm} = \frac{mi\omega}{e\tau} \frac{1 - \sigma_o R_{\pm}}{1 - i\beta\sigma_o R_{\pm}} \xi_{\pm} \tag{8.62}$$

For the left-hand polarization we obtain

$$\xi_+ = -\left[e(\omega_g - \omega_H)/m\omega^2\omega_c\right]E_+ \tag{8.63}$$

In particular, for the crossing branches at the frequency ω_d we find the relation

$$\xi_+ = \pm \frac{eg_d}{m\omega_d\omega_c}\left(\frac{\Omega_c}{2g_d\omega_d}\right)^{1/2} E_+ , \tag{8.64}$$

where the $\pm$ sign correspond to the two branches in Eq. (8.61). A simple calculation shows that at the crossover the elastic energy density is equal to the electromagnetic energy density as expected.

The strong coupling between helicon and transverse acoustic waves in the region of the crossover suggests the possibility of exciting the latter modes by electromagnetic means. It is, of course, also possible to use this effect for the detection of transverse acoustic modes. Finally, it is interesting to notice that for some values of the magnetic field Eq. (8.58) can have up to three solutions for w_d while ordinary it only has one. This effect has been observed in potassium by Grimes and Buchsbaum[18].

REFERENCES

1. J. R. Reitz, Vol. 1, "Solid State Physics" by F. Seitz and D. Turnbull, ed.
2. F. Bloch, Z. Physik, 52, 555 (1928).
3. R. E. Peierls, "Quantum Theory of Solids", p. 94 (The Clarendon Press, Oxford, 1955).
4. L. Onsager, Phil. Mag. 43, 1006 (1952).
5. See for example, A. B. Pippard, "Dynamics of Conduction Electrons" in Low Temperature Physics, edited by C. De Witt, B. Dreyfus, and P. G. de Gennes, Gordon and Breach, New York 1962.
6. M. I. Azbel and E. A. Kaner, Soviet Phys. JETP 3, 772 (1956).
7. H. Barkhausen, Physik Zeit. 20, 401 (1919).
8. T. L. Eckersley, Nature 135, 104 (1935).

9. O. V. Konstantinov and V. I. Perel, Soviet Phys., JETP 38, 161 (1960).

10. P. Aigrain, Proceedings of the International Conference on Semiconductor Physics, Prague, 1961.

11. H. E. Bömmel, Phys. Rev. 96, 220 (1954).

12. L. Mackinnon, Phys. Rev. 100, 655 (1955).

13. W. P. Mason, Phys. Rev. 97, 557 (1955).

14. C. Kittel, Acta Met. 3, 295 (1955).

15. R. W. Morse, Phys. Rev. 97, 1716 (1955).

16. See for example, J. J. Quinn and S. Rodríguez, Phys. Rev. 128, 2487 (1962) and D. N. Langenberg, J. J. Quinn and S. Rodríguez, Phys. Rev. Letters 12, 104 (1964). Other references are given in these papers.

17. See for example, J. J. Quinn and S. Rodríguez, Phys. Rev. 133, A1589 (1964).

18. C. C. Grimes and S. J. Buchsbaum, Phys. Rev. Letters 12, 357 (1964).

11

THE ELECTRONIC STRUCTURE AND OPTICAL PROPERTIES OF INSULATORS

R. F. Wood
Solid State Division Oak Ridge National Laboratory(°)

(°) Operated by UNION CARBIDE CORPORATION for the U.S. Atomic Energy Commission Oak Ridge, Tennessee

1. INTRODUCTION

In this series of lectures, selected topics from the general area of the electronic structure and optical properties of insulators will be discussed. Although references to experimental work will be taken almost exclusively from the literature on alkali halide crystals, many aspects of the theory will apply to a much wider class of materials. The main emphasis will be on theory, models, and methods of calculation, but an effort will be made to give a fairly complete survey of the experimental results in the areas chosen for discussion.

The plan of the lectures is as follows: After this brief introduction, the energy expressions for a many-electron system going with a single determinant wave function will be derived. Hartree-Fock theory and various approximations to excited state wave functions and energy states will be covered lightly. Then in succeeding lectures reviews of band theory and exciton theory will be given and some aspects of electronic and ionic polar-on effects will be mentioned. Then, the experimental data on the intrinsic optical absorption of alkali halide crystals and its current interpretation will be given. Finally, in the last two or three lectures, the electronic structure and optical absorption of a typical point defect (F center) in alkali halides will be discussed and the role played by lattice relaxation in luminescence processes of both the F center and excitons will be outlined.

2. DETERMINANTAL WAVE FUNCTIONS AND THE HARTREE-FOCK APPROXIMATION[1]

Let us assume that the system in which we are interested is composed of N electrons and M nuclei, of which the ν-th has charge Z_ν. The physical properties of this system can be obtained in principle from Scrödinger's equation

$$H\psi = E\psi \tag{2.1}$$

with H given by

$$H = H_1 + H_2 \tag{2.2}$$

$$H_1 = \sum_{i=1}^{N} h_i \qquad h_i = -\frac{1}{2}\nabla_i^2 + V(r_i) \tag{2.3}$$

$$H_2 = \frac{1}{2}\sum_{i,j}{}' g_{ij} + \frac{1}{2}\sum_{\mu,\nu} G_{\mu\nu} \tag{2.4}$$

$$g_{ij} = \left|\underline{r}_i - \underline{r}_j\right|^{-1} \quad ; \quad G_{\mu\nu} = Z_\mu Z_\nu \left|\underline{R}_\mu - \underline{R}_\nu\right|^{-1} \tag{2.5}$$

$\underline{r}_i$ is the position coordinate of the i-th electron and $\underline{R}_\mu$ that of the μ-th nucleus. Note that h_i is the same for all electrons. For the present we assume the Born-Oppenheimer approximation to be adequate for our purposes and fix the nuclei in their equilibrium positions. This makes $\frac{1}{2} \sum_{\mu,\nu} G_{\mu\nu}$ a constant, which we shall simply drop until much later.

The wave function ψ is an enormously complicated function of the space and spin coordinates of the N electrons, which is often approximated by an antisymmetrized product of one-electron functions or orbitals. Thus,

$$\psi(1,2\ldots N) = (N!)^{1/2} A\phi_1(1)\phi_2(2)\ldots\phi_N(N) \tag{2.6}$$

in which A is an antisymmetrizing operator given by

$$A = (N!)^{-1} \sum_P (-1)^p P \tag{2.7}$$

Here, P is a permutation operator and p is its parity. The sum runs over the N! permutations of the electrons among the functions ϕ. It is easily shown that A is a projection operator, that is, it has the property

$$A^2 = A \tag{2.8}$$

$\psi(1,2\ldots N)$ as given by Eq. (2.6) will be normalized if the functions ϕ are orthonormal as is usually assumed. This assumption is not necessary but it greatly simplifies the algebra involved later, although the construction of orthonormal orbitals can in itself become rather laborious. It should be noted that

$$\psi(1,2\ldots N) = (N!)^{-1/2} \det|\phi_1(1)\phi_2(2)\ldots\phi_N(N)| \tag{2.9}$$

and that it therefore follows from the properties of determinants that if any two electrons are placed in the same orbital ϕ, ψ will vanish. Thus the exclusion principle for fermions is automatically satisfied.

The expectation value of H with respect to this approximate N-particle wave function is easily worked out. Thus, for H_1, we have

$$\int \psi^* H_1 \psi d\tau = (N!) \int \left[A \phi_1(1) \phi_2(2) \ldots \phi_N(N) \right]^* H_1 A\phi_1(1)\phi_2(2)\ldots\phi_N(N) d\tau_1 \ldots d\tau_N$$

$$\int \psi^* H_1 \psi d\tau = (N!) \int \phi_1^*(1) \ldots \phi_N^*(N) H_1 A\phi_1(1) \ldots \phi_N(N) d\tau_1 \ldots d\tau_N$$

$$= \sum_{i=1}^{N} \sum_{P} (-1)^P \int \phi_1^*(1) \ldots \phi_N^*(N) h_i P \phi_i(1) \ldots \phi_N(N) d\tau_1 \ldots d\tau_N \qquad (2.10)$$

Because of the orthogonality of the ϕ's, the integral will vanish for all permutations, P, except the identity, in which case it just becomes

$$\int \phi_i^*(i) h_i \phi_i(i) d\tau_1 ,$$

so that

$$\int \psi^* H_1 \Phi d\tau = \sum_{i=1}^{N} \int \phi_i^*(1) h(1) \phi_i(1) d\tau_1 \equiv \sum_{i=1}^{N} (i | h | i) \qquad (2.11)$$

The last symbol is just meant to introduce a shorter notation for the integral.

For H_2, we have

$$\int \psi^* H_2 \psi d\tau = N! \; \phi_1^*(1)\ldots\phi_N^*(N) H_2 A \phi_1(1)\ldots\phi_N(N) d\tau_1 \ldots d\tau_N$$

$$= \frac{1}{2} \sum_{i,j} \sum_P (-1)^p \int \phi_1^*(1)\ldots\phi_N^*(N) g_{ij}$$

$$P\phi_1(1)\ldots\phi_N(N) d\tau_1 \ldots d\tau_N \tag{2.12}$$

Because of the presence of the two-particle operator, g_{ij}, the integral will be non-vanishing both for the identity permutation and for the permutation which interchanges particles i and j. Hence, we find

$$\int \psi^* H_2 \psi d\tau = \frac{1}{2} \sum_{i,j}{}' \int \phi_1^*(1)\ldots\phi_N^*(N) g_{ij} (1 - P_{ij}) \phi_1(1)\ldots\phi_N$$

$$d\tau_1 \ldots d\tau_N = \frac{1}{2} \sum_{i,j} \int \phi_i^*(1)\phi_j^*(2) g_{12} (1 - P_{12})$$

$$\phi_i(1)\phi_j(2) d\tau_1 d\tau_2 \tag{2.13}$$

Note that we can remove the prime from the summation because when i = j the two integrals cancel each other. As a shorthand notation for the integrals we shall often write

$$\int \phi_i^*(1)\phi_j^*(2) g_{12} (1 - P_{12}) \phi_i(1)\phi_j(2) d\tau_1 d\tau_2 = (ij|ij) - (ij|ji) \tag{2.14}$$

Here the vertical bar implies the presence of g_{12}.

The total electronic energy of the system is thus given by

$$E_N = \int \psi^* H \psi d\tau = \sum_{i=1}^{N} (i|h|i) + \frac{1}{2} \sum_{i,j}^{N} \left[(ij|ij) - (ij|ji) \right] \tag{2.15}$$

To find the best single determinant approximation to the true ground state energy of the system, we can proceed as follows. First, we note that Schrödinger's equation can be derived from the following variation theorem. Define the functional

$$E[\psi] = \int \psi^* H \psi d\tau / \int \psi^* \psi d\tau \qquad (2.16)$$

and require

$$\delta E = 0 \qquad (2.17)$$

Treating ψ^* and ψ as independent functions and taking the variation of E with respect to ψ^*, we have

$$\int \delta\psi^* (E - H)\psi d\tau = 0 \ , \qquad (2.18)$$

from which it follows

$$H\psi = E\psi \qquad (2.19)$$

Now consider a normalized function, Φ, not necessarily an eigenfunction of H but obeying the same boundary conditions, and write

$$E[\Phi] - E_o = \int \Phi^* (H - E_o)\Phi d\tau \qquad (2.20)$$

with E_o the lowest eigenvalue of H. Expand Φ in terms of the eigenfunctions of H, so that

$$\Phi = \sum_n C_n \psi_n \quad ; \quad C_n = \int \psi_n^* \Phi d\tau \qquad (2.21)$$

We then have

$$E[\Phi] - E_o = \sum_{n=0} \int \Phi^* (E_n - E_o) C_n \psi_n d\tau = \sum_{n=0} C_n^2 (E_n - E_o) \qquad (2.22)$$

Since C_n^2 is always positive and E_o is always less than or equal to E_n, it follows that

$$E[\Phi] \geqslant E_o \tag{2.23}$$

Thus, from a class of trial functions, Φ, of a given type we can select the "best" by requiring

$$\delta E[\Phi] = 0 \tag{2.24}$$

and still be assured of having the ground state energy as a lower bound. The same variation principle can be applied to excited states, but we shall not go into it here.

Returning now to trial functions of the single determinant type, we can take the variation of Eq. (2.15) with respect to the single-particle function and obtain

$$\delta E = \sum_{i=1}^{N} \int \delta \phi_i^*(1) h \phi_i(1) d\tau_1 + \sum_{i,j} \int \delta \phi_i^*(1) \phi_j^*(2) g_{12}(1 - P_{12}) \phi_i(1) \phi_j(2) d\tau_1 d\tau_2 = 0 \tag{2.25}$$

However, we also wish to maintain the normality of the trial function while varying the orbitals, so we also have the condition

$$\int \delta\psi^* \psi d\tau = \sum_i \int \delta \phi_i^*(1) \phi(1) d\tau_1 = 0 \tag{2.26}$$

to fulfill. Equations (2.25) and (2.26) can be combined by introducing a Lagrangian multiplier ε_i. Then, since the $\delta \phi_i$ are independent variations, we obtain

$$\varepsilon_i \phi_i(1) = h\phi_i(1) + \sum_{j=1}^{N} \int d\tau_2 \phi_j^*(2) g_{12}(1 - P_{12}) \phi_j(2) \phi_i(1) \tag{2.27}$$

or, putting $\rho(2,1) = \sum_j \phi_j^*(2)\phi_j(1)$,

$$(\varepsilon_i + h)\phi_i(1) + \int d\tau_2 g_{12}\left[\rho(2,2) - \rho(2,1) P'_{12}\right]\phi_i(1) = 0 \tag{2.28}$$

The operator P'_{12} simply replaces 1 with 2 in the orbital to its right.

Multiplying Eq. (2.27) or (2.28) from the left, integrating over variable 1 and summing over i, we have

$$\sum_{i=1}^{N} \varepsilon_i = \sum_{i=1}^{N} \int \phi_i^*(1) h \phi_i(1) d\tau_1$$

$$+ \sum_{i,j}^{N} d\tau_2 d\tau_1 \phi_i^*(1) \phi_j^*(2) g_{12}(1 - P_{12}) \phi_j(2) \phi_i(1) \tag{2.29}$$

Comparing this to Eq. (2.15), we see that

$$E_N = \sum_{i=1}^{N} \varepsilon_i - \frac{1}{2} \sum_{i,j} d\tau_2 d\tau_1 \phi_i^*(1) \phi_j(2) g_{12}(1 - P_{12}) \phi_j(2) \phi_i(1)$$

The expression corresponding to Eq. (2.15) for the N-1 electron case can be written as

$$E_{N-1} = \sum_{i=1}^{N-1} \int \phi^*_i(1) h \phi_i(1) d\tau_1$$

$$+ \frac{1}{2} \sum_{i,j=1}^{N-1} d\tau_2 d\tau_1 \phi^*_i(1) \phi^*_j(2) g_{12}(1-P_{12}) \phi_j(2) \phi_i(1)$$

$$= \sum_{i=1}^{N} \int \phi^*_i(1) h \phi_i(1) d\tau_1 - \int \phi^*_N(1) h \phi_N(1) d\tau_1$$

$$+ \frac{1}{2} \sum_{i,j=1}^{N} d\tau_2 d\tau_1 \phi^*_i(1) \phi^*_j(2) g_{12}(1-P_{12}) \phi_j(2) \phi_i(1)$$

$$- \sum_{j=1}^{N} d\tau_2 d\tau_1 \phi^*_N(1) \phi^*_j(2) g_{12}(1-P_{12}) \phi_j(2) \phi_i(1) \tag{2.30}$$

$$E_{N-1} = E_N - \varepsilon_N.$$

This last relationship, known as Koopman's theorem, follows if it is assumed that the orbitals involved in the N and N-1 problems are eigenfunctions of the same effective Hamiltonian. Note, however, that the more rigorous procedure would be to reminimize E_{N-1} with respect to all of the orbitals.

Let us consider the excited states of the N electron problems formed by placing a single electron, originally in the N-th orbital, in an excited one-electron orbital denoted by a prime. We have

$$E^*_N = \sum_{i=1}^{N-1} (i|h|i) + (N'|h|N') + \frac{1}{2} \sum_{i,j}^{N-1} \left[(ij|ij) - (ij|ji)\right]$$

$$+ \sum_{j=1}^{N-1} \left[(N'j|N'j) - (N'j|jN')\right] \tag{2.31}$$

The most rigorous calculation of the excited state energies within the Hartree-Fock scheme would proceed by minimizing E_N^* with respect to all of the orbitals. One would then encounter all of the problems of self-consistency just as in the ground state. In solid state problems, two approximations are commonly made. The first assumes that the N-1 orbitals involved in the ground state are unchanged in form when the one electron is excited. Minimization of the excited state energy then involves only the variation of the N'-th orbital. An even more common approximation is to assume that an excited state is formed simply by placing an electron in one of the virtual orbitals calculated with the same effective one-electron Hamiltonian appropriate for the ground state orbitals. Let us add and subtract terms to Eq. (2.31) to obtain

$$E_N^* = \sum_{i=1}^{N}(i|h|i) - (N|h|N) + (N'|h|N')$$

$$+ \frac{1}{2}\sum_{i,j}^{N}\left[(ij|ij) - (ij|ji)\right] - \sum_{j=1}^{N}\left[(Nj|Nj) - (Nj|jN)\right]$$

$$+ \sum_{j=1}^{N}\left[(N'j|N'j) - (N'j|jN')\right]$$

$$- \left[(N'N|N'N) - (N'N|NN')\right] \qquad (2.32)$$

Since all orbitals are eigenfunctions of the ground state one-electron Hamiltonian, we have

$$E_N^* = E_N - \varepsilon_N + \varepsilon_{N'} - \left[(N'N|N'N) - (N'N|NN')\right] \qquad (2.33)$$

In comparing the results of band theory calculations the term in square brackets is usually neglected. In some materials such as metals this may be a fairly good approximation; however, in others such as semiconductors and insulators the term in brackets is responsible for the form of exciton states.

3. BAND THEORY[2]

In this lecture I shall very briefly remind you of some of the elements of band theory and then review some of the more recent calculations on the band structure of KCl and KI.

Thus far in solid state physics band theory has been essentially the theory of the one-electron approximation for a periodic potential. Let us assume then that we have been supplied with a one-electron Hamiltonian of the form

$$h = -\frac{1}{2}\nabla^2 + V(r) \tag{3.1}$$

The periodicity of the lattice is reflected in the periodicity of the potential as expressed by the condition that

$$V(\mathbf{r} + \mathbf{R}_\nu) = V(\mathbf{r}) \tag{3.2}$$

where $\mathbf{R}_\nu$ is vector connecting equivalent lattice sites. $\mathbf{R}_\nu$ can be expressed in terms of three primitive lattice translation vectors, $\mathbf{a}_1$, $\mathbf{a}_2$, and $\mathbf{a}_3$ by

$$\mathbf{R}_\nu = \nu_1\mathbf{a}_1 + \nu_2\mathbf{a}_2 + \nu_3\mathbf{a}_3 \tag{3.3}$$

Since the potential is periodic in $\mathbf{r}$ space, h is unaffected by a translation of the crystal through any one of the $\mathbf{R}_\nu$. If the translation operator $T(\mathbf{R}_\nu)$ is defined by

$$T(\mathbf{R}_\nu)\psi(\mathbf{r}) = \psi(\mathbf{r} + \mathbf{R}_\nu), \tag{3.4}$$

then

$$T(\mathbf{R}_\nu)h(\mathbf{r})\psi(\mathbf{r}) = h(\mathbf{r} + \mathbf{R}_\nu)\psi(\mathbf{r} + \mathbf{R}_\nu)$$

$$= h(\mathbf{r})T(\mathbf{R}_\nu)\psi(\mathbf{r}) \tag{3.5}$$

Also,

$$T(\mathbf{R}_\mu)T(\mathbf{R}_\nu)\psi(\mathbf{r}) = (\mathbf{r} + \mathbf{R}_\nu + \mathbf{R}_\mu) = \psi(\mathbf{r} + \mathbf{R}_\mu + \mathbf{R}_\nu)$$

$$= T(\mathbf{R}_\nu)T(\mathbf{R}_\mu)\psi(\mathbf{r}) \tag{3.6}$$

So, the translation operators commute with h and with each other. Therefore, functions which are simultaneoulsy eigenfunctions of h and of the T's can be constructed, and it is this property that makes the periodic potential problem tractable. Consider first the simple operation of translation through one of the primitive vectors and let $T\psi = \lambda\psi$; then

$$T(\mathbf{a}_1)\psi(\mathbf{r}) = \psi(\mathbf{r} + \mathbf{a}_1) = \lambda\psi(\mathbf{r})$$

In order to maintain the normalization of the wave function after a translation it is necessary to have $\lambda^2 = 1$. But, also,

$$T^n(\mathbf{a}_1)\psi(\mathbf{r}) = T(n\mathbf{a}_1)\psi = \lambda_1^n\psi = \psi(\mathbf{r} + n\mathbf{a}_1)$$

and therefore, $|\lambda_1^n|$ must be unity, which suggests the choice $\lambda_1 = e^{i\theta_1}$. Furthermore, if we put $\theta_1 = \mathbf{k}\ \mathbf{a}_1$, we have

$$\lambda_1^n = e^{i\mathbf{k}\cdot n\mathbf{a}_1}$$

It follows that

$$\begin{aligned} T(\mathbf{R}_\nu)\psi(\mathbf{r}) &= T(\nu_1\mathbf{a}_1 + \nu_2\mathbf{a}_2 + \nu_3\mathbf{a}_3)\psi(\mathbf{r}) \\ &= T(\nu_1\mathbf{a}_1)T(\nu_2\mathbf{a}_2)T(\nu_3\mathbf{a}_3)\psi(\mathbf{r}) \\ &= \lambda_1^{1}\lambda_2^{2}\lambda_3^{3}\psi(\mathbf{r}) = e^{i\mathbf{k}\cdot\nu_1\mathbf{a}_1}e^{i\mathbf{k}\cdot\nu_2\mathbf{a}_2}e^{i\mathbf{k}\cdot\nu_3\mathbf{a}_3}(\mathbf{r}) \\ &= e^{i\mathbf{k}\cdot\mathbf{R}_\nu}\psi(\mathbf{r}) \end{aligned} \tag{3.7}$$

This is Bloch's theorem.

We also note the following. Write

$$\psi(\mathbf{r}) = e^{i\mathbf{k}\cdot\mathbf{r}}w(\mathbf{r}),$$

then

$$T(\mathbf{R}_\nu)\psi(\mathbf{r}) = e^{i\mathbf{k}\cdot(\mathbf{r}+\mathbf{R}_\nu)}w(\mathbf{r}+\mathbf{R}_\nu) = e^{i\mathbf{k}\cdot\mathbf{R}_\nu}e^{i\mathbf{k}\cdot\mathbf{r}}w(\mathbf{r}+\mathbf{R}_\nu)$$

Thus, if $w(\mathbf{r}+\mathbf{R}_\nu)$ is itself periodic with $w(\mathbf{r}) = w(\mathbf{r}+\mathbf{R}_\nu)$, we have

$$T(\mathbf{R}_\nu)\psi(\mathbf{r}) = e^{i\mathbf{k}\cdot\mathbf{R}_\nu}\psi(\mathbf{r}) \tag{3.8}$$

The vectors **k** can be related to three primitive vectors, $\mathbf{b}_i$, reciprocal to the **a**'s in the sense that

$$\mathbf{a}_i \cdot \mathbf{b}_i = \delta_{ij}$$

Then vectors of the reciprocal lattice can be expressed as

$$\mathbf{K}_n = 2\pi(n_1\mathbf{b}_1 + n_2\mathbf{b}_2 + n_3\mathbf{b}_3)$$

It follows that

$$e^{i\mathbf{K}_n \cdot \mathbf{R}_\nu} = e^{i(n_1\nu_1 + n_2\nu_2 + n_3\nu_3)} = e^{i2\pi(\text{integer})} = 1$$

so that

$$T(\mathbf{R}_\nu)\, e^{i\mathbf{K}_n \cdot \mathbf{r}} = e^{i\mathbf{K}_n \cdot (\mathbf{r} + \mathbf{R}_\nu)} = e^{i\mathbf{K}_n \cdot \mathbf{r}} \qquad (3.9)$$

Therefore, $e^{i\mathbf{K}_n \cdot \mathbf{r}}$ is a periodic function of $\mathbf{r}$ and we can write

$$\psi(\mathbf{r}) = e^{i(\mathbf{k} + \mathbf{K}_n) \cdot \mathbf{r}}$$

Unit cells can be constructed in both k and r space and they will be related to each other through the relationship between the unit vectors. It is usually convenient to choose unit cells which reflect the full symmetry of the lattice. This can be done in the manner first used by Wigner and Seitz in constructing unit cells in real space. The result is that the unit cell is that geometrical figure of least volume containing the origin and bounded by planes perpendicularly bisecting the vectors from the origin to the lattice points. In k space this figure is called the Brillouin zone.

In addition to the translational symmetry of the crystal, there are symmetry properties associated with various rotation and reflection operations which constitute the point group of the crystal.

The combined operations of the translation and point groups comprise the space group of the crystal whose elements are usually denoted by $\{\alpha | \mathbf{R}_\nu\}$. The $\mathbf{R}_\nu$ refers to the translation operation previously denoted by $T(\mathbf{R}_\nu)$ and the $\boldsymbol{\alpha}$ refers to one of the operations of the point group. The intricacies of a full group theoretical discussion of space groups are well beyond the scope of this brief review. The most important points are the following.

It can be shown that the real and reciprocal lattices are invariant under the operations of the point group. More specifically, the effect of operating on a lattice vector of the real lattice with an element of the point group is equivalent to operating on a lattice vector of the reciprocal lattice with the inverse element, in the sense that

$$\boldsymbol{\alpha}\mathbf{R}_\nu \cdot \mathbf{k}_j \equiv \mathbf{R}_\nu \cdot \boldsymbol{\alpha}^{-1}\mathbf{K}_j$$

If an arbitrary vector in the BZ is transformed with all of the elements of the point group, the so-called "star" of the wave vector is generated. For a general point in a cubic lattice the star will have 48 points, since each of the 48 operations of the group transforms the vector into a new and equivalent vector. For k vectors at the symmetry points it may happen that the star of the wave vector is much smaller because the operations transform the wave vector into itself or an equivalent vector, i.e.,

$$\alpha\mathbf{k} = \mathbf{k} + \mathbf{K}_j$$

The operations for which this occurs form the "group of the wave vector" $\mathbf{k}$. For a general point the group of the wave vector will consist of just the identity operation, but for symmetry points and along symmetry directions the group will be much larger.

Even after the foregoing general considerations one is still left with the formidable problem of solving Schrödinger equation $h\psi = \varepsilon\psi$ for the various irreducible representations of the group of the wave vector. A number of methods have been developed for doing this and I shall now remind you of some of these.

a. Tight binding method. In the tight binding method, one approximates ψ by a linear combination of Bloch sums, thus

$$\psi_n(\mathbf{k}, \mathbf{r}) = \sum_m C_{nm}(\mathbf{k}) U_m(\mathbf{k}, \mathbf{r}) \tag{3.10}$$

with

$$U_m(\mathbf{k}, \mathbf{r}) = \sum_{\nu=1}^{N} e^{i\mathbf{k}\cdot\mathbf{R}_\nu} \phi_m(\mathbf{r} - \mathbf{R}_\nu) \tag{3.11}$$

In these equations, n is a band index and $\phi_m(\mathbf{r} - \mathbf{R}_\nu)$ is an atomic orbital centered at the ν-th ion. The index m stands for a set of quantum numbers specifying the symmetry of the atomic orbital. Schrödinger's equation becomes

$$\varepsilon_{k,n}\psi_n(\mathbf{k}, \mathbf{r}) = h\psi_n(\mathbf{k}, \mathbf{r}) \tag{3.12}$$

Multiplying through from the left by $\psi_n(k, r)$, integrating and applying the variation principle $\delta\varepsilon_{k,n} = 0$, gives the usual secular determinant, i.e.,

$$\left| h_{nm} - S_{nm}\varepsilon_k \right| = 0 \tag{3.13}$$

Here,

$$h_{nm} = \int U_n^* h U_m \, d\tau = \sum_{\mu,\nu} e^{i\mathbf{k}\cdot(\mathbf{R}_\nu - \mathbf{R}_\mu)} \int \phi_n^*(\mathbf{r}-\mathbf{R}_\mu) h \phi_m(\mathbf{r}-\mathbf{R}_\nu) d\tau$$

$$= N \sum_\mu e^{i\mathbf{k}\cdot\mathbf{R}_\mu} \Big[\varepsilon_m S^a_{nm}(\mathbf{R}_\mu, 0)$$

$$+ \int \phi_n^*(\mathbf{r} - \mathbf{R}_\mu) v(\mathbf{r}) \phi_m(\mathbf{r}) d\tau \Big]$$

ε_m, the energy of the m-th atomic orbital, is obtained by splitting h into an atomic Hamiltonian, h_a, of which ϕ_m is an eigenfunction, and that part of the potential ($v = V - V_a$) which is not included in h_a. S^a_{nm} is the overlap integral between $\phi_n(r - \mathbf{R}_\mu)$ and $\phi_m(r)$. S_{nm} is the overlap integral between Bloch functions and is given by

$$S_{nm} = N \sum_\mu e^{i\mathbf{k}\cdot\mathbf{R}_\mu} S^a_{nm}(\mathbf{R}_\mu, 0)$$

The secular equation becomes

$$\left| \sum_\mu e^{i\mathbf{k}\cdot\mathbf{R}_\mu} \left[(\varepsilon_m - \varepsilon_{\mathbf{k}}) S^a_{nm}(\mathbf{R}_\mu, 0) + v_{nm}(\mathbf{R}_\mu, 0) \right] \right| = 0 \qquad (3.14)$$

in which

$$v_{nm}(\mathbf{R}_\mu, 0) = \int \phi_n^*(\mathbf{r} - \mathbf{R}_\mu) v(r) \phi_m(\mathbf{r}) d\tau$$

Solution of the secular equation for E for different values of **k** gives the dispersion curve. Note that the size of the secular equation is determined by the number of different Bloch sums. The tight binding method is sometimes used for approximate work, interpolation and for purposes of discussion. With a little more work, one important aspect of band theory can be seen already from Eq. (3.14). Let us assume that we have a simple cubic crystal with one atom per unit cell and consider that we have formed Bloch sums from s, p_x, p_y and p_z atomic orbitals. Also we assume that the sum over μ is negligible after first nearest neighbors. Then if the elements of the secular determinant are worked out, the off diagonal elements between the s and p functions will be of the form $2i\alpha \sin k_x a$, with α the appropriate integral of the form of $v_{nm}(\mathbf{R}_\mu, 0)$. The important point to notice is that because of the $\sin k_x a$ term the off diagonal elements will vanish for $k_x = 0$ and π/a (the zone boundary in this case) and there will be no mixing of s and p functions. At all values of k_x in between, however, there will be mixing and the bands cannot be described as s bands or p bands.

Howland's[3] calculation on the core and valence bands of KCl is probably the most complete application of the tight binding method. The method is usually considered to be quite inadequate for calculations on any but highly ionic crystals because of the slow convergence of the sums over R_μ and the occurrence of three- and four-center integrals. In an important recent development, however, C. C. Lin and coworkers[4] have shown that the method becomes tractable even for metals if one assumes a "muffin tin" potential of the form usually employed by methods described below.

b. Orthogonalized plane wave (OPW) and pseudopotential methods[5].
In the OPW method the one-electron functions are expressed as linear combinations of orthogonalized plane waves. A single orthogonalized plane wave is given by

$$\psi_j(\mathbf{k}, \mathbf{r}) = (N\Omega_o)^{-1/2} e^{i(\mathbf{k}+\mathbf{K}_j)\cdot\mathbf{r}} - \sum_n C_n(\mathbf{k}+\mathbf{K}_j)U_n(\mathbf{k}, \mathbf{r}) \tag{3.15}$$

in which $U_n(k, r)$ is a Bloch sum defined above in Eq. (3.11) for the n-th core band. N is the number of atoms and Ω_o the atomic volume. The constants $C_n(\mathbf{k}+\mathbf{K}_j)$ are determined by the condition

$$\int U_n^*(\mathbf{k}, \mathbf{r})\,\psi_j(\mathbf{k}, \mathbf{r})d\tau = 0 \quad ,$$

that is, the ψ_j are forced to be orthogonal to the lower core band functions. In working out the matrix elements of the one-electron Hamiltonian, h, it is usually assumed that

$$hU_n(\mathbf{k}, \mathbf{r}) = \varepsilon_n(\mathbf{k})U_n(\mathbf{k}, \mathbf{r}) \tag{3.16}$$

and that the $\varepsilon_n(k)$ are known.

Expressing the linear combination of OPW's as

$$\psi(k, r) = \sum d_j\,\psi_j(k, r) \quad ,$$

the usual secular determinant $|h_{ij} - \delta_{ij}\varepsilon| = 0$ is obtained, with

$$h_{ij} = (N\Omega_o)^{-1}\left[\frac{1}{2}(\mathbf{k}+\mathbf{K}_j)^2\delta_{ij} + w(\mathbf{K}_i - \mathbf{K}_j)\right]$$

$$- \sum_n C_n^*(\mathbf{k}+\mathbf{K}_i)C_n(\mathbf{k}+\mathbf{K}_j)\,\varepsilon_n$$

$w(\mathbf{K}_i - \mathbf{K}_j)$ is a matrix element of the periodic potential. You will recall that the OPW method is much more rapidly convergent than an ordinary plane wave expansion. This is because the violent oscillations of the wave function in the vicinity of an ion are taken care of by the presence of the core function rather than by a very large number of plane waves of large K value.

The OPW method can be cast in a slightly different form, as follows. Write

$$h\psi_j(\mathbf{k},\mathbf{r}) = h\phi^o_j(\mathbf{k},\mathbf{r}) - \sum_n \left(U_n(\mathbf{k}) \middle| \phi^o_j(\mathbf{k})\right) \varepsilon_n(\mathbf{k}) U_n(\mathbf{k})$$

$$= \varepsilon\left\{\phi^o_j(\mathbf{k},\mathbf{r}) - \sum_n \left(U_n(\mathbf{k}) \middle| \phi^o_j(\mathbf{k})\right) U_n(\mathbf{k})\right\} \qquad (3.17)$$

where

$$\phi^o_j(k, r) = (N\Omega_o)^{-1/2} e^{i(\mathbf{k}+\mathbf{K}_j)\cdot\mathbf{r}}$$

and

$$(U_n | \phi^o_j) \equiv \int U^*_n(\mathbf{r}) \phi^o_j(\mathbf{r}) d\mathbf{r}$$

Or

$$h\phi^o_j(\mathbf{k},\mathbf{r}) + \sum_n (\varepsilon - \varepsilon_n)(U_n | \phi^o_j) U_n = \varepsilon \phi^o_j(\mathbf{k},\mathbf{r})$$

which can be written as

$$h\phi^o_j(\mathbf{k},\mathbf{r}) + \sum_n (\varepsilon - \varepsilon_n) \int d\tau' U_n(\mathbf{r}') U_n(\mathbf{r}) \phi^o_j(\mathbf{r}') = \varepsilon \phi^o_j(\mathbf{r}) \qquad (3.18)$$

The term

$$V_{ps}(r, r') \equiv \sum_n (\varepsilon - \varepsilon_n) \int d\tau' U_n(r') U_n(r)$$

can be thought of as pseudopotential which takes into account the orthogonalization of the smooth function ϕ^o_j to the cores. It should be noted that the pseudopotential is repulsive, non-local and angular-momentum-dependent since the core states to which ϕ_j^o must be orthogonalized will depend on the angular dependence of ϕ_j^o. Although it is probably very difficult to construct a truly accurate pseudopotential, the method has been very useful as a semi-empirical scheme. It also gives considerable insight into the reasons for the nearly free electron behavior of many mono- and divalent metals, and gives promise of being useful in lattice dynamics.

c. The augmented plane wave (APW) method[6]. This method is somewhat similar to the OPW method in that it employs plane waves suitably modified in the vicinity of the ions. To construct an APW, one assumes that the crystal potential can be approximated well by one of the "muffin tin" form, that is, one which is spherically symmetric inside a sphere of a given radius R drawn around the ion and constant outside. In the region inside of the sphere the wave function is given by

$$\psi_i = \sum_{\ell=0}^{\infty} \sum_{m=-\ell}^{+\ell} C_{\ell,m} (2\ell+1) i^{\ell} \frac{(\ell-|m|)!}{(\ell+|m|)!} \frac{j_\ell(k_i R)}{U_\ell(R)}$$

$$U_\ell(r) F_\ell^{|m|}(\theta, \theta_i, \phi, \phi_i) \qquad (3.19)$$

and outside by

$$\psi_i = e^{i(\mathbf{k}+\mathbf{K}_i)\cdot\mathbf{r}} = \sum_{\ell=0}^{\infty} \sum_{m=-\ell}^{\ell} (2\ell+1) i^{\ell} \frac{(\ell-|m|)!}{(\ell+|m|)!} j_\ell(k_i r)$$

$$F_\ell^{|m|}(\theta, \theta_i, \phi, \phi_i) \qquad (3.20)$$

with $k_i = |\mathbf{k} + \mathbf{K}_i|$ and

$$F_\ell^{|m|}(\theta, \theta_i, \phi, \phi_i) = P_\ell^{|m|}(\cos\theta) P_\ell^{|m|}(\cos\theta_i) e^{im(\phi - \phi_i)}$$

The j's are spherical Bessel functions and the U's are the radial solutions of the spherical potential. θ_i and ϕ_i are the angles of $\mathbf{k}_i$ referred to the chosen axis. The coefficients $C_{\ell,m}$ are chosen so as to make the wave function continuous at R. Note, however, that the first derivative cannot also be made continuous at R. To get around this difficulty one must then expand the trial function in a series of APW's, set up a secular determinant and find those values of the energy for which its zeros occur.

d. <u>Korringa-Kohn-Rostoker (KKR) method</u>[7,8]. Consider once again the one-electron Schrödinger equation

$$\left[-\frac{1}{2}\nabla^2 + V(r)\right]\psi(r) = \varepsilon\,\psi(r)$$

and introduce the free particle Green's function defined by

$$\left[-\frac{1}{2}\nabla^2 - \varepsilon\right] G(\mathbf{r}, \mathbf{r}') = \delta(\mathbf{r} - \mathbf{r}') \qquad (3.21)$$

It is easily shown that

$$\psi(\mathbf{r}) = \int G(\mathbf{r}, \mathbf{r}') V(\mathbf{r}') \psi(\mathbf{r}') d\tau \qquad (3.22)$$

Both $G(\mathbf{r}, \mathbf{r}')$ and its first derivative have the periodicity of the lattice, since $G(\mathbf{r}, \mathbf{r}')$ can be constructed from plane waves. Kohn and Rostoker showed that Eq. (3.22) is equivalent to the variation principle

$$\delta\Lambda = 0$$

where

$$\Lambda = \int_\tau \psi^*(\mathbf{r})V(\mathbf{r})\psi(\mathbf{r})d\tau - \iint_{\tau\tau'} \psi^*(\mathbf{r})V(\mathbf{r})G(\mathbf{r},\mathbf{r}')V(\mathbf{r}')\psi(\mathbf{r}')d\tau d\tau' \tag{3.23}$$

ψ can be expanded in a convenient set of basis functions to obtain the secular equation

$$|\Lambda_{ij}| = 0$$

The Λ_{ij} are functions only of $\mathbf{k}$ and E so that $\mathbf{k}$ can be fixed and those values of E found which satisfy this equation or the converse procedure may be taken. Here, as in the APW method, great simplification results if the crystal potential is assumed to be of the "mufin tin" form. Then the interior solution is again of the form given in Eq. (3.19). With this potential, Kohn and Rostoker arrive after much algebraic manipulation at the equation

$$\left| A_{\ell m;\ell' m'} + K\delta_{\ell\ell'}\delta_{mm'} \frac{n_\ell' - n_\ell L_\ell}{j_\ell' - j_\ell L_\ell} \right| = 0 \tag{3.24}$$

Here L_ℓ is the logarithmic derivative evaluated at the radius of the muffin tin, j_ℓ and n_ℓ are the spherical Bessel and Neuman functions, respectively, and j_ℓ' and n_ℓ' their derivatives. The $A_{\ell m;\ell' m'}$ are the famous "structure factor" constants which are rather difficult to evaluate. As a matter of fact, it was formerly thought that the evaluation of the structure factor constants was a serious drawback of the KKR method. However, recently Davis, Faulkner and Joy[9] have shown that the KKR method, when efficiently programmed, is an extremely fast method and we can expect it or modifications of it to be used frequently in future calculations. Johnson[10] has recently given a useful discussion of the similarities and differences of the APW and KKR methods.

We now turn to a discussion of the results obtained by the application of these methods to the calculation of band structure in alkali halide crystals with the Na Cl structure. The NaCl structure consists of two interpenetrating face-centered cubic structures. The crystal is generated by the fcc lattice with one ion of each type in the primitive unit cell. The Brillouin zone for the face-centered cubic lattice is shown in Fig. 1.

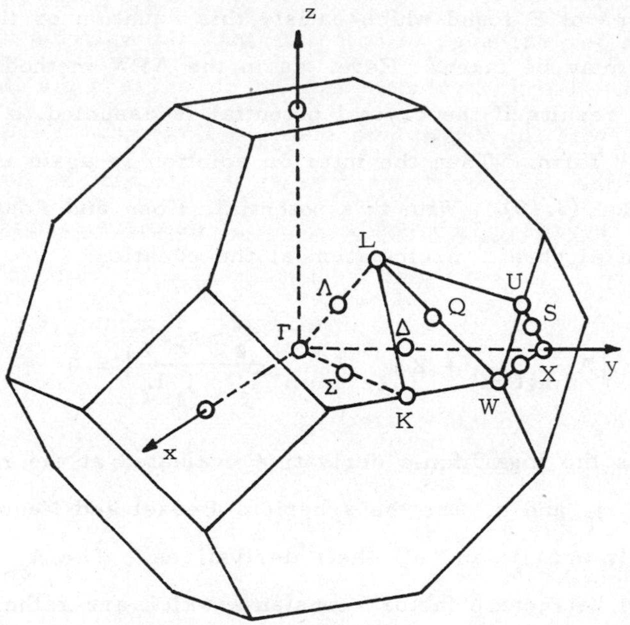

Fig. 1

Howland has carried out a very complete tight binding calculation on the core and valence bands in KCl. He obtains a width of 1.52 eV for the valence band with the minimum coming at the L point and the maximum (located at -0.7862 rydbergs) at a point along the Σ direction. Howland considers it possible that in a more accurate calculation the band maximum might shift to the L point or to a point on the L-K line but unlikely that it would occur in any other region of the BZ. The calculated width of 1.52 eV is roughly twice the width obtained by Parratt and Jossem[11] from the x-ray emission spectrum of KCl. It is not clear, however, that this discrepancy is to be attributed entirely to inadequacies in the calculations.

There are two other calculations on KCl in the literature. DeCicco[12] has used the APW method with the Slater $\rho^{1/3}$ approximation[13] for exchange to calculate both the valence and conduction bands. For the valence band he obtains a width in better agreement with the x-ray data than did Howland. Furthermore, the top of the valence band comes at the Γ point as does the bottom of the conduction band. Also of great importance to exciton theory is the fact that the minimum of the next highest conduction band comes at the X point rather than at the L point as suggested by Phillips[14]. The separation in energy between the states at X and L is not small.

Oyama and Miyakawa[15] have also carried out calculations on the conduction band of KCl using the OPW method with a potential based closely on Howland's calculation. Their results are generally in fairly good agreement with those of DeCicco, and, in particular, also show that the energy at the X point is lower than that at the L point.

Finally, there is the calculation of Onodera, Okazaki and Inui[16] on the valence and conduction bands of KI using the relativistic KKR method. Their results are very similar to those of DeCicco; the top of the valence band and the bottom of the conduction band are at the Γ point and the states near the X point are lower than those at the X point.

4. REVIEW OF THE THEORY OF EXCITONS[17]

In the section on determinantal wave functions, we obtained an expression for the excited state of an N-particle system in terms of the occupied and virtual orbitals of an effective one-electron Hamiltonian; the expression was

$$E_N^* = E_N^o + (N'|h_{eff}|N') - (n|h_{eff}|N) - \{(N'N|N'N) - (N'N|NN')\} \qquad (4.1)$$

In the last section, the band states arising when the terms in curly brackets are neglected were discussed. When these terms are included, the resulting interaction between the hole (orbital ϕ_N) and the excited electron (orbital $\phi_{N'}$) can give rise to exciton states (bound electron-hole pairs) whose effects are readily discernible in the optical spectra of insulators.

In the "exciton representation", the wave function is written as

$$\Psi_{vc}(\mathbf{K},\boldsymbol{\beta}) = N^{-1/2} \sum_{\mu} e^{i\mathbf{K}\cdot\mathbf{R}_\mu} A_{vc}(\mathbf{R}_\mu, \mathbf{R}_\mu + \boldsymbol{\beta}) \qquad (4.2)$$

A_{vc} is a determinantal wave function, formed from atomic or Wannier functions, in which an electron has been taken from a valence band Wannier orbital at $\mathbf{R}_\mu$ and placed in a conduction band Wannier orbital at $\mathbf{R}_\mu + \boldsymbol{\beta}$. The translational degeneracy of this function is accounted for in the usual way by multiplying by the exponential and summing over lattice sites.

Because h_{eff} in Eq. (4.1) has Bloch functions as eigenvectors, it is convenient to have $\Psi_{vc}(\mathbf{K}, \boldsymbol{\beta})$ in terms of these functions. By manipulating determinantal wave functions it can be shown that

$$A_{vc}(\mathbf{R}_\mu, \mathbf{R}_\mu + \boldsymbol{\beta}) = N^{-1} \sum_{\mathbf{k}_h \mathbf{k}_e} e^{-i\mathbf{k}_e \cdot (\mathbf{R}_\mu + \boldsymbol{\beta})} e^{i\mathbf{k}_h \cdot \mathbf{R}_\mu} B_{vc}(\mathbf{k}_h, \mathbf{k}_e) \tag{4.3}$$

in which $\mathbf{k}_h$ is the wave vector of the hole Bloch orbital and $\mathbf{k}_e$ that of the electron. Inserting this into (4.2), we find

$$\begin{aligned} \Psi_{vc}(\mathbf{K}, \boldsymbol{\beta}) &= N^{-3/2} \sum_{\mathbf{k}_e \mathbf{k}_h} \sum_{\mu} e^{i(\mathbf{K} - \mathbf{k}_e + \mathbf{k}_h) \cdot \mathbf{R}_\mu} e^{-i\mathbf{k}_e \cdot \boldsymbol{\beta}} B_{vc}(\mathbf{k}_h, \mathbf{k}_e) \\ &= N^{-1/2} \sum_{\mathbf{k}_e \mathbf{k}_h} \delta(\mathbf{K} - \mathbf{k}_e + \mathbf{k}_h) e^{-i\mathbf{k}_e \cdot \boldsymbol{\beta}} B_{vc}(\mathbf{k}_h, \mathbf{k}_e) \\ &= N^{-1/2} \sum_{\mathbf{k}} e^{-i\mathbf{k} \cdot \boldsymbol{\beta}} B_{vc}(\mathbf{k} - \mathbf{K}, \mathbf{k}) \end{aligned} \tag{4.4}$$

where $\mathbf{k} \equiv \mathbf{k}_e$ and $\mathbf{k}_h = \mathbf{k} - \mathbf{K}$.

The matrix elements of the Hamiltonian with respect to the exciton representation can be found readily using the results of the first lecture. We find

$$\left[\Psi_{vc}(\mathbf{K},\boldsymbol{\beta}')\,|\,H\,|\,\Psi_{vc}(\mathbf{K},\boldsymbol{\beta})\right] = N^{-1}\sum_{\mathbf{k}'}\sum_{\mathbf{k}} e^{i(\mathbf{k}'\cdot\boldsymbol{\beta}'-\mathbf{k}\cdot\boldsymbol{\beta})}$$

$$\times\left\{\left[E_N^o + \varepsilon_c(\mathbf{k}) - \varepsilon_v(\mathbf{k}-\mathbf{K})\right]\delta_{\mathbf{k}-\mathbf{K},\mathbf{k}'-\mathbf{K}}\,\delta_{\mathbf{k},\mathbf{k}'}\right.$$

$$\left.-\,(\mathbf{k}'+\mathbf{K},\mathbf{k}'\,|\,\mathbf{k}+\mathbf{K},\mathbf{k}')\right\}$$

$$= N^{-1}\left\{\sum_{\mathbf{k}} e^{i\mathbf{k}\cdot(\boldsymbol{\beta}-\boldsymbol{\beta}')} E_N^o + \sum_{\mathbf{k}} e^{i\mathbf{k}\cdot(\boldsymbol{\beta}-\boldsymbol{\beta}')}\varepsilon_c(\mathbf{k})\right.$$

$$-\sum_{\mathbf{k}} e^{i\mathbf{k}\cdot(\boldsymbol{\beta}'-\boldsymbol{\beta})}\varepsilon_v(\mathbf{k}-\mathbf{K}) - N^{-1}\sum_{\mathbf{k}',\mathbf{k}} e^{i(\mathbf{k}'\cdot\boldsymbol{\beta}'-\mathbf{k}\cdot\boldsymbol{\beta})}$$

$$\left.\times\left[(\mathbf{k}'+\mathbf{K},\mathbf{k}'\,|\,\mathbf{k}+\mathbf{K},\mathbf{k}) - (\mathbf{k}'+\mathbf{K},\mathbf{k}'\,|\,\mathbf{k},\mathbf{k}+\mathbf{K})\right]\right\} \tag{4.5}$$

The last term in this equation is somewhat easier to treat if it is written in the localized representation. Carrying out the transformation to Wannier functions, we have

$$\left[\Psi_{vc}(\mathbf{K},\boldsymbol{\beta}')\,|\,H\,|\,\Psi_{vc}(\mathbf{K},\boldsymbol{\beta})\right] = E_N^o\,\delta_{\boldsymbol{\beta}\boldsymbol{\beta}'} + N^{-1}\sum_{\mathbf{k}} e^{i\mathbf{k}\cdot(\boldsymbol{\beta}-\boldsymbol{\beta}')}$$

$$\times\ \varepsilon_c(\mathbf{k}) - N^{-1}\sum_{\mathbf{k}} e^{i\mathbf{k}\cdot(\boldsymbol{\beta}-\boldsymbol{\beta}')}\varepsilon_v(\mathbf{k}-\mathbf{K})$$

$$-\sum_{\mu} e^{i\mathbf{K}\cdot\mathbf{R}_\mu}\left[\left(a_v(0)a_c(\boldsymbol{\beta}')\,|\,a_v(\mathbf{R}_\mu)a_c(\boldsymbol{\beta})\right)\right.$$

$$- (a_v(0)a_c(\boldsymbol{\beta}')\,|\,a_c(\boldsymbol{\beta})a_v(\mathbf{R}_\mu))\Big] \tag{4.6}$$

Linear combinations of the $\psi_{vc}(\mathbf{K}, \boldsymbol{\beta})$ for different values of $\boldsymbol{\beta}$ must now be taken and the usual secular determinant set up, thus

$$\psi_{vc}(\mathbf{K}) = \sum_{\boldsymbol{\beta}} U_{vc}(\mathbf{K}, \boldsymbol{\beta})\psi_{vc}(\mathbf{K}, \boldsymbol{\beta})$$

with the U's related by

$$\sum_{\boldsymbol{\beta}'} (\psi_{vc}(\mathbf{K}, \boldsymbol{\beta}')\,|\,H\,|\,\psi_{vc}(\mathbf{K}, \boldsymbol{\beta}))U(\mathbf{K}, \boldsymbol{\beta}') = EU(\mathbf{K}, \boldsymbol{\beta}) \tag{4.7}$$

Equations (4.6) and (4.7) are, in general, quite difficult to solve but there are two limits in which the problem becomes tractable. Frenkel[18] was the first to consider the limiting case in which the electron and hole are on the same atom so that $\boldsymbol{\beta} = \boldsymbol{\beta}'$. Wannier[19] treated the opposite case of large electron-hole separation and this approximation has been particularly fruitful in explaining a large body of experimental data in narrow-band-gap semi-conductors. We consider it first and then return to the Frenkel case later.

a. <u>Wannier excitons.</u> In the matrix element given by Eq. (4.6), we note that the electron-hole exchange term is very short-range and can be neglected in the Wannier approximation. Furthermore, the Coulomb term will be large only when R = 0 and $\boldsymbol{\beta} = \boldsymbol{\beta}'$, and we now consider this case; then

$$\int a_v^*(\mathbf{r}_1)a_c^*(\mathbf{r}_2 - \boldsymbol{\beta})\,|\,\mathbf{r}_1 - \mathbf{r}_2\,|^{-1}\,a_v(\mathbf{r}_1)a_c(\mathbf{r}_2 - \boldsymbol{\beta})d\tau_1 d\tau_2 \simeq \frac{1}{\boldsymbol{\beta}} \tag{4.8}$$

large $\boldsymbol{\beta}$

Equation (4.7) becomes

$$N^{-1} \sum_{\boldsymbol{\beta}'} \sum_{\mathbf{k}} e^{i\mathbf{k}\cdot(\boldsymbol{\beta} - \boldsymbol{\beta}')} \left[\varepsilon_c(\mathbf{k}) - \varepsilon_v(\mathbf{k} - \mathbf{K}) \right] U(\mathbf{K}, \boldsymbol{\beta}')$$

$$- \boldsymbol{\beta}^{-1} U(\mathbf{K}, \boldsymbol{\beta}) = (E - E_N^o) U(\mathbf{K}, \boldsymbol{\beta}) \qquad (4.9)$$

It is convenient to make this somewhat more symmetrical by replacing $\mathbf{k}$ by $\mathbf{k} + \mathbf{K}/2$ and then $\mathbf{k} - \mathbf{K} \rightarrow \mathbf{k} - \mathbf{K}/2$. At the same time we can multiply through by $e^{-i\mathbf{k}\cdot\boldsymbol{\beta}}$ to get

$$N^{-1} \sum_{\boldsymbol{\beta}'} \sum_{\mathbf{k}} e^{-i\mathbf{k}\cdot\boldsymbol{\beta}'} \left[\varepsilon_c(\mathbf{k} + \mathbf{K}/2) - \varepsilon_v(\mathbf{k} - \mathbf{K}/2) \right] U'(\mathbf{K}, \boldsymbol{\beta}')$$

$$- \boldsymbol{\beta}^{-1} U'(\mathbf{K}, \boldsymbol{\beta}) = (E - E^o) U'(\mathbf{K}, \boldsymbol{\beta}) \qquad (4.10)$$

where

$$U'(\mathbf{K}, \boldsymbol{\beta}) = e^{-i\mathbf{K}\cdot\boldsymbol{\beta}/2} U(\mathbf{K}, \boldsymbol{\beta})$$

The conversion of this difference equation to differential form has been discussed by Wannier. One gets

$$\left[\varepsilon_c(-i\nabla_{\boldsymbol{\beta}} + \mathbf{K}/2) - \varepsilon_v(-i\nabla_{\boldsymbol{\beta}} - \mathbf{K}/2) - \boldsymbol{\beta}^{-1} \right] U'(\boldsymbol{\beta}) =$$

$$= (E - E^o) U'(\boldsymbol{\beta}) \qquad (4.11)$$

Next, the assumption is made that the valence and conduction bands are of standard form and that they can be expanded as

$$\varepsilon_c = \varepsilon_c^o + k^2/2m_e^*$$

$$\varepsilon_v = \varepsilon_v^o - k^2/2m_h^* \tag{4.12}$$

where m_e^* and m_h^* are the effective masses of the electron and hole and ε_c^o and ε_v^o are the bottom of the conduction band and the top of the valence band, respectively. When these expressions are substituted into Eq. (4.11), one gets

$$\left[-\frac{1}{2m_+}\nabla_{\boldsymbol{\beta}}^2 - \boldsymbol{\beta}^{-1} + \frac{i}{2m_-}\mathbf{K}\cdot\boldsymbol{\nabla}\right]U' = \left[E - E_N^o - E_G - \frac{K^2}{8m_+}\right]U' \tag{4.13}$$

Here, $m_+^{-1} \equiv (m_h^{*-1} + m_e^{*-1})$; $m_-^{-1} \equiv (m_h^{*-1} - m_e^{*-1})$; E_N^o is the total ground state energy; E_G is the band gap. Carrying out the same transformation used in the $\mathbf{K}\cdot\mathbf{P}$ perturbation approach in band theory $\left(U'(\boldsymbol{\beta}) = e^{i\alpha\mathbf{K}\cdot\boldsymbol{\beta}}F(\boldsymbol{\beta})\right)$, one obtains an equation for $F(\boldsymbol{\beta})$, i.e.,

$$\left(-\frac{1}{2m_+}\nabla^2 - \beta^{-1}\right)F(\beta) = \left[E - E^o - E_G - \frac{K^2}{2(m_e^* + m_h^*)}\right]F(\beta) \tag{4.14}$$

with $\alpha = \frac{1}{2}(m_e^* - m_h^*)/(m_e^* + m_h^*)$. From the solution of the corresponding equation of the hydrogen atom it is easily seen that

$$E(K) = E_N^o + E_G - \frac{m_+}{2n^2} + \frac{K^2}{2(m_e^* + m_h^*)} \tag{4.15}$$

Equation (4.14) can be extended to the more general case[21] occurring when the valence and conduction bands do not have isotropic effective masses and do not have their maximum and minimum respectively at $\mathbf{k} = 0$. Thus, instead of Eqs. (4.12), we have

$$\varepsilon_c(\mathbf{k}_e) = \varepsilon_c(\mathbf{k}_e^o) + \sum_{\mu,\nu} (1/2m^*_e)_{\mu\nu} (\mathbf{k} - \mathbf{k}^o_e)_\mu (\mathbf{k} - \mathbf{k}^o_e)_\nu$$

$$\varepsilon_v(\mathbf{k}_h) = \varepsilon_v(\mathbf{k}_h^o) - \sum_{\mu,\nu} (1/2m^*_h)_{\mu\nu} (\mathbf{k} - \mathbf{k}^o_h)_\mu (\mathbf{k} - \mathbf{k}^o_h)_\nu \qquad (4.16)$$

b. Frenkel excitons. As stated earlier, Frenkel considered the case arising when the excited electron remains always associated with the same atom as the hole. The wave function for this case can be obtained from Eq. (4.6) by putting $\beta = \beta' = 0$. One finds for a highly simplified model

$$E(K) = E_{oo} + \sum_{\mu} e^{i\mathbf{k}\cdot\mathbf{R}_\mu} \Big[(a_v(0)a_c(\mu) \,|\, a_c(0)a_v(\mu)) - (a_v(0)a_c(\mu) \,|\, a_v(\mu)a_c(0)) \Big] \qquad (4.17)$$

E_{oo} contains the ground state energy plus the energy of excitation of an atom. Note that the sum over μ gives a contribution even when the Wannier functions do not overlap. The most extensive calculations using the Frenkel model are those by Knox on argon.

c. Excitation model. There is another model which has been employed frequently in the literature --the so-called excitation model[22]. In this model, the hole is considered to be localized at a particular lattice site and the wave function of the electron is approximated in various ways. The problem becomes essentially the same as that for a point defect in an ionic crystal, which will be discussed later.

5. MANY-BODY EFFECTS

Throughout the discussion of Wannier excitons in the preceding section, the effect of the dielectric media on the electron-hole interaction was neglected. But since both the electron and hole when well separated, as assumed in the Wannier model, can very efficiently polarize the lattice, we must expect this neglect to be inadmissible. The simplest procedure and one arrived at very quickly on intuitive grounds is to introduce an effective dielectric constant into the electron-hole interaction. Thus,

$$V_{\text{el-hole}} = (\kappa_{\text{eff}} r)^{-1}$$

Furthermore, one might expect that in the region of very large electron-hole separations it would be appropriate to put $\kappa_{\text{eff}} \equiv \kappa_{\text{static}}$, whereas at smaller values of r when the internal kinetic energy of the pair is higher, $\kappa_{\text{eff}} \simeq \kappa_{\infty}$. When the electron and hole are very close together, even the electrons on the ions cannot follow the electron and hole adiabatically, and $\kappa_{\text{eff}} \rightarrow 1$.

The problem of the choice of κ_{eff} for various regions of the electron-hole separation has been discussed often in the literature. Here we shall follow the work of Toyozawa[23] and Haken and Schottky[24]. Since the theory is quite involved, it cannot be covered in any great detail in these lectures. Instead, let me just indicate the approach of Haken and Schottky and give their final result with most of the intermediate steps left out.

To write the Hamiltonian for a many-body system in second quantized notation, we proceed as follows. From field theoretical considerations, we write

$$H = \int \psi^{+}(\mathbf{r}_1) H_1 \psi(\mathbf{r}_1) d^3\mathbf{r}_1 + \frac{1}{2}\iint \psi^{+}(\mathbf{r}_1)\psi^{+}(\mathbf{r}_2) V_{12} \psi(\mathbf{r}_2)$$

$$\times \psi(\mathbf{r}_1) d^3\mathbf{r}_1 d^3\mathbf{r}_2 \qquad (5.1)$$

and put

$$\psi^{+}(\mathbf{r}) = \sum_{\nu} \alpha_{\nu} a_{\nu}(\mathbf{r}) + \sum_{\nu} \bar{\alpha}^{+}_{\nu} \bar{a}^{+}_{\nu}(\mathbf{r}) + \bar{c}^{+}_{\nu} \bar{\phi}^{+}_{\nu}(\mathbf{r})$$

with

$$a(\mathbf{r} - \mathbf{R}_{\nu}) = N^{-1/2} \sum_{k} e^{i\mathbf{k}\cdot\mathbf{R}_{\nu}} \psi(\mathbf{k}, \mathbf{r})$$

and

$$\psi(\mathbf{r}) = \sum_{\nu} \alpha^{+}_{\nu} a^{+}_{\nu}(\mathbf{r}) + \sum_{\nu} \bar{\alpha}_{\nu} \bar{a}_{\nu}(\mathbf{r}) + \bar{c}_{\nu} \bar{\phi}_{\nu}(\mathbf{r})$$

a_{ν} is a valence band Wannier function which is so well localized that there is negligible overlap between functions on different sites. $\bar{a}_{\nu}$ is an excited state Wannier function which is also assumed to have zero overlap with the a's and $\bar{a}$'s on different sites. Obviously this corresponds to a highly idealized model. $\bar{\alpha}^{+}_{\nu}$ and α^{+}_{ν} are electron and hole creation operators for the Wannier functions and $\bar{\alpha}_{\nu}$ and α_{ν} are the corresponding destruction operators. As we shall see, the α's and $\bar{\alpha}$'s will be used to form Frenkel excitons and therefore other quantities ($\bar{c}^{+}$, $\bar{\phi}^{+}_{\nu}(r)$ and $\bar{c}_{\nu}$, $\bar{\phi}_{\nu}(r)$) have been introduced explicitly to describe a free electron or one involved in a more loosely bound exciton.

Inserting $\psi(r)$ and $\psi^{+}(r)$ into Eq. (5.1) and considering only those terms not involving $\bar{\phi}^{+}_{o}(r)$ or $\phi_{o}(r)$, we get for H_1

$$H_1 = \sum_{\mu,\nu} \{ \alpha^{+}_{\mu} \alpha_{\nu} (\xi | H_1 | \nu) + \bar{\alpha}^{+}_{\mu} \bar{\alpha}_{\nu} (\bar{\mu} | H_1 | \bar{\nu})$$

$$+ \alpha_\mu^+ \bar{\alpha}_\nu(\mu | H_1 | \bar{\nu}) + \bar{\alpha}_\mu^+ \alpha_\nu(\bar{\mu} | H_1 | \nu)\} \qquad (5.2)$$

We assume H_1 is an effective Hamiltonian for both the barred and unbarred functions. This in conjunction with our assumption about overlap gives

$$H_1 = \sum_\nu (\varepsilon \alpha_\nu^+ \alpha_\nu + \bar{\varepsilon} \bar{\alpha}_\nu^+ \bar{\alpha}_\nu) \qquad (5.3)$$

Next, we use the fermion commutation relations

$$[\alpha_\mu^+, \alpha_\nu]_+ = \delta_{\mu\nu}, \qquad [\bar{\alpha}_\mu^+, \bar{\alpha}_\nu]_+ = \delta_{\mu\nu}$$

to write $\alpha_\nu^+ \alpha_\nu$ as

$$\alpha_\nu^+ \alpha_\nu = \alpha_\nu^+ [\bar{\alpha}_\nu^+ \bar{\alpha}_\nu + \bar{\alpha}_\nu \bar{\alpha}_\nu^+] \alpha_\nu = \alpha_\nu^+ \bar{\alpha}_\nu^+ \bar{\alpha}_\nu \alpha_\nu + \alpha_\nu^+ \bar{\alpha}_\nu \bar{\alpha}_\nu^+ \alpha_\nu$$

Localized pair creation and annihilation operators are defined by

$$\beta_\nu^+ \equiv \bar{\alpha}_\nu^+ \alpha_\nu^+ \quad \text{and} \quad \beta_\nu \equiv \alpha_\nu \bar{\alpha}_\nu$$

This gives (barred quantities commute with unbarred)

$$\alpha_\nu^+ \alpha_\nu = \beta_\nu^+ \beta_\nu + \bar{\alpha}_\nu \beta_\nu^+ \alpha_\nu$$

There are no holes in the ground state so $\alpha_\nu | 0 \rangle = 0$ and we can neglect the last term. Carrying out a similar calculation for $\bar{\alpha}_\nu^+ \bar{\alpha}_\nu$, we finally obtain

$$H_1 = \sum_\nu (\varepsilon + \bar{\varepsilon}) \beta_\nu^+ \beta_\nu \qquad (5.4)$$

Keep in mind that the energy of a hole, ε, in this case is positive, whereas $\bar{\varepsilon}$ is negative.

Turning to H_2 and again considering all terms not involving ϕ_o, we find that there are sixteen of them of the form

$$< \mu\nu \,|\, \nu\mu > \alpha^{+}_{\mu} \alpha^{+}_{\nu} \alpha_{\nu} \alpha_{\mu}$$

with all possible combinations of barred and unbarred quantities. These sixteen terms can be classified as follows:

hole-hole	$(\mu\nu \,\vert\, \nu\mu)\, \alpha_{\mu} \alpha_{\nu} \alpha^{+}_{\nu} \alpha^{+}_{\mu}$	one term
hole-pair	$(\mu\nu \,\vert\, \nu\bar{\mu})\, \alpha_{\mu} \alpha_{\nu} \alpha^{+}_{\nu} \bar{\alpha}_{\nu}$	four terms
pair-pair	$(\mu\nu \,\vert\, \bar{\nu}\bar{\mu})\, \alpha_{\mu} \alpha_{\nu} \bar{\alpha}_{\nu} \bar{\alpha}_{\mu}$	two terms
pair-pair	$(\mu\bar{\nu} \,\vert\, \nu\bar{\mu})\, \alpha_{\mu} \bar{\alpha}^{+}_{\nu} \alpha^{+}_{\nu} \bar{\alpha}_{\mu}$	two terms
el-pair	$(\mu\bar{\nu} \,\vert\, \bar{\nu}\bar{\mu})\, \alpha_{\mu} \bar{\alpha}^{+}_{\nu} \bar{\alpha}_{\nu} \bar{\alpha}_{\nu}$	four terms
el-el	$(\bar{\mu}\bar{\nu} \,\vert\, \bar{\nu}\bar{\mu})\, \bar{\alpha}^{+}_{\mu} \bar{\alpha}^{+}_{\nu} \bar{\alpha}_{\nu} \bar{\alpha}_{\mu}$	one term
el-hole	$(\mu\bar{\nu} \,\vert\, \bar{\nu}\mu)\, \alpha_{\nu} \bar{\alpha}^{+}_{\mu} \bar{\alpha}_{\mu} \alpha^{+}_{\nu}$	two terms

We now assume that an electron and hole created on the ν-th ion, by $\bar{\alpha}^{+}_{\nu}$ and α^{+}_{ν}, will remain tighly bound together, i.e., they will form a Frenkel exciton. The following reductions will then occur for $\mu \neq \nu$. The hole-pair terms will cancel with the electron-pair terms and the hole-hole and electron-electron terms will cancel the electron-hole terms. When $\mu = \nu$, on the other hand, the restriction that no more than one hole or one electron can be on a given site at the same time causes all terms to vanish except the electron-hole interaction and the pair-pair terms of the form $\alpha_\nu \bar{\alpha}_\nu^+ \alpha_\nu^+ \bar{\alpha}_\nu = \beta_\nu^+ \beta_\nu$ which now just correspond to the number operator for a pair state on a given site. We must also require the commutation relation, $[\alpha_\nu, \beta_\nu^+] = 0$. Thus, we get

$$H_1 = \sum_\nu \{(\varepsilon + \bar{\varepsilon}) + (\bar{\nu}\nu|\nu\bar{\nu}) - (\bar{\nu}\nu|\bar{\nu}\nu)\} \beta_\nu^+ \beta_\nu$$

$$+ \sum_{\mu,\nu} (\nu\bar{\mu}|\mu\bar{\nu}) \beta_\mu^+ \beta_\nu \qquad (5.5)$$

The translational invariance of the system makes it possible to diagonalize this expression by the transformation

$$\beta_\nu^+ = N^{-1/2} \sum_k \beta_k^+ e^{-i\mathbf{k}\cdot\mathbf{R}_\nu} \qquad (5.6)$$

We obtain

$$H_1 = \sum_k E(K) \beta_k^+ \beta_k^+ \qquad (5.7)$$

From Eq. (5.6) it can be seen that E(K) is the energy of a Frenkel exciton. Thus, fy forcing the electron and hole to always be created together and to remain tightly bound together as they move through the crystal, we have been able to reduce the Hamiltonian to that for Frenkel excitons.

Now we consider that the electron and hole are created on different ions or that an additional electron is added to the system. This is the reason for including $\bar{c}_\nu^+$ and $\bar{c}_\nu$ explicitly.

The same type terms as those listed above will be present again, but now the hole-pair and electron-pair terms will not cancel. The analysis of these terms given by Haken and Schottky is too complicated to go into in detail here. Besides effective

Hamiltonians for the electron and hole they obtain interaction terms between the electron and Frenkel excitons and between the hole and the Frenkel excitons. For the former the term is of the form

$$H_{\text{el-pair}} = \sum_{\mu,\nu} \left\{ (\bar{\mu}\bar{\nu}\,|\,\nu\bar{\mu})\,\bar{\alpha}_{\nu}^{+}\,\bar{\alpha}_{\nu}\,\beta_{\mu}^{+} + \text{comp. conj.} \right\} \tag{5.8}$$

The interparticle potential in the integral can be expanded in terms of the ratio of the atomic radius to the interatomic distance $\mathbf{R}_{\mu} - \mathbf{R}_{\nu}$. The lowest order term surviving in this integral is the monopole-dipole interaction which gives, on introducing Eq. (5.6),

$$H_{\text{el-pair}} = \sum_{\nu} \sum_{k} e^{i\mathbf{k}\cdot\mathbf{R}_{\nu}}\, \Gamma_k\, \bar{\alpha}_{\nu}^{+}\,\bar{\alpha}_{\nu}\,\beta_{k}^{+} \tag{5.9}$$

where

$$\Gamma_k = N^{-1/2} \sum_{\lambda} e^{i\mathbf{k}\cdot\mathbf{R}_{\lambda}} (\mathbf{R}_{\lambda} \cdot \boldsymbol{\mu} / \ell^3)$$

and

$$\mu_{\nu} = \int a^{*}(\mathbf{r} - \mathbf{R}_{\nu})\,\mathbf{r}\,\mathbf{a}(\mathbf{r} - \mathbf{R}_{\nu})\,d\tau$$

Proceeding in this way, Haken and Schottky obtain

$$H = E_o^e - E_o^h - \frac{\nabla_1^2}{2m_e^*} - \frac{\nabla_2^2}{2m_h^*} - |\mathbf{r}_e - \mathbf{r}_h|^{-1}$$

$$+ \sum_k \beta_k^{+} \beta_k\, E(K) + \sum_k \left(e^{-i\mathbf{k}\cdot\mathbf{r}_e} - e^{-i\mathbf{k}\cdot\mathbf{r}_h}\right) \Gamma_k \beta_k^{+} + cc \tag{5.10}$$

This Hamiltonian is basically the same as that obtained earlier by others for the polaron problem. For a discussion of it see reference 23. The final form for the Wannier exciton equation obtained by Haken and Schottky is

$$\left[- \frac{\nabla_e^2}{2m_e^{**}} - \frac{\nabla_h^2}{2m_h^{**}} - \frac{1}{\kappa_{eff} r} \right] \Psi = E\Psi \tag{5.11}$$

with

$$\frac{1}{\kappa_{eff}} = 1 - (1 - \kappa_\infty^{-1})(1 - \frac{e^{-\rho_e r} + e^{-\rho_h r}}{2}) \tag{5.12}$$

The ** on m_e and m_h indicate that these are somewhat different from the usual effective masses due to inclusion of many-body effects. ρ_e and ρ_h are constants related roughly to the band gap. Note that

$$\kappa_{eff}^{-1} \rightarrow \kappa_\infty^{-1} \quad \text{as} \quad r \rightarrow \infty$$

and (5.13)

$$\kappa_{eff}^{-1} \rightarrow 1 \quad \text{as} \quad r \rightarrow 0$$

The above value of κ_{eff}^{-1} was obtained on the assumption that the ions cannot follow the motion of the electron or hole. This restriction can easily be lifted and the following expression is then obtained:

$$\frac{1}{\kappa_{eff}} = 1 - (1 - \kappa_\infty^{-1})(1 - \frac{e^{-\rho_e r} + e^{-\rho_h r}}{2}) - (\kappa_\infty^{-1} - \kappa_{st}^{-1})(1 - \frac{e^{-v_e r} + e^{-v_h r}}{2}) \tag{5.14}$$

where v_e and v_h are constants related to the longitudinal optical phonon frequency. From this expression we see that $\kappa_{eff}^{-1} \rightarrow \kappa_{st}^{-1}$ as r becomes large. The extent to which these forms for κ_{eff} are reliable remains to be seen. Preliminary results on defect calculations, to be discussed later, indicated that Eq. (5.14) can give very promising results. In any case, the fact that there exists an analytical form for κ_{eff} which gives the correct limiting behavior is interesting in itself.

6. OPTICAL ABSORPTION SPECTRA AND THEIR INTERPRETATION

The intrinsic optical absorption spectra of large-band-gap ionic and rare gas crystals have a number of interesting features which indicate the occurrence of both excitonic and band-to-band transitions. The experimental data on the alkali halides is particularly rich due to the work of Teegarden and coworkers[25], and I shall concentrate on these crystals.

In Figs. 2, 3 and 4, the results of Teegarden and Baldini for NaCl, KCl and KBr are shown[26]. The spectra of KCl and RbCl are very similar, as are those of KBr and RbBr. Indeed, there are certain similarities among many of the spectra, but here we need emphasize only the following. In both NaCl and KCl the lowest energy peak has an appreciable splitting, whereas in KBr thair spectra appear to be two distinct low energy peaks (~6.8 eV and ~7.3 eV). These splittings and peaks correlate very nicely with the spin-orbit splitting of the free negative halide ion and there seems little doubt that spin-orbit splittings play a major role in the interpretation of all of the spectra and especially those of crystals

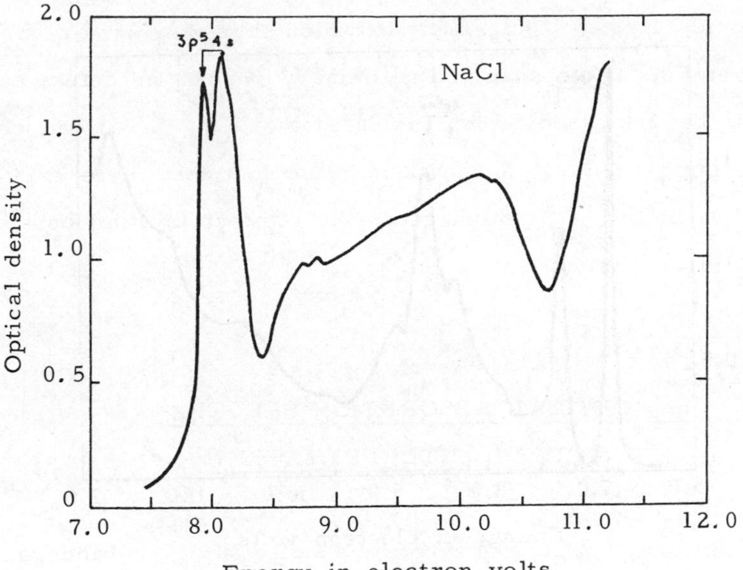
3p⁵4s
NaCl
2.0
1.5
1.0
0.5
0
Optical density
7.0
8.0
9.0
10.0
11.0
12.0
Energy in electron volts

Fig. 2

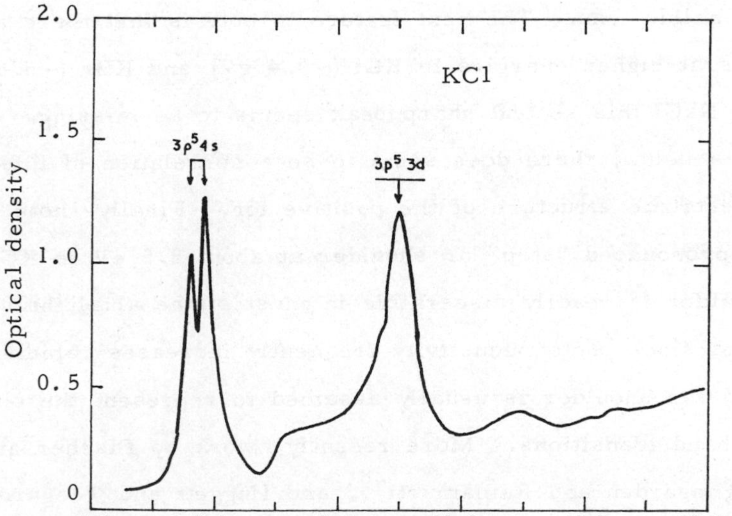
3p⁵4s
3p⁵3d
KCl
2.0
1.5
1.0
0.5
0
Optical density
7.0
8.0
9.0
10.0
11.0
12.0
Energy in electron volts

Fig. 3

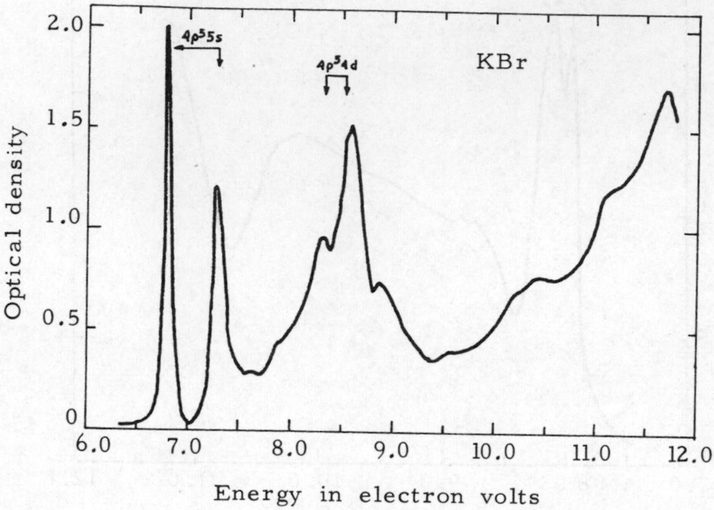

Fig. 4

with heavy halide ions. The next feature to note is that there are sharp peaks at higher energies in KCl (~9.4 eV) and KBr (~8.5 eV), whereas in NaCl this second sharp peak seems to be missing. As we shall see below, there does seem to be a correlation of this peak with the electronic structure of the positive ion. Finally, note that there is a pronounced "step" or shoulder at about 8.5 eV in KCl. Such a shoulder is readily discernible in most of the alkali halide spectra, and since photoconductivity frequently increases rapidly in this region, the shoulder is usually assumed to represent the onset of band-to-band transitions. More recently, work by Fischer and Hilsch[27], Teegarden and Ramamurti[28], and Huggett and Teegarden[29] has indicated that there is considerable structure in the shoulder region. The work of Hopfield and Worlock[30] on two-photon absorption is also quite interesting in this connection.

The interpretation of the spectra below and in the shoulder region appears to be quite straightforward. The first intense peak is due to a transition from the valence band to an exciton state which is well localized although probably not sufficiently to be considered a true Frenkel exciton. This first peak is spin-orbit split and in crystals with heavy halide ions this splitting may throw the high energy component in or above the shoulder region. In most cases, the structure in the shoulder region now appears to be due to transitions to Wannier or nealy Wannier-like exciton states. The onset of band-to-band transitions evidently occurs somewhat further into the shoulder region than was formerly believed, but the exact position is somewhat difficult to determine because of the lack of well resolved peaks. It does appear, however, that a very nice M_o edge (see Cardona's lectures) can be hidden in the shoulder region.

The interpretation of the structure beyond the onset of band-to-band transitions is more difficult and has been the subject of much controversy recently. For example, the second strong peak in KCl (which is almost certainly not a spin-orbit effect) apparently lies well within the region of band-to-band transitions. Is it to be associated with a density of state condition, i.e., an M_1 and M_2 edge in very close proximity, or is it due to an excitonic resonance such as one might obtain form a Lifschitz[31] - Koster - Slater[32] (LKS) type approach?

The first suggestion that this peak (and corresponding peaks in other alkali halides) is due to transitions to metastable exciton states is frequently attributed to Phillips[33]. He called them L excitons because he felt that they were most likely associated with the hyperbolic critical point (M_1) at the L point in the Brillouin zone.

Three papers[34] have appeared recently discussing the existence or nonexistence of "hyperbolic" excitons. Morita and Azuma[35] actually published a parameterized calculation of this excitonic resonance in KCl using a Koster-Slater model some time before Phillips' suggestion. The agreement which he obtained with the experimental data is impressive. He associated the resonance with an M_o edge at the Γ point. More recently, as mentioned in the section on band theory, calculations have indicated that the energy of the lowest conduction band at the X point is lower than it is at the L point. Since there is an M_o critical point at X, the indication would again seem to be that the second peak is due to a parabolic excitonic resonance. Since the conduction band function at X in KCl, etc., contains a considerable alkali d orbital contribution, the absence of a resonance in Na and Li halides may be associated with the higher energy of a d orbital in these ions. The actual calculation of excitonic resonances beyond the simple parameterized Koster-Slater-type calculation carried out by Morita can become quite involved. At Oak Ridge, we have been carrying out calculations based on the excitation model described earlier. We have actually been trying to calculate phase shifts as a function of energy by a variational principle due to Kohn. Thus far, we have been unsuccessful in detecting any resonances, but this may very well be due to inadequacies in the model.

7. POINT DEFECTS IN IONIC CRYSTALS

Now let us turn to the consideration of some aspects of the optical absorption of ionic crystals containing point defects (frequently called color centers). This branch of solid state physics began in the twenties with the experimental work of Pohl and coworkers[36]. Initially, interest in the field was not great, but in the last ten years it has increased rapidly in spite of the fact that there has, as yet, been no really important technological application of the rapidly accruing knowledge. Thus far, most of the work has been done in the alkali halide crystals, but recently much attention has been given to two-six compounds such as MgO and CaO and to other ionic crystals such as CaF_2.

The simplest point defect is the F center, which consists of an electron trapped at a negative ion vacancy. It has also been found that F centers can combine to form new agglomerate centers; the M center consists of two F centers bound together at neighboring negative ion sites; the N centers consist of three and four neighboring F centers. Another modification on the basic F center is the F_a center, which consists of an F center with a neighboring alkali ion of the host crystal replaced by some other alkali ion. Also, there is the F' center, which consists of two electrons trapped at a negative ion vacancy. F centers and probably many of these other defects occur in MgO, CaF_2, and other ionic crystals. Another very interesting defect is the U center, which is an H^- ion at a site normally occupied by a negative halide ion. There has been considerable interest in this problem recently because of its vibrational properties.

In addition to these "electron" centers, there are various "hole" centers which, with one exception, we shall not consider. The exception is the V_K center, which can be thought of as the negative ion of a halide diatomic molecule embedded in the crystal and oriented in a [110] direction. This center is of interest in connection with the relaxation of exciton states.

You can see that there is a large number of color centers, which, perhaps, helps to explain the increasing interest in them. Here, we shall consider only the F center, which is the most basic of the color centers. For discussions of other centers see reference 36.

Let us assume we have a one-electron Hamiltonian of the form

$$h = -\frac{1}{2}\nabla^2 + V_{cr}(\mathbf{r}) \tag{7.1}$$

and consider some of the models which have been used for calculations on the F center. We shall specify the crystal potential V_{cr} as we go along.

a. Semi-continuum models. Tibbs[37] was the first to attempt a calculation of F-center energy levels and wave functions. He based his calculations on a model in which the crystal is treated as a continuous dielectric medium of dielectric constant, κ_{eff}, in which there exists a spherical cavity where $\kappa_{eff} = 1$. This has become known as the semi-continuum model. Tibbs chose V_{cr} as follows:

$$\begin{aligned} V_{cr} &\equiv V_{in} = -\alpha_M/a + (1 - \kappa_\infty^{-1})R^{-1}, \quad && r < R_o \\ V_{cr} &\equiv V_{out} = -(\kappa_\infty r)^{-1} && r > R_o \end{aligned} \tag{7.2}$$

α_M is the Madelung constant, a the nearest neighbor distance in the crystal, and κ_∞ the high-frequency dielectric constant. The radius R was chosen to be 0.95a, based on earlier work of Mott and Littleton[38], and R_o, the radius of the hole, was obtained by equating V_{in} and V_{out}. Hence the distances involved are

$a = 5.33$ a.u., $R = 5.06$ a.u., and $R_o = 2.0$ a.u.

The interior solutions of Eq. (7.1) with the potential Eq. (7.2) are just those for a particle in a spherical box, i.e., spherical Bessel functions. The exterior solutions can be obtained by numerical integration and the conditions that both ψ and its first derivative be continuous at $r = R_o$ determine the eigenvalue E. For NaCl, Tibbs obtained with this model a value of 1.26 eV for the first transition energy, whereas the experimental value is 2.72 eV.

Tibbs carried out the calculation of the transition more successfully on a somewhat different model. First, he referred the potential of the defect electron to the bottom of the conduction band by writing

$$V_{in} = -\alpha_M/a + (1 - \kappa_\infty^{-1})R^{-1} - \chi \qquad (7.3)$$

and

$$V_{out} = V_L - (\kappa_\infty)^{-1}$$

χ is the experimental electron affinity of the crystal, which is assumed to measure the energy of the bottom of the conduction band. V_L is the potential energy of the electron in the field of the perfect lattice. The principal difference between the two models appears to be the use of a larger value of R_o in the second, i.e., $R_o = 5.0$ a.u. In any case, with his second model Tibbs obtained 2.5 eV for the transition energy, in fairly good agreement with experiment.

Many other workers[39] have used the semi-continuum model, with varying degrees of success depending on the assumptions made about well depth, well radius and polarization potential.

b. MO-LCAO method. The letters here indicate that the F-center wave function thought of as a molecular orbital is to be constructed from linear combinations of the unoccupied atomic orbitals on the neighboring ions. This is a difficult method to work with from first principles. The reason is that one is frequently trying to construct a localized function centered on one site from a linear combination of diffuse functions centered on other sites. The result is that if an accurate calculation is to be obtained many two-, three- and four-center integrals must be evaluated, and this is both time consuming and expensive.

c. Point ion model. This model, used extensively by Gourary and Adrian[40], treats all ions as point charges. An expansion of the potential about the center of the vacancy results in a spherically symmetric term which is constant within the lnn distance and then undergoes a series of oscillations as more and more shells of ions are taken into account. Gourary and Adrian's most successful calculations were carried out with wave functions which were made up of spherical Bessel functions inside the nearest neighbor radius and some form of exponentially decreasing functions outside. Their results for the transition energies for a series of alkali halides are in general about 20 per cent too low but follow the experimental trend of energy vs crystal lattice parameter rather well. Gourary and Adrian came to the conclusion that polarization effects are of little importance in determining the energy of the states involved in absorption. This is interesting in light of the occurrence of κ_∞ in the semi-continuum model.

d. Hartree-Fock calculations[41]. The point ion model can be extended by taking into account the electronic structure on the ions neighboring the vacancy within the Hartree-Fock approximation. Thus, for the potential of the crystal one might take

$$V_{cr}(\mathbf{r}_1) = -\sum Z_\nu/|\mathbf{r}_1 - \mathbf{R}_\nu| + \int d\tau_2\left[\rho(2,2) - \rho(2,1)P'_{12}\right] \tag{7.4}$$

where the Fock-Dirac density matrix, ρ, is given by

$$\rho(2,1) = \sum_{\nu,j} a^*_{\nu,j}(1')$$

$a_{\nu,j}$ is the j-th Wannier or atomic orbital on the ν-th ion. Energy terms involving $\rho(2,2)$ give the Coulomb interaction and $\rho(2,1)$ the exchange interaction with the electrons on the neighboring ions. Note that when the point ion model is assumed the exchange terms vanish and the Coulomb terms combine with the nuclear terms to give the point ion potential. The wave function of the F-center can be assumed to be of the form

$$\psi(\mathbf{r}) = N\left[\phi_o(\mathbf{r}) - \sum_{\nu,j} (a_{\nu,j}|\phi_o)a_{\nu,j}(\mathbf{r} - \mathbf{R}_\nu)\right] \tag{7.5}$$

where $\phi_o(r)$ is a smooth function containing both linear and non-linear parameters whose "best" values can be found from a variational calculation. The above form of $\psi(\mathbf{r})$ results from a simple Schmidt orthogonalization to the neighboring ion functions.

Calculations along this line with structure on the lnn ions only give a considerable improvement over the point ion results.

e. <u>Hartree with polarization effects included.</u> At Oak Ridge, we have now greatly extended earlier Hartree-Fock calculations by Wood and Joy. These extensions account rigorously for the structure on the lnn, 2nn and 3nn ions and approximately for all the ions in the crystal. Furthermore, the polarization of the crystal is taken account of by the Toyozawa, Haken and Schottky theory discussed earlier. The trial functions, ϕ_o, of Eq. (7.5) are expressed as linear combinations of Slater orbitals, i.e.,

$$\phi_o(r) = \sum_n c_n \phi_n(r)$$
$$\phi_n(r) \sim r^{n-1} e^{-\beta_n r} \tag{7.6}$$

Both β_n and c_n are variation parameters so that considerable flexibility is introduced into the trial functions. Quite good agreement with experiment has been found thus far in NaCl and KCl.

Perhaps the most obvious conclusion to be drawn from our discussion of this simple defect is that the problem of calculating the electronic wave functions and energy levels is not simple. Unlike the impurity problem in semiconductors, the deviations from simple effective mass theory are of paramount importance to some of the states. To take these deviations into account satisfactorily is rather difficult. Furthermore, the above discussion has been concerned only with those states involved in the most prominent absorption of the center. In addition, there are other states which are very nearly effective mass states (K band). There are also weak absorptions (L bands) which appear to require the excited states involved to be degenerate with the conduction band states, or at least associated with the conduction band in some way. The exact nature of these states is still an unresolved problem.

8. LATTICE RELAXATION AND LUMINESCENCE

A crystal will usually not emit light at the same frequency that it absorbs, and, in fact, the luminescence is often completely quenched. In alkali halide and other ionic crystals, the difference in frequency between the absorbed and emitted light (often called the Stokes shift) may be quite large. This is true of both the intrinsic luminescence and the luminescence of crystals with defects, e.g., the F center. The occurrence of a large Stokes shift suggests substantial changes in the lattice configuration in the vicinity of localized excitations. Here I want to consider some aspects of the lattice relaxation and luminescence of excitons and F centers.

a. Coupling of electronic and nuclear motion[42]. Let us write the total Hamiltonian of the system as

$$H = T_{el} + T_N + U(\mathbf{r}, \mathbf{R}) \tag{8.1}$$

in which T_{el} and T_N are the total kinetic energies of the electrons and nuclei, respectively, and $U(\mathbf{r}, \mathbf{R})$ is the total potential energy of the system including that due to the interaction of the nuclei. $\mathbf{r}$ represents the coordinates of all of the electrons and $\mathbf{R}$ of all of the nuclei. The corresponding Schrödinger equation is

$$H(\mathbf{r}, \mathbf{R})\Psi(\mathbf{r}, \mathbf{R}) = \varepsilon\,\Psi(\mathbf{r}, \mathbf{R}) \tag{8.2}$$

For fixed nuclei, T_N contributes nothing and the Hamiltonian can be written as

$$H_o = T_{el} + U(\mathbf{r}, \mathbf{R}) \tag{8.3}$$

with the eigenvalue and eigenvectors given by

$$H_o\psi_n(\mathbf{r},\mathbf{R}) = E_n(\mathbf{R})\psi_n(\mathbf{r},\mathbf{R}) \tag{8.4}$$

The notation is meant to indicate that the energy of the n-th state of the electronic system depends on the positions of the nuclei. We now expand Ψ in terms of the ψ_n, i.e.,

$$\Psi(\mathbf{r},\mathbf{R}) = \sum_n \chi_n(\mathbf{R})\psi_n(\mathbf{r},\mathbf{R}) \tag{8.5}$$

and substitute into Eq. (8.2) to get

$$\sum_n T_N\left[\chi_n(R)\psi_n(\mathbf{r},\mathbf{R})\right] + \sum_n E_n(R)\psi_n(\mathbf{r},\mathbf{R}) =$$

$$= \varepsilon \sum_n \chi_n(\mathbf{R})\psi_n(\mathbf{r},\mathbf{R}) \tag{8.6}$$

When expanded, a single term in the first sum gives, with

$$T_N = \frac{1}{2}\sum_\nu P_\nu^2/M_\nu ,$$

$$T_N\left[\chi_n(\mathbf{R})\psi_n(\mathbf{r},\mathbf{R})\right] = \frac{1}{2}\sum_\nu M_\nu^{-1}\left\{\left[P_\nu^2\chi_n(\mathbf{R})\right]\chi_n(\mathbf{r},\mathbf{R})\right.$$

$$\left. + 2\left[P_\nu\chi_n(\mathbf{R})\right]\left[P_\nu\psi_n(\mathbf{r},\mathbf{R})\right] + \chi_n(\mathbf{R})P_\nu^2\psi_n(\mathbf{r},\mathbf{R})\right\} \tag{8.7}$$

Inserting this into Eq. (8.6), multiplying through by $\psi_m(\mathbf{r},\mathbf{R})$, and integrating, we obtain

$$\left[T_N + E_m(\mathbf{R}) - \epsilon\right]\chi_m(\mathbf{R}) + \sum_{n,\nu} M^{-1}\Big\{(\psi_m|P_\nu|\psi_n)P_\nu + \frac{1}{2}(\psi_m|P^2|\psi_n)\Big\}\chi_n(\mathbf{R}) = 0 \qquad (8.8)$$

The last two terms in this equation, from which the electron-phonon interaction can be extracted, can be neglected for the relaxation of systems we are considering (large band gap insulators) here. See reference 42 for a discussion of this. We are then left with the equation

$$\left[T_N + E_m(\mathbf{R})\right]\chi_m(\mathbf{R}) = \epsilon\chi_m(\mathbf{R}) \qquad (8.9)$$

It tells us that in this approximation the electronic energy (including the interaction of the nuclei) in the n-th quantum state plays the role of an effective potential for the nuclear motion in that state. Actually, the diagonal element from the last term of Eq. (8.8) also contributes to the effective potential, but we shall ignore this in this rather qualitative discussion. In any case, we know that if the electronic system is excited we can expect the nuclear motion to change also and phonons may be emitted or absorbed. If the electronic system stays in an excited state long enough, the nuclei may have sufficient time to relax to new equilibrium positions before the system returns to the ground state. We then expect

$$\left.\frac{\partial E_m(\mathbf{R})}{\partial \mathbf{R}_\nu}\right|_{\mathbf{R}_m} = 0 \quad , \qquad (8.10)$$

where $\mathbf{R}_m$ represents the equilibrium position of the nuclei in the m-th excited state. When the electronic system does return to its ground state, the nuclei will be out of their ground state equilibrium positions and the nuclear system must then relax back to these positions.

When we come to apply these considerations to actual systems and attempt fairly detailed calculations of the relaxation and emission processes, we immediately encounter a difficulty which can be illustrated by considering the F center. We have seen that the ground and first excited state of the F-center electron can be treated quantum mechanically in fairly good approximation when the surrounding ions are held fixed. During the relaxation process, however, the ions neighboring the defect site move and the change in their interaction energy must be calculated. It would be extremely difficult to do this from a "first principles" quantum mechanical formulation, and we must look for an easier way. For ionic crystals an obvious choice is to use classical ionic crystal theory for calculating the interaction energy of closed shell ions, and this is what we shall do in the following.

b. F-center luminescence[43]. Let us write the Hamiltonian of a crystal with a single defect, in an obvious notation, as

$$H(1,2\ldots M) = H_d(1,2\ldots i) + H_{cr}(i+1,\ldots M) + H_{int}(1,2\ldots M) \qquad (8.11)$$

where the numbers stand for both the space and spin coordinates of the electrons, i of which are associated with the defect and M-i with the rest of the crystal. For the wave function, let us write

$$\Psi(1,2\ldots M) = M^{1/2} A\psi(1)\psi_{cr}(2\ldots M) \qquad (8.12)$$

in which A is an anti-symmetric operator given by

$$A = M^{-1} \sum_P (-1)^p P(1, cr)$$

The operator P(1, cr) interchanges electron 1 with all of the electrons in the group 2...M but does not interchange electrons within ψ_{cr}, which is assumed to be separately anti-symmetrized.

It is straightforward to find the expectation value of H(1, 2...M) with respect to $\Psi(1, 2...M)$ and, after some manipulation, one obtains

$$E \equiv \int \Psi^* H \Psi d\tau = E_F(\beta, c, \mathbf{R}) + E_{cr}(R) \qquad (8.13)$$

with

$$E_F = \int \psi^* h \psi d$$

h can be taken as one of the F-center Hamiltonians discussed earlier, e.g., Eqs. (5.1) and (5.4). The notation is meant to emphasize that E_F depends on a set of nonlinear parameters $\{\beta\}$ and a set of linear parameters $\{c\}$ as well as the positions of the neighboring ions denoted by **R**. E_{cr} is the energy of the rest of the crystal, given by

$$E_{cr} = \int \psi^*_{cr} H \psi_{cr} d\tau$$

which we shall treat by classical ionic crystal theory. It depends only on the position of the ions. Care must be taken in working with Eq. (8.13) not to count the Coulomb and exchange interactions between the defect electron and the rest of the crystal twice.

In actual calculations, it is usually practical to let only the lnn neighbors relax. Calculations of the changes in E_{cr} as a function of ionic displacements around a vacant lattice site have been carried out in great detail. The calculations can become quite involved if one takes into account induced dipole moments, deformation of ion shells, etc. Thus far, in defect calculations of the type being discussed here, only Coulomb interactions and repulsive interactions of the form

$$V_{rep} = A e^{-r/\rho} \tag{8.14}$$

have been considered.

In calculating the total energy from Eq. (8.13), the procedure is to minimize the energy with respect to the set of variation parameters $\{c\}$ and $\{\beta\}$ for a number of values of the lnn displacements in, say, a "breathing mode" relaxation. In this way, a "configuration coordinate" curve is mapped out. A typical example for the F center is shown in Fig. 5.

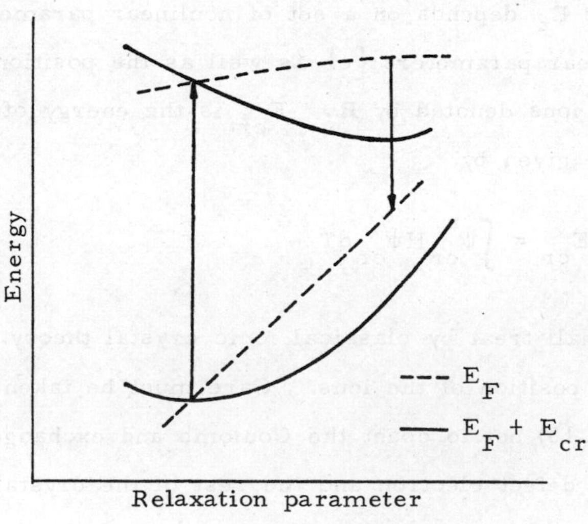

Fig. 5

The origin of the large Stokes shift for this center is now fairly well understood, as follows: During the absorption process the ground state of the F-center electron is well localized and the excited state somewhat less so. Therefore, in the excited state, the charge density at the defect site is somewhat less than it is in the ground state. The result is that on excitation the attraction of the neighboring positive ions to the defect site is reduced, and they begin to relax outward. The major effect of this relaxation is to reduce the Madelung potential at the defect site, and this in turn causes the excited state wave function to become delocalized to the extent that the excited state energy is no longer very sensitive to further changes in the Madelung potential. The ground state wave function, on the other hand, always remains fairly well localized with the result that the energy of this state is quite sensitive to changes in the Madelung potential. The relative sensitivities of the electronic part of the ground and excited state energies (E_F in Eq. 8.13) to lattice relaxation are shown clearly in Fig. 5 by the dashed curves.

The above picture is substantiated by the long lifetime ($\sim 10^{-6}$ sec) of the excited state of the F center in most alkali halides, which can be understood as follows. The lifetime, τ, is proportional to the ratio of the squares of the dipole matrix elements in emission and absorption. As the excited state wave function spreads out as a result of lattice relaxation, the ratio become quite large. The important role played by the effective dielectric constant for these diffuse states must be emphasized. After lattice relaxation, the excited state is apparently described quite well by an effective-mass-like treatment with an effective dielectric constant only slightly smaller than the static dielectric constant.

c. Relaxation of exciton states. The intrinsic luminescence of alkali halide crystals has been found to be quite rich in detail. The most important single fact about the luminescence is that it appears to be identical in most every respect to the recombination luminescence of electrons with self-trapped holes or V_K centers mentioned earlier. This implies that the exciton relaxes into a configuration which is identical to a V_K center plus a trapped electron. You will recall, however, that the V_K center looks like a diatomic molecule embedded in the crystal and oriented in a [110] direction. Thus, the crystal, while in an exciton state, evidently relaxes in such a way that the original cubic symmetry is destroyed.

A number of luminescence bands are usually observed and they frequently have quite large Stokes shifts associated with them --even larger than the shift associated with the F center. This appears to be related to the formation of the diatomic molecule which, when the electron and hole recombine, leaves two halide negative ions tightly squeezed together along a [110] direction. In fact, this compressional energy has been used by Pooley in a suggested mechanism for the formation of F centers by ultraviolet irradiation. The idea is that the two ions experience such violent repulsion that one may be ejected from its normal lattice site.

The excited levels of the relaxed exciton are also found to have widely differing lifetimes associated with them. The long lifetimes of some of the states may be brought about by the occurrence of a dipole matrix element between a diffuse excited state and a compact ground state just as in the case of the F center. However, one should not overlook the role which may possibly be played by triplet states in explaining the long lifetimes.

REFERENCES

1. A recommended general reference for this section is A. Messiah, Quantum Mechanics, Vol. II (North Holland Publishing Co., Amsterdam, 1962), p. 762. See also P. O. Löwdin, Phys. Rev. 97, 1474 (1955).
2. General references for this section are J. Callaway, Energy Band Theory (Academic Press, New York and London, 1964); and J. C. Slater, Quantum Theory of Molecules and Solids, Vol. 2 (McGraw-Hill, New York, 1965).
3. L. P. Howland, Phys. Rev. 109, 1927 (1958).
4. E. E. Lafon and C. C. Lin, Phys. Rev. 152, 579 (1966).
5. C. Herring, Phys. Rev. 57, 1169 (1940).
6. J. C. Slater, Phys. Rev. 51, 846 (1937).
7. J. Korringa, Physica 13, 392 (1947).
8. W. Kohn and N. Rostoker, Phys. Rev. 94, 1111 (1954).
9. H. L. Davis, J. S. Faulkner and H. W. Joy, Phys. Rev. (to be published).
10. K. H. Johnson, Phys. Rev. 150, 429 (1966).
11. L. G. Parratt and E. L. Jossem, Phys. Rev. 97, 916 (1955).
12. P. D. DeCicco, Phys. Rev. 153, 931 (1967).
13. J. C. Slater, Phys. Rev. 81, 385 (1951).
14. J. C. Phillips, Phys. Rev. Letters 12, 142 (1964).
15. S. Oyama and T Miyakawa, J. Phys. Soc. Japan 21, 868 (1966).
16. Y. Onodera, M. Okazaki and T. Inui, J. Phys. Soc. Japan 21, 2229 (1966).
17. A general reference for this section is R. S. Knox, "Theory of Excitons", Solid State Physics, Suppl. 5, F. Seitz and D. Turnbull, editors (Academic Press, New York and London, 1963).

18. J. Frenkel, Phys. Rev. 37, 17 and 1276 (1931).

19. G. H. Wannier, Phys. Rev. 52, 191 (1937).

20. R. S. Knox, J. Phys. Chem. Solids 9, 265 (1959).

21. G. Dresselhaus, J. Phys. Chem. Solids 1, 14 (1956).

22. D. L. Dexter, Phys. Re . 83, 435 (1951); T. Muto, Prog. Theor. Phys. (Kyoto), Suppl. 12, 3 (1959); R. F. Wood, Phys. Rev. Letters 15, 449 (1965).

23. Y. Toyozawa, Prog. Theor. Phys. 12, 422 (1954).

24. H. Haken and W. Schottky, Z. Phys. Chem., N.F. 16, 218 (1958).

25. J. E. Eby, K. J. Teegarden and D. B. Dutton, Phys. Rev. 116, 1099 (1959); K. Teegarden and G. Baldini, Phys. Rev. 155, 896 (1967).

26. I want to thank Professor Teegarden for permission to use these figures.

27. F. Fischer and R. Hilsch, Nachr. Akad. Wiss. Göttingen, II. Math. Physik KL. 1959, No. 8, 241 (1959); F. Fischer, Z. Physik 160, 194 (1960).

28. J. Ramamurti and K. Teegarden, Phys. Rev. 145, 698 (1966).

29. R. Huggett and K. Teegarden, Phys. Rev. 141, 797 (1966).

30. J. J. Hopfield and J. M. Worlock, Phys. Rev. 137, A1455 (1965).

31. I. M. Lifshitz, Nuovo Cimento 3 (Suppl. 4), 716 (1956) and references therein.

32. G. F. Koster and J. C. Slater, Phys. Rev. 96, 1208 (1954).

33. See reference 14.

34. B. Velicky and J. Sak, Phys. Stat. Sol. 16, 147 (1966); C. B. Duke and B. Segall, Phys. Rev. Letters 17, 19 (1966); J. Hermanson, Phys. Rev. Letters 18, 170 (1966).

35. A. Morita and M. Azuma, J. Phys. Soc. Japan, 18, 1273 (1963).

36. See J. H. Schulman and W. D. Compton, Color Centers in Solids (pergamon Press, New York, 1962) for background information on references on color centers.

37. S. R. Tibbs, Trans. Faraday Soc. 35, 1471 (1939).

38. N. F. Mott and M. J. Littleton, Trans. Faraday Soc. 34, 485 (1938).

39. See, for example, J. A. Krumhansl and N. Schwartz, Phys. Rev. 89, 1154 (1953) and W. B. Fowler, Phys. Rev. 135, A1725 (1964).

40. B. S. Gourary and F. J. Adrian, Phys. Rev. 105, 1180 (1957).

41. T. Kojima, J. Phys. Soc. Japan 12, 918 (1957); B. S. Gourary and F. J. Adrian, Solid State Physics 10, 127 (1960); R. F. Wood and H. W. Joy, Phys. Rev. 136, A451 (1964).

42. M. Born and K. Huang, Dynamical Theory of Crystal Lattices (Clarendon Press, Oxford, England, 1954), p. 406.

43. See references to W. B. Fowler and R. F. Wood and H. W. Joy given above.

44. M. N. Kabler, Phys. Rev. 136, A1296 (1964); R. B. Murray and F. J. Keller, Phys. Rev. 137, A942 (1965); R. F. Wood, Phys. Rev. 151, 629 (1966).

12
ELECTRONIC OPTICAL PROPERTIES OF SOLIDS

Manuel Cardona
Brown University, Providence, R. I., U.S.A.

INTRODUCTION

The linear optical behavior of a solid (non-magnetic) is determined by the **k** and **ω**-dependent dielectric constant tensor $\underline{\underline{\varepsilon}}(\mathbf{k},\omega)$, which relates the Fourier transforms in time and space of the electric displacement and the electric field.

$$\mathbf{D}(\mathbf{k},\omega) = \underline{\underline{\varepsilon}}(\mathbf{k},\omega) \cdot \mathbf{E}(\mathbf{k},\omega) \quad ; \quad \mathbf{D}(\mathbf{k},\omega) \sim e^{i(\mathbf{k}\cdot\mathbf{r} - \omega t)}$$

The dielectric constant tensor is related to the conductivity tensor by the relationship $\underline{\underline{\varepsilon}} = 1 + \frac{4\pi}{\omega}\underline{\underline{\sigma}}\, i$. The components of $\underline{\underline{\sigma}}$ and $\underline{\underline{\varepsilon}}$ are in general, complex numbers. The nine components of $\underline{\underline{\varepsilon}}$ (or $\underline{\underline{\sigma}}$) are not all independent. Thermodynamics requires that these tensors be symmetric in the absence of an external d.c. magnetic field (Onsager relations[1]).

In the optical regions of the spectrum the "wavelength" (or the penetration depth) of the light is much larger than any characteristic atomic dimensions (Bohr radii, lattice constants). As such, **k** can, in general, be assumed equal to zero in the dielectric constant. A few optical effects connected with the finite nature of **k** have been observed and they constitute the field of "Spacial Dispersion"[2]. We shall only consider dielectric constants for **k** = 0 in these notes.

If the medium under consideration is isotropic (glass or liquid) or cubic, the dielectric tensor reduces to a scalar: The quadric defined by the tensor must have cubic symmetry and hence must reduce to a sphere. In this case $\mathbf{D} = \varepsilon \mathbf{E}$. Eliminating the magnetic field in Maxwell's equations we obtain, for scalar ε, the wave equation

$$\nabla^2 E = \frac{\varepsilon}{c^2} \frac{\partial^2 E}{\partial t^2} \tag{1}$$

Let us define the complex refractive index $n = \sqrt{\varepsilon}$. The real and imaginary components of n are related to these of ε by

$$\left.\begin{aligned} n_r^2 - n_i^2 &= \varepsilon_r \\ 2 n_r n_i &= \varepsilon_i \end{aligned}\right\} \tag{2}$$

A plane-wave solution of Eq. (1) has the form

$$\mathbf{E} = \mathbf{E}_o \, e^{-i\omega\left[t - \frac{x n_r}{c}\right]} \, e^{-\frac{\alpha}{2} x} \tag{3}$$

where the <u>absorption coefficient</u> $\alpha = \frac{2\omega n_i}{c}$

Equation (3) represents a decaying wave whose energy decreases in space like $e^{-\alpha x}$. Maximum absorption coefficients found in solids are of the order of 10^6 cm^{-1}

DIELECTRIC CONSTANT OF A SOLID

The one-electron Hamiltonian of a solid in the presence of an electromagnetic wave of vector potential $A = A_o e^{i(k \cdot r - \omega t)}$ (we shall assume $\mathbf{k} \approx 0$) is, in atomic units (see Appendix A),

$$H = \frac{1}{2}\left[\mathbf{p} + \frac{1}{c}\mathbf{A}\right]^2 + V(r) \tag{4}$$

where $\mathbf{p}$ is the linear momentum operator and V(r) the self-consistent crystal potential. For the study of linear dielectric constants we shall linearize Eq. (4) and write

$$H = \frac{1}{2}\mathbf{p}^2 + \frac{1}{c}p \cdot A_o e^{-i\omega t} = H_o + H' \tag{5}$$

We shall assume that the band structure problem of the unperturbed Hamiltonian H_o is solved, i.e., that its eigenvalues and eigenfunctions (Bloch functions) are known. The Schrödinger equation for the perturbed wavefunctions is, in the interaction representation (see Appendix B)

$$i \frac{\partial \psi_I(t)}{\partial t} = H_I'(t)\, \psi_I(t) \tag{6}$$

where $\psi_I(t) = e^{iH_o(t - t_o)}\, \psi(t)$ [$\psi(t)$ is the wave function in the Schrödinger representation]

$$H_I'(t) = e^{iH_o(t - t_o)} H_I(t) e^{-H_o(t - t_o)}$$

By integrating Eq. (6) we obtain

$$\Psi_I(t) = \Psi(t_o) - i \int_{t_o}^{t} H_I'(t')\, \Psi_I(t')dt' \qquad (7)$$

In order to obtain the <u>linear</u> response, we can replace in the integral of Eq. (7) $\Psi_I(t')$ by the unperturbed $\Psi_I(t_o) = \Psi(t_o)$. Also, we shall apply the perturbation in an adiabatic manner, that is, we shall write the vector potential as $A = A_o e^{-i(\omega + i\eta)t}$ with $\eta \rightarrow +0$. That means that for $t_o \rightarrow -\infty$ the perturbation disappears and hence $\Psi(t_o)$ becomes a Bloch function solution of the unperturbed problem. The j-th component of the current density vector at the point $\mathbf{r}$ becomes

$$J(r,t) = -\frac{i}{2} \sum_{k \text{ occupied}} \Big[\Psi_k^*(r,t) p_j \Psi_k(r,t) - \Psi_k(r,t) p_j \times \Psi_k^*(r,t) + \frac{2}{ci} A_j(r) \Psi_k^*(r) \Psi_k(r)\Big] \qquad (8)$$

Equation (8) gives the microscopic current.

The macroscopic current is obtained by averaging Eq. (8) over a volume v large compared with a lattice constant. The last term in Eq. (8) is the diamagnetic term. For linear response, its contribution to the current is found by replacing the wave functions Ψ_k by the unperturbed Bloch functions $\varphi_k(r)$. It becomes

$$J_{\text{diamag.}} = -\frac{1}{v} \sum_{k \text{ occupied}} \int_v \frac{1}{c} A_j(r) \varphi_k^*(r) \varphi_k(r) dr = -\frac{1}{c} A_j N$$

where N is the <u>total</u> electron density. From Maxwell's equations we obtain $A_j = -\frac{i}{\omega} E_j c$ and hence the contribution of the diamagnetic current to the dielectric constant becomes

$$\Delta\varepsilon_{\text{diamag.}} = -\frac{4\pi}{\omega^2} N \tag{9}$$

The contribution of the first two terms in Eq. (8) to the current density is evaluated by replacing the wave functions by a sum of a Bloch function plus the perturbation. Four types of terms appear:

a) ψ unperturbed $\quad p\psi$ unperturbed

b) ψ perturbed $\quad p\psi$ unperturbed

c) ψ unperturbed $\quad p\psi$ perturbed

d) ψ perturbed $\quad p\psi$ perturbed

The a) terms give no contribution to the current since the unperturbed crystal carries no current. The d) terms give only higher order contributions, hence the only contributions of interest come from b) and c) (four of them). Let us evaluate a typical one using for all vectors and operators the interaction representation:

$$\sum \frac{1}{v} \frac{i}{2c} \int e^{i\omega_k (t - t_o)} \varphi_k^*(r, t_o) p_j \Big[e^{-iH_o(t - t_o)}$$

$$\int_{t_o \to -\infty}^{t} e^{iH_o(t' - t_o)} \mathbf{p} \cdot \mathbf{A}_o \, e^{-i(\omega + i\eta + \omega_k)t'}$$

$$\times \, e^{i\omega_k t_o} \varphi_k(r, t_o) dt \Big] dr \tag{10}$$

Introducing the completeness relation

$$\sum_{\ell} \varphi_{\ell}^*(r') \varphi_{\ell}(r) = \delta(r, r')$$

we can write Eq. (10) in the form

$$\frac{A_o^J}{v}\frac{i}{2c}\sum_{\ell}\sum_{k\ \text{occupied}}\iint dr\,dr'\,e^{i\omega_k(t-t_o)}\Psi_k^*(r')p_j$$

$$\Psi_\ell(r')e^{-i\omega_\ell\cdot t}\int_{t_o}^{t}\Psi_\ell^*(r)e^{i\omega_\ell\cdot t'}p_j\varphi_k(r)e^{-i(\omega+i\eta+\omega_k)t'}$$

which yields

$$\frac{E^J}{2v\omega}\sum_\ell <k|p_j|\ell><\ell|p_j|k>\frac{e^{-i(\omega+i\eta)t}}{-i(\omega+i\eta-\omega_{\ell k})}$$

where $\omega_{\ell k} = \omega_\ell - \omega_k$.

The contribution of this term to the j-th diagonal component of the dielectric constant ε_{jj} is

$$-\frac{4\pi}{v\omega^2}\sum_{\substack{k\ \text{occupied}\\ \ell}}\frac{|<k|p_j|\ell>|^2}{\omega-\omega_{\ell k}+i\eta} \tag{11}$$

Equation (8) yields another term like Eq. (11) and two of the form

$$+\frac{4\pi}{v\omega^2}\sum_{\substack{k\ \text{occupied}\\ \ell}}\frac{|<k|p_j|\ell>|^2}{\omega_{\ell k}+\omega+i\eta}$$

Summing all these contributions and the diamagnetic term we finally obtain

$$\varepsilon_{jj} = 1+\frac{4\pi}{\omega^2}\sum_{\substack{k\ \text{occupied}\\ \ell}}\frac{2|<k|p_j|\ell>|^2\omega_{\ell k}}{\omega_{\ell k}^2-(\omega+i\eta)^2}-\frac{4\pi}{\omega^2}N \tag{12}$$

$$\eta\to+0$$

In Equation (12) the summation over ℓ may be taken either over all states or only over unoccupied states since terms connecting two occupied states k and ℓ cancel out ($\omega_{k\ell} = -\omega_{\ell k}$). The volume v has been taken equal to unity in Eq. (12).

In a solid, the only matrix elements of p which can appear in Eq. (12) are those which connect states of the same crystal momentum **k** (in the reduced-zone scheme), since p_j has translational invariance. The transitions involved are called direct transitions.

Equation (12) shows that the dielectric constant at high frequencies ($|\omega| \longrightarrow \infty$) always becomes

$$\varepsilon = 1 - \frac{4\pi}{\omega^2} N \qquad (13)$$

The remaining term in Eq. (12) varies like $1/\omega^4$ at high frequencies and hence is negligible.

Broadening effects can be introduced in a phenomenological manner in Eq. (12) by leaving η finite and equal to the broadening or collision frequency. η can be considered constant or else k and ℓ-dependent. The last choice agrees perhaps more closely with the many-body quasi-particle description of the solid. Broadening can also be introduced in the diamagnetic term in the usual manner, by replacing ω by $\omega + i\omega_c$ (ω_c = collision frequency). Depending on whether we perform this replacement in σ or in ε we obtain

$$\varepsilon = 1 - \frac{4\pi N}{(\omega + i\omega_c)^2} \qquad (14a)$$

or

$$\varepsilon = 1 - \frac{4\pi N}{\omega(\omega + i\omega_{c'})} \qquad (14b)$$

Equations (14a) and (14b) are equivalent for $\omega >> \omega_c(\omega_{c'})$ except for the definition of ω_c ($\omega_{c'} = 2\omega_c$)[3]. Eq. (14b) is the standard Drude formula which is easily obtained classically (do it as an exercise).

Equation (12) can be conveniently transformed by means of the **k · p** (or F) sum rule (see Appendix C)[4]:

$$-1 = -\frac{\partial^2 \omega_k}{\partial k_j^2} - \sum_{\ell \neq k} \frac{2|\langle k|p_j|\ell\rangle|^2}{\omega_{\ell k}} \tag{15}$$

Multiplying Eq. (15) by $4\pi/\omega^2$ and summing with respect to the occupied states k we build up in the left-hand side the diamagnetic term of ϵ. Replacing it in Eq. (12), we obtain

$$\epsilon_{jj} = 1 + \frac{4\pi}{\omega^2} \sum_{\substack{k \text{ occupied} \\ \ell}} 2|\langle|p_j|\rangle|^2 \left\{\frac{\omega_{\ell k}}{\omega_{\ell k}^2 - (\omega + i\eta)^2} - \frac{1}{\omega_{\ell k}}\right\} - \frac{4\pi}{\omega^2} \sum_{k \text{ occupied}} \frac{\partial^2 \omega_k}{\partial k_j^2}$$

$$= 1 + \frac{4\pi}{\omega^2} \sum_{\substack{k \text{ occupied} \\ \ell}} \frac{2|\langle k|p_i|\ell\rangle|^2/\omega_{\ell k}}{\omega_{\ell k}^2 - (\omega + i\eta)^2} - \frac{4\pi}{\omega^2} \sum_{\substack{k \text{ occupied} \\ \ell}} \frac{\partial^2 \omega_k}{\partial k_j^2} \tag{16}$$

or

$$\epsilon_{jj} = 1 - \frac{4\pi}{\omega^2} \sum_{k \text{ occupied}} \frac{\partial^2 \omega_k}{\partial k_j^2} + 4\pi \sum_{\substack{k \text{ occupied} \\ \ell}} \frac{F_{k\ell}^{jj}}{\omega_{\ell k}^2 - (\omega + i\eta)^2} \tag{17}$$

We have introduced in Eq. (17) the oscillator strength

$$F^{jj}_{k\ell} = \frac{2|\langle k|p_j|\ell\rangle|^2}{\omega_{\ell k}}$$

The second term in the right-hand side of Eq. (17) is called the intraband contribution to ε. It is easy to see that it is zero for a completely filled band. Let us consider, for instance, the case of a cubic crystal. The intraband term $\Delta\varepsilon^b$ is

$$\Delta\varepsilon^b = \frac{1}{3}(\Delta\varepsilon^b_{11} + \Delta\varepsilon^b_{22} + \Delta\varepsilon^b_{33}) = -\frac{4\pi}{3\omega^2} \sum_{k \text{ occupied}} \nabla^2_{\mathbf{k}}\omega_{\mathbf{k}}$$

$$= -\frac{4\pi}{3\omega^2} \cdot \frac{1}{4\pi^3} \iiint \nabla^2_{\mathbf{k}}\omega_{\mathbf{k}} \cdot d\mathbf{k}$$

$$= -\frac{4\pi}{3\omega^2} \cdot \frac{1}{4\pi^3} \iint_S \boldsymbol{\nabla}_k(\omega_k) \cdot d\mathbf{S}_k \qquad (18)$$

For a half-filled band, the surface integral in Eq. (18) is extended to the Fermi sphere. For a filled band it is extended to the entire boundary of the Brillouin zone. In this case, it is easy to see that the surface integral becomes zero, due to the periodicity of the bands in k space. (See Fig. 1).

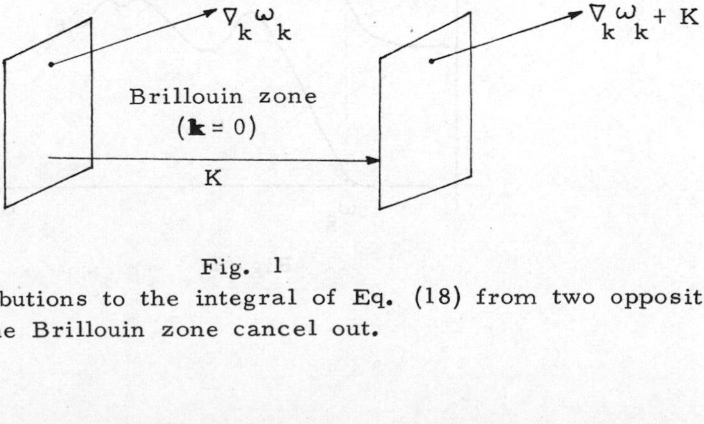

Fig. 1

The contributions to the integral of Eq. (18) from two opposite faces of the Brillouin zone cancel out.

Hence the only contributions to the intraband term come from half-filled bands (metals, semimetals, and doped or extrinsic semiconductors).

The dielectric constant of an insulator is therefore given by the <u>interband</u> terms only:

$$\varepsilon_{jj} = 1 - 4\pi \sum_{\substack{k \\ \ell} \text{ occupied}} \left. \frac{F^{jj}_{k\ell}}{\omega^2_{\ell k} - (\omega + i\eta)^2} \right|_{\eta \to +0} \tag{19}$$

The imaginary part of Eq. (19) is zero unless $\omega^2_{\ell k} = \omega^2$, i.e., unless there are possible direct transitions (with $F^{jj}_k \neq 0$) between states whose difference in energy is $\omega_{\ell k} = \omega$. If the material has an energy gap (insulator) no such transitions are possible below the gap ω_g and hence $\varepsilon_i = 0$ for $\omega < \omega_g$. For $\omega << \omega_g$,

$$\varepsilon_{jj} = \varepsilon_{jj,r} \simeq 1 - 4\pi \sum_{\substack{k \\ \ell} \text{ occupied}} \frac{F^{jj}_{k\ell}}{\omega^2_{\ell k}}$$

and is hence frequency independent:

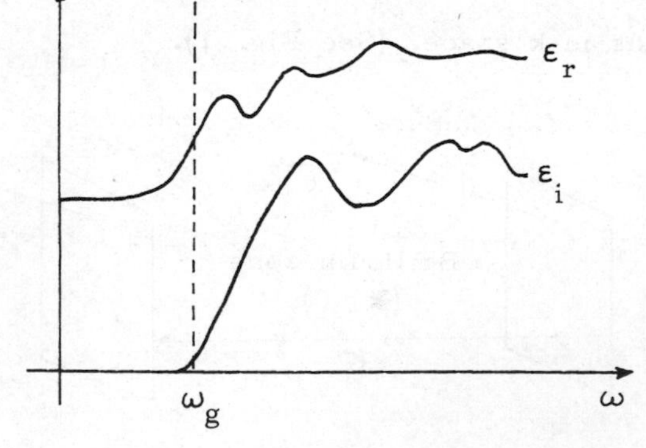

Fig. 2

It occurs frequently that the allowed frequencies $\omega_{\ell k}$ are clustered in two (or more) well-separated groups (see reference 3). Well above the group ① (lower energy group) the dielectric constant is produced by two contributions: a diamagnetic-like contribution from the electrons in group

$$① \quad \Delta\varepsilon_r^{①} = -\frac{4\pi N_\ell}{\omega^2} \quad ; \quad \Delta\varepsilon_i^{①} = 0$$

plus a non-dispersive contribution of the electrons group ② to the real part of the dielectric constant:

$$\varepsilon = 1 - \frac{4\pi N_\ell}{\omega^2} + \Delta\varepsilon_r^{②} \tag{20}$$

for $\omega_{\ell k}^{②} >> \omega >> \omega_{\ell k}^{①}$

The diamagnetic contribution to ε is sometimes written in terms of the plasma frequency at which $\varepsilon = 0$:

$$\varepsilon = 1 - \frac{\omega_p^2}{\omega^2} \quad \text{(below } \omega_p \text{ no propagation occurs)}$$

When several groups of well separated transition frequencies occur, one must define several plasma frequencies:

$$\varepsilon = 1 + \Delta\varepsilon_r - \frac{4\pi N_\ell}{\omega^2} = (1 + \Delta\varepsilon_r)(1 - \frac{\omega_{p,\ell}^2}{\omega^2}) \tag{21}$$

where $\Delta\varepsilon_r$ is the non-dispersive contribution to the real part of the dielectric constant produced by all transition frequencies <u>higher</u> than ω, N_ℓ is the density of electrons which correspond to transition frequencies lower than ω, and $\omega_{p,\ell}^2 = 4\pi N_\ell/(1 + \Delta\varepsilon_r)$. Eq. (21)

is only valid for ω in a region where no $\omega_{\ell k}$ occur.

A natural separation into two groups can be made in many insulators[5,6] (and semiconductors) for the core and valence electrons. The contribution of the core electrons to $\Delta\varepsilon_r$ is generally quite small and is often neglected. The plasma frequency of the valence electrons is around 16 eV for many insulators and semiconductors (e.g. Ge, Si). In order to interpret experimental results broadening must be added in the manner described by Eqs. (14a) and (14b). We show in Fig. 3 the experimental results σ for SnTe and a fit using as adjustable parameter the broadening parameter ω_c. Best fit is obtained for $\omega_c = 5.2$ eV.

The interband contribution to the dielectric constant is usually evaluated by replacing the sum of Eq. (19) by an integral over **k**-space:

$$\varepsilon_{jj} = 1 + \frac{1}{\pi^2} \iiint \frac{F_{k\ell}}{\omega_{\ell k}^2 - (\omega + i\eta)^2} \, d\mathbf{k}$$

$$= 1 + \frac{1}{\pi^2} \int d\omega_{\ell k} \int_{\omega_{\ell k}=\text{const.}} dS_{\mathbf{k}} \frac{1}{|\nabla_k \omega_{\ell k}|} \frac{F_{k\ell}^{jj}}{\omega_{\ell k}^2 - (\omega + i\eta)^2} \tag{22}$$

The surface integral of Eq. (22) is extended over a surface such that $\omega_{\ell k}$ = constant for all points of the surface (in k-space). For cubic materials we shall symmetrize the oscillator strength:

$$F_{k\ell}^{jj} = \frac{1}{3} \sum_{j=1}^{3} F_{k\ell}^{jj} = \frac{2}{3} \frac{|\langle k|\mathbf{p}|\ell\rangle|^2}{\omega_{\ell k}} = F_{k\ell} \tag{23}$$

It is now convenient to separate real and imaginary parts in

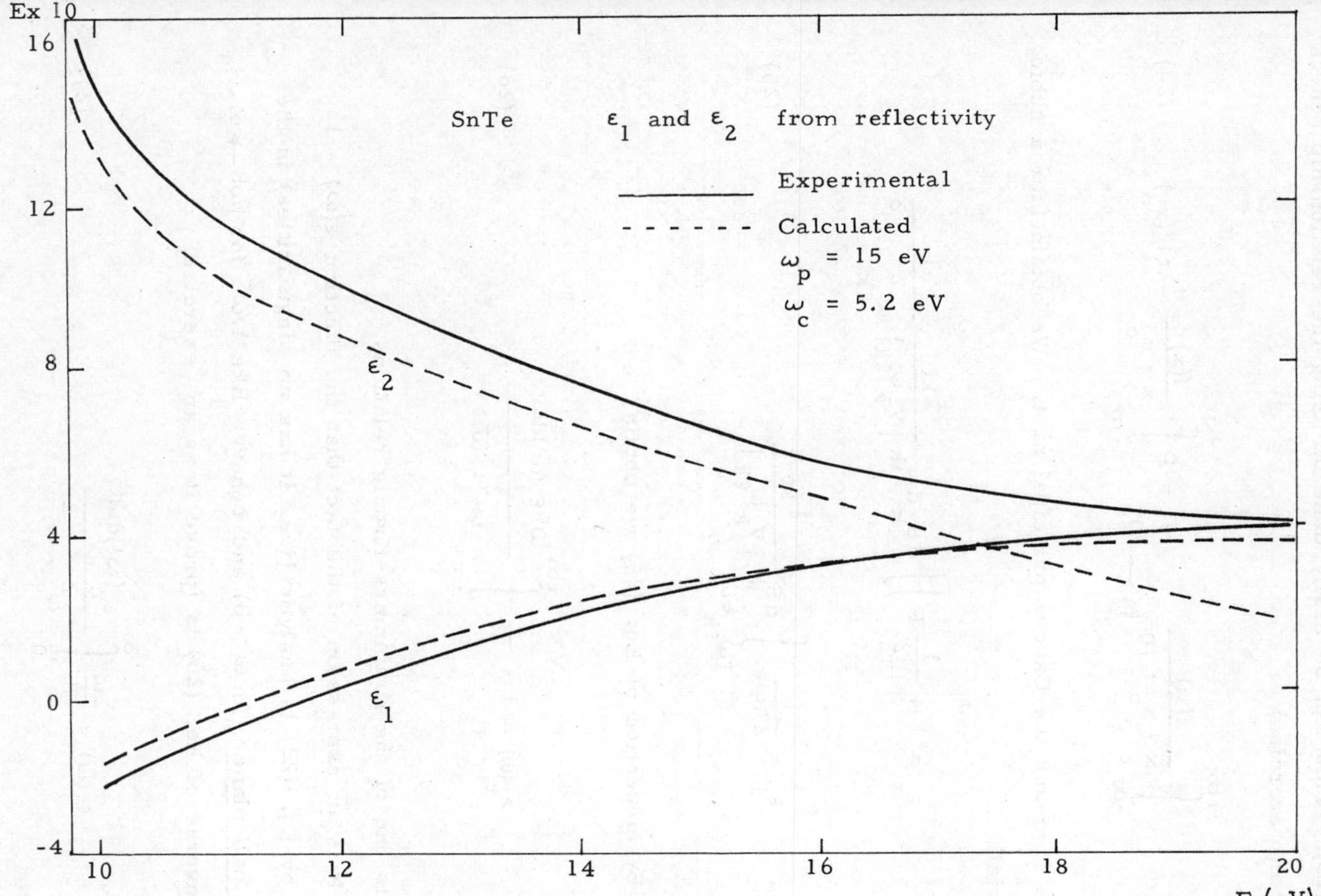

Ex 10
16
12
8
4
0
-4
10
12
14
16
18
20
E (eV)
SnTe
ε1 and ε2 from reflectivity
Experimental
Calculated
ωp = 15 eV
ωc = 5.2 eV
ε2
ε1

Fig. 3

Eq. (22). This can be easily done by using the relationship (check it as an exercise)

$$\int_{-\infty}^{+\infty} \frac{f(x)}{x - x_o + i\eta} \; (\eta \to +0) = P\int_{-\infty}^{+\infty} \frac{f(x)}{x - x_o} - \pi i f(x_o) \tag{24}$$

where P means the Cauchy principal part. We obtain (for a cubic material)

$$\varepsilon_r = 1 + \frac{1}{\pi^2} P \iint dS_k \, d\omega_{\ell k} \frac{F_{k\ell}}{|\nabla_k \omega_{\ell k}|} \frac{1}{\omega_{\ell k}^2 - \omega^2}$$

$$\varepsilon_i = \frac{1}{2\pi\omega} \int_{(\omega_{\ell k} = \omega)} dS_k \frac{F_{k\ell}}{|\nabla_k \omega_{\ell k}|} \tag{25}$$

By inspection of Eq. (25) we obtain

$$\varepsilon_r(\omega) = 1 + \frac{2}{\pi} \int_{-\infty}^{+\infty} \frac{\omega' \varepsilon_i(\omega') d\omega'}{\omega'^2 - \omega^2} \tag{26}$$

This is one of the Krammers-Kronig relations.

It is an expression of the fact that the function $\varepsilon(\omega) - 1$ given by Eq. (22) is analytic (i.e. it has no singularities) in the <u>upper half plane</u> ($\mathrm{Im}\,\omega > 0$) and behaves like $1/\omega^2$ for $|\omega| \to \infty$. The inverse of Eq. (26) is (prove it as an exercise)

$$\varepsilon_i(\omega) = \frac{2\omega}{\pi} \int_0^{\infty} \frac{\varepsilon_r(\omega') d\omega'}{\omega^2 - \omega'^2} \tag{27}$$

As is well known, Eqs. (26) and (27) guarantee the causality of the electromagnetic response: no **D** can appear before an **E** is applied.

Eqs. (15), (26) and (27) are <u>sum-rules</u>. Another important sum rule can be derived from the asymptotic behavior of ε,

$$\varepsilon \underset{\omega \to \infty}{\longrightarrow} 1 - \frac{\omega_p^2}{\omega^2} \qquad (\omega_p^2 = 4\pi N)$$

Let us evaluate the integral

$$\int_{-\infty}^{\infty} \omega\left[\varepsilon(\omega) - 1\right] d\omega \tag{28}$$

with ε given by Eq. (22), using the contour indicated in Fig. 4.

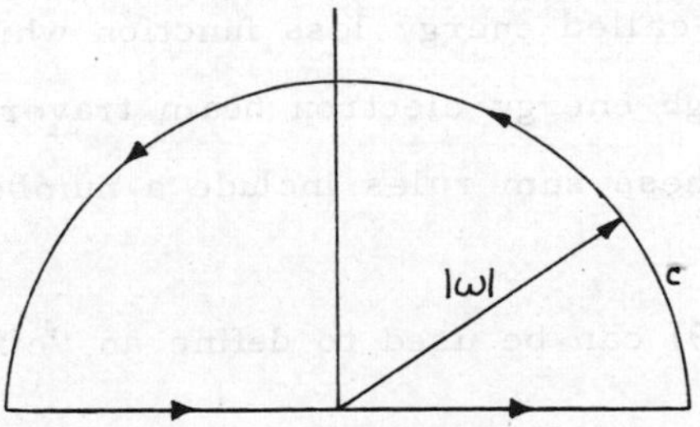

Fig. 4

The integral (28) is equal to minus the integral along the half circle. For $|\omega| \to \infty$ this integral is $(\varepsilon \to 1 - \omega_p^2/\omega^2)$

$$\int_{-\infty}^{\infty} \omega(\varepsilon - 1) d\omega = + \int_c \omega \times \frac{\omega_p^2}{\omega^2} d\omega = + \pi i \omega_p^2$$

Hence

$$\int_{-\infty}^{+\infty} \omega[\varepsilon_r(\omega) + i\,\varepsilon_i(\omega) - 1]\, d\omega = +\pi i \omega_p^2 = 2i \int_0^{\infty} \omega\varepsilon_i(\omega) d\omega$$

And we obtain the useful sum rule

$$\int_0^{\infty} \omega\varepsilon_i(\omega) d\omega = \frac{\pi}{2}\omega_p^2 = \frac{\pi}{2}(4\pi N) \tag{29}$$

We can also show by a similar method that

$$\int_0^{\infty} \omega \,\mathrm{Im}\; \varepsilon^{-1}(\omega) d\omega = -\frac{\pi}{2}\omega_p^2 \tag{30}$$

The interest of the sum rule of Eq. (30) resides in that $\mathrm{Im}\;\varepsilon^{-1}$ is the so-called energy loss function which is proportional to losses of a high energy electron beam traversing a thin film of the material. These sum rules include a number of many-body corrections[7].

Equation (29) can be used to define an "effective" electron density[5] $N_{eff}(\omega)$:

$$\int_0^{\omega} \omega'\,\varepsilon_i(\omega') d\omega' = 2\pi^2 N_{eff}(\omega) \tag{31}$$

$N_{eff}(\omega)$ gives a qualitative idea of the electron density involved in transitions at energies lower than ω. Between two groups of well-separated bands ① and ②, it would be equal to $N^{①}$, the electron density of the low-energy group.

Figure 5 shows N_{eff}/N_{at} (N_{at} = total number of atoms) for SnTe.[8] It tends to the average number of valence electrons (5) for atom at high frequencies. At 5 eV there is a hump in the curve due to the onset of a new group of electrons.

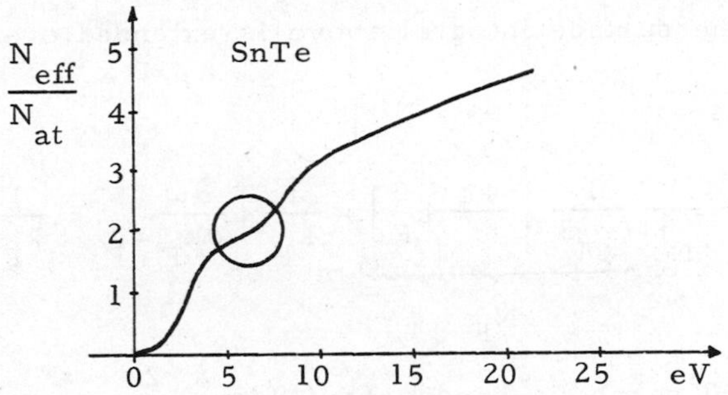

Fig. 5

FREE CARRIER (INTRABAND) EFFECTS

Let us write the intraband contribution to ε_{jj} :

$$\varepsilon^{f}_{jj} = -\frac{4\pi}{\omega^2} \sum_{k\ \text{occupied}} \frac{\partial^2\omega_k}{\partial k_j^2} = -\frac{4\pi N^f}{\omega^2 m^*_{jj}} \tag{32}$$

(Although not explicitly stated, it is obvious that Eq. (32) is referred to the principal axes of $\underset{\approx}{\varepsilon}$). Equation (32) defines the optical (or conductivity) effective-mass tensor

$$\frac{1}{m^*_{jj}} = \frac{1}{N^f} \sum_{k\ \text{occupied}} \frac{\partial^2\omega_k}{(\partial k_j)^2} \tag{33}$$

where N^f is the density of electrons in an unfilled band. For bands with spherical symmetry:

$$\frac{1}{m^*_{jj}} = \frac{1}{m^*} = \frac{1}{N^f} \cdot \frac{1}{4\pi^3} \cdot \frac{1}{3} \iint_{S_F} \nabla_k(\omega_k) \cdot dS_k$$

(see Eq. 18). The surface integral above is extended over the Fermi surface. Or:

$$\frac{1}{m^*} = \frac{1}{N^f} \underbrace{\frac{1}{4\pi^3}\left[\frac{4\pi}{3} k_F^3\right]}_{N_F} \cdot \frac{1}{k_F}\left[\frac{\partial\omega}{\partial k_F}\right]_F = \frac{1}{k_F}\left[\frac{\partial\omega}{\partial k}\right]_F \tag{34}$$

For spherical and parabolic bands $\omega = (1/2\mathbf{m}^*)k^2$, $m^* = \mathbf{m}^*$. For non-spherical parabolic bands

$$\omega = \frac{k_x^2}{\mathbf{m}_{xx}} + \frac{k_y^2}{\mathbf{m}_{yy}} + \frac{k_z^2}{\mathbf{m}_{zz}} ,$$

it is trivial to show that $m^*_{xx} = \mathbf{m}_{xx}$, $m^*_{yy} = \mathbf{m}_{yy}$, and $m^*_{zz} = \mathbf{m}_{zz}$. For cubic materials with a collection of equivalent non-spherical parabolic bands one has to symmetrize the $\underset{\approx}{\varepsilon}$ and thus:

$$\frac{1}{m^*} = \frac{1}{3}\left[\frac{1}{\mathbf{m}_{xx}} + \frac{1}{\mathbf{m}_{yy}} + \frac{1}{\mathbf{m}_{zz}}\right] \tag{35}$$

In the region well below the lowest interband gap the dielectric constant of a metal or a doped semiconductor can thus be written (assume it cubic, for simplicity)

$$\varepsilon = \varepsilon_o - \frac{4\pi N^f}{m^* \omega^2} \tag{36}$$

where ε_o is the non-dispersive interband dielectric constant.

Equation (36) is very similar to Eq. (20) except that the free-electron mass ($m = 1$) of Eq. (20) has been replaced by an effective mass in Eq. (36). Thus we reach the important conclusion that while "bound" (filled band) electrons behave at high frequencies like free electrons with a free electron mass, electrons in half-filled bands also give a free electron term at low frequencies, but with a mass replaced by an effective mass. This mass m^* must also be replaced at high frequencies by the free-electron mass.

Equation (36) offers us a method for determining effective masses if we measure N^f (Hall effect) and $\varepsilon(\omega)$[9]. This method has the advantage with respect to cyclotron resonance that one does not require high purity and low temperatures. The cyclotron resonance requirement $\omega_{coll} \ll \omega_{cyclotron}$ now becomes $\omega_{coll} \ll \omega$ and hence, in the visible and infrared this condition is not very stringent. The method has, however, the drawback that only an average m^* is obtained with it.

ε is real without including collision effects below the lowest interband edge and hence it can be measured by measuring the reflectivity:

$$R = \left[\frac{\sqrt{\varepsilon} - 1}{\sqrt{\varepsilon} + 1}\right]^2 \qquad (37)$$

Figure 6 gives a sketch of the reflectivity as a function of ω for a typical metal or doped semiconductor.

The full line gives the unbroadened results while the dotted line includes the effects of broadening. The effective mass of the conduction electrons in Na and K determined by this method by Althoff and Hertz[10] is

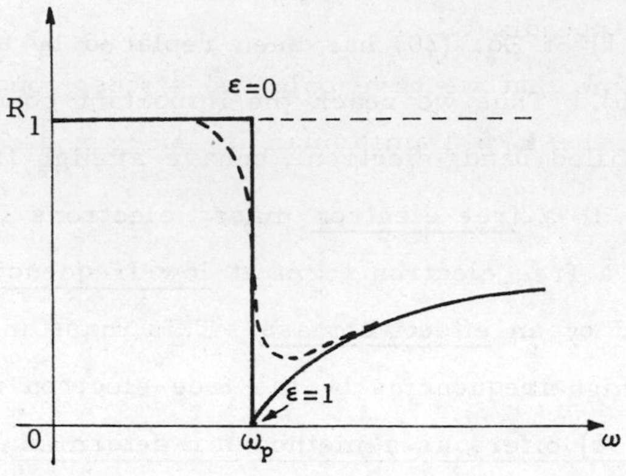

Fig. 6

	Na	K
m^* measured	0.99	1.17
m^* calculated	1.00	1.02

The method described above has been very fruitful to study the variation with doping of the effective mass in semiconductors, which is due to non-parabolicity in the bands[11]. A number of III-V compounds have been measured (In As, In Sb, Ga As) and shown to have non-parabolic bands, that is, m^* varies with doping (see Fig. 7).[12]

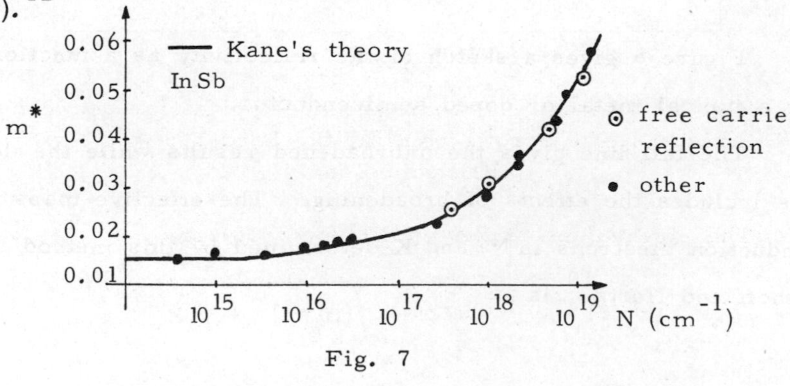

Fig. 7

Non-parabolicity effects can be easily calculated using the $\mathbf{k}\cdot\mathbf{p}$ Hamiltonian of Appendix C.

If we assume that we have only two states (conduction and valence) at $\mathbf{k} = 0$, the $\mathbf{k}\cdot\mathbf{p}$ Hamiltonian is (along x direction)

$$\begin{vmatrix} \omega_g + k^2/2 & k_x p_x \\ k_x p_x & k^2/2 \end{vmatrix} \tag{38}$$

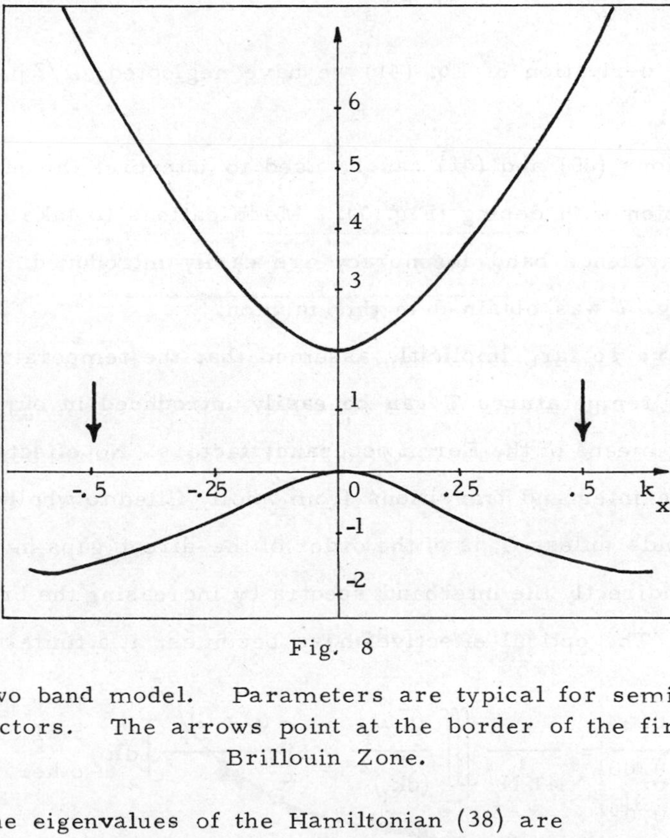

Fig. 8

Two band model. Parameters are typical for semiconductors. The arrows point at the border of the first Brillouin Zone.

The eigenvalues of the Hamiltonian (38) are

$$-(k_x^2/2) + \omega = \omega_g/2 \pm \sqrt{(\omega_g/2)^2 + p_x^2 k_x^2} \tag{39}$$

(Notice that Eq. 39 is the equivalent of Dirac's equations with holes corresponding to positrons). Assuming spherical bands we obtain from Eq. 39, by expanding in powers of k_x^2 and replacing in Eq. 34

$$\frac{1}{m^*} = \left[\frac{1}{m_o^*} - 1\right]\left[1 - \frac{2\omega_F}{\omega_g}\right] + 1 \quad (\omega_F = \text{Fermi level}) \tag{40}$$

where m_o^* is the mass at the bottom of the band:

$$(1/m_o^*) - 1 = 2(p_x^2/\omega_g) \tag{41}$$

In the derivation of Eq. (41) we have neglected $\omega_g/2p^2$ in relation to 1.

Equations (40) and (41) can be used to interpret the effective mass variation with doping (Fig. 7). Modifications to take into account the valence band degeneracy are easily introduced. Kane's curve in Fig. 7 was obtained in this fashion.

We have so far, implicitly assumed that the temperature is 0 °K. Finite temperatures T can be easily introduced in our expression by means of the Fermi occupancy factors. No effect is obtained on the interband transitions from wholly filled to wholly unoccupied bands unless T is of the order of the direct gaps involved. (T affects indirectly the interband spectra by increasing the broadening parameter). The optical effective mass becomes, at a finite temperature T

$$\frac{1}{m_{jj}^*} = \frac{1}{4\pi^3 N_f} \iiint \frac{\partial^2 \omega_k}{(\partial k_j)^2} \cdot f\left[\frac{\omega - \omega_F}{T}\right] d\mathbf{k} \tag{42}$$

with the Fermi level defined by

$$N_f = (1/4\pi^3) \iiint f(\omega - \omega_F/T)\, d\mathbf{k} \tag{43}$$

Obviously $(1/m^*_{jj})$ is temperature independent if the bands are parabolic $(\partial^2\omega_k/\partial k_j^2)$ can be taken out of the integral in Eq. 42). If the bands have the shape of Eq. (39) the carriers are shifted towards higher-mass regions as T is increased: an increase in m^* with increasing T is normally obtained. This increase is often partially compensated by the decrease in the gap ω_g with T (Eq. 41) since p_x is normally T-independent. These effects have been studied in detail for GaAs, InAs and InSb.

FARADAY ROTATION

As shown by Prof. Rodríguez in his lectures, Eq. (36) becomes, in the presence of a uniform magnetic field B

$$\varepsilon_{\pm} = \varepsilon_o - \frac{4\pi N^f}{m^*\omega(\omega \pm \omega_c)} \qquad (44)$$

where ω_c is the cyclotron frequency. For spherical bands $\omega_c = B/m^*c$ and m^* is given by Eq. (34). The double sign in Eq. (44) corresponds to the two possible directions of circular polarization. Then linearly polarized light is propagated along the direction of B, the two circularly polarized components propagate at different velocities and hence their relative phase is changed after traversing the material. Hence, a rotation of the plane of polarization results. It is easy to see that this rotation is, to first order in B (do it as an exercise)[12]

$$\theta = + \frac{2\pi N^f B d}{\omega^2 cn(m^*)^2} \quad (\text{for } \omega_c \ll \omega) \qquad (45)$$

$n = \sqrt{\varepsilon(B=0)}$ = index of refraction without magnetic field

d = thickness of sample

m^* can be measured by measuring θ and N^f (Hall effect). The method is more sensitive than the ε measurement since $\theta \sim 1/m^{*2}$.

The need for a Hall measurement can be eliminated if one measures ε (Eq. 36) and θ

VOIGT EFFECT[12]

The uniform magnetic field B is perpendicular to the direction of propagation. The electric field of the radiation is linearly polarized at 45° with B. After traversing the sample, a difference in phase β appears between the components of E parallel and perpendicular to B; thus the light is elliptically polarized. The ratio of the axes of the ellipse is $\tan \frac{\beta}{2}$

Thus a measurement of the ellipticity yields the Voigt angle β:

$$\beta = - \frac{2\pi N^f B^2 d}{\omega^3 cn(m^*)^3} \quad \text{(Do it as an excercise)} \qquad (46)$$

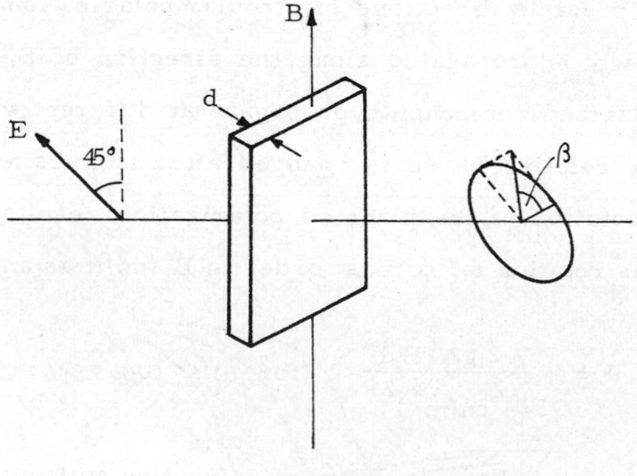

Fig. 9

Hence we have a rather sensitive method of determining effective masses ($\beta \sim m^{*-3}$). For non-spherical constant-energy surfaces, the measurements of ε, θ, and β do not yield the same average effective mass. In cubic materials the Faraday effect is isotropic but the Voigt effect is anisotropic[14].

MAGNETOPLASMA REFLECTION[12]

The free carrier reflectivity has a minimum (Fig. 6) for

$$\varepsilon = \varepsilon_o - \frac{4\pi N^f}{\omega^2} = 1 \quad \text{(for } B = 0\text{)}$$

In the Faraday configuration and for $B \neq 0$ this condition becomes for the two possible directions of circular polarization:

$$1 = \varepsilon_o - \frac{4\pi N^f}{\omega(\omega \pm \omega_c)}$$

and therefore the minimum is split and shifted from the B = 0 minimum by a frequency shift $\Delta\omega = \pm \omega_c/2$ (to first order in ω_c). Thus we have another method to determine ω_c and hence m^*. This method does not require the knowledge of N^f. Figure 10 shows the magnetoplasma shift obtained by Palik et al, for InSb.[15]

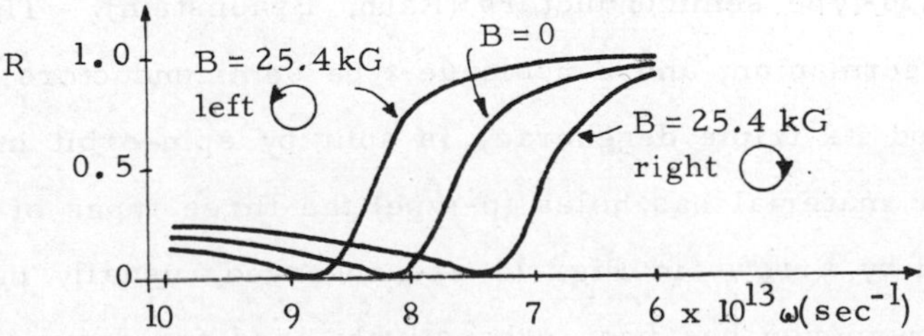

Fig. 10

FREE-CARRIER PIEZOBIRREFRINGENCE[16]

We have mentioned that in cubic materials with anisotropic constant-energy surfaces only an average effective mass

$$\left\langle \frac{1}{m^*} = \frac{1}{m_x} + \frac{1}{m_y} + \frac{1}{m_z} \right.$$

(for ellipsoidal surfaces and from reflectivity measurements) is obtained from the experiments discussed above. If uniaxial stress is applied to the material, the degeneracy of the equivalent minima is often broken and therefore birrefringence appears. For instance, the degeneracy of the equivalent [100] conduction-band minima of silicon is broken by application of a [100] stress since the [100] minimum becomes unequivalent to [010] and [001]. This type of measurement can be used to extract <u>all</u> of the components of m^*_{jj} and not only the average discussed above.

FREE-CARRIER INTERBAND EFFECTS[17]

When a semiconductor is doped, the interband transitions are modified since the state occupancy changes. Several related effects have been observed, the most important of which is perhaps the absorption of light produced by transitions between the various valence bands in p-type semiconductors (Kahn, Braunstein). The valence band of germanium and Zincblende-type semiconductors is (at $\mathbf{k} = 0$) p-like and its triple degeneracy is split by spin-orbit interaction. When the material has holes (p-type) the three types of transitions indicated by arrows in Fig. 11 are observed, usually in the infrared. This phenomenon has been exhaustively used for determining spin-orbit splittings Δ_o and effective masses.

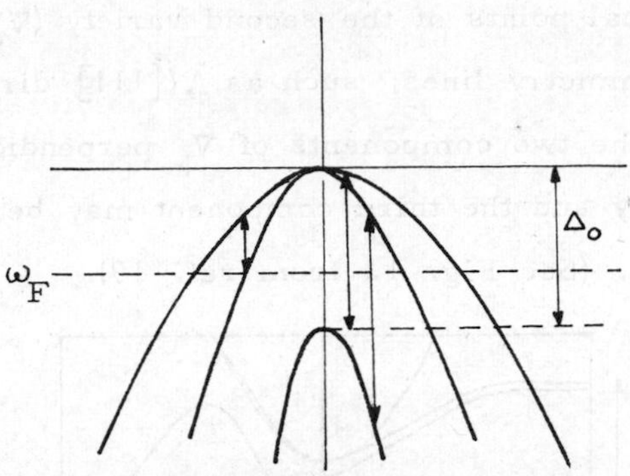

Fig. 11

INTERBAND EFFECTS

(Direct transitions)

Equation (25),

$$\varepsilon_i = \frac{1}{2\pi\omega}\int dS_v \frac{F_{k\ell}}{|\nabla_k \omega_{\ell k}|},$$

indicates that structure in ε_i will occur possibly for $|\nabla_k \omega_{\ell k}| = 0$ since the integrand blows up. We treat cubic materials but the restriction is not essential. The points where this occurs are called Van Hove singularities or Critical Points[18]. Since:

$$\nabla_k \omega_{\ell k} = \nabla_k \omega_\ell - \nabla_k \omega_k \tag{47}$$

there will be two types of critical points, those for which $\nabla_k(\omega_\ell) = \nabla_k(\omega_k) = 0$ and those for which only the difference of both gradients is zero. Critical points of the first variety usually occur at high symmetry points of **k** space where the band gradients are zero by symmetry (for f.c.c. lattices, at Γ, L, X, etc,..., see Dr. Wood's lectures). Critical points of the second variety ($\nabla_k \omega_\ell \neq 0$) often occur at high-symmetry lines, such as Λ([111] direction) for f.c.c., along this line, the two components of ∇_k perpendicular to [111] are zero by symmetry and the third component may be zero at some point along [111]. (See Fig. 12 from ref. 19).

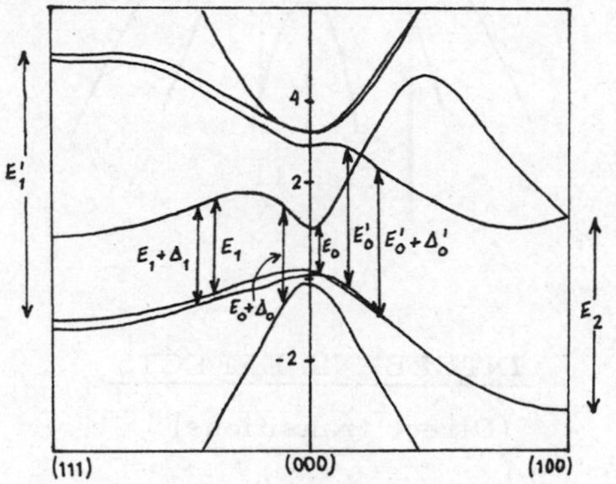

Fig. 12

Band structure of germanium indicating critical points. $E_1 - E_1 + \Delta_1$ and $E'_o - E'_o + \Delta'_o$ are of the $\nabla_k \omega_\ell \neq 0$ variety.

In order to find the shape of ε_r and ε_i near a critical point, we shall expand $\omega_{\ell k}$ in power series of **k** and keep only 0 and 2nd order terms (first order terms are zero since $\nabla_k \omega_{\ell k} = 0$)

Referred to principal axes we have

$$\omega_{\ell k} = \omega_g(k_o) + \frac{1}{2}\left[\frac{\Delta k_x^2}{m_x} + \frac{\Delta k_y^2}{m_y} + \frac{\Delta k_z^2}{m_z}\right] \qquad (48)$$

where ω_g is the gap at the critical point and m_x, m_y, m_z are the principal components of the "reduced" mass tensor. $\Delta k_x, \Delta k_y, \Delta k_z$ are the displacements from the point k_o. Critical points are classified into four categories according to the signs of m_x, m_y, m_z. If the three masses are positive we have a minimum in the conduction-valence-band separation (M_o). If one or two masses are negative one has saddle points (M_1 and M_2 for one or two negative masses respectively). When all masses are negative one has a maximum (M_3). In order to find the behavior of ε near ω_g, we shall replace $F_{k\ell}$ in Eq. (25) by an average F and take it out of the integral sign (in general F is not singular at $\omega_g(k_o)$).

The behavior of ε_i is then determined by that of the combined density of states for the transitions:

$$\varepsilon_i(\omega) \sim N_d(\omega) \sim \int_{\omega_{\ell k}=\omega} dS_k \frac{1}{|\nabla_k \omega_{\ell k}|} \tag{49}$$

Near an M_o critical point, and assuming $m_k = m_y = m_z$ (the case of unequal masses can be reduced to this by changing the lengths of the coordinate axes):

$$\varepsilon_i(\omega) \sim N_d(\omega) = \frac{1}{4\pi^3} \int \frac{dS_k}{|\nabla_k \omega_{\ell k}|} = \frac{1}{\pi^2} k^2 \frac{dk}{d\omega_{\ell k}} \Bigg|_{\omega_{\ell k} = \omega} \tag{50}$$

$$= \frac{1}{2\pi^2} (m)^{3/2} (\omega - \omega_g)^{1/2} \qquad \omega \gtrless \omega_g$$

$$= 0 \quad \text{for} \quad \omega \lessgtr \omega_g$$

For ellipsoidal constant energy surface, we must write $m = (m_x m_y m_z)^{1/3}$ in Eq. (50). For M_3 critical points the result is similar:

$$\varepsilon_i = 0 \quad \text{for} \quad \omega > \omega_g \qquad \varepsilon_i \sim \sqrt{(\omega_g - \omega)} \quad \text{for} \quad \omega < \omega_g.$$

We must add to this contribution to ε_i a smooth background due to all other non-singular transitions present.

Let us now calculate the shape of ε_i around an M_1 singularity. Without significant loss in generality we can assume (otherwise one can adjust the lengths of the axes),

$$\omega - \omega_g = \frac{1}{2m}\left[k_x^2 + k_y^2 - k_z^2\right] = \frac{1}{2m}\left[k_\rho^2 - k_z^2\right] \tag{51}$$

we have

$$dS = 2\pi k_\rho \sqrt{1 + \left(\frac{dk_\rho}{dk_z}\right)^2}\, dk_z = 2\pi k_\rho \cdot \frac{1}{k_\rho}\sqrt{k_\rho^2 + k_z^2}\, dk_z$$

and

$$\left|\nabla\omega_{\ell k}\right| = \frac{1}{m}\sqrt{k_\rho^2 + k_z^2}$$

therefore:

$$N_d(\omega) = \frac{1}{4\pi^3} \times 2\pi \times m' \times 2 \int_{|k_z|_{min}}^{|k_z|_{max}} dk_z$$

$$= \frac{m}{\pi^2}\left\{|k_z|_{max} - |k_z|_{min}\right\} \tag{52}$$

If we assume that the parabolic band of Eq. (51) extends to infinite k, the integral of Eq. (52) diverges, hence we must impose a cut-off in k_z of the order of the B Zone. $|k_z|_{min}$ is equal to zero for $\omega > \omega_g$ and to $\sqrt{2m(\omega_g - \omega)}$ for $\omega < \omega_g$. Hence:

$$\left.\begin{aligned} N_d(\omega) &= \frac{m}{\pi^2}|k_z|_{max} \quad \text{for} \quad \omega \geqslant \omega_g \\ &= \frac{m}{\pi^2}|k_z|_{max} - \sqrt{2(\omega_g - \omega)} \quad \text{for} \quad \omega \leqslant \omega_g \end{aligned}\right\} \tag{53}$$

A similar result is obtained for an M_2 critical point with the $\omega \gtrless \omega_g$ condition reversed. These results are sketched in Fig. 13.

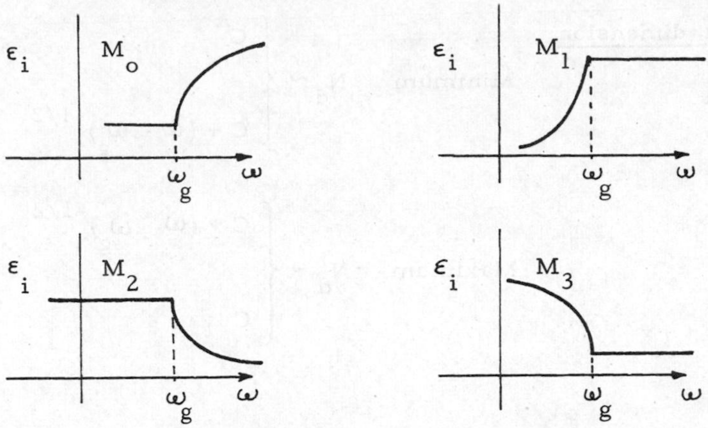

Fig. 13

It is also of interest to consider critical points in two- and one-dimensional bands since their shape approximately indicates the shapes encountered with three-dimensional bands when one or two masses are very large (flat bands). One-dimensional bands are also of interest in treating spectra in the presence of a magnetic field (see Prof. Rodríguez's lectures). The surface integral giving the density of states in three dimensions becomes a line integral in two dimensions and no integral at all in one dimension.

One obtains (do it!)

$$\text{2 dimensions:}\left\{\begin{array}{l} \text{Minimum} \quad N_d \sim \begin{cases} = C_1 & \omega < \omega_g \\ = C_2 & \omega > \omega_g \end{cases} \qquad C_2 < C_1 \\[2ex] \text{Maximum, the same with } C_2 > C_1 \\[2ex] \text{Saddle point } N_d \sim \begin{cases} C_1 \ln(\omega_g - \omega) & \omega < \omega_g \\ C_2 \ln(\omega - \omega_g) & \omega > \omega_g \end{cases} \end{array}\right. \qquad (54)$$

1 dimension

$$\text{Minimum} \quad N_d \sim \begin{cases} C & \omega < \omega_g \\ C + (\omega - \omega_g)^{-1/2} & \omega > \omega_g \end{cases}$$

$$\text{Maximum} \quad N_d \sim \begin{cases} C + (\omega - \omega_g)^{-1/2} & \omega < \omega_g \\ C & \omega > \omega_g \end{cases}$$

(55)

The behavior of ε_r near a critical point can be calculated with the help of Eq. ( ). We have, near a three-dimensional M_o critical point,

$$\varepsilon_r(\omega) - 1 \sim P \int_{\omega_g}^{\infty} \frac{(\omega' - \omega_g)^{1/2}}{\omega'(\omega^2 - \omega'^2)} d\omega' + \text{smooth background} \tag{56}$$

This integral can be easily evaluated with the help of the contour:

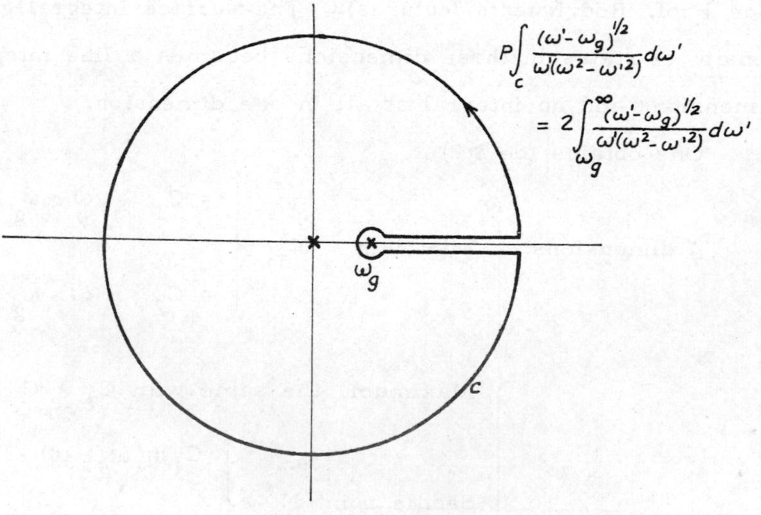

Fig. 14

Poles occur for $\omega < \omega_g$ at $\omega' = \pm\omega$ and $\omega' = 0$ and for $\omega > \omega_g$ at $\omega' = -\omega$ and $\omega' = 0$. We obtain (do it!) (for $\omega > 0$)

$$\varepsilon_r(\omega) - 1 \sim \begin{cases} \dfrac{\omega^{-2}}{2}\left[-2\omega_g^{1/2} + (\omega + \omega_g)^{1/2}\right] & \omega > \omega_g \\ \dfrac{\omega^{-2}}{2}\left[-2\omega_g^{1/2} - (\omega_g - \omega)^{1/2} + (\omega + \omega_g)^{1/2}\right] & \omega < \omega_g \end{cases} \tag{57}$$

The results for other three-dimensional singularities can be obtained from Eq. (57) by noticing that a reflection of the $\varepsilon_i(\omega)$ curve with respect to a horizontal line (parallel to ω axis), gives the same reflection in ε_r, while a reflection of $\varepsilon_i(\omega)$ with respect to a vertical line gives a reflection and a change in sign in ε_r (because of the energy denominator in Eq. 56).

Thus we obtain

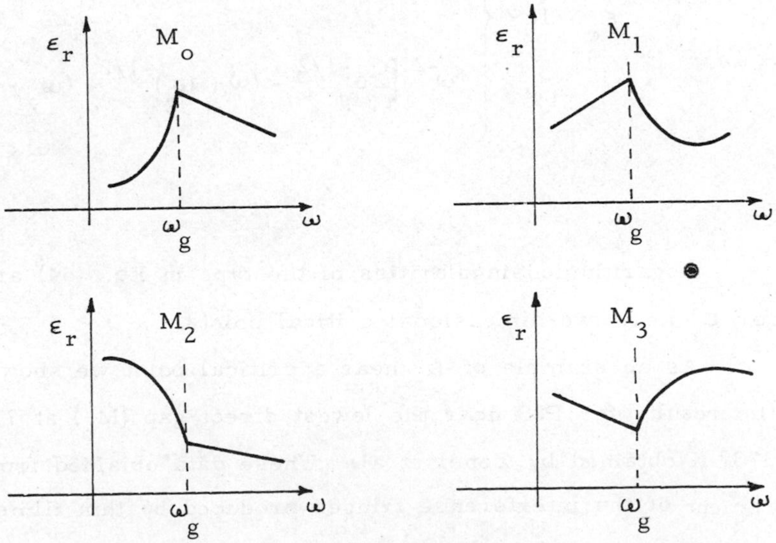

Fig. 15

Notice that the common characteristic of all critical points is the existence of a square root singularity (infinite slope). In general we have

$$\left.\begin{array}{lll} & \varepsilon \sim b\sqrt{\omega - \omega_g} + \text{constant} & \\ & b = i \quad \text{near} \quad M_o & \\ b = i^{m+1} & b = 1 \quad \text{near} \quad M_1 & \\ \text{for an } M_m & b = -i \quad \text{near} \quad M_2 & \\ \text{critical point} & b = 1 \quad \text{near} \quad M_3 & \end{array}\right\} \qquad (58)$$

A similar analysis can be made for one --and two-dimensional critical points. For a one-dimensional minimum we have

$$\varepsilon_r - 1 \sim \begin{cases} \omega^{-2}\left[2\omega_g^{-1/2} - (\omega + \omega_g)^{-1/2}\right] & \omega > \omega_g \\ \omega^{-2}\left[2\omega_g^{-1/2} - (\omega + \omega_g)^{-1/2} - (\omega_g - \omega)^{-1/2}\right] & \omega < \omega_g \end{cases} \qquad (59)$$

Logarithmic singularities of the type in Eq. (54) are found for ε_r near two-dimensional critical points.

As an example of ε_r near a critical point we show in Fig. 16 the results for PbS near the lowest direct gap (M_o) at 77° K and 373° K obtained by Zenel et al. These data obtained from a measurement of the interference fringes produced by thin films of PbS. The full line has been obtained with the expressions:

(A, B, and C have been treated as fitting parameters)

$$= C + B\left[\frac{\omega_g}{\omega}\right]\left[2 - \left(1 + \frac{\omega}{\omega_g}\right)^{1/2} - \left(1 - \frac{\omega}{\omega_g}\right)^{1/2}\right] - \frac{A}{\omega^2} \qquad (60)$$

The first term in Eq. (60) corresponds to the structureless (constant) inter-band background. The second term is the critical point contribution and the third term is a free-electron contribution. If the free electron concentration were known, the optical effective mass could be determined from A. The parameters A, B, and C used for the fit of Fig. 15 are

	A	B	C
77° K	17.54	6.95	2.30×10^{-2}
373° K	14.64	7.45	1.87×10^{-2}

Keeping track of the proportionality constants in Eqs. (25), (26) and (50) we find (do it !)

$$B \cong \frac{2}{3}(2m^*)^{3/2} \cdot |\langle|\mathbf{p}|\rangle|^2 \cdot \omega_g^{-3/2} \qquad (61)$$

where $|\langle|\mathbf{p}|\rangle|$ is the average matrix element of $\mathbf{p}$.

It is well known that the critical point under consideration occurs at the L-point (edge of zone, [111] direction) and $(m^*)^{3/2} = 4(m_{11} m_\perp^2)$ (the factor of 4 takes into account the Valley multiplicity. Hence from the fitted value of B we calculate (77° K data)

$$2^{3/2}(m_{11} m_\perp^2)^{3/2} \cdot |\langle|\mathbf{p}|\rangle|^2 = 2.85 \times 10^{-3} \qquad (62)$$

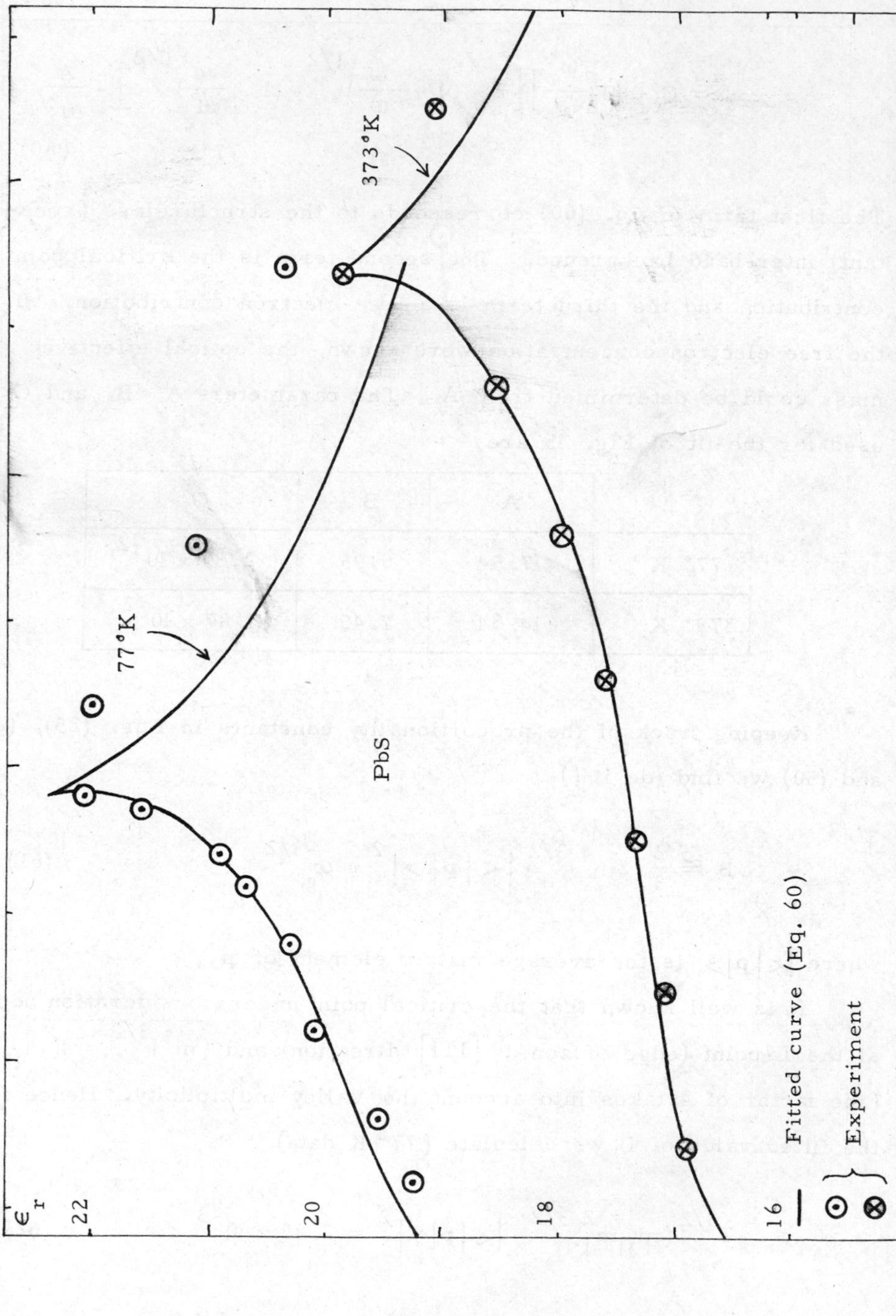

ϵ_r
22
20
18
16
0.2
0.3
0.4
0.5
77°K
373°K
PbS
Fitted curve (Eq. 60)
Experiment

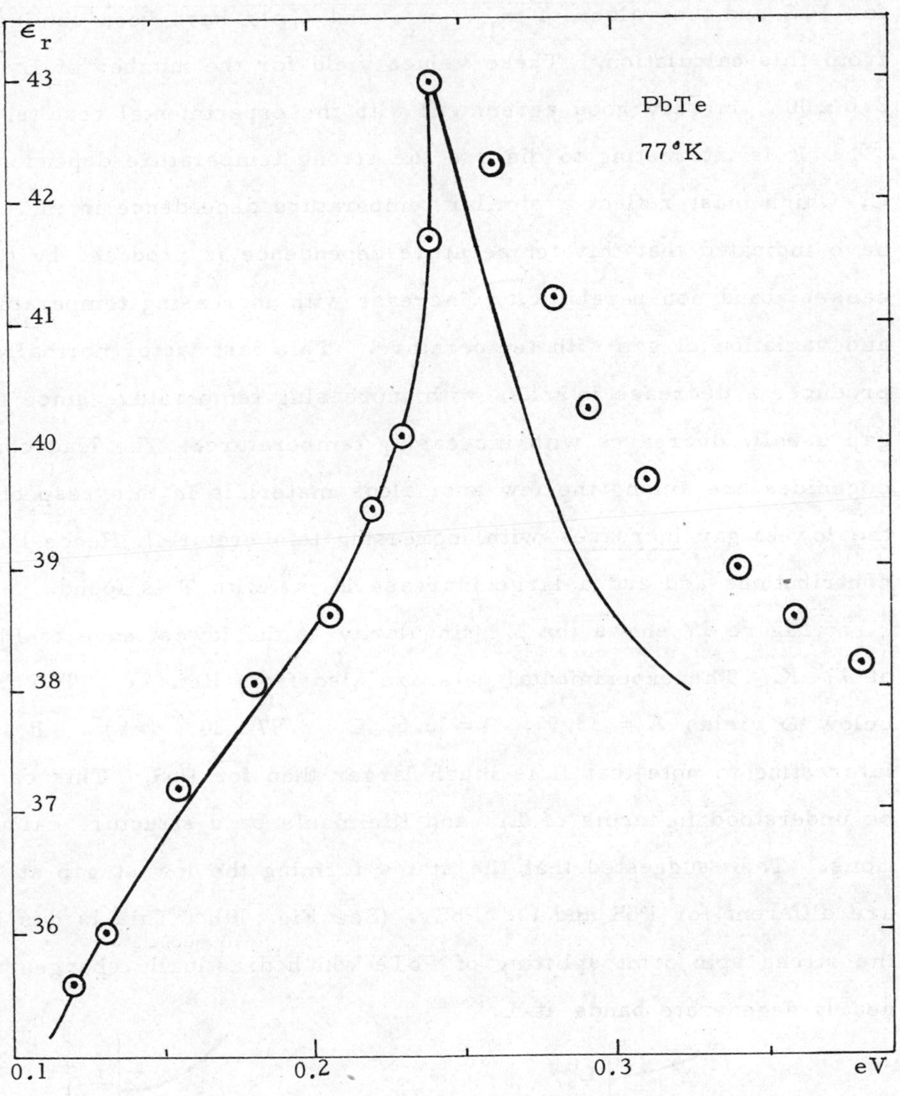

Fig. 17

A band calculation (pseudopotential, Lin and Kleiman[23]) is available for PbS and the values of m_{ll}, $m_{\perp}$, and $<|\mathbf{p}|>$ have been obtained from this calculation. These values yield for the number of Eq. (62) 2.6×10^{-3} in very good agreement with the experimental results.

It is interesting to discuss the strong temperature dependence of C, which must reflect a similar temperature dependence in m^*. We have indicated that this temperature dependence is produced by two causes: band non-parabolicity (increase with increasing temperature) and variation of gap with temperature. This last factor normally produces a decrease in mass with increasing temperature since the gap usually decreases with increasing temperature. The lead chalcogenides are among the few anomalous materials in this respect: the lowest gap increases with increasing temperature. Hence both contributions add and a large increase in m^* with T is found.

Figure 17 shows the E_r singularity at the lowest edge of PbTe at 77° K. The experimental data are also from Ref. 22. The fit below ω_g yields $A = 33.97$, $B = 16.6$, $C = 3.97 \times 10^{-2}$ $(eV)^2$. It is interesting to note that B is much larger than for PbS. This can be understood in terms of Lin and Kleiman's band structure calculations. They suggested that the states forming the lowest gap at L are different for PbS and for PbTe. (See Fig. 18). This is due to the strong spin orbit splitting of PbTe which drastically changes the nearly-degenerate bands at L.

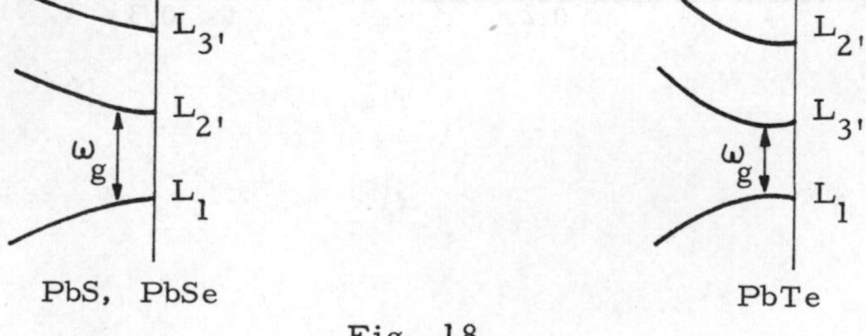

Fig. 18

LONG-WAVELENGTH ELECTRONIC DIELECTRIC CONSTANT OF AN INSULATOR (PENN)[24]

It occurs commonly that the gaps at the edge of the B. Z. are roughly isotropic (fig. 19). We can therefore approximate the Brillouin Zone by a sphere in order to calculate $\varepsilon_r(0)$, and assume $\omega_{\ell k} = \omega_{\ell k}(|k|)$, a function of the magnitude of $\mathbf{k}$ only. The density of states around ω_g becomes that for one-dimensional bands. We replace the solid by a free-electron gas with an energy gap ω_g at the edge of the spherical B. Z. Fig. 20 gives the ε_i for a real solid and for our model.

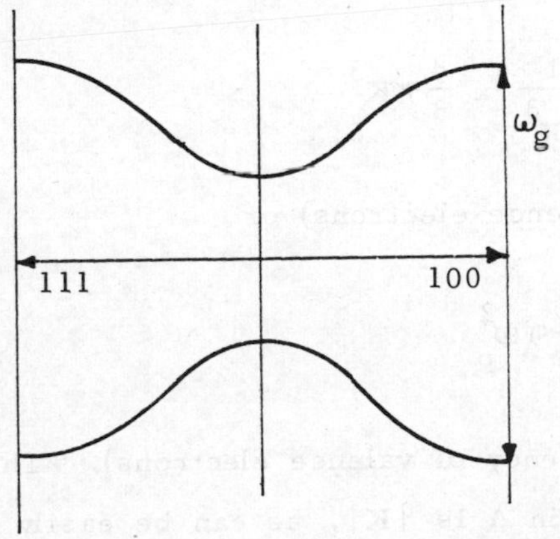

Fig. 19

We shall equate the gap ω_g of our model to the energy at which ε_i (experimental) has a maximum. We obtain from Eq. (59), keeping track of proportionality constants:

$$\varepsilon_r(0) = 1 + \frac{3}{4} A \, \omega_g^{-5/2} \tag{63}$$

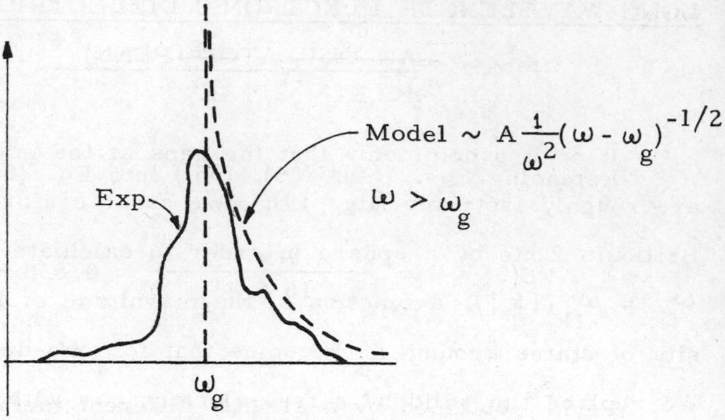

Fig. 20

Let us call K the radius of the spherical B. Z. K is given by

$$N = \frac{1}{4\pi^3} \times \frac{4}{3}\pi K^3$$

(N = number of valence electrons) or

$$K^3 = \frac{3}{4}\pi\omega_p^2 \qquad (63')$$

(ω_p = plasma frequency of valence electrons). The matrix element of **p** which enters in A is $|K|$, as can be easily obtained from the wave functions across the gap (free electrons):

$$\left.\begin{array}{l} \frac{1}{\sqrt{2}}(e^{ikr} + e^{-ikr}) \\ \\ \frac{1}{\sqrt{2}}(e^{ikr} - e^{-ikr}) \end{array}\right\} \qquad (64)$$

Hence

$$A = \frac{1}{2\pi}\ \frac{2}{3}K^2 \times 4\,T\,K^2\left(\frac{m^*}{2}\right)^{1/2}$$

with

$$m^* \cong \frac{\omega_g}{4|\langle \mid K \mid \rangle|^2} = \frac{\omega_g}{4K^2} \tag{65}$$

Replacing Eqs. (64), (65), (63') into Eq. (63) we find (check!)

$$\varepsilon(0) - 1 = \frac{\sqrt{2} \times 3 \times \pi}{16} \frac{\omega_p^2}{\omega_g^2} = 0,835 \frac{\omega_p^2}{\omega_g^2} \tag{66}$$

Penn[24] obtained by a slightly different method $\varepsilon(0) = \frac{\omega_p^2}{\omega_g^2}$

He also obtained the **k** dependence of this dielectric constant.

The results calculated from Eq. (66) for a number of materials and their experimental counterparts are[8]

	Calculated	Experimental
S_i	12.5	12.0
ZnS	5.7	5.2
ZnSe	5.8	5.9
ZnTe	7.0	7.3
CdTe	6.4	7.2

Eq. (59) also enables us to calculate the low frequency dispersion. By expanding it in power series of ω/ω_g we get

$$\varepsilon_o(\omega) = A \times \frac{3}{4} \omega_g^{-5/2} \left[1 + 0,73 \frac{\omega^2}{\omega_g^2} + \ldots\right] \tag{67}$$

INDIRECT TRANSITIONS

We have, so far, considered first order transitions induced only by the electromagnetic field. Since a phonon field is present, second order transitions involving the absorption of a phonon and the absorption or emission of a phonon are also possible. These transitions are generally only observable when they occur below the lowest direct gap since their intensity is quite low. The phonons may have a finite crystal momentum $\mathbf{k}_{phon}$ and therefore indirect transitions are possible from a valence band state of crystal momentum $\mathbf{k}_v$ to a conduction band state of $\mathbf{k}_c \neq \mathbf{k}_v$ (indirect transitions[25]). Such is the case in Ge and Si where the smallest gap is indirect. The energy and momentum conservation conditions are

$$\left.\begin{aligned} \omega &= \omega_f - \omega_o \pm \omega_{phon} \\ \mathbf{k}_f &= \mathbf{k}_i \mp \mathbf{k}_{phon} \end{aligned}\right\} \tag{68}$$

Upper sign for phonon emission; lower sign for phonon absorption.

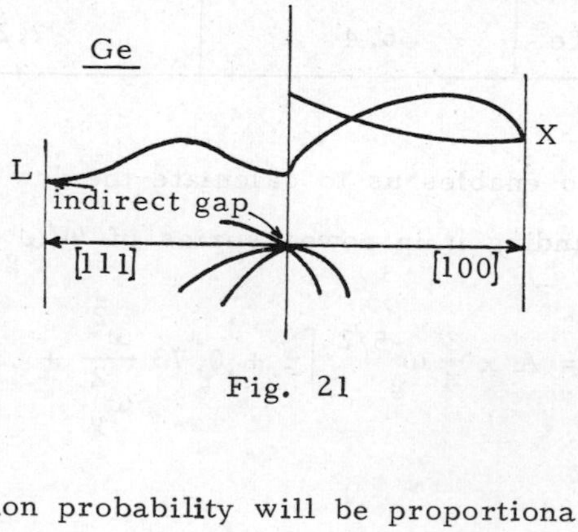

Fig. 21

The transition probability will be proportional to the density of initial states times the density of final states since each initial state is now connected with each final state. Hence

$$\varepsilon_i \sim \int_0^{\omega - \omega_g \mp \omega_{phon}} \omega_c^{1/2} (\omega - \omega_g - \omega_c \mp \omega_{phon})^{1/2} d\omega_c$$

$$= (\omega - \omega_g \mp \omega_{phon})^2 \int_0^1 x^{1/2} (1 - x)^{1/2} dx \qquad (69)$$

$$(x = \frac{\omega_c}{\omega - \omega_g \mp \omega_{phon}})$$

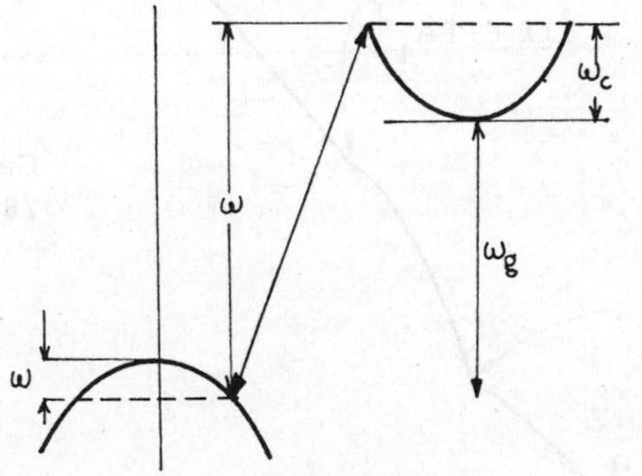

Fig. 22

Therefore the ε_i is proportional to $(\omega - \omega_g \mp \omega_{phon})^2$. ε_i is also proportional to the phonon occupation number $1 + f_B$ for phonon emission and f_B for phonon absorption: The absorption processes disappear at low temperatures. It is conventional to plot $\varepsilon_i^{1/2}$ (or $\alpha^{1/2}$, which is approximately proportional to $\varepsilon_i^{1/2}$

below the lowest gap) in order to exhibit the dependence shown above. Several straight branches are found corresponding to various phonon branches (absorption and emission). Data for GaP are shown in Fig. 23 (Gershenson et al[26]). Deviations from straight lines are due to exciton effects[27].

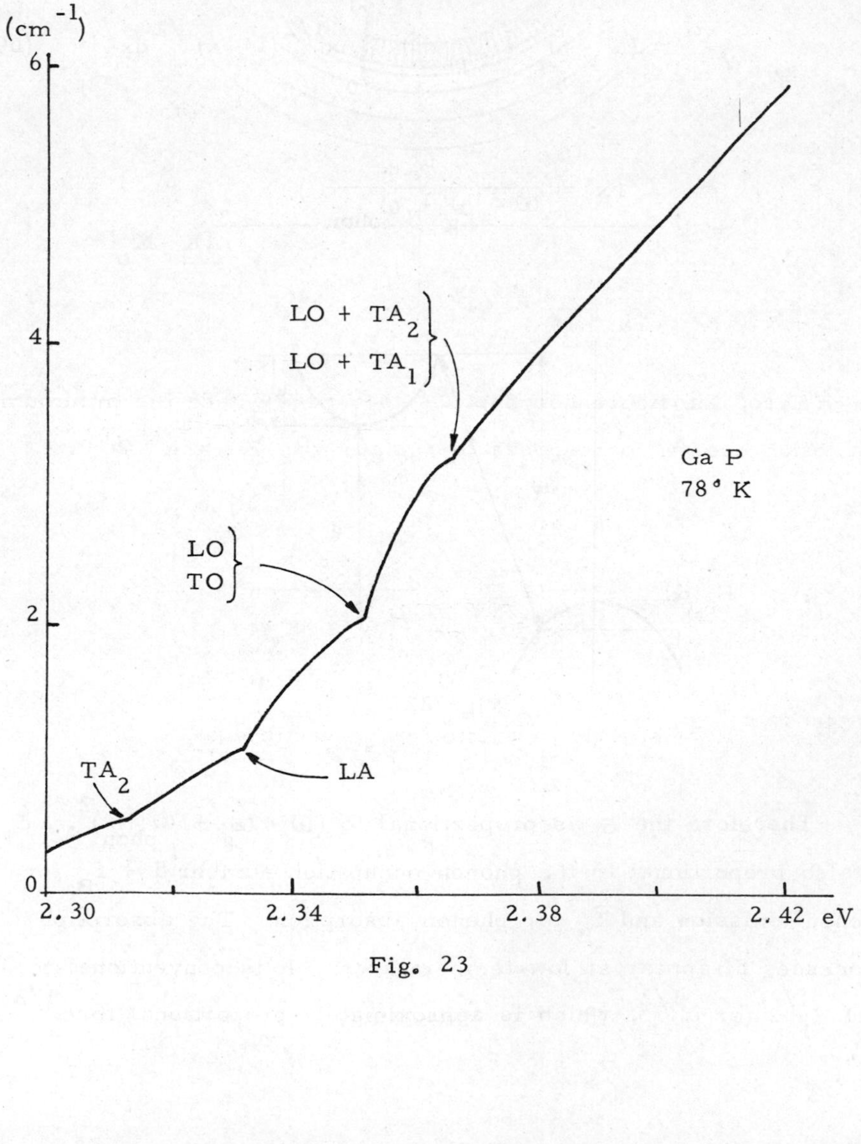

Fig. 23

In the case of exciton states, what we must consider is a many body ground states, plus a spectrum of infinitely many bands:

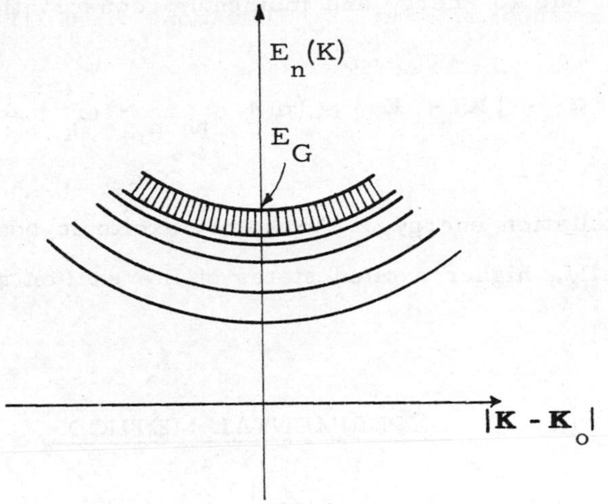

Here, the figure corresponds to a case where the minimum excitation energy corresponds to a state with $\mathbf{K}_o = \mathbf{k}_v \neq 0$.

$$E_n(K) = -\frac{R}{n^2} + E_G + \frac{(K - K_o)^2}{2(m_c^* + m_v^*)}$$

$K = k_c + k_v$ = exciton wave vector.

If we limit ourselves to the n = 1 exciton band, we see that, again, there is only one density of states over which we can integrate, and due to energy and momentum conservation, we obtain

$$\alpha \sim |\mathbf{K} - \mathbf{K}_o| \sim (\omega \pm \omega_{phon} - \omega_g + \omega^o_{exc})^{1/2}$$

ω^o_{exc} = excitation energy of the lowest excitonic bound state (n = 1).

Usually, higher excited states of the exciton are much weaker.

EXPERIMENTAL METHODS

For an insulator it is possible to determine ε_r and ε_i near and below the fundamental edge by measuring the transmission and the reflection of a slab of material. If the slab is thick (or irregular) enough that interference effects can be neglected we have for the transmission τ and the reflection R at normal incidence:

$$\left.\begin{aligned} \tau &= \frac{(1 - R)^2 \, e^{-\alpha d}}{1 - R^2 \, e^{-2\alpha d}} \\ R &= R\left[1 + \tau e^{-\alpha d}\right] \end{aligned}\right\} \qquad (70)$$

where R is the reflectivity of the sample. The optical constants (n_r and n_i are then found from

$$\left.\begin{aligned} R &= \frac{(n_r - 1)^2 + n_i^2}{(n_r + 1)^2 + n_i^2} \\ \alpha &= \frac{2\omega n_i}{c} \end{aligned}\right\} \qquad (71)$$

In order to use this method, one must have a sample thick enough so that "some" absorption occurs and thin enough so that "some" transmission occurs ($e^{-\alpha d} \approx 1$). Above the lowest gap ω_g the absorption coefficient soon climbs to values of the order of $10^5 - 10^6$ cm^{-1}. Hence for "some" transmission to occur the sample thickness must be $\approx$ 1000 Å. The preparation of such samples, of good crystalline quality, poses serious difficulties. We have already mentioned the use of epitaxial samples (PbS, PbTe)[22,28]. This method has received relatively little attention and is very promising. Samples can, sometimes, be prepared by chemical etching of thin ground and polished samples[29]. Most of the available data have, however, been obtained by reflection techniques. These techniques can be divided into two categories: Measurements with polarized light, in which the optical constants are derived from two measured quantities (such as the reflectivity for a given angle of incidence and the two normal modes of polarization[30]) and measurements of only one parameter over a broad spectral range with a dispersion relation so as to obtain two equations from which ε_r and ε_i are determined[31,32,28].

Among the methods based on two measurements with polarized light we shall note the ellipsometric method in which light linearly polarized at 45° with the plane of incidence is reflected at oblique incidence (Archer[33]). The ellipticity and ellipse orientation of the reflected light are measured and from these parameters the optical constants are obtained. A promising method based on the pseudo-Brewster angle has been recently developed (Potter[34]). For a non-absorbing medium the reflectivity for E polarized parallel to the plane of incidence vanishes at the Brewster angle φ_B: $\tan \varphi_B = n_r$. If the medium is absorbing, the reflectivity still has, in general, a minimum at the pseudo-Brewster angle φ_{pB}. The optical constants can be found from φ_{pB} and the reflectivity at φ_{pB}.

The most popular method for determining the optical constants over a large spectral region involves the measurement of the reflectivity R at normal incidence[31, 32, 28] (for a cubic material). In order to find the optical constants, the change in phase under reflection must be obtained with the help of a dispersion relation. The optical constants are found by solving

$$r(\omega) = R^{1/2} e^{i\theta} = \frac{n_r - 1 + in_i}{n_r + 1 + in_i} = \frac{n - 1}{n + 1} \qquad (72)$$

for n_r and n_i. Let us derive the dispersion relation for θ. We consider the function $\ln\left[R^{1/2} e^{i\theta}\right] = \frac{1}{2} \ln R + i\theta$. This function is analytic in the upper half plane (since n is analytic), except for $|\omega| \rightarrow \infty$ ($R \rightarrow 0$ and $\ln R \rightarrow -\infty$).

In order to elliminate this singularity we multiply $\ln r(\omega)$ by $\frac{1 + \omega\omega'}{1 + \omega'^2}$. We integrate $\frac{1 + \omega\omega'}{1 + \omega'^2} \frac{\ln r(\omega')}{\omega' - \omega}$ along the contour of Fig. 24.

Poles now occur for $\omega' = i$ and $\omega' = \omega$. We obtain

Fig. 24

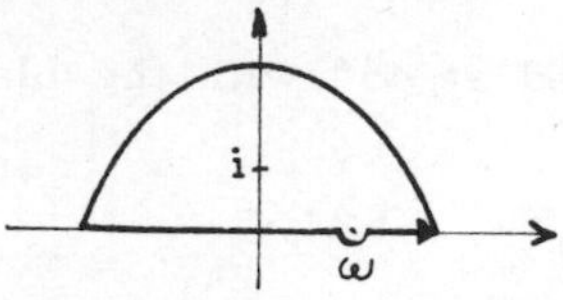

$$\pi i \frac{1+\omega^2}{1+\omega^2} \ln r(\omega) + 2\pi i \frac{1+i\omega}{1+1} \frac{\ln r(i)}{(1+i\omega_r)i} \tag{73}$$

$$= P \int_{-\infty}^{+\infty} \frac{1+\omega\omega'}{1+\omega'^2} \ln r(\omega') \frac{d\omega'}{\omega'-\omega}$$

It is easy to see from Eq. (25) and (72) that ln r(i) is a real number. Equating the real parts of both sides of Eq. (73) we find[35]

$$\theta(\omega) = \frac{1}{\pi} P \int_{-\infty}^{+\infty} \frac{1+\omega\omega'}{1+\omega'^2} \ln R^{1/2}(\omega') \frac{d\omega'}{\omega'-\omega}$$

$$= \frac{\omega}{\pi} P \int_0^{\infty} \ln R(\omega') \frac{d\omega'}{\omega'^2 - \omega^2} \tag{74}$$

The integral of Eq. (74) has to be evaluated with a computer after removing the singularity in the integrand by adding to it

$$\frac{\omega}{\pi} P \int_0^{\infty} \ln R(\omega) \frac{d\omega'}{\omega'^2 - \omega^2} = 0$$

The integral

$$\theta(\omega) = \frac{\omega}{\pi} P \int_0^{\infty} \frac{\ln R(\omega') - \ln R(\omega)}{\omega'^2 - \omega^2} d\omega' \tag{75}$$

is non-singular since the slope of $R(\omega')$ found experimentally is never infinite (due to broadening).

The integral of Eq. (75) is evaluated numerically with a computer (Simpson's rule). In order to evaluate it, $R(\omega)$ must be known over as broad an energy range as possible and extrapolations must be used in order to cover the whole range $0 \leq \omega \leq \infty$. On the low-frequency side $R(\omega)$ is usually measured down to a frequency for which it is constant ($\omega_{min} < \omega_g$, the lowest gap for an insulator). On the high frequency side, measurements are performed up to a frequency at which the oscillator strengths for the valence electrons has been exhausted. This involves work in the vacuum ultraviolet; a typical cutoff frequency is 25 eV. Equation (21) yields (for $\Delta\varepsilon_r \simeq 0$) $R \sim \omega^{-4}$ for frequencies higher than the cutoff. This expression is used to extrapolate $R(\omega)$ beyond the maximum available experimental frequency to infinity. Figure 25 shows experimental values of ε_i for silicon obtained by Philipp and Taft[36] using the method just discussed, together with calculated values to be discussed later.

IDENTIFICATION OF CRITICAL POINTS

The assignement of the observed optical structure to specific critical points for direct interband transitions is a rather complicated process[20]. It is hard to determine the shape of the observed structure in relationship to the theoretical shape since critical points are normally broadened by collisions and either broadened (M_2, M_3) or sharpened (M_o, M_1) by electron-hole Coulomb interaction (excitons). Many of the assignements made so far are to be considered as tentative.

The family of materials for which most reliable assignements exist and that which has been most exhaustively studied is the germanium-zincblende-Wurtzite family. The existence of a number of critical points with spin-orbit splittings has made assignements particularly easy and was responsible for the breakthrough in the field around 1960[20]. We shall now discuss in an elementary fashion the

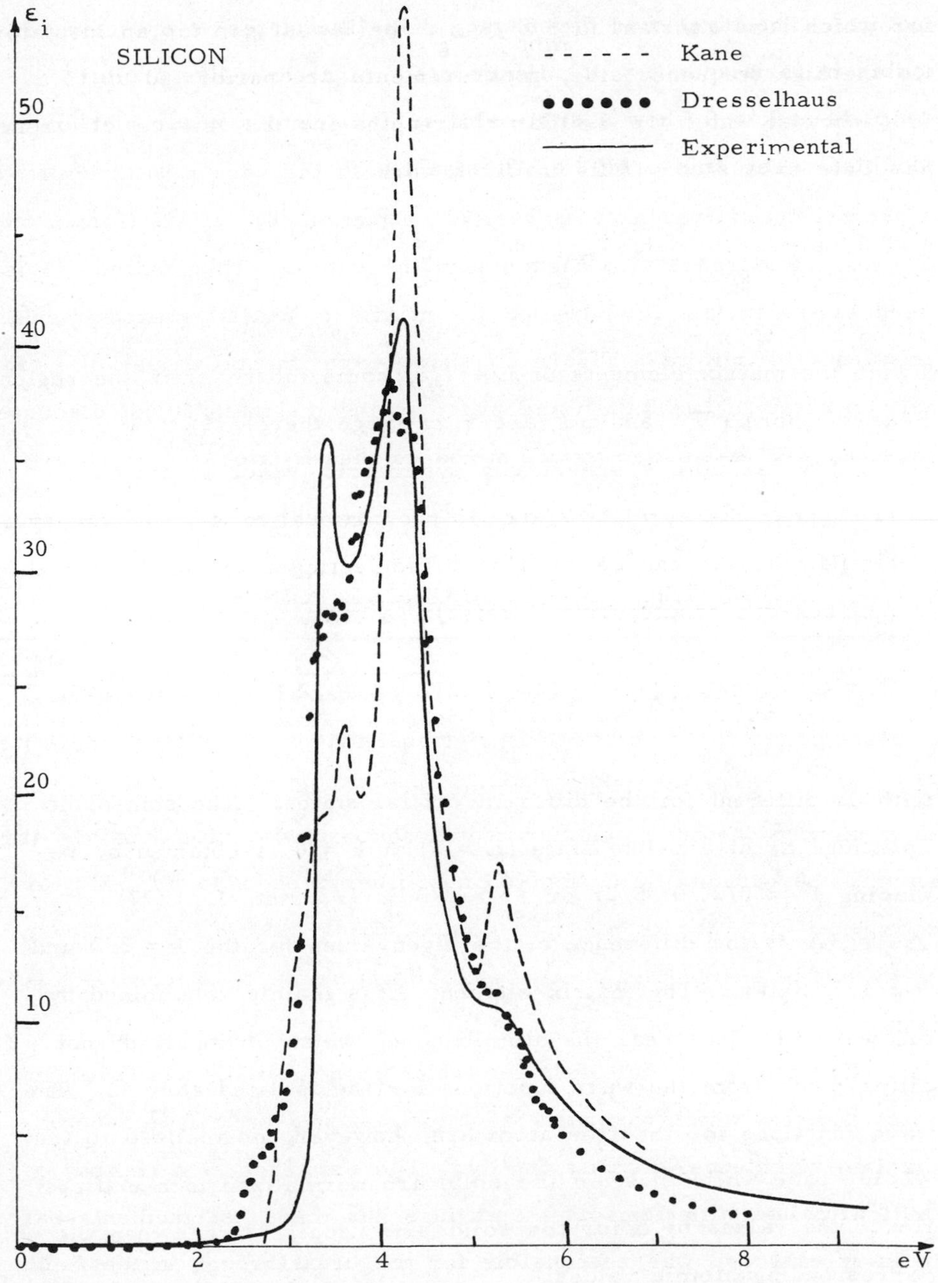

ε i
SILICON
Kane
Dresselhaus
Experimental
50
40
30
20
10
0
2
4
6
8
eV

Fig. 25

possible uses of spin-orbit splittings for the identification of critical points. The three-fold degeneracy of p-like states is preserved in cubic materials at $k = 0$. Hence predominantly p-like orbital triplets at $k = 0$ show a spin-orbit splitting into a quadruplet and a doublet. The spin-orbit Hamiltonian is

$$H_{so} = \frac{1}{4c^2}\left[\nabla V \times p\right] \cdot \sigma \qquad (76)$$

hence the matrix elements of Eq. (76) come mostly from the region near the core (∇V and $p\cdot\psi$ are very large there).

If we assume V spherically symmetric (which is certainly correct near the core), $\partial V/\partial \mathbf{r}$ is proportional to $\mathbf{r}$, and the spin-orbit Hamiltonian can be written as (neglecting coupling between different non-degenerate orbital states):

$$H_{so} = 2\Delta L \cdot S = \Delta\left[J^2 - S^2 - L^2\right] \qquad (77)$$

with Δ different for the different orbital states. The spin-orbit splitting Δ_o of a p-like state ($L = 1$) at $k = 0$ is obtained by replacing $J^2 = 3/2 \times 5/2$, or $J^2 = 3/2 \times 1/2$, into Eq. (77): $\Delta_o = 3\Delta$ is the difference of the eigenvalues for the $J = 3/2$ and $J = 1/2$ states. The matrix element Δ is mainly determined by the wave functions near the atomic core, which obviously do not differ much from the wave functions for the isolated atom[37]. The wave functions for the free atom are, however, normalized to the whole space while those of the solid are normalized to a unit cell. Hence the values of Δ for the solid are usually larger than the corresponding atomic values:

$$\Delta^{solid} = A\,\Delta^{atomic} \qquad (78)$$

(We are considering elemental solids). A can be assumed to be the same for all materials of a given family.

We have listed in Table I the values of $3\,\Delta^{atomic}$ extracted from atomic spectroscopic data (C. E. Moore[38]) by the Russell-Saunders scheme (Condon Shortley[39]) and also the values calculated by Herman and Skillman[40]. From Δ^{solid} for the valence band of germanium we obtain $\Delta = 1.4$; we shall use this number for all materials of the germanium-zincblende family.

In a material composed of two different atoms, we must weigh the wave functions and spin-orbit splittings of the two components properly:

$$\Delta_o^{solid} = A\left[\xi^{(1)}\,\Delta_o^{(1)} + \xi^{(2)}\,\Delta_o^{(2)}\right] \qquad (79)$$

where $\Delta_o^{(i)}$ are the atomic spin-orbit splittings of the two constituents and $\xi^{(i)}$ the relative contribution of the atomic wave functions to the wave function of the valence band at $\mathbf{k} = 0$.

A good approximation to the experimental spin-orbit splittings of the III - V compounds is obtained for $\xi^{III} = 0.35$ and $\xi^{V} = 0.65$ and to that of the II - VI compounds for $\xi^{II} = 0.2$ and $\xi^{VI} = 0.8$.

Table II lists the experimental values of Δ_o for a number of group IV, III-V, II-VI, I-VII, and VIII solids obtained by several methods. We also list the values calculated from the spectroscopic data of Table I (A = 1.1 for alkali halides and A = 1 for solid rare gases). If a measured splitting agrees with the calculated one, it is plausible to assign the corresponding transitions to transitions at $\mathbf{k} = 0$ involving p-like states. This assignement can be strikingly confirmed by applying uniaxial stress to the material: the spin-quadruplet splits. Spin quadruplets can only exist (other than accidental degeneracies) for cubic materials and at $\mathbf{k} = 0$.

Away from $\mathbf{k} = 0$ the three-fold orbital degeneracy of p-like states is split by the $\mathbf{k} \cdot \mathbf{p}$ "crystal field" (the $\mathbf{k} \cdot \mathbf{p}$ term in the Hamiltonian of Appendix C). Along [100] and [111] a two-fold orbital degeneracy remains, but is split by the spin-orbit interaction. If z is the direction of $\mathbf{k}$ (either [100] or [111]), the wave functions of the orbital doublet have symmetries $(1/\sqrt{2})(x + iy)$ and $(1/\sqrt{2})(x - iy)$. From Eq. (77) we see that this orbital state is split into $(1/\sqrt{2})(x+iy)\uparrow$ and $(1/\sqrt{2})(x - iy)\uparrow$ (and the time reversed states):

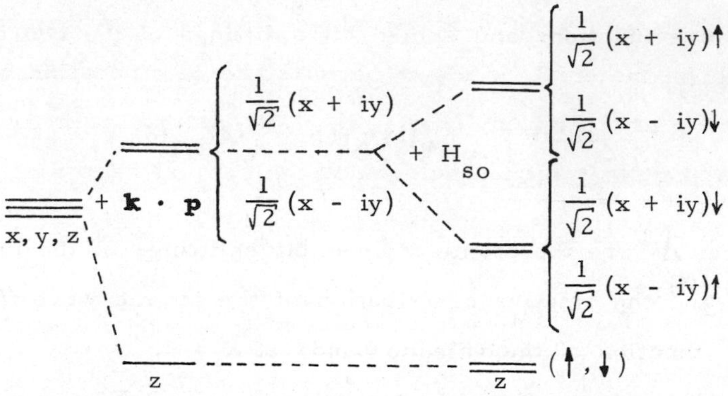

The wave functions $(1/\sqrt{2})(x + iy)\uparrow$ and $(1/\sqrt{2})(x + iy)\downarrow$ (and their time-reversed) diagonalize the spin-orbit Hamiltonian 2 L.S:

$$\left\langle \frac{1}{\sqrt{2}}(x + iy)\uparrow \middle| 2\ \mathrm{L.S} \middle| \frac{1}{\sqrt{2}}(x + iy)\uparrow \right\rangle = +1$$

$$\left\langle \frac{1}{\sqrt{2}}(x + iy)\downarrow \middle| 2\ \mathrm{L.S} \middle| \frac{1}{\sqrt{2}}(x + iy)\downarrow \right\rangle = -1 \qquad (80)$$

Hence the spin-orbit splitting of the orbital doublet is 2Δ where Δ is the matrix element of the spin-orbit Hamiltonian evaluated for the pertinent wave functions. As **k** moves along the high-symmetry direction of **k** space ([111] or [100]) Δ may vary. If it doesn't, we conclude that the doublet splitting is two-thirds of the Δ_o splitting (we assume that the **k** · **p** splitting of Z - X is much larger than Δ). Detailed calculations[41] must be performed in order to see how Δ varies with **k**. In germanium-zincblende materials Δ is independent of **k** along [111]. However along [100] Δ decreases as **k** increases. This can be understood by looking at Fig. 12: Symmetry requires that the spin-orbit splitting be zero at the X point (the splittings of the two constituent atoms subtract instead of adding as they do along [111]).

The spin-orbit splitting along [111] is very important in this family of materials since it permits the identification of the E_1, $E_1 + \Delta_1$ critical point (Fig. 12). We list in Table III the splittings Δ_o and $\frac{3}{2}\Delta_1$, which should be roughly equal according to the discussion above, for a number of materials of this family.

TABLE III[19]

	Δ_o	$\frac{3}{2}\Delta_1$
Ge	0.29	0.30
GeAs	0.34	0.33
InAs	0.43	0.40
GaSb	0.80	0.69
CdTe	0.92	0.89
ZnTe	0.93	0.86

ε_r AND ε_i CALCULATIONS FROM BAND STRUCTURE

The most reliable confirmation of assignments of optical structure is obtained when a calculation of ε from a reliable band structure is performed. If broadening is neglected, ε_i is calculated first with Eq. (25). $\underset{\approx}{\varepsilon}_r$ is obtained through the Kramers-Kronig relation [Eq. (26)]. It is sometimes convenient to introduce broadening (an energy-independent scattering time) in order to fit the height of the experimental curves and also to avoid the singularity in the integrand of the Kramers-Kronig relation. In order to calculate ε_i one must obtain the energy eigenvalues and eigenfunctions at a large number of points in the Brillouin zone. Symmetry considerations reduce the size of the zone to an irreducible section from which all other points are generated by applying the symmetry operations of the point group. For the full cubic group, the irreducible volume is $\frac{1}{48}$th of the Brillouin zone. Of the order of 1000 diagonalizations of the Hamiltonian are usually performed to calculate $\underset{\approx}{\varepsilon}$ in this case: This number is so large that it usually becomes prohibitive to use one of the "first-principles" methods, such as OPW or APW. Parametrization techniques, which simplify the structure of the Hamiltonian (pseudopotential[42, 44], $\mathbf{k} \cdot \mathbf{p}$[41], Fourier expansion[43]) are usually employed.

The calculation of the matrix element of $\mathbf{p}$ does not present any difficulties once the wave functions are known. However, since, as mentioned above, these matrix elements do not vary drastically with $\mathbf{k}$, they are assumed constant sometimes and hence the ε_i calculation is reduced to a density of states calculation. This can be done by two different methods:

a. Generating the points at which the Hamiltonian is diagonalized at random (Monte Carlo[42,44]) and counting how many have energies between ω and $\omega + \Delta\omega$ (density of states; $\Delta\omega$ could be 0.01 eV for instance); b. approximating the energy band differences by tangent planes (perpendicular to $\langle p \rangle$) at points on a regular mesh (cubic for a cubic material) and measuring the volume within each cube comprised between the planes ω and $\omega + \Delta\omega$ (Gilat + Raubenheimer[45]). Summing the volumes within each cube we get the density of states.

The calculations of Fig. 25 were obtained by the Monte Carlo method. We show in Fig. 26 ε_r and ε_i for gray tin obtained by the $\mathbf{k} \cdot \mathbf{p}$ method including spin-orbit coupling effects (they are not included in Fig. 24)[46]. No experimental data are available for comparison. The density of states was obtained by the method of Gilat + Raubenheimer[45].

MODULATION TECHNIQUES

As mentioned above, the identification of a Van Hove singularity in an optical spectrum is not always an easy task. While such singularity is characterized by the infinite slope associated with the square root singularity, the fact that it occurs in general on a broad, possibly large, background, makes its observation difficult since it may be lost in the noise of the background. Also, broadening may round off the singularity. Excitons sharpen or broaden it. For instance near an M_3 critical point, the effective electron-hole Coulomb interaction is repulsive (the mass is negative) and this

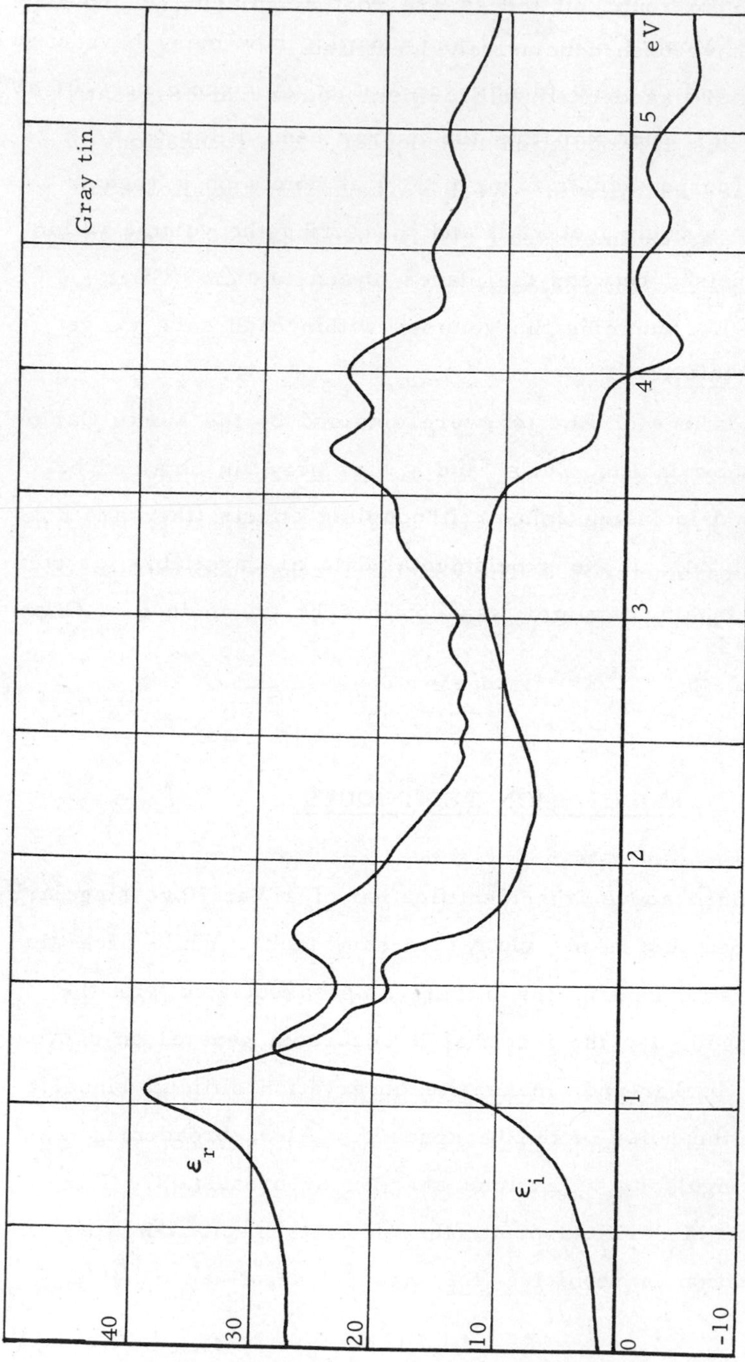

Fig. 26

interaction tends to round off the square root singularity[47]: no M_3' critical points have been conclusively identified.

The structure associated with critical points can be greatly enhanced by means of modulation techniques. The foundations of these methods are as follows. We have seen that the dielectric constant near a three-dimensional critical point (similar reasonings apply to one- and two-dimensional singularities) is:

$$\varepsilon \sim B(\omega - \omega_g)^{1/2} + \text{constant} \tag{81}$$

Since the constant background may be large, it is advantageous to measure, instead of ε, the derivative of ε with respect to some as yet unspecified parameter ξ. The constant background is then eliminated and the singularity becomes:

$$\frac{d\varepsilon}{d\xi} = B(\omega - \omega_g)^{-1/2} \frac{d(\omega - \omega_g)}{d\xi} + \frac{dB}{d\xi}(\omega - \omega_g)^{1/2} \tag{82}$$

Since the derivative of Eq. (82) blows up for $\omega = \omega_g$, easy detectability of the singularity should result. The term $\frac{dB}{d\xi}(\omega - \omega_g)^{1/2}$ is usually negligible with respect to the singular term.

Two distinct possibilities appear for the parameter ξ in Eq. (82). We either take the derivative with respect to frequency ω, or with respect to the energy gap ω_g. Let us first discuss the frequency (or wavelength) derivative technique[48, 49]. In order to obtain the derivative of an optical "constant" with respect to ω we apply to the sample a frequency-modulated monochromatic beam of frequency

$$\omega = \omega_o + (\Delta\omega) \cos \Omega t \tag{83}$$

with $\Delta\omega << \omega_o$. The measured dielectric constant is then given by (similar reasoning would apply to the reflectivity R and the transmissivity τ):

$$\varepsilon = \varepsilon(\omega_o) + \Delta\varepsilon \cos \Omega t \tag{84}$$

If we measure the modulation $\Delta\varepsilon$ we obtain

$$\frac{d\varepsilon}{d\omega} = \frac{\Delta\varepsilon}{\Delta\omega} \qquad \Delta\omega \rightarrow 0 \tag{85}$$

Hence if $\Delta\omega$ is kept small and constant over the spectral range of interest, $\Delta\varepsilon$ is proportional to $d\varepsilon/d\omega$. The frequency modulation of the incident beam is easily accomplished by vibrating the exit slit, or same mirror in the system[48, 49]

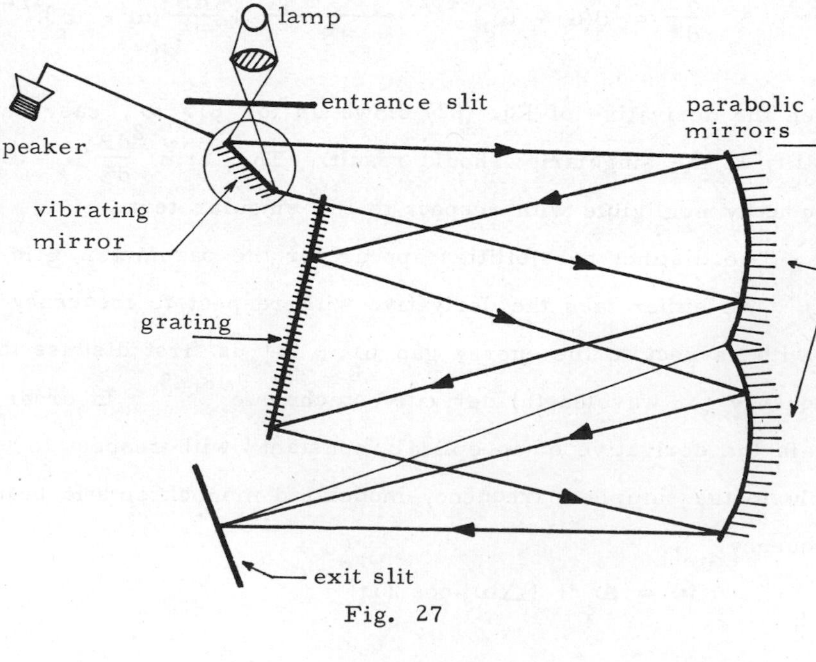

Fig. 27

Another method consists in rotating a parallel plate interposed in the beam inside the monochrometer at an angle. The shift in the beam by the rotating plate produces the frequency modulation.

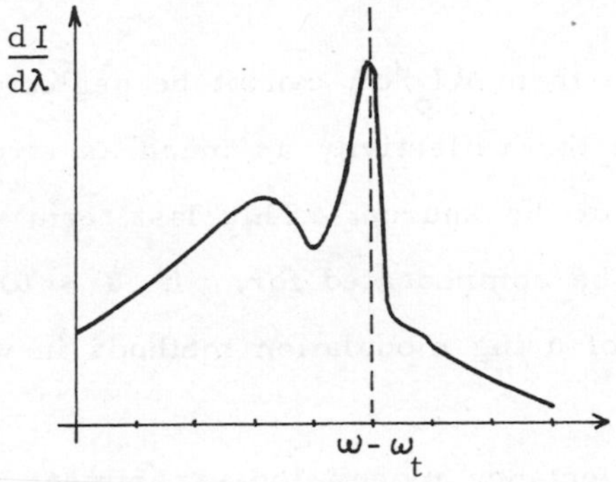

Fig. 28

Figure 28 shows the wavelength modulation spectrum of silicon obtained by transmission by I. Bälslev[49] (we plot the derivative of the transmitted intensity). ω_t is equal to the indirect gap plus the transverse optical phonon energy (the peak corresponds to indirect transitions with phonon emission). The slope of the peak is obviously reminescent of a $(\omega - \omega_t)^{-1/2}$ singularity, as expected for indirect transitions with exciton interactions.

The wavelength modulation method has a number of disadvantages. It is difficult to keep $\Delta\omega$ frequency independent and, for the case of a vibrating mirror or slit, the stability of the center frequency ω_o is usually poor.

Another more fundamental difficulty comes from the fact that the experimentally measured quantity is not ε_r, nor ε_i, nor α, nor R but $I_o \cdot R$ (in the case of reflection modulation) or $I_o \cdot \tau$ in the case of transmission modulation. Hence in a reflectance modulation experiment what we measure is

$$\frac{dI}{d\xi} = R\frac{dI_o}{d\xi} + I_o\frac{dR}{d\xi} \qquad (86)$$

For $\xi = \omega$, the term $dI_o/d\xi$ cannot be neglected and thus we measure structure in the reflectivity as much as structure in the spectral distribution of the source. This last term will be large in general and must be compensated for. If $\xi \sim \omega_g$, $dI_o/d\xi = 0$, hence the advantage of using modulation methods in which the sample itself is modulated.

In a typical reflectance modulation experiment with sample modulation one can measure the d.c. component of the reflected intensity $I_o \cdot R$ and the a.c. component $I_o \Delta R$; dividing one by the other, one obtains $\Delta R/R$ and the incident intensity I_o is eliminated. Here lies the great advantage of the sample modulation methods: If this division is done with a computing element of some kind, no moving parts are required to obtain $\Delta R/R$ and the lamp stability, one of the main sources of error in conventional reflectivity and other static optical measurements, is eliminated as a problem. The division of $I_o \Delta R$ by $I_o R$ can be done in many different ways. When a photomultiplier is used as a detector, the division is easily performed[19] by varying the d.c. voltage on the photomultiplier so as to keep the d.c. output ($\sim I_o R$) equal to 1 Volt. The a.c. output is then $\Delta R/R$. The d.v. voltage on the photomultiplier is applied by means of a "helipot", which is controlled by a servo that keeps the d.c. output equal to 1 Volt. The modulation voltage, proportional to $I_o R$, is measured with a lock-in amplifier (phase sensitive detection). It is not difficult to measure ratios $\Delta R/R$ of the order of 10^{-6}.

We shall now discuss the various ways in which an energy gap ω_g can be modulated by the application of an external, sinusoidally varying parameter (it is possible and sometimes advantageous to use square wave modulation). Uniaxial stress[50], temperature[51], and electric field modulation[52,19], have been, so far, successfully used. We should, however, make from the start a distinction between uniaxial stress and electric field modulation. When uniaxial stress is applied to a crystal, this does not destroy the three-dimensional translation lattice and thus it keeps, in general, the shape of the critical points. The modulation response is indeed proportional to $(\omega - \omega_g)^{-1/2} \cdot \frac{d\omega_g}{d\xi}$ ($\xi \equiv$ stress). A uniform electric field, on the other hand, introduces a term in the Hamiltonian of the form

$$+e\,\mathbf{E} \cdot \mathbf{r} \tag{87}$$

Eq. (87) is <u>not</u> invariant under translations and hence the three-dimensional translation lattice under which the crystal was invariant is lost by the application of **E**. If **E** is oriented (in a cubic crystal) along one of the crystal axes, then only those translation operations containing primitive translations along this axis are lost. The crystal still keeps a two-dimensional translation lattice.

It is easy to see that in the case of electric field modulation one does not obtain the derivative of the optical parameter measured with respect to ω_g. In fact, it is easy to see that ω_g becomes zero in the presence of a uniform electric field (Franz-Keldysh effect). Figure 28 illustrates this fact. The field is along X and small so that we can define a "local" band structure varying from point to point.

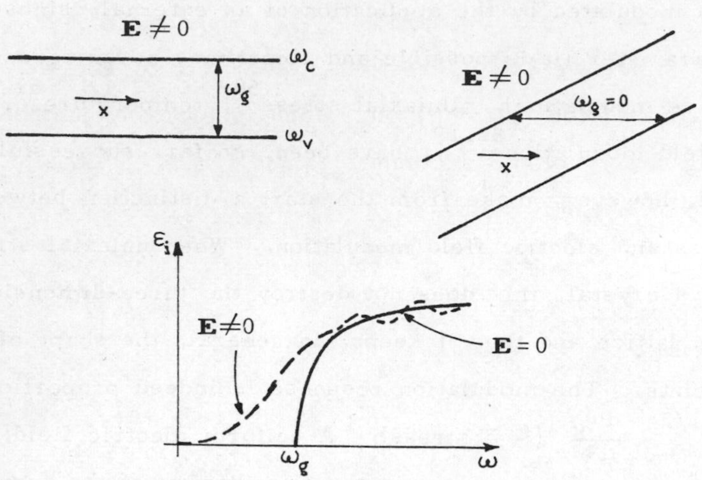

Fig. 29

As shown in Fig. 29, a tilt in the bands as a function of x is introduced by the electric field. Interband transitions are now possible with an arbitrarily small ω, since we can bring a valence electron to a different point in real space. The probability of doing this is proportional to the overlap of the corresponding electron and hole wave functions[53]:

$$\varepsilon_i \sim |\phi(\mathbf{r}=0)|^2 \qquad (88)$$

where $\phi(\mathbf{r})$ is the functional dependence of the electron-hole pair wave-function on the relative coordinate $\mathbf{r} = \mathbf{r}_e - \mathbf{r}_h$. ϕ satisfies, in the effective mass approximation the equation

$$\left[-\frac{1}{2m^*}\nabla^2 + V(r) - \mathbf{E}\cdot\mathbf{r}\right]\phi(\mathbf{r}) = \omega\phi(\mathbf{r}) \qquad (89)$$

where V(r) is the Coulomb attractive potential between electron and hole. Equation (89) is hard to treat unless we make V(r) = 0, or **E** = 0. Since we are interested in the effect of **E**, we shall make the assumption that V(r) = 0, which is probably justified if the binding energy of the excitons obtained for **E** = 0 is smaller than |E| x (the Bohr radius of the excitons). For a general direction of **E**, Eq. (89) can be separated by making $\phi(\mathbf{r}) = \phi_1(x_1)\phi_2(x_2)\phi_3(x_3)$. One obtains three equations of the form (referred to principal axes of $1/\underset{\approx}{m}$)

$$\left.\begin{aligned} &\left[\frac{1}{2m_i^*}\frac{\partial^2}{\partial x_i^2} + E_i x_i\right]\phi_i(x_i) = -\omega_i \phi_i(x_i) \\ &-\omega = \omega_1 + \omega_2 + \omega_3 \end{aligned}\right\} \qquad (89')$$

If the electric field is along one of the crystal axis (for a cubic material), we only have to solve <u>one</u> equation, of the form of Eq. (89'); the two remaining components of the wave function are free-electron-like (plane waves). Eqs. (89') can be easily transformed by means of a change of variables, into Airy's equation.

$$\frac{d^2F(\xi)}{d\xi^2} = \xi F(\xi) \qquad (90)$$

The change of variables is

$$-\xi_i = \left(\frac{\omega_i}{E_i} + x_i\right)(2m_i^* \cdot E_i)^{1/3} \qquad (91)$$

The solutions of Airy's equation are Airy functions which have the form (check it)

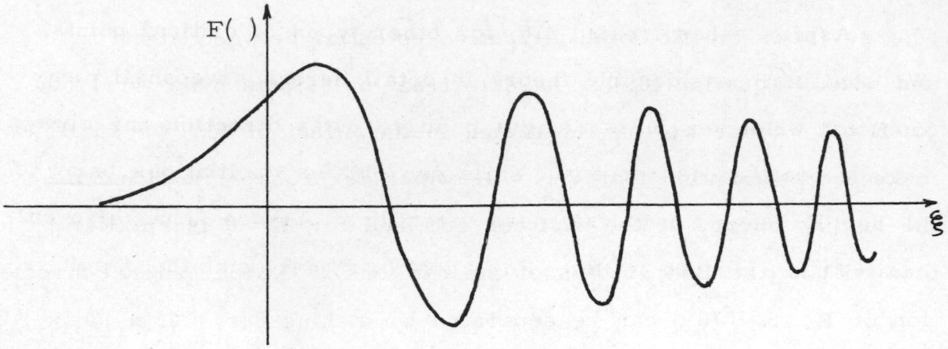

Fig. 30

Since $-\omega = \omega_1 + \omega_2 + \omega_3$, there is a double multiplicity of functions corresponding to a given ω. After performing the integration, one obtains for an M_o edge

$$\varepsilon_i(E) \sim \frac{N^2}{\pi}\left[A_i'^2(\eta) - \eta A_i(\eta)\right] - (-\eta)^{1/2}\, H(-\eta)$$

with $\quad \eta = \dfrac{\omega_g - \omega}{\theta} \quad$ and $\quad \theta^3 = \dfrac{|E|^2}{2\mu}$

$$\frac{1}{\mu} = \frac{1}{|E|^2}\left[\frac{E_i^2}{m_1^*} + \frac{E_2^2}{m_2^*} + \frac{E_3^2}{m_3^*}\right] \tag{92}$$

The change induced by the electric field in ε_i, $\Delta\varepsilon_i = \varepsilon_i(E) - \varepsilon_i(0)$ has the form (Fig. 1 of Ref. 53)

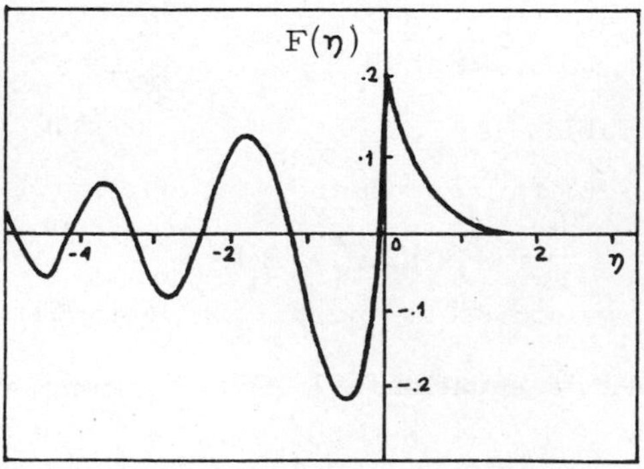

Fig. 31

Aspnes[53] has treated $\Delta\varepsilon_i$ for other types of critical points. We shall not consider the theory in detail here but we shall mention that whenever **E** is along a positive mass direction one always obtians oscillations <u>above</u> ω_g while one obtains oscillations <u>below</u> ω_g for **E** along a negative mass direction. Aspnes[54] has also calculated $\Delta\varepsilon_r$ induced by **E**. For an M_o critical point the result is

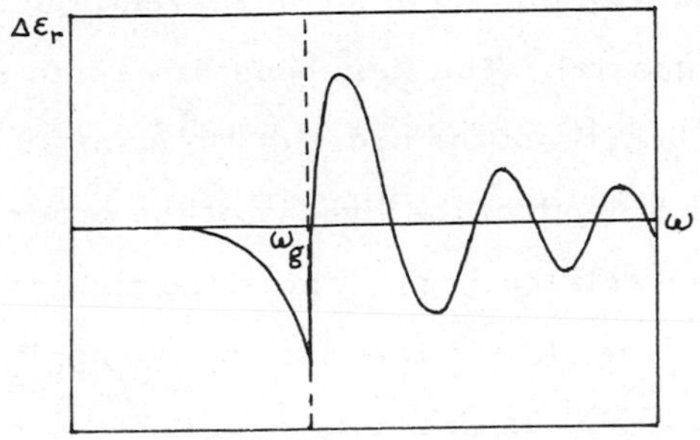

Fig. 32

Oscillations in $\Delta\varepsilon_r$ also occur above ω_g for **E** along a positive-mass direction and below ω_g for a negative-mass direction. For E along an arbitrary direction the "effective" electro-optical mass is[53, 54]

$$\frac{1}{m^*_{eo}} = \frac{1}{|E|^2}\left[\frac{E_1^2}{m_1^*} + \frac{E_2^2}{m_2^*} + \frac{E_3^2}{m_3^*}\right]$$

The sign of m^*_{eo} determines whether the oscillations occur above or below ω_g.

We want now to discuss briefly the methods employed to apply the electric field. In an insulator, one can apply the electric field by "brute force"[55,56] between parallel electrodes evaporated on the sample with a gap of approximately 1 mm between them. The electric field can then be determined accurately by solving the corresponding electrostatic problem of conformal mapping.

A more versatile technique is that used originally by Seraphin and Hess[52]. This technique is useful for semiconductors with a carrier concentration range between 10^{13} and 10^{10} carriers x cm^{-3}. The field is applied with the aid of a transparent electrode (usually S_nO_2-coated fused quartz). The field penetrates into the sample through a Debye screening length (of the order of 10^4 Å for 10^{16} carriers x cm^{-3}). Since the penetration depth of the light is of the order of 10^4 - 10^3 Å, the light samples fairly well the region where the applied field is appreciable. The field strength is determined by the applied voltage divided by the thickness of the insulating foil.

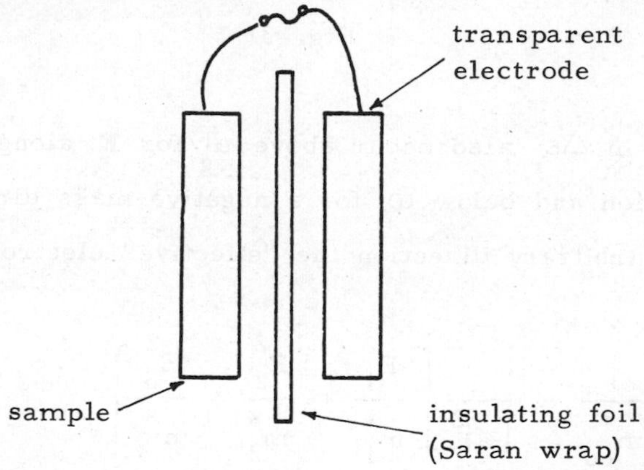

Fig. 33

The method described above has the disadvantage that it is not usable in the u.v. range, since the absorption edge of S_nO_2 lies around 3.5 eV. In the search of a better transparent electrode one encounters the fact that water is transparent up to about 7 eV and can be made highly conducting with an ionic solute. This and the fact that a blocking contact is formed when a semiconductor-electrolyte contact is properly biased (usually ⊖ sign for the semiconductor) constitutes the foundation of the electrolytic method of electroreflectance[19] sketched in Fig. 34 (Fig. 6 of Ref. 19).

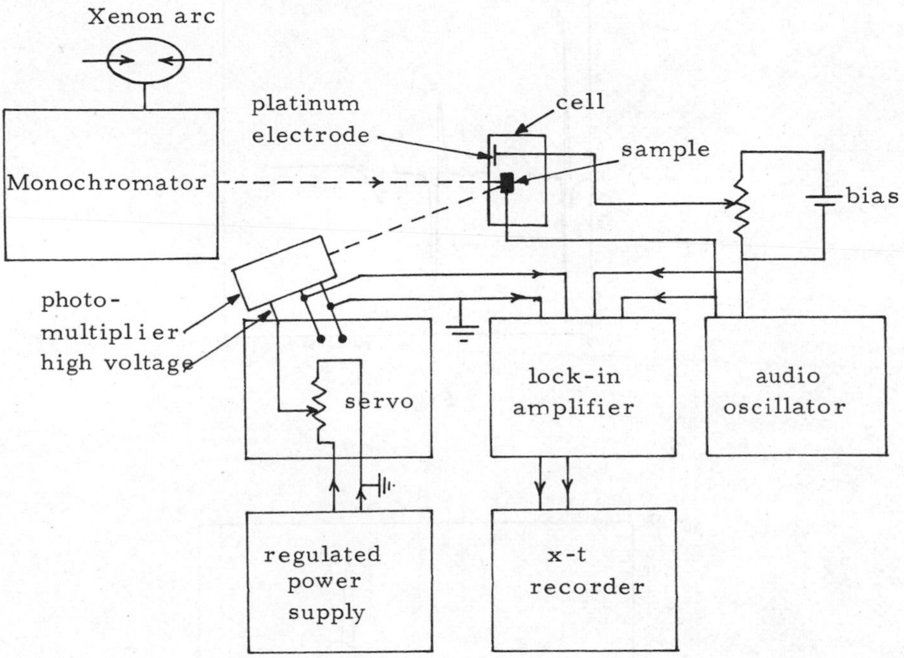

Fig. 34

The voltage which has to be applied to the sample is now small (~ 1 Volt) since the field is determined by the Debye penetration depth (there is no "Saran wrap"). Fields of the order of 10^4 - 10^5 V x cm^{-1} are then obtained.

Figure 35 shows the electroreflectance spectrum of ZnTe

obtained by the electrolytic method. The E_o, $E_o + \Delta_o$, E_1 and $E_1 + \Delta_1$ peaks appear very clearly. The power of the method is best examplified in Fig. 36. The electroreflectance spectrum resolves very well the spin-orbit splitting Δ_1 of the E_1 peaks of InP while the ordinary reflection spectrum doesn't.

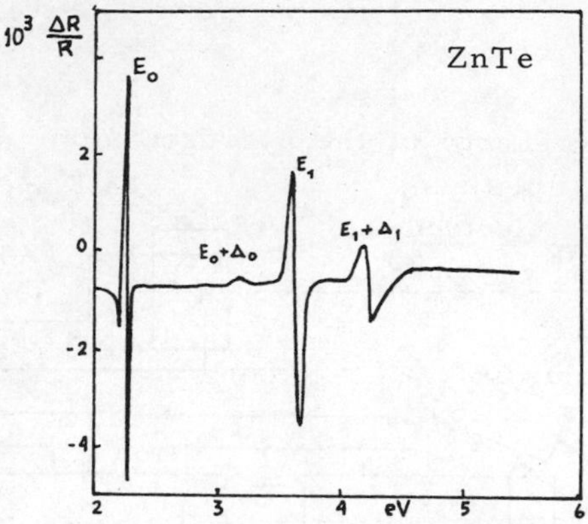

Fig. 35

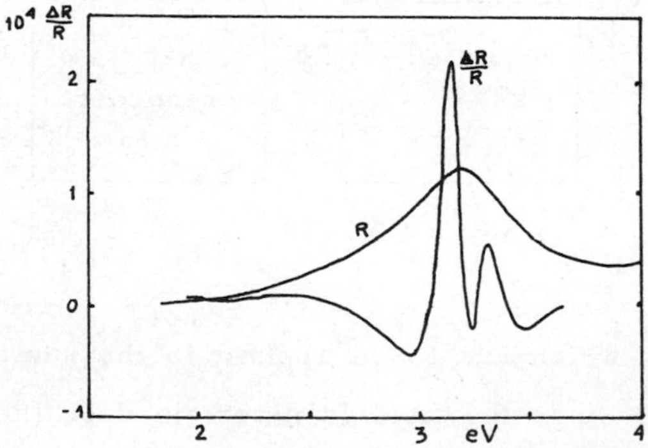

Fig. 36

The electroreflectance spectrum resolves very well the spin orbit splitting Δ_1 of the E_1 peaks of InP, while the ordinary reflection spectrum does not.

APPENDIX A

The ionization energy of the hydrogen atom is

$$1 \text{ Rydberg} = \frac{me^4}{2\hbar^2}$$

The Bohr radius is $a_o = \dfrac{\hbar^2}{me^2}$

Two types of atomic units are used

1. 1 Hartree = unit of energy = 2 Rydbergs
   unit of length = a_o = 1
   unit of action $\hbar$
   } In this system $m = 1, \; |e| = 1$

2. unit of energy = 1 Rydberg
   unit of length = a_o
   unit of action = $\hbar$
   } In this system $m = \frac{1}{2}, \; |e| = 2$

We shall use throughout these lectures system 1.

APPENDIX B

Interaction representation. Consider the Hamiltonian $H = H_o + H'$ and the wavefunction ψ which in the Schrödinger representation evolves with time according to

$$H\psi(r,t) = i\frac{\partial\psi(r,t)}{\partial t} = (H_o + H')\psi(r,t) \qquad (A.1)$$

The wavefunction $\psi(t)$ is transformed to the interaction representation $\psi_I(t)$ by the canonical transformation

$$\psi_I(r,t) = e^{iH_o(t-t_o)}\psi(r,t) \qquad (A.2)$$

where t_o is an arbitrary origin of time. The transformed operator H'_I is

$$H'_I(t) = e^{iH_o(t-t_o)} H'(t)\, e^{-iH_o(t-t_o)} \qquad (A.3)$$

Applying this transformation to Eq. (A.2) we obtain

$$i\frac{\partial\psi_I(r,t)}{\partial t} = H'_I(t)\,\psi_I(r,t) \qquad (A.4)$$

Hence if $H' = 0$, ψ_I is time-independent (Heisenberg representation). The evolution of ψ_I with time is due exclusively to the interaction (perturbation) Hamiltonian H'.

APPENDIX C

k · p Sum Rule. Replace in the one-electron Schrödinger's equation for a crystal

$$\left[\frac{1}{2}p^2 - V\right]\varphi = \omega\varphi \;; \tag{A. 5}$$

φ by a Bloch function

$$\varphi_{\mathbf{k},n}(r) = e^{i\mathbf{k}\cdot\mathbf{r}} u_{\mathbf{k},n}(r) \tag{A. 6}$$

$$\left[\frac{1}{2}p^2 + \mathbf{k}\cdot\mathbf{p} + V\right] u_{\mathbf{k},n}(\mathbf{r}) = \left[\omega_{\mathbf{k},n} - \frac{k^2}{2}\right] u_{\mathbf{k},n}(\mathbf{r}) \tag{A. 7}$$

Equation (A. 7) can be used to expand the bands around a point $\mathbf{k}_o$ by treating terms in $(\mathbf{k} - \mathbf{k}_o)$ as a small perturbation.

$$\omega_n(k) = \omega_n(k_o) + \langle p \rangle \, (k - k_o) + \sum_{\ell \neq n} \frac{|\langle \mathbf{k}_o, n | \mathbf{p} \cdot (\mathbf{k} - \mathbf{k}_o) | \mathbf{k}_o, \ell \rangle|^2}{\omega_n(\mathbf{k}_o) - \omega_\ell(\mathbf{k}_o)} + \frac{k^2}{2} - \frac{k_o^2}{2} + \ldots.. \tag{A. 8}$$

Differentiating Eq. (A. 8) we find

$$\frac{\partial^2 \omega_n}{(\partial k_j)^2} = 1 - \sum_{\ell \neq n} \frac{2|\langle k_o, n | p_j | k_o, \ell \rangle|^2}{\omega_{\ell n}} \tag{A. 9}$$

which is the **k · p** (or F) sum rule.

TABLE I

Atomic spin-orbit splittings of p- and d-valence levels, as obtained from one-electron Hartree-Fock calculations and from spectroscopic data. The splittings of d-levels are those with the superscript "a"; all other entries are for p-levels.

a d-level splittings.
b Obtained from spectroscopic data of singly-ionized atom.
c Russel-Saunders coupling breaks down.

	Spect.	Calc.		Spect.	Calc.		Spect.	Calc.		Spect.	Calc.		Spect.	Calc.
Ia			Ib			III			V			VII		
Li	0.000					B	0.002	0.004	N	0.011	0.025	F	0.050	0.093
Na	0.002					Al	0.016	0.018	P	0.046	0.062	Cl	0.110	0.150
K	0.006		Cu	-0.15[b]	-0.19[a]	Ga	0.120	0.120	A	0.290	0.310	Br	0.460	0.550
Rb	0.029		Ag	-0.33[a]	-0.35[a]	In	0.270	0.310	Sb	0.670	0.670	I	0.945	1.060
Cs	0.067		Au	-0.91[b]	-1.00[a]	Tl	0.960	0.860	Bi	----[c]	1.680			
IIa			IIb			IV			VI			VIII		
Be	0.000	0.001				C	0.005	0.011	O	0.027	0.051	Ne	0.10[b]	0.120
Mg	0.007	0.059				Si	0.028	0.035	S	0.069	0.096	A	0.18[b]	0.200
Ca	0.020		Zn	0.071	0.054	Ge	0.210	0.210	Si	0.370	0.420	Kr	0.67[b]	0.690
Sr	0.072		Cd	0.210	0.150	Sn	0.600	0.475	Te	0.890	0.860	Xe	1.31[b]	1.270
Ba	0.150		Hg	0.760	0.460	Pb	----[c]	1.270						

TABLE II

Spin-orbit splittings at $\mathbf{k} = 0$ of the valence band of group IV, III-V, IIb-VI, Ib-VII materials, the alkali halides and the solidified rare gases. The calculated splittings were obtained with the expression

$$\Delta_o = A\left[\xi^{(1)}\,\Delta_o^{(1)} + \xi^{(2)}\,\Delta_o^{(2)}\right].$$

A was taken equal to 1.4 for all germanium-zinchblende-wurtzite-type materials, equal to 1.0 for the solidified rare gases, and equal to 1.1 for the alkali halides for which we also took $\xi^{(1)} = 0$ (the contribution of the cation to Δ_o). For the III-V compounds we took $\xi^{(III)} = 0.35$ and $\xi^{(V)} = 0.65$. For the II-VI compounds we took $\xi^{(II)} = 0.2$ and $\xi^{(VI)} = 0.8$. The spectroscopic values of Table I were used for $\Delta_o^{(i)}$.

	Trans.	Reflec.	Reflect. modul.	Intrav. band Trans.	Other Experim.	Calculated
C					0.006[a]	0.007
Si					0.044[b]	0.039
Ge	0.29[c]		0.290[d]	0.29[c]		0.29
Sn						
AlN						0.018
AlP						0.049
AlAs						0.27
AlSb			0.7[f]	0.75[c]		0.60
GaN						0.069
GaP	0.09[g]	0.1[h]	0.10[f]	0.127[i]		0.10
GaAs	0.35[j]		0.340[f]	0.33[e]		0.33
GaSb			0.80[f]	0.80[h]		0.66
InN						0.14
InP			0.11[f]			0.17
InAs			0.45	0.43[m]		0.40
InSb			0.82[n]			0.72
ZnO		-0.0087[o]				0.050
ZnS		0.1[p]	0.1[p]			0.097
ZnSe		0.43[q]				0.43
ZnTe		0.91[r]	0.93[f]	0.98		1.01
CdO						0.089
CdS	0.066		0.066[f]			0.14

(Table II continued)

	Trans.	Reflec.	Reflect. modul.	Intrav. Band Trans.	Other Experim.	Calculated
CdSe	0.408[q]		0.404[f]			0.47
CdTe		0.9	0.92[f]		0.9[t]	1.05
HgS						0.29
HgSe						0.63
HgTe						1.21
CuCl	-0.049[u]					+0.15
CuBr	0.147[u]					0.64
CuI	0.633[u]					1.3
AgCl	0.10[v]					0.15
AgBr	0.55[v]					0.64
AgI	0.837[u]					1.3
LiF						0.055
LiCl						0.12
LiBr	0.52[x]					0.51
LiI						
NaF						0.055
NaCl	0.13[x]					0.12
NaBr	0.52[x]					0.51
NaI	1.17[x]					1.04
KF	0.05[x]					0.055
KCl	0.11[x]					0.12
KBr	0.49[x]					0.51
KI	1.34[x]					1.04
RbF	0.1					0.055
RbCl	0.13					0.12
RbBr	0.48					0.51
RbI	1.22					1.04
CsF	0.10					0.055
CsCl	0.17					0.12
CsBr						0.51
CsI						1.04
Ne						0.10
A	0.2					0.18
K	0.65					0.67
Xe	1.17					1.31

a. C. J. Rauch, Ref. 26, p. 276.

b. S. Zwerdling, K. J. Button, B. Lax and L. M. Roth, Phys. Rev. Letters 4, 173 (1960).

c. M. V. Hobden, J. Phys. Chem. Solids 23, 821 (1962).

d. B. O. Seraphin and R. B. Hess, Phys. Rev. Letters 14, 38 (1965).

e. R. Braunstein and E. Okane, Ref. 37.

f. M. Cardona, K. L. Shahlee and F. M. Pollak, Ref. 19.

g. W. K. Subashiew and S. A. Abagyan, Proceedings of the International Conference on Physics of Semiconductors, Academic Press, ed. by M. Hulin.

h. R. Zallen and W. Paul, Phys. Rev. 134, 1628 (1964).

i. J. W. Hodby, Proc. Phys. Soc. (London) 82, 324 (1963).

j. M. D. Sturge, Phys. Rev. 127, 768 (1962).

k. B. B. Kosicki and W. Paul, Bull. Am. Phys. Soc. 11, 52 (1966).

l. C. R. Pidgeon, Bull. Am. Phys. Soc., Chicago Meeting, March 1967.

m. F. Matossi and F. Stern, Phys. Rev. 111, 472 (1958).

n. M. Cardona, F. M. Pollak and K. L. Shaklee, Phys, Rev. Letters 16, 942 (1966).

o. P. G. Thomas, J. Phys. Chem. Solids 15, 86 (1966).

p. M. Cardona, J. Appl. Phys. 32S, 958 (1961).

q. J. O. Dimmak and R. G. Wheeler, Phys. Rev. 125, 1805 (1962).

r. M. Cardona and D. L. Greenaway, Phys. Rev. 131, 98 (1963).

s. N. Watanabe and S. Usui, J. Appl. Phys. (Japan) 4, 467 (1965).

t. D. T. F. Marple and H. Ehrenreich, Phys. Rev. Letters 8, 87 (1962).

u. M. Cardona, Phys. Rev. 129, 69 (1963).

v. Y. Okamoto, Nach. Gött. Acad. a. Wissenschaften 14, 275 (1956).

x. J. E. Eby, K. J. Teegarden and D. B. Dutton, Phys. Rev. 116, 1099 (1959).

y. G. Baldini, Phys. Rev. 136 A248 (1964).

REFERENCES

1. L. Onsager, Phys. Rev. 37, 405 (1931). Phys. Rev. 38, 2265 (1931).
2. S. I. Pekar, Sov. Phys. Sol. State, 4, 953 (1962).
3. A discussion of the role of collisions in E is given by H. R. Philipp and H. Ehrenreich in Semiconductors and Semimetals, edited by R. Willardson and A. S. Beer (Academic Press Inc., New York, N.Y., 1967, Vol. 3) p. 93.
4. F. Seitz, Modern Theory of Solids, Mc Graw Hill Book Co., Inc. New York and London, 1940.
5. H. R. Philipp and H. Ehrenreich, Phys. Rev. 129, 1550 (1963).
6. M. Cardona and D. L. Greenway, Phys. Rev. 133, A 1685 (1964).
7. P. Nozieres and D. Pines, Phys. Rev. 113, 1254 (1959).
8. M. Cardona, J. Appl. Phys. 36, 2185 (1965).
9. W. G. Spitzer and H. Y. Fan, Phys. Rev. 106, 882 (1957).
10. Althoff and Hertz, Phys. Stat. Sol.
11. H. Y. Fan, Ref. 3, p. 406.
12. Fig. 7 is Fig. 19 of E. D. Palik and G. B. Wright, Ref. 3, p. 455.
13. M. Cardona, Phys. Rev. 121, 752 (1961).
14. M. Cardona, Helv. Phys. Acta 34, 796 (1961).

15. Figure 10 is figure 4 of the article of Ref. 12.

16. Schmidt-Tiedemann, K. J., "Semiconductors Conference", Exeter, 1962, p. 419-30. A. Feldman, Phys. Rev. Vol. 150 748 (1966).

17. A. H. Kahn, Phys. Rev. 97, 1647 (1955).
R. Braunstein, J. Phys, Chem. Solids, 8, 280 (1959).

18. L. Van Hove, Phys. Rev. 89, 1189 (1953).

19. M. Cardona, F. H. Pollak and K. L. Shaklee, Phys. Rev. 154, 696 (1967).

20. J. C. Phillips, Solid State Physics, edited by F. Seitz and D. Turnbull (Academic Press Inc., New York, N.Y.).

21. L. I. Korovin, Soviet Phys., Solid State 1, 1202 (1959).

22. J. N. Zemel, J. D. Jensen and R. B. Schoolar, Phys. Rev. 140A, 330 (1965).

23. P. J. Lin and Kleinman, Phys. Rev. 142, 978 (1966).

24. D. Penn, Phys. Rev. 128, 2093 (1962).

25. J. Bardeen, F. J. Blatt and L. H. Hall, in Photoconductivity Conference, edited by R. G. Breckenridge (J. Wiley and Sons Inc., New York, N.Y., 1954) p. 146.

26. M. Gershenzon, D. G. Thomas and R. E. Dietz, Proceedings of the International Conference on the Physics of Semiconductors, Exeter 1962, (The Institute of Physics and the Physical Society, London 1962) p. 752.

27. R. J. Elliott, Polarons and Excitons edited by C. G. Kuper and G. D. Whitfield, (Plenum Press, New York, 1963) p. 269.

28. M. Cardona and D. L. Greenaway, Phys. Rev. 133, A1685 (1964).

29. G. Harbeke, Z. Naturf, 19a, 548 (1964).

30. D. G. Avery, Proc. Phys. Soc. 65B, 425 (1952).

31. F. C. Jahoda, Phys. Rev. 107, 1261 (1957).

32. H. R. Phillip and E. A. Taft, Phys. Rev. 113, 1002 (1959).

33. R. J. Archer, Phys. Rev. 110, 354 (1958).

34. R. F. Potter, Phys. Rev. 150, 562 (1966).

35. B. Velicky, Czech, J. Phys. B11, 541 (1961).

36. H. R. Philipp and E. A. Taft, Phys. Rev. 120, 37 (1960).

37. R. Braunstein and E. O. Kane, J. Phys. Chem. Solids 23, 1423 (1962).

38. C. E. Moore, Atomic Energy Levels (National Bureau of Standards Circular Number 467, Vol. 1 (1949), Vol 2 (1952), Vol. 3 (1958).

39. Condon and Shortley, The Theory of Atomic Spectra.

40. F. Herman and S. Skillman, Atomic Structure Calculations (Prentice-Hall Inc., Englewood Cliffs, N. J., 1963).

41. M. Cardona and F. H. Pollak, Phys. Rev. 142, 530 (1966). F. H. Pollak, C. W. Higginbotham and M. Cardona, J. Phys. Soc. Japan Suppl. 21, 20 (1966).

42. D. Boust, Phys. Rev. 134, A 1337 (1964).

43. M. S. Dresselhaus and G. Dresselhaus, Phys. Rev., in press.

44. E. O. Kane, Phys. Rev. 146, 558 (1966).

45. G. Gilat and L. J. Raubenheimer, Phys. Rev. 144, 390 (1966).

46. C. W. Higginbotham, M. Cardona and F. H. Pollak, Solid State Commun, in press.

47. B. Velicky and J. Sak, Phys. Stat. Sol. 16, 147 (1966).

48. G. Bonfiglioli and P. Brovetto, Phys. Letters 5, 248 (1963).

49. I. Balslev, Phys. Rev. 143, 636 (1966).

50. W. E. Engeler, M. Garfinkel and J. J. Tiemann, Phys. Rev. Letters 16, 239 (1966). G. O. Gobeli and E. O. Kane, ibid 15, 142 (1965).

51. C. N. Berglund, J. Appl. Phys. 37, 3019 (1966).

52. B. O. Seraphin and R. B. Hess, Phys. Rev. Letters 14, 138 (1965).

53. D. E. Aspnes, Phys. Rev. 147, 554 (1966).

54. D. E. Aspnes, Phys. Rev. 153, 972 (1967).

55. V. Rehn and D. S. Kyser, Phys. Rev. Letters 18, 848 (1967).

56. R. Forman and M. Cardona, Bull. Am. Phys. Soc. Toronto Meeting, 1967.

57. K. L. Shaklee, F. H. Pollak and M. Cardona, Phys. Rev. Letters 15, 883 (1965).

13

A MEASUREMENT OF THE FINE STRUCTURE CONSTANT BY LEVEL CROSSING IN ATOMIC HYDROGEN (Seminar)

Harold Metcalf, John Brandenberger and James C. Baird

The primary purpose of the experiment described here is to obtain a precision value of the Sommerfeld fine structure constant α. The value of α is of particular interest because of its role as the expansion parameter in many of the formulas of quantum electrodynamics (Q. E. D.). Since experimental checks of the accuracy of some quantum electrodynamic predictions are presently limited by the uncertainty associated with the value of α, there is need for a more precise α because of the very high precision of the experiments.

Fig. 1 provides a partial summary of our knowledge of α. If we examine the third and fourth lines of Fig. 1, we find a discrepancy of 45 ppm between the calculated and measured values of the hyperfine separation in the ground state of atomic hydrogen. The theoretical value of the frequency of the hyperfine separation is[1]

$$\Delta\nu_{hfs}(H) = \frac{16}{3}\alpha^2 R_{\infty}c\left[\frac{\mu_p}{\mu_o}\right]\left[\frac{\mu_e}{\mu_o}\right]\left[\frac{M}{M+m}\right]^3\left[1-(1-\ln 2)\alpha^2-\delta_p\right],$$

---

1. J. DuMond and E. R. Cohen, Rev. Mod. Phys., 37, 537 (1965). This expression was taken from Eq. 18 on p. 571 which has an error. The mass term should be cubed.

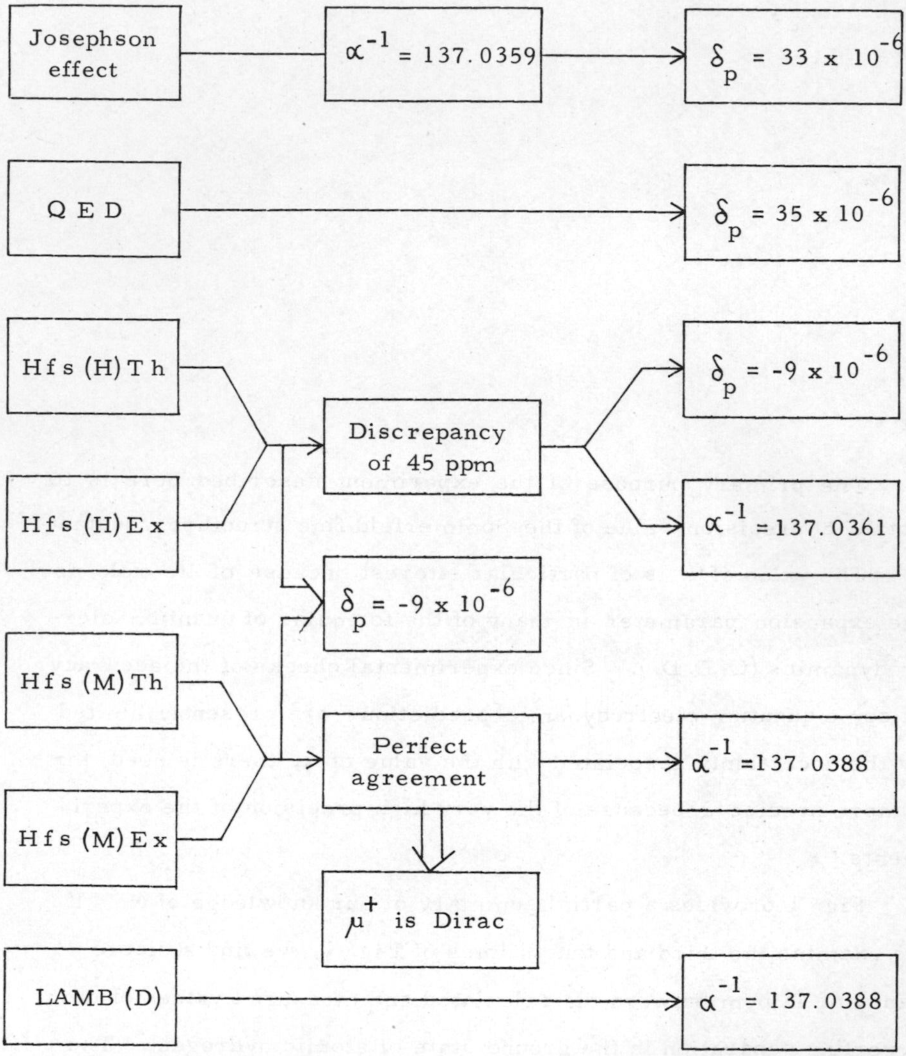
Josephson effect
α^-1 = 137.0359
δ_p = 33 x 10^-6
Q E D
δ_p = 35 x 10^-6
Hfs (H) Th
Hfs (H) Ex
Discrepancy of 45 ppm
δ_p = -9 x 10^-6
α^-1 = 137.0361
δ_p = -9 x 10^-6
Hfs (M) Th
Hfs (M) Ex
Perfect agreement
α^-1 = 137.0388
μ+ is Dirac
LAMB (D)
α^-1 = 137.0388

Fig. 1

where the symbols are conventionally defined[1]. This discrepancy can be resolved by bringing the theoretical value up to the (extremely precise) experimental value in one of two ways. The first possibility is to readjust the correction δ_p introduced into the hfs formula for the finite extent of the proton from 35 ppm to -9 ppm. The value of 35 ppm was calculated from Q.E.D and is believed to be correct to within 20%; thus a change of its value by 125% does not seem very likely. The second way to remove the hydrogen hyperfine discrepancy is to choose a value of α which is 22 ppm higher than the original value used in the calculation. This original value was obtained from the fine structure splitting in deuterium measured by Lamb[2] and his co-workers in 1953. Their formula for the fine structure has been modified by the reevaluation of the anomalous magnetic moment of the electron, and their measurements yield the value of α shown in the last line of Fig. 1. These two alternatives for removing the discrepancy are represented by the diverging arrows in Fig. 1.

Hughes and his associates[3] have measured the hyperfine interval in the ground state of muonium. Their experimental value coincides with the theoretical value to six significant figures if one uses Lamb's value of α to evaluate the theoretical expression for the muonium hfs. This close agreement was interpreted as an excellent confirmation of the theory that the muon is a Dirac particle. It was also interpreted as an indication that Lamb's value of α was correct and therefore the Q.E.D. calculation of

---

2. Dayhoff, Triebwasser and Lamb, Phys. Rev., 89, 106 (1953). Note that the numerical coefficient in Eq. (264) is in error because of the error in g.
3. Cleland, Bailey, Eckhause, Hughes, Mobely, Prepost and Rothberg, Phys. Rev. Lett., 13, 202 (1964).

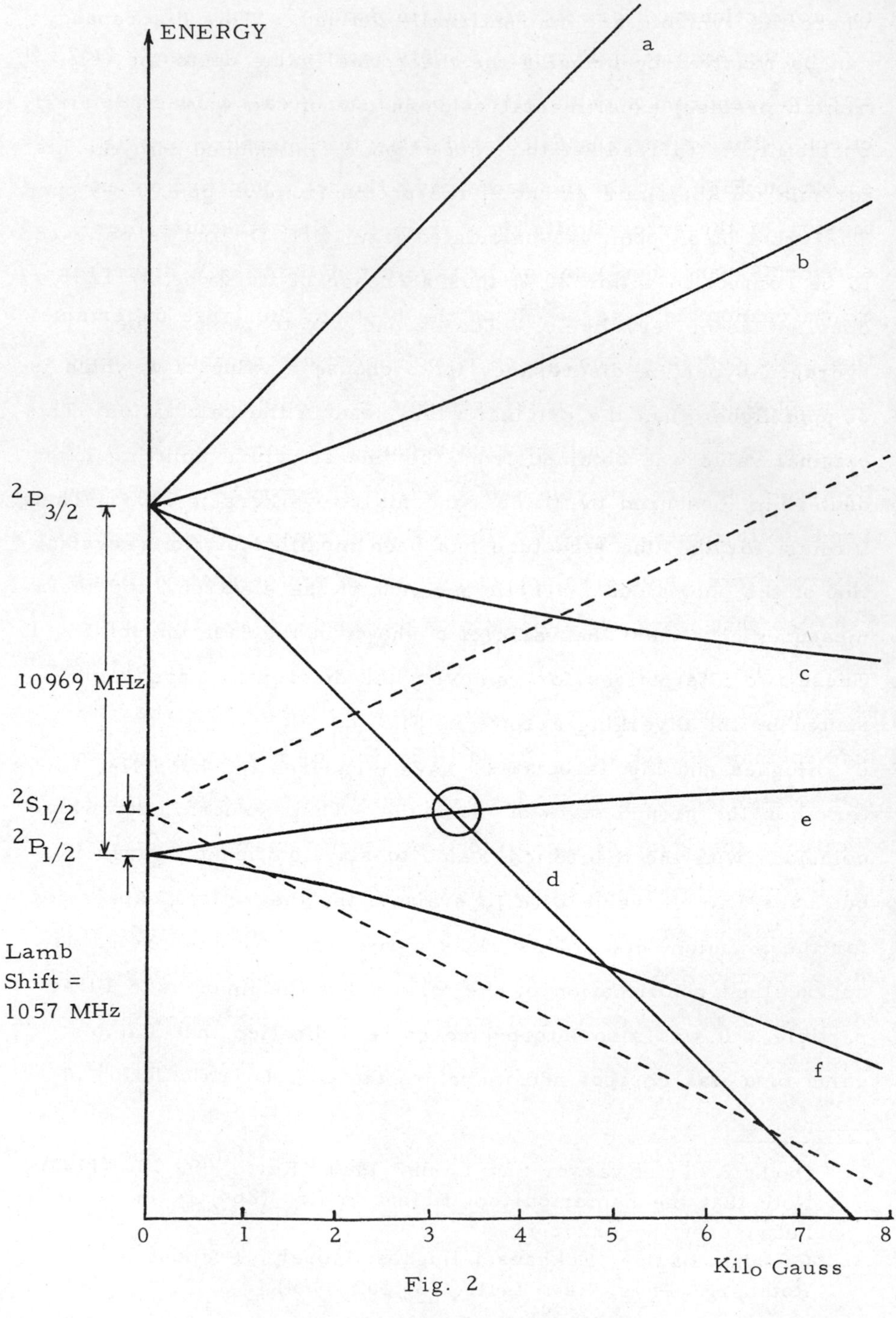
ENERGY
a
b
c
d
e
f
$^2P_{3/2}$
10969 MHz
$^2S_{1/2}$
$^2P_{1/2}$
Lamb
Shift =
1057 MHz
0
1
2
3
4
5
6
7
8
Kilo Gauss

Fig. 2

the correction to hydrogen hfs was in doubt.

At the American Physical Society meeting in January, 1967, Parker[4] reported a value of e/h based on the a.c. Josephson effect. The value of α calculated from this measurement is shown on Fig. 1. On the same day, Hughes[5] justified an extension of the error limits on α from the fine structure measurements, and then went on to say that if there is a discrepancy we cannot claim to see it on the basis of the large uncertainties. He concluded that there is no major discrepancy in the value of α based on the measurements of atomic physics.

The most recent information about alpha comes from Robiscoe[6] who has discovered an error in the analysis of his Lamb shift remeasurement. His value of alpha, which originally differed from Lamb's value, is now to be shifted toward Lamb's value so that there is substantial agreement. Also, the error bars of the composite number calculated by Hughes[5] should now be reduced leaving the measured values of alpha more sharply divided than he implied. There may now be a real discrepancy and independent values of alpha are desirable to resolve the conflict over the value of the proton structure factor correction to the hydrogen hyperfine separation.

In this experiment we measure α by observing a level crossing of atomic hydrogen in a magnetic field The field dependence of some of the eigenvalues of hydrogen (neglecting hyperfine structure) is shown in Fig 2. We detect the crossing of the level

---

4. Parker, Taylor and Langenberg, Bull. Am. Phys. Soc., 12, 76 EH4; also Phys. Rev. Lett., 18, 287 (1967).
5. Hughes, Bull. Am. Phys Soc., 12, 83 FB4 (1967).
6. R. T. Robiscoe, private communication.

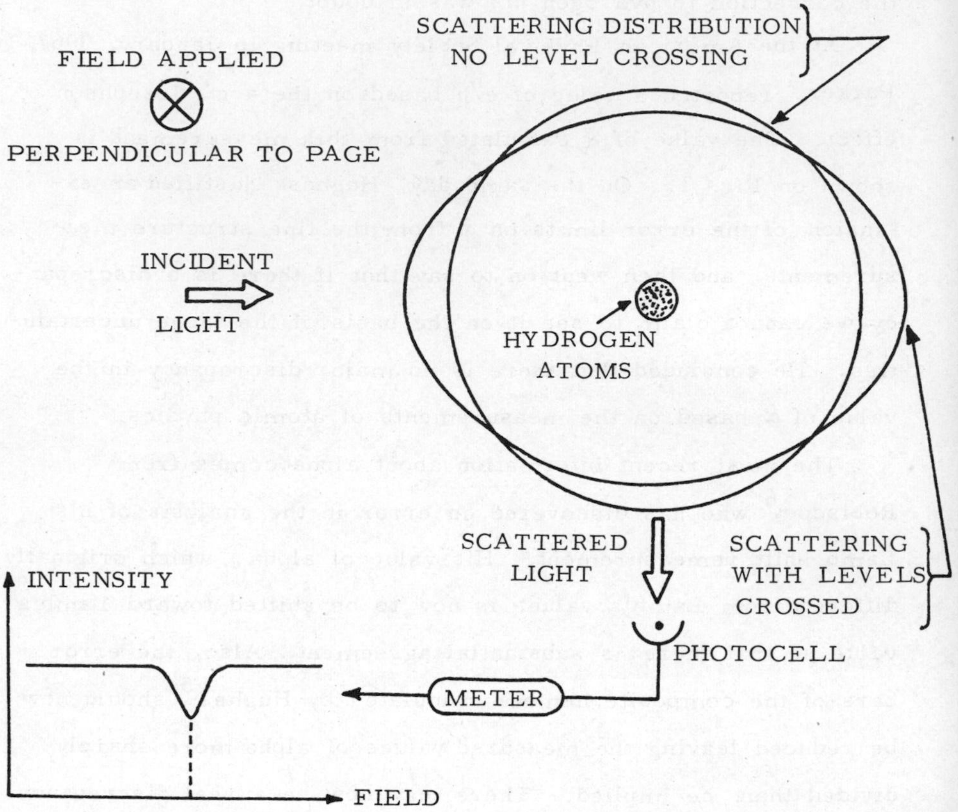

Fig. 3. Schematic diagram of level crossing experiment.

d with the level e by observing part of the change in the spatial distribution of the resonantly scattered Lyman-α radiation. The change of the scattering distribution, which occurs in the region of field where the levels cross[7] is pictured in Fig. 3. The apparatus is arranged so that resonance radiation is incident on free hydrogen atoms in a magnetic field which is perpendicular to the direction of incidence. A detector measures the amount of radiation scattered into a small solid angle centered about the direction perpendicular to both the field and the incident light. When the field is swept the detector output shows a dip as the levels cross.

The ultimate precision of this experiment is limited by the width of the level crossing signal. In order to measure α to 5 ppm it is necessary to determine the position of the center of the signal to one thousandth of its width. Some of the factors affecting the shape of the signal are the hyperfine interaction, the geometry of the apparatus, magnetic field inhomogeneity, and optical effects such as radiation trapping. The available data is not yet sufficient for an accurate determination of α but more data is currently being accumulated.

---

7. There are many discussions of the phenomenon of level crossing in the literature. See Franken, Phys. Rev., <u>121</u>, 508, (1961); Eck and Wieder, Phys. Rev., <u>153</u>, 91, (1967).

14

CRITICAL PHENOMENA IN HEISENBERG MODELS OF MAGNETISM+

H. Eugene Stanley
Massachusetts Institute of Technology and Harvard University, U.S.A.

+ Operated with support from the U. S. Air Force

Considerable attention has focused in recent years upon phenomena occurring near the critical points of various model systems. Here we'll consider the Heisenberg model, $H = -\Sigma_{\mathbf{fg}} J(\mathbf{f},\mathbf{g}) \mathbf{S}_{\mathbf{f}} \cdot \mathbf{S}_{\mathbf{g}}$ in which spins $\mathbf{S}_{\mathbf{f}}$ and $\mathbf{S}_{\mathbf{g}}$ are assumed to be localized on sites **f** and **g** and to interact isotropically via an exchange parameter $J(\mathbf{f},\mathbf{g})$.

First off, it is important to stress that even as simple a model as Heisenberg's model of isotropic interactions between localized spins has not been solved exactly for general temperature T and exchange parameter J. However, ingenious approximation schemes have been developed --e.g., the various cluster approximation, in which the Heisenberg Hamiltonian is replaced by an approximate Hamiltonian for a small cluster of k spins. The basic idea is to replace the spin operators of all but a small cluster of spins by their thermal averages at temperature T, and to then look for a self-consistent solution for the thermal properties. If there is only 1 single spin in the cluster, we have the "molecular field approximation" (MFA) of Pierre Weiss --the simplest of the cluster approximations.[1] Even the simple MFA has had some astounding successes, but other predictions of the MFA are not so good, and most of the shortcomings don't go away by using larger clusters. For example, the MFA cannot even predict the location of the critical temperature T_c to better than about 50 %.

It was this question of the value of T_c which first attracted a lot of people to high-temperature series expansions. The basic idea of the high-T method is the expansion of the exponential $e^{-H/kT}$ as a power series in 1/kT. The principle motivation for such a series expansion is that this exponential occurs in the partition function Z, from which one can obtain (just by differentiation) all of the macroscopic thermodynamic quantities of interest (e.g., F, U, C, S, and χ) as power series in 1/kT. Thus, e.g., we can obtain the expansion $\chi = \sum_{n=0}^{\infty} a_n(1/kT)^n$ for the zero-field susceptibility χ.

The successive coefficients in such power series representations become increasingly difficult to calculate as n increases --"The labour of calculating one more term in one of the series is considerably greater that that of calculating all the previous terms".[2] Nevertheless, the series for some functions of interest (e.g., χ) have been pushed quite a way, at the cost of rather considerable "labour". Extrapolations from the first few terms of these high temperature series expansions have done so well that, even for temperatures as low as T_c, they have come to serve as standards of comparison by which to judge the various "one-shot" Green's function decouplings and cluster approximations.[3]

Sometimes the high-temperature expansion methods are referred to as being "exact" --this is certainly misleading. All that is "exact" are the values of the coefficients in the series expansions; there is nothing rigorous whatsoever about extrapolating from the first few terms of infinite series, and there don't even exist any theorems that the infinite series themselves converge. However, the high-temperature extrapolation methods do perform considerably better on one "test" than do the various other approximation methods: There is excellent agreement between the extrapolated value of T_c and the exact value for the two-dimensional (S = 1/2) Ising model with nearest-neighbor ferromagnetic interactions.[4]

1. SPIN CORRELATION FUNCTION

There are other physically-interesting properties of the system which are not directly obtainable from the macroscopic thermodynamic functions, but which are easily related to the static spin correlation function

$$\langle \mathbf{S}_f \cdot \mathbf{S}_g \rangle = \frac{\text{trace } \mathbf{S}_f \cdot \mathbf{S}_g \, e^{-H/kT}}{\text{trace } e^{-H/kT}}$$

The idea is exactly the same as for the partition function, only now there are 2 exponentials to expand. However, it was not difficult to develop the appropriate diagrammatic representation[5], and quite a few terms in the expansion have been obtained.[6]

The motivation for considering $\langle \mathbf{S}_f \cdot \mathbf{S}_g \rangle$ rather than the customary thermodynamic quantities (susceptibility, specific heat, ...) is that $\langle \mathbf{S}_f \cdot \mathbf{S}_g \rangle$ not only yields all of the thermodynamic functions of interest but also provides additional physical information -- namely, (i) information concerning the short-range (SR) magnetic order to be expected for $T > T_c$ (as measured by the elastic paramagnetic neutron scattering cross section)[6, 7] and (ii) information concerning the type of long-range (LR) magnetic ordering to be expected for $T < T_c$ (as measured by neutron diffraction).[8]

(i) Although the LR order (which gives rise to huge Bragg peaks) vanishes above T_c, neutron scattering patterns often possess broad "humps" which presist at temperatures 5 or 10 times larger than T_c.[9] These so-called liquid peaks have been associated with the persistence of SR magnetic order above T_c. Such peaks are not predicted by the molecular field approximation (MFA), since the MFA allows for no SR order whatsoever above T_c. Now the MFA is recovered if one calculates just the first term in the high-temperature expansions, so that one might expect that the "correlation effects" taken into account by the addition of higher-order terms would predict the observed hump in the scattering pattern. This is indeed the case: as an example of the applicability of the series expansion $< \mathbf{S_f} \cdot \mathbf{S_g} >$ to provide information concerning the SR order, a calculation of the elastic paramagnetic neutron cross section for a normal cubic spinel with nearest-neighbor AB and BB exchange interactions is presented in Ref. 6.

(ii) Previous applications of the high-temperature series to the study of critical phenomena have assumed the type of LR ordering to be given at the outset and, furthermore, have been restricted to only two types of LR ordering --ferromagnetic and antiferromagnetic. Thus this previous work is not applicable to the class of substances which order at $T = T_c$ to a spiral spin configuration. Question: Can the high temperature expansion of $< \mathbf{S_f} \cdot \mathbf{S_g} >$ tell us for a given model what type of LR Magnetic order will set in as $T \rightarrow T_c^+$? The answer is "yes" --at least in principle. For a Bravais lattice one need only study which "Fourier component" $\sum_R e^{i\mathbf{Q} \cdot \mathbf{R}} < \mathbf{S_o} \cdot \mathbf{S_R} >$ diverges fastest as one decreases the temperature to determine the wavevector $\mathbf{Q}_o$ of the spiral spin configuration which will set in at T_c. ($\mathbf{Q}_o = 0$, π/a correspond to ferro- and antiferromagnetic spin configurations). The above argument is made more explicit, generalized to non-Bravais lattices, and applied to a particular example in Ref. 8.

2. CLASSICAL HEISENBERG MODEL

The extension of high-temperature expansions for the Heisenberg model with arbitrary spin quantum number S seems to be highly impractical because of the enormous "labour" involved. For example, the series for the zero-field susceptibility χ appears to be limited for general S to the six terms a_n published in 1958 by Rushbrooke and Wood[10]. Nevertheless, there exists a considerable need for more terms in order to study several unresolved problems. In Ref. 5, it is pointed out that order-of-magnitude simplifications occur in treating the quantum-mechanical spin operators in the Heisenberg Hamiltonian as isotropically-interacting classical vectors of length $[S(S+1)]^{1/2}$. This semi-classical approximation --the "classical" Heisenberg model-- appears to be excellent for some critical properties of interest if $S > 1/2$. For the $S = 1/2$ case other simplifications arise; these simplifications have recently been exploited to obtain additional terms in the susceptibility series[11, 12]. Thus a corresponding extension of the classical calculation may be expected to complement this recent advance for the case $S = 1/2$.

Although the simplifications in the high-temperature expansion method which occur when one assumes the spin operators commute were first pointed out by Stanley and Kaplan[5], two other groups of workers claim (in letters published immediately after the appearance in press of Ref. 5) to have had the "idea" independently. In the first of these, Joyce and Bowers[13] re-stated the simplifications pointed out by Stanley and Kaplan but using an altogether different diagrammatic representation. In the second letter, Wood and Rushbrooke[14] actually added two additional terms to the expansion (which had already been carried out to six terms for general spin quantum number S --and hence for the limiting $S = \infty$ case of the classical Heisenberg model).

Very recently the high-temperature series for the suceptibility of the classical Heisenberg model has been re-expanded in the new expansion parameter $u = \mathcal{L}(K) = \coth K - 1/K$ where $K = 2J/kT$.[16] This new series is found to provide more reliable extrapolations --especially for one- and two-dimensional lattices-- than heretofore. Stanley[16] has very recently solved the model of isotropically-interacting classical spins of arbitrary dimensionality D exactly for a linear chain lattice, and obtained nine terms in the high-temperature series for general lattices. Stanley's calculation differed from the Wood-Rushbrooke moment expansion in that (i) he obtained the coefficients a_n in the susceptibility series directly from the diagrammatic representation of the spin-spin correlation function,[6] and (ii) he made use of a recursion relation to obviate the need to consider the sizable class of "tree diagrams".

3. POSSIBLE PHASE TRANSITION IN TWO-DIMENSIONS

It has commonly been supposed that the two-dimensional Heisenberg model with nearest-neighbor ferromagnetic interactions will not undergo a phase transition (i.e., $T_c^{(2)} = 0$). Recently Stanley and Kaplan pointed out[17,18] that the standard spin wave argument against the existence of such a phase transition is invalid. They further pointed out that standard extrapolation methods based upon high-temperature series expansion indicate the presence of a well-defined $T_c^{(2)}$ --for the plane square, triangular and honeycomb lattices-- which is nowhere near zero but rather has a value which is an appreciable fraction of T_M, the ordering temperature predicted the MFA. Moreover, the extrapolated values of $T_c^{(2)}$ vary smoothly with lattice coordination number z and spin quantum number S and may be fit by a simple formula quite analogous to that proposed by Rushbrooke and Wood[10] for the critical temperatures of the fcc, bcc, and s.c. three-dimensional lattices.

What, then, happens below the critical temperature? In addition to the conventional low-temperature phase with nonzero spontaneous magnetization M, we suggested the possibility of a phase transition to a low-temperature state with M = 0 but with $\chi = \infty$ for $0 < T \leqslant T_c$. At the 1966 Brandeis Summer Institute in Theoretical Physics, I discussed with Professor Freeman Dyson the evidence from high-temperature expansions that $T_c^{(2)} > 0$. A few days latter he displayed an argument (based upon an intuitive generalization of spin-wave theory) that at low temperature the spin correlation function $< \mathbf{S}_\mathbf{o} \cdot \mathbf{S}_\mathbf{R} >$ falls off at large distance R as $R^{-\lambda}$ with λ linear in T. Thus M = 0 for T > 0, yet $\chi \propto \sum_R < \mathbf{S}_\mathbf{o} \cdot \mathbf{S}_\mathbf{R} >$ is infinite at low temperature. In fact, the value of T such that $\lambda = 2$ is in crude agreement with the value of $T_c^{(2)}$ I had predicted by the high-temperature extrapolation methods!

Shortly after our proposal that there might be a phase transition in the two-dimensional Heisenberg model, Mermin and Wagner[20] proved rigorously that M = 0. With the conventional M > 0 low-temperature phase thus ruled out, there remains only the "non-conventional" --and novel-- M = 0 possibility.

Mubayi and Lange have recently applied Mubayi's refined Green's function decoupling procedure to the two-dimensional (S = 1/2)

Heisenberg model[21]. For the plane square lattice they find M = 0 for all positive T, and that χ diverges at a nonzero temperature.

One should not forget that the high-temperature extrapolation methods and the Green's function decoupling procedures are not rigorous; nevertheless, the preliminary developments described above are intriguing.

It is certainly legitimate to ask if all this isn't perhaps rather academic, since no one has ever "built" a two-dimensional magnet in the laboratory. When one attempts to make metallic films thinner than several atomic layers, the film breaks up into little droplets or "islands" --experimental problems appear to be unsurmountable, indeed[22]. There seem to be two directions one can go from here: (1) to make a three-dimensional structure containing only one two-dimensional magnetic "layer", and (2) to build an "ideal" two-dimensional Heisenberg model on a computer.

(1) No one has succeeded in making structures with only a single magnetic layer, but there does exist one material, K_2NiF_4, for which the spins within a plane interact antiferromagnetically and tend to form an antiferromagnetic square lattice. Spins within the plane have an equal number of parallel and anti-parallel nearest-neighbors on adjacent planes, so that to find forces favorable to ordering one must go out to next-neighbor exchange --via 5 anions![23] Plumier's neutron diffraction work indicates that some sort of "long-range order" within the two-dimensional layers sets in below 180°K, but he finds no sign of a three-dimensional ordering all the way down to 4°K[24]. Hence it would appear that for all practical purposes, K_2NiF_4 provides a simple example of a two-dimensional antiferromagnet.

(2) Computers have been used quite dramatically to model statistical systems like gases and fluids. Very recently Vineyard,

Blume, and Watson at Brookhaven have succeeded in simulating the classical Heisenberg model on a computer[25]. Their preliminary results suggest the persistence of a rather considerable degree of order above T = 0 for the two-dimensional square lattice.

4. CRITICAL BEHAVIOR OF THE ZERO-FIELD SUSCEPTIBILITY

High-temperature extrapolation methods have been used recently to estimate not only the location of the critical temperature T_c but also the form of the divergence of the various thermodynamic functions as $T \rightarrow T_c^+$. Here we limit our considerations to the zero-field magnetic susceptibility for the Heisenberg model with nearest-neighbor ferromagnetic interactions.

The first studies concerned with this problem were independently carried out by Domb and Sykes (DS) at Wheatstone Laboratory[26] and by Gammel, Marshall and Morgan (GMM) at Harwell[27]. Both groups assumed that χ diverged with a power law form, $\chi \sim (T - T_c)^{-\gamma}$, and both groups proposed the value $\gamma = 4/3$ for all values of the spin quantum number S and for all three-dimensional lattices. In the period following these studies, the DS and GMM proposal has been widely quoted as a fact which has been "shown"; that $\gamma = 4/3$ independent of spin and lattice has come to be accepted as "universally true" for the Heisenberg model.

In Ref. 28 we argue that the conclusion that γ is independent of S and lattice is unwarranted. We find instead a slow but nevertheless clear variation of γ with S for the fcc, bcc and s.c. lattices[29], and we further point out that there exists at least one three-dimensional lattice for which the evidence indicates the value of γ is nowhere near 4/3 but rather may be near 1 --the value predicted by the MFA[28]. This lattice --a normal cubic spinel with nearest-neighbor interactions between the B-site cations-- is of more than academic interest, for within the last year a great deal of attention has focused upon insulating ferromagnets with exactly this structure: the cadmium chromium chalcogenides. Meniuk and Dwight are currently measuring γ for two such compounds ($CdCr_2S_4$ and $CdCr_2Se_4$); their preliminary results indicate γ may indeed be appreciably lower than 4/3.

REFERENCES

1. A very readable survey of the many "cluster approximations" (e.g. molecular field approximation, Oguchi-Van Vleck two-spin cluster, Bethe-Peierls-Weiss method) is given in J. S. Smart, Effective Field Theories of Magnetism (W. B. Saunders, Philadelphia, 1966).
2. P. J. Wood, thesis, King's College, Newcastle-upon-Tyne, 1958 (unpublished).
3. See, e.g., Smart's monograph (Ref. 1) and H. B. Callen, Phys. Rev. 130, 890 (1963).
4. The exact value of T_c was first obtained by H. Kramers and G. Wannier, Phys. Rev. 60, 252 (1941).
5. H. E. Stanley and T. A. Kaplan, Phys. Rev. Letters 16, 981 (1966).
6. H. E. Stanley, Phys. Rev. 158, 537 (1967).
7. K. Dwight, N. Menyuk and T.A. Kaplan, J. Appl. Phys. 36, 1090 (1965).

8. T. A. Kaplan, H. E. Stanley, K. Dwight and N. Menyuk, J. Appl. Phys. 36, 1129 (1965).

9. J. M. Hastings and L. M. Corliss, Phys. Rev. 126, 556 (1962).

10. G. S. Rushbrooke and P. J. Wood, Mol. Phys. 1, 257 (1958).

11. C. Domb and D. W. Wood, Proc. Phys. Soc. 86, 1 (1965).

12. G. A. Baker, H. E. Gilbert, J. Eve and G. S. Rushbrooke, Phys. Letters 20, 146 (1966).

13. G. S. Joyce and R. G. Bowers, Proc. Phys. Soc. 88, 1053 (1966).

14. P. J. Wood and G. S. Rushbrooke, Phys. Rev. Letters 17, 307 (1966).

15. H. E. Stanley, Phys. Rev. 164, 709 (1967).

16. H. E. Stanley, Phys. Rev. Letters, 20, 579 (1968).

17. H. E. Stanley and T. A. Kaplan, Phys. Rev. Letters 17, 913 (1966).

18. H. E. Stanley and T. A. Kaplan, J. Appl. Phys. 38, 975 (1967).

19. F. Bloch, Z. Physik 61, 206 (1930).

20. N. D. Mermin and H. Wagner, Phys. Rev. Letters 17, 1133 (1966).

21. V. Mubayi and R. Lange, to be published.

22. Private communication of P. E. Tannenwald and E. Grünbaum.

23. M. E. Lines, Phys. Letters 24A, 591 (1967).

24. R. Plumier, J. Appl. Phys. 35, 950 (1964).

25. G. Vineyard, M. Blume and R. Watson, to be published.

26. C. Domb and M. F. Sykes, Phys. Rev. 128, 168 (1962).

27. J. Gammel, W. Marshall and L. Morgan, Proc. Roy. Soc. (London) A275, 257 (1963).

28. H. E. Stanley and T. A. Kaplan, J. Appl. Phys. 38, 977 (1967).

29. In Ref. 28 we argued that for the fcc, bcc and s.c. lattices $\gamma(S) = \gamma(\infty) + 0.05/S$, with $\gamma(\infty) \cong 4/3$. The more sophisticated extrapolation procedures developed in Ref. 15 suggest instead that $\gamma(\infty) \cong 1.38$ (for the fcc and bcc lattices, with $\gamma(\infty) \cong 1.4$ for the s.c.) and that perhaps

$$\gamma(S) \cong \begin{cases} 1.43 & S = 1/2 \\ 1.38 & S > 1/2 \end{cases}$$

Further work on the spin dependence of γ is underway.